GLOBAL KARST CORRELATION

UNESCO/IUGS
International Geological Correlation Program
Project 299: Geology, Climate, Hydrology
and Karst Formation (1990 - 1994)
Final Report

Global Karst Correlation

Edited by

Yuan Daoxian Liu Zaihua
(*Institute of Karst Geology, CAGS, Guilin, China*)

Supported by
National Natural Science Foundation of China
Ministry of Geology and Mineral Resources of China

Science Press
Beijing, New York

VSP
Utrecht, The Netherlands
Tokyo, Japan

Responsible Editor: Bin PENG

Science Press
16 Donghuangchenggen North Street
Beijing, 100717
P. R. China

VSP BV
P. O. Box 346
3700 AH Zeist
The Netherlands
Tel: +31 30 692 5790
Fax: +31 30 693 2081
E-mail: vsppub@compuserve.com
Home Page: http://www.vsppub.com

First published in 1998

ISBN 7-03-006837-8 (Science Press, Beijing)
ISBN 1-880132-32-X (Science Press, New York)
ISBN 90-6764-286-X (VSP)

Printed in Beijing

Preface

This is the final report of the UNESCO/IUGS supported International Geological Correlation Program (IGCP) Project 299 "Geology, Climate, Hydrology and Karst Formation" (1990 – 1994). The project is the first of this kind in IGCP that dedicated to karst problems since it started in 1972.

Karst covers approximately 12% of the world's land surface. It is not only rich in resources, such as water, mineral deposits, fossil fuels, and tourism attractions, but also suffers from a series of particular environmental problems and natural disasters, including leakage of surface water, drought, flood, surface collapse, and rock desertification. Karst area is therefore regarded as a fragile environment by world scientific community. The sustainable development of karst area depends largely on a better understanding on the mechanism of karst formation and its variations at different parts of the world. Like other IGCP projects, IGCP 299 has improved our knowledge in this field remarkably through worldwide karst comparison. It benefits people in tackling resources and environmental problems of karst, and proves itself in keeping with the aim of IGCP — "Geoscience in the Service of Society".

The involvement of CO_2 in karst processes requires karst study to go beyond the consideration simply of water-rock interaction, and necessitates incorporation of an Earth System Science approach. The latter is considered to be the principal melody of Earth Science at the turn of the Centuries, and appeals to study the sum of processes operating in the atmosphere, hydrosphere, biosphere and lithosphere, and the interactions between them. Following the guideline of Earth System Science, and multidisciplinary cooperation between geologists, geographers, speleologists, physicists, biologists, and chemists, IGCP 299 has adopted systematic methodologies, and got many new findings on karst processes. The project thus contributed to the development of modern karstology.

The karst in China totals 3443000 km^2 including buried, covered and exposed types. Moreover, karst in mainland China is unique in the world because of its hard, compact, old phase carbonate rocks; remarkable Cenozoic uplift; water-heat matching monsoon climate; and devoid of scouring by ice sheet of the last glaciation. We are glad that karsts of China have provided key patterns for world karst correlation. Meanwhile, Chinese karst workers have learnt a lot from many correlations abroad. The fruitful results of the project are crystallized in the publication of this final report.

I would like to take this chance to thank IGCP Board and National IGCP Committees of Australia, Austria, France, Italy, UK, USA, former USSR and Yugoslavia for continuous support and advices for the project; all the 254 participants of IGCP 299 from 41 countries, and the Karst Commissions of IAH and IGU, the UIS for enthusiastic cooperation. I would also like to thank the National Natural Science Foundation of China, and the Ministry of Geology and Mineral Resources for financial support for the implementation of the Project in China.

Now the successor project IGCP 379 "Karst Processes and the Carbon Cycle" (1994 – 1999) is on-going. I wish the new cooperation would be as successful as before!

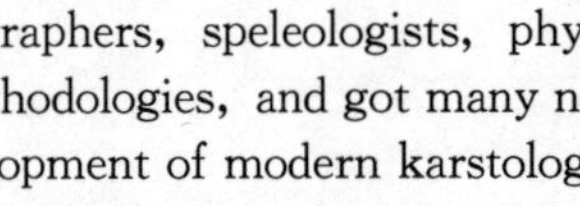

Prof. Cheng Yuqi
Academician of CAS
Chairman, IGCP National Committee of China

Contents

Global Karst Correlation
Edited by Yuan Daoxian and Liu Zaihua
Science Press and VSP BV, 1998

Chapter 1 Basic Ideas, Methodologies And Major Results of IGCP 299

Yuan Daoxian
Institute of Karst Geology, CAGS, Guilin, China

1.1 Background

The term karst is designated to the natural processes characterized by chemical dissolution (deposition) of soluble rocks in (from) water but cooperating with mechanical erosion or gravitational collapses, and various features thus formed. Consequently, the meanings of the term karst could be karst process; karst features; or even karst regions under different occasions of its use.

While talking about karst, people always first refer to tourism, because karst processes can usually bring about unique landforms, such as big cave system in Postojna, Slovenia and Mammoth Cave in USA, spectacular tower karst (or cockpit karst) in southeast Asia and Puerto Rico, which are all well-known scenic resorts for many years, and attract millions of visitors annually.

However, during the past decades, resources and environment problems in karst which covers approximately 12% of the continental part of the Earth surface(Fig. 1-1, Ford and Williams, 1989) have become a major concern for more and more people. Karst areas are not only rich in water, mineral deposits, oil and gas, and tourism resources, but also suffer from a series of particular environmental problems and natural disasters, including rock desertification, leakage of surface water and drought, flood, surface collapse, and water/mud gush into mines and constructing tunnels for various uses (traffic or aqueduct). Karst has been recognized as a fragile environment by the scientific community since at least 1983, when a symposium entitled "Degradation and Rehabilitation of Fragile Environments: Karst Areas and Desert Margin" was held at the 149th Conference of the American Association for the Advancement of Science (AAAS, 1983). The key to karst is the development of its unusual subsurface hydrology(Ford and Williams, 1989). All the resources and environmental problems in karst are controlled by various surface and subsurface karst forms, and varied at different karst areas of the world.

Accordingly, an understanding on the space distribution, the size and the integration pattern of various karst features becomes the bases for the survey and evaluation of the karst-related resources, and the prediction, mitigation and remedation of karst environmental problems and natural disasters. However, our abilities on such understanding are still limited. It depends largely on the progress in the knowledge about the mechanism and controlling factors of karst formation, which are explored and made headway continuously by world scientists for hundreds of years, and thus a discipline named as karstology has been formed. It has gone through stages of different academic thinkings: From stage of dialectics on the bases of geological-geographical description, through stage of physical-chemical experiment; and to the stage of Earth System Science. The latter has been developed in the last decades of the century, and appeals to study the Earth as a whole, and to study the sum of processes operating in the atmosphere, hydrosphere, biosphere and lithosphere and the interactions between these compartments(Mackenzie and Mackenzie, 1995). These ideas turn out to be very essential in the development of modern karstology.

Contemporary with the development of the ideas of the Earth System Science, international

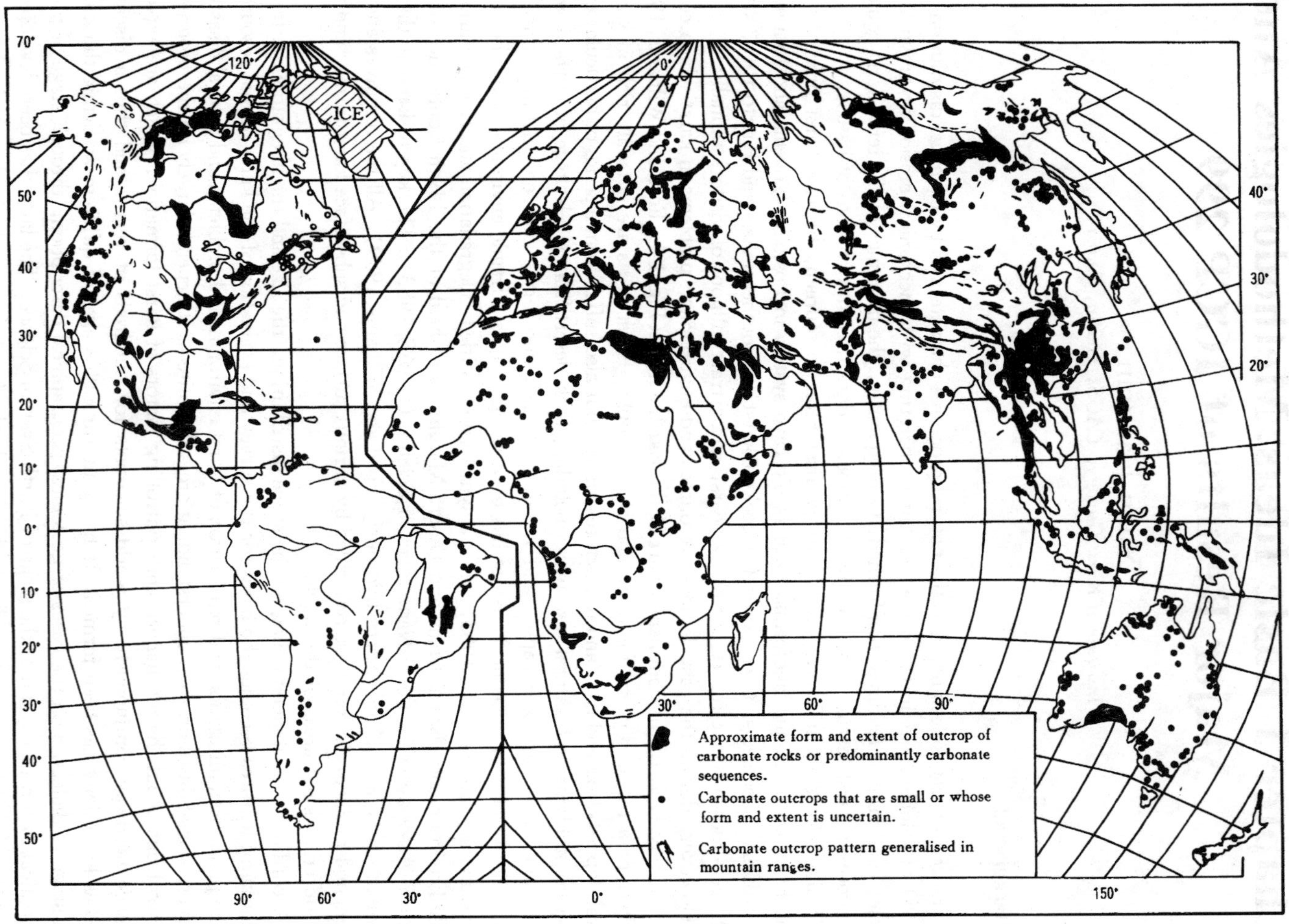

Fig. 1-1 Major karst areas of the world (Ford and Williams, 1989)

correlation has brought about many breakthroughs for all field of geoscience. The UNESCO/IUGS supported International Geological Correlation Program (IGCP) started from 1972 has played major role in improving such international correlation. Through comparing tectonism, volcanism, metallogenesis, geological history of various periods, paleoecosystem and surface processes such as glaciation, desertification, soil erosion or deposition and many natural disasters at different parts of the world, great achievements have been got in discovering mineral resources, understanding earth environments and interpreting earth processes and evolution. All the new knowledges will not only help people in sustainable development, but also the formation of modern earth science.

It was not until 1990, we got the first world karst correlation project among hundreds of IGCP projects, namely, the IGCP299 "Geology, Climate, Hydrology and Karst Formation" (1990 – 1994). It was 18 years after the beginning of IGCP, nevertheless, individual karst researchers had started world karst comparison as early as 1936, when H. Lehmann recognized the coincidence of Kegelkarst relief with the humid tropic climate in Java, Indonesia (Lehmann, 1936). Lehmann's finding was followed by decades of comparison by geomorphologists on the karst from tropics to the arctic, but concluded in a dilemma between the impacts of climatic and geological (lithology and structure) factors on karst features (Ford and Williams, 1989). However, the lessons from the karst geomorphologists are very helpful for the initiation and implementation of IGCP 299.

1.2 Basic Ideas of IGCP 299, Objectives and Methodologies

The project was supported by three karst-related International Academic Organizations including the Karst Commission of the International Association of Hydrogeologists (IAH), Karst Commission of International Geographical Union (IGU), and Union of International Speleology (UIS). It had also got written supports from 9 National Committees of IGCP (Australia, Austria, China, France, Italy, UK, USA, former Soviet Union and Yugoslavia), and 18 geoscientists from 9 countries (China, France, Germany, Hungary, Ireland, the Netherlands, Switzerland, USA and Yugoslavia).

The project was first discussed and endorsed by the Karst Commission of IAH at its 18th meeting in Guilin, China from Oct. 11 to 14, 1988. Later in 1988, Yuan Daoxian filled in a formal IGCP application form for the project and sent it to the IGCP Secretariat (UNESCO, Paris) and relevant IGCP national committees and scientists for review. Meanwhile, Dr. H. Paloc, the then president of Karst Commission of IAH, sent a formal supporting letter on behalf of the Commission to the IGCP Secretariat on Feb. 2, 1989. On July 21, 1989, the proposal was discussed again by the Karst Commission of IAH during its 19th meeting in Orlando, Florida, USA. The project was accepted for implementation in 1990 – 1994 by IGCP Board during its 18th meeting in Feb., 1990. The inaugural meeting of IGCP 299 was held from Oct. 7 to 11, 1990 in Antalya, Turkey. Yuan Daoxian (China) was elected as the leader and Heinz Hoetzl (Germany), John W. Hess (USA) the coleaders of the project. During the 20th meeting of IAH Karst Commission (Antalya), all its members were nominated as active participants. The Institute of Karst Geology, Guilin served as the Project's Secretariat.

1.2.1 *Earth System Science in Karst Correlation*

In contrast to the world karst comparison concentrated on karst landform between the 1930s and 1970s, the new karst correlation under the basic idea of Earth System Science is carried out in a more comprehensive way. The guideline for IGCP 299 is to investigate karst morphology and its associated environmental background (features of solid earth, with water, heat, chemical and biogenic energy) and then determine the physical-chemical mechanisms of karst formation.

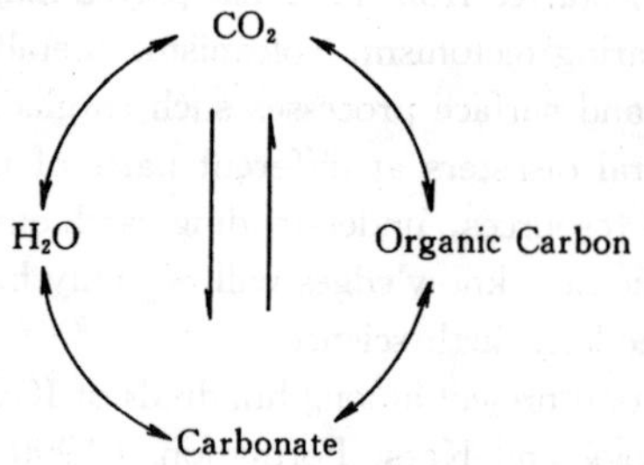

Fig. 1-2 Global carbon cycle

Karst processes are part of world carbon, water and calcium (magnesium) cycles that occur at the interfaces between lithosphere, hydrosphere, atmosphere and biosphere. The different forms of global carbon cycle are conceptualized in Fig. 1-2, which include not only the short-term, medium-term and long-term carbon cycling suggested by Mackenzie & Mackenize (1995), but also karst processes expressed at the left part of Fig. 1-2. Short-term cycling includes modern photosynthesis and respiration, whereas medium-term cycling includes the formation and burning of coal, oil and gas, as well as kerogen dispersed in sedimentary rocks. Long-term cycling refers to rock weathering, sedimentation and plate subduction processes. Karst processes are mainly implicated in the latter. It is accepted to be important over geological time (responsible for warming in Cretaceous and cooling in the Permo-Carboniferous), but not on a human time scale (Berner and Berner, 1987). Recent work, including that in IGCP 299, shows that carbonate rocks, which constitute the biggest carbon reservoir on Earth, are still actively involved in the modern carbon cycle as part of the karst dynamic system (KDS).

A karst dynamic system involves the transfer of energy and matter within the carbon, water and calcium (and magnesium) cycle. It occurs at the interfaces of the atmosphere, lithosphere, hydrosphere and biosphere and controls the formation and evolution of karst, but is moderated by already formed karst features.

The traditional CO_2-H_2O-$CaCO_3$ system model is conceptually presented in Fig. 1-3. It can be found in similar form in various works, such as by Bogli (1960), Sweeting (1972), Trudgill (1985), and Ford and Williams (1989). Its clear expression of the involvement of CO_2 in karst pro-

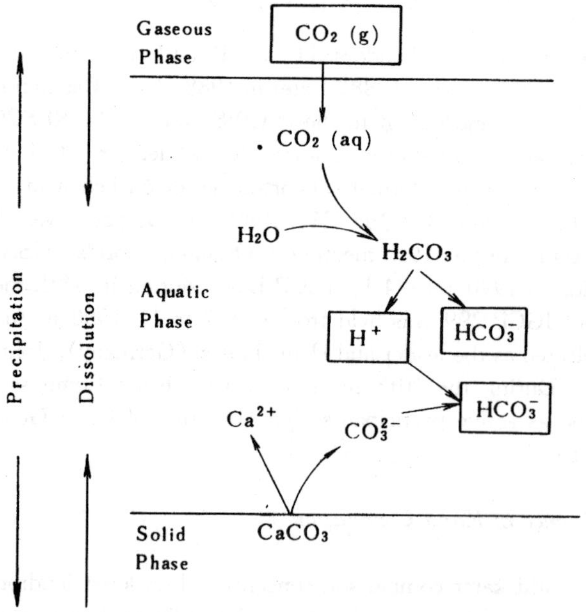

Fig. 1-3 Conceptual model of a karst dynamic system (modified after Bogli, 1960)

cesses requires karst study to go beyond a consideration simply of water-rock interactions and necessitates incorporation of an earth system science approach.

The KDS is composed of solid, liquid and gaseous phases. Part of the solid phase is dominated by different types of carbonate rocks with complex networks of fissures and joints. The liquid phase involves water flow with Ca^{2+} (and Mg^{2+}), HCO_3^-, CO_3^{2-}, H^+ and dissolved CO_2 as its major chemical constituents. There is a boundary layer in the liquid phase bordering the solid surface, with its thickness controlled by the hydrodynamic condition of the flow. The layer plays an important role in karst processes for both dissolution and precipitation (Liu et al, 1995). The gaseous phase involves CO_2 as a gas and in a dissolved state.

Because the KDS is an open system, its boundaries are not only configured by the already formed karst features, but also closely interlinked with the lithosphere, hydrosphere, atmosphere and biosphere. For instance, the solid phase at its lower part is not only connected with the whole lithosphere through the carbonate rocks and the networks of fissures within it, but also linked with the mantle through modern active deep faults. Thus CO_2 originating from the mantle takes an active part in the operation of the KDS. The aqueous phase plays the key role in the system by introducing biospheric, atmospheric and human activities into karst processes through actions such as absorbing water and carbon from the system by photosynthesis, and changing hydrodynamic conditions by hydroengineering construction.

A basic characteristic of the karst system is the sensitivity of its responsiveness to environmental change, as a part of the world carbon and water cycles. The behaviour of the KDS can be identified by the mutual relationship between four parameters, i.e., temperature, pH, HCO_3^- and CO_2 (Fig. 1-3). Data from two years' (1993 and 1994) monitoring of 7 karst systems with different environmental backgrounds (Fig. 1-4) has provided repeated evidence that shows the sensitivity of the systems to environmental conditions of rainfall, temperature, vegetation, P_{CO_2} and water flow. All these conditions can change the intensity and direction of CO_2 flux in the system, and thus can alter the intensity, manner, and even the direction of karst processes (dissolution versus precipitation). The time scale of such sensitivity is not only seasonal, but also could be daily, hourly or less.

The sensitivity of KDS to environmental change makes the field monitoring essential in world karst correlation. Moreover, because of the complicated movement of matter and energy between the lithosphere, hydrosphere, biosphere and atmosphere, isotopic approaches and physical and mathematical modeling are important for a real understanding of the operation of the KDS.

The principal function of the KDS is to drive karstification, or the formation of karst feature. Nevertheless, it has other functions, for example, to regulate the greenhouse gases in the atmosphere (and help mitigate environmental acidification); to drive the migration, enrichment and precipitation of a number of elements (and thus influence both the formation of mineral deposits and the biodiversity of life in karst areas); and to record the course of environmental change. These functions and their close relation with environmental change are shown clearly and repeatedly from many KDS monitoring sites. One site from China, as an example, illustrates this. In Yudong underground stream, Zhen'an County (Fig. 1-4), Shaanxi Province, monitoring was carried out in 1993 and 1994.

The HCO_3^- data in water shows intensive dissolution in the system, but also great seasonal variation (Fig. 1-5) from about 150 − 160 mg/l in winter to 210 − 220 mg/l in summer. It also appears to show positive correlation with soil CO_2 and negative correlation with pH value of water. The time of greatest HCO_3^- concentration in August is not coincident with the period of highest soil CO_2 content in June. Both years' data seem to show a 2-month lag. However, comparing CO_2 at depth of 20 cm and 50 cm indicates the time of highest dissolution to coincide with the greatest CO_2 difference (or CO_2 gradient), just after the month of highest rainfall (July). The findings show that it is the movement of CO_2 from atmosphere into water rather than just its absolute concentration in

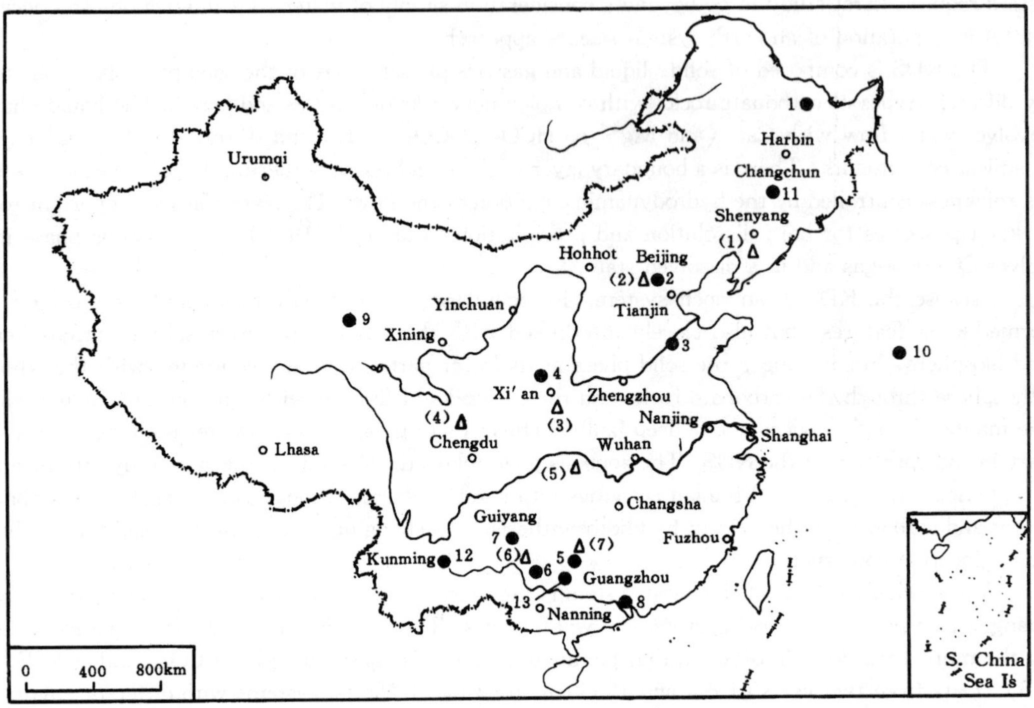

Fig. 1-4 Sites for monitoring the dynamics of karst systems in China. Δmonitoring stations for system dynamics: (1) Taizihe; (2) Beijing; (3) Zhen'an; (4) Huanglong; (5) Changyang; (6) Libo; (7) Guilin.
● monitoring stations for limestone denudation: (1) Yichun; (2) Beijing; (3) Jinan; (4) Binxian; (5) Guilin; (6) Huanjiang; (7) Guiyang; (8) Guangzhou; (9) Golmud; (10) Akioshidai, Japan; (11) Changchun; (12) Kunming; (13) Liuzhou

air that plays a most important role in karstification.

The structure and function of KDS (Fig. 1-3) show that karst processes can be both sink and source of atmospheric CO_2. However, so far as IGCP 299 is concerned, epigenetic karst processes are considered to act more often as a sink of atmospheric CO_2 than a source. In contrast, in karst areas with active faults and geothermal or volcanic activity, CO_2 is commonly measured emitting into atmosphere at concentrations of 23～90% (measured by the author during the 8 excursions of IGCP 299) and large amount of calcareous tufa are often deposited. In Huanglong Ravine, western Sichuan [Fig. 1-4 (4)], the high content of ^{13}C of the emitted CO_2 (−0.679% and −0.482%) and some noble gas isotopic data indicate that they originate mainly in the mantle (Liu et al., 1995). The deep source CO_2 outgassing can also be identified by the rapid change of hydrochemical parameters (rising up of pH and lowing down of HCO_3^-), as exemplified at the outlet of Pamukale geothermal spring, Turkey (Fig. 1-6, Photo 1) during the Project's 1990 excursion. International review shows that hydrothermal outgassing through karst is widespread in the world, especially in the Pacific Realm and the Tethys Belt, extending from Tibet westward through Iran, Turkey, Italy and southeast France, leaving a lot of calcareous tufa (Photo 2). This is an important source of atmospheric CO_2.

From the viewpoint of Earth System Science, karst processes are the dissolution or deposition of carbonate rocks in the system of carbon cycle with its coupled water cycle and calcium (magnesium) cycle (KDS), and various karst features are the tracks remained by the movement of this

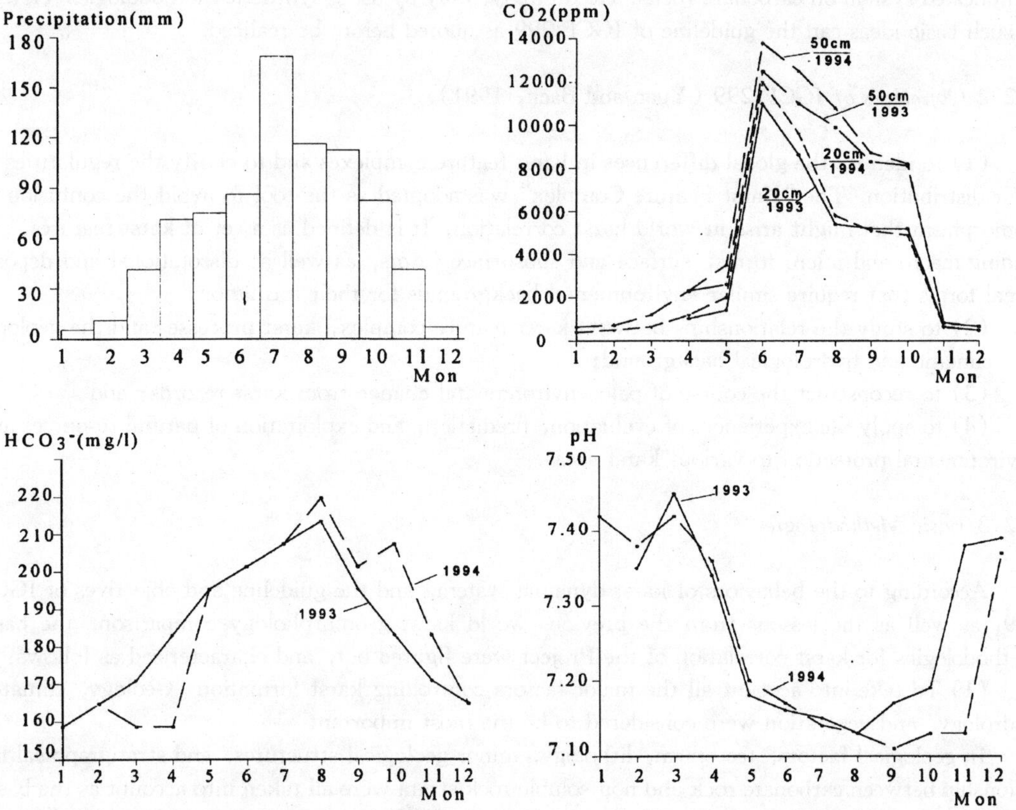

Fig. 1-5 Seasonal variations and relationships between soil CO_2 at two depths (20 and 50 cm), water pH, HCO_3^- and mean monthly precipitation at Yudong underground stream, Zhen'an County, Shaanxi Province

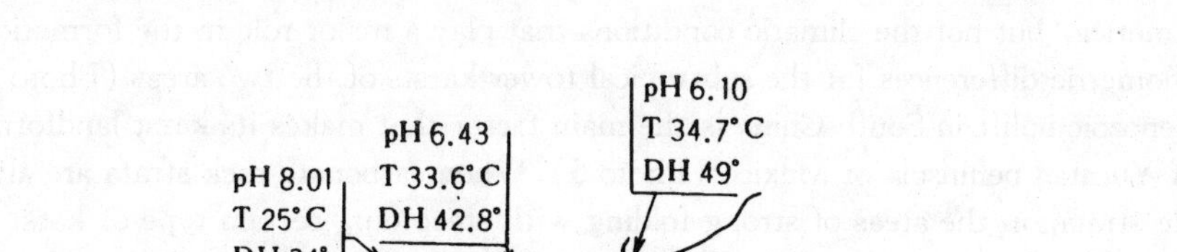

Fig. 1-6 Changing hydrochemistry as an indicator of CO_2 outgassing from a karst system. The example of Pamukale geothermal spring, Turkey (Nature and Resources, 1994)

complicated system on carbonate rocks. Accordingly, only by using synthetic methodologies relevant to such basic ideas can the guideline of IGCP 299 as quoted before be realized.

1.2.2 *Objectives of IGCP* 299 (Yuan and Back, 1991)

(1) to identify the global differences in karst feature complexes and to clarify the regularities of their distribution. The "Karst Feature Complex" was adopted as the tool to avoid the confusion of isomorphism that might arise in world karst correlation. It is defined as a set of karst features, including macro and micro forms, surface and subsurface forms, as well as dissolutional and depositional forms that require similar environmental backgrounds for their formation;

(2) to study the relationships between karst feature complex, karst processes and the geological, climatic and hydrological background;

(3) to reconstruct the course of paleoenvironmental change from karst records; and

(4) to apply the experiences of evaluation, prediction, and exploitation of natural resources and environmental protection to various karst areas.

1.2.3 *Basic Methodologies*

According to the behaviors of karst dynamic system, and the guideline and objectives of IGCP 299, as well as the lessons from the previous world karst geomorphology comparison, the basic methodologies for karst correlation of the Project were figured out, and characterized as follows:

(1) To take into account all the major factors controlling karst formation. Geology, climate, hydrology, and vegetation were considered to be the most important.

In geological factors, tectonism, lithology, minor geological structures, and stratigraphical relationship between carbonate rock and non-soluble rock strata were all taken into account as the bases for karst morphology comparison. For example, in comparison to intraplate karst, plate margin karsts are unique at features related to CO_2 of mantle origin, and carbonate rocks exposed at structural windows under nappes. It is the difference between the lithology of the hard, compact Paleozoic carbonate rocks of south China and the porous Cenozoic carbonate rocks of Puerto Rico, Central America, but not the climatic conditions that play a major role in the formation of remarkable morphometric differences for the subtropical tower karsts of the two areas (Photo 3, 4). Again, strong Cenozoic uplift in South China is the main factor that makes its karst landform different from those of Yucatan peninsula of Mexico (Photo 5). When carbonate rock strata are alternate with non-soluble strata, in the areas of strong folding with steep dip, certain type of karst landscape will be distributed only in a narrow belt, but in the areas of gentle dip, it will be more widespread. Lithological features are also important in the comparison on some micro karst features. For instance, the size of karren could be a measure of humidity (Photo 6, 7), but it can scarcely developed on porous limestone or dolomite. Moreover, it can hard develop under dense forest. Consequently, while taking any karst feature as an indicator of climate, the same geological background should be a prerequisite.

As climate is a synthetic factor of water, heat, CO_2 and biogenic energy, which are all driving forces of a karst dynamic system, it goes without saying that climate is an important element in global karst correlation. According to monitoring data, precipitation seems to be the most active factor affecting KDS, but other parameters including evaporation, temperature, snow and ice accumulation, permafrost should all be considered.

Hydrology could be considered as a derivative factor of climate, but sometimes it appears as a combination of geology and climate. For instance, when there are abundant allogenic water accumulation in non-soluble rock areas flowing into a carbonate rock system, the karstification will be remarkably intensified because of its stronger fluvial action, and higher aggressiveness to carbonate minerals. This situation is important for the evolution of tower karst (Fenglin), and the formation of some gigantic cave systems even in semi-arid region. So, hydrology is taken as a factor parallel with climate for world karst correlation. Hydrological pattern (vadose, phreatic, or deep slow flow), water table, amplitude of fluctuation in discharge and water table, and availability of allogenic water are taken for comparison.

Vegetation is also relevant with climate, but as it has close relation with soil and CO_2 generation, it is also used as one of the major elements for world karst correlation.

(2) to use Karst Feature Complex (KFC) as a tool for morphological correlation on karst. Various karst features are the results of karst processes under different environments, it is therefore reasonable to take them as indicators of correlation. However, confusion of isomorphism usually happens when the comparison is carried out for individual karst form. For example, similar form of isolated stone peaks being risen up abruptly from a plain, could be resulted from different origins, such as the karst process in humid tropical region, the erosion process on quartzose sandstone, and even wind abrasion in desert. However, if one matches it with micro karst features such as doline, karren, depositional feature such as red soil or limestone scree, and subsurface features like cave, speleothems, in a word, to take karst feature complex (KFC) as a tool of correlation, one can easily sort out what is the real tower karst formed under humid tropical environment. The advantages of taking KFC as indicator for world karst correlation is to avoid confusion of isomorphism. Although the karst features of the world are voluminous and colourful, the international correlation on karst is possible by means of distinguishing them carefully into sets of KFC.

At the beginning stage of IGCP 299, a table summarizing the available knowledges (basically from China and few other karst regions abroad) on the relationship between Karst Feature Complex and climate (Appendix 1 in this book) was given to every participants for reference.

(3) To monitor the behaviors of karst dynamic system. All the karst features except paleokarst are relying on the behaviors of KDS. So the latter is also essential for international correlation on karst. However, the KDS is very sensitive to environmental change, the only way to understand its behaviors is field monitoring for KDS at different environments, which is emphasized in IGCP 299.

Moreover, it is stressed that the monitoring work should be done in a systematic way, i.e., to do every efforts to understand the transfer of energy and matter within the carbon, water and calcium (and/or magnesium) cycle in the lithosphere, hydrosphere, atmosphere, and biosphere part of a KDS, and its impacts on karstification. Practically, for a karst dynamic system, the measurements should include CO_2 in atmosphere and soil air; precipitation and air temperature; hydrochemistry, especially pH, HCO_3^-, Ca^{2+}, Mg^{2+}, temperature of rain water, soil water, and karst water in the underlying carbonate rocks; and the discharge of spring. If autorecorders are not available, the measurements should be repeated in different seasons. Daily variation and the changes after some extreme events, such as storm, cold front, should be understood through experiments. In the karst area with geothermal activities, CO_2 emission on the surface of spring, and the rapid change of hydrochemical parameters should be measured. Moreover, information on lithology, organic content in soil, and seasonal change of vegetation should also be collected.

(4) Methodologies for paleoenvironment reconstruction with karst records. The first step is to sort out all the karst features that are not matching with the present environmental condition, such as red soil or doline in a semiarid karst area, so as to get a general idea about the past environment of the region. As a record of carbon, water, and calcium cycle in karst, speleothems, especially carefully selected stalagmites are often used for high resolution paleoenvironmental reconstruction. Priorities are to those areas where other paleoenvironmental proxies (ice core, lacustrine deposit, and etc.) are not available, and karst records show advantages.

Drilling on stalagmite to get small core sample has the advantage for cave protection and less engineering work, but for more objective sampling, it is recommended to bring back the whole stalagmite, and to take samples according to its sedimentological structure exposed by cutting along its growth axis. Dating methods include C-14, AMS C-14, U-series, TIMS U-series, paleomagnetism, and other approaches to be chosen according to the characteristics of the cave sediments and the aim of research. Stable isotopic and geochemical studies are usually necessary for paleoclimatic reconstruction. Detrital deposits in cave, doline or karst lake can also be used for paleoenvironmental reconstruction by traditional methods, such as paleomagnetism, C-14 dating, spore and pollen analysis.

(5) Registration form for typical correlation site. The form along with a detailed instruction was sent to all the participants of the project at its beginning stage. It is the basic approach to make the international karst correlation carrying out on a common basement, and includes all the contents for correlation and methodologies as described before. The form is put at the end of this book as Appendix 2.

1.3 Major Results of World Karst Correlation

254 participants from 41 countries were involved in this project. 33 typical karst areas with different geological, climatic, hydrological and ecological background were provided for world correlation (Fig. 1-7). Many of them were included in the 8 excursions in Turkey, China, Russia, USA, Australia, Canada, Iran, and UK. Among them, National Working Groups of Australia, Russia, USA, UK, China provided relevant chapters in this final book. In addition, NWG of Norway,

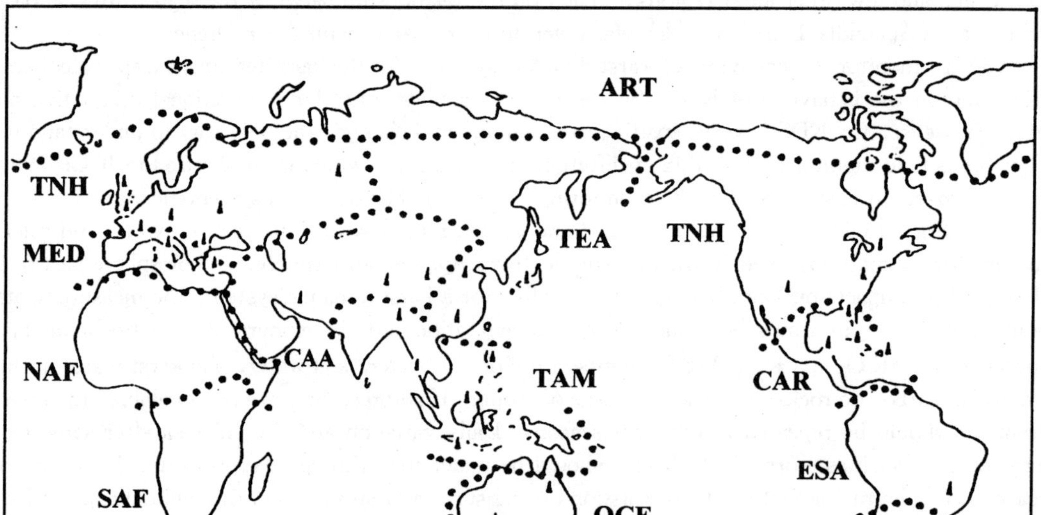

Fig. 1-7 World distribution of IGCP 299 karst correlation sites in relation to International Geosphere-Biosphere Programme (IGBP) ecological division (IGBP, 1992). ANT — Antarctica, ART — Arctic, CAA — Central Arid Asia, CAR — Caribbean, ESA — Equatorial South America, MED — Mediterranean, NAF — North Africa, OCE — Oceania, SAF — South and East Africa, TAM — Tropical Asian Monsoon region, TEA — Temperate East Asia, TNH — Temperate Northern Hemisphere, TSA — Temperate South America

Japan, Romania, Slovenia, Brazil, Vietnam, Bulgaria, and a joint group of Baltic countries (Lithuania, Latvia, Estonia) each wrote a chapter. Prof. W. Dreybrodt of Bremen University (Germany) led a thematic group "Physicochemical mechanism of karst processes" for the project. His contribution chapter is also in this book.

Besides this book, the major publications of the project include 8 books, 2 field excursion guidebooks, IGCP 299 Newsletters 1990, 1991, 1992, 1993, and 1994, and many papers published in international journals. A list of major publications is available as Appendix 4 in this book.

However, the 8 field excursions, each including 20 to more than hundred participants, provided the most important opportunities of on-the-spot field correlations, and more intimate discussions on ideas of karst formation and other topics of the Project. Therefore, it is pertinent to summarize here what we saw, what we discussed, and the accumulation and changing of ideas from one excursion to another.

1.3.1 *Karst of Plate Margin and Mediterranean Climate-Western Taurus Mt., SW Turkey* (1990)

The excursion took place from Oct. 7 to Oct. 17, 1990, in conjunction with the international symposium on hydrogeological processes in karst terrains, organized by Prof. Gultekin-Gunay, Dr. William Back, and Dr. Ivan Johnson.

About one third of Turkey is underlain by carbonate rocks that have been subdivided into four karst regions of which the Taurus Mountains at its southwest are the most extensive. The carbonate rock units are about 200 km wide along the Taurus Mts. which attain elevations of 2500m. Moreover, as Turkey is in a plate margin zone, there are many geothermal springs (Fig. 1-8). The tectonic features along with its typical Mediterranean climate make the karst features of the region being characterized as follows:

(1) The nappe structures which make the Jurassic and Cretaceous marble alternate with ophiolite or Tertiary Flysch both on the plane and vertical profile, cast strong influence on karst formation. The most spectacular features are many big karst springs or submarine springs flowing out from structural windows where carbonate rocks are exposed from ophiolite (photo 8), and a series of geothermal karst springs are along major expansional grabens, usually with high carbonate hardness (50 German degree), which form splendid travertine cascades (photo 1) as a result of rapid outgassing of CO_2(pH rises from 6.1 to 8.1 in a short distance less than 100m, Fig. 1-6).

(2) The karst features complex of the region reflects a combination of karst features of both humid environment, such as underground streams (photo 9) and arid environment, such as limestone scree (photo 10), which are usually distinct to each other in monsoon and hurricane region. This is considered to be the result of Mediterranean climate characterized by dry summer and wet winter, and yearly longer time of snow cover on the mountain regions. Thus mechanical weathering is as important as chemical corrosion. Coastal karst of the region is, in contrast with Caribbean and Southeast Asia, featured by less biogenic process because of lower water temperature.

(3) Karst hydrological characteristics of the Western Taurus region, as controlled by the karst feature complex, can be distinguished into two types. The karst hydrological systems recharged by poljes on lower plateau are characterized by higher fluctuation in discharge, higher temperature (above 17℃), higher carbonate hardness (up to 22° German degree), and extensive travertine deposit, whereas those mainly recharged from high mountains with long time of snow cover are characterized by stabler regime of discharge, lower temperature (less than 13℃), lower carbonate hardness (less than 10° German degree) and very few travertine deposit(Photo 8).

(4) The rock desertification problems are more serious than monsoon area. This is related not only to human activities and the general reason of two layer space structure and thin soil in karst re-

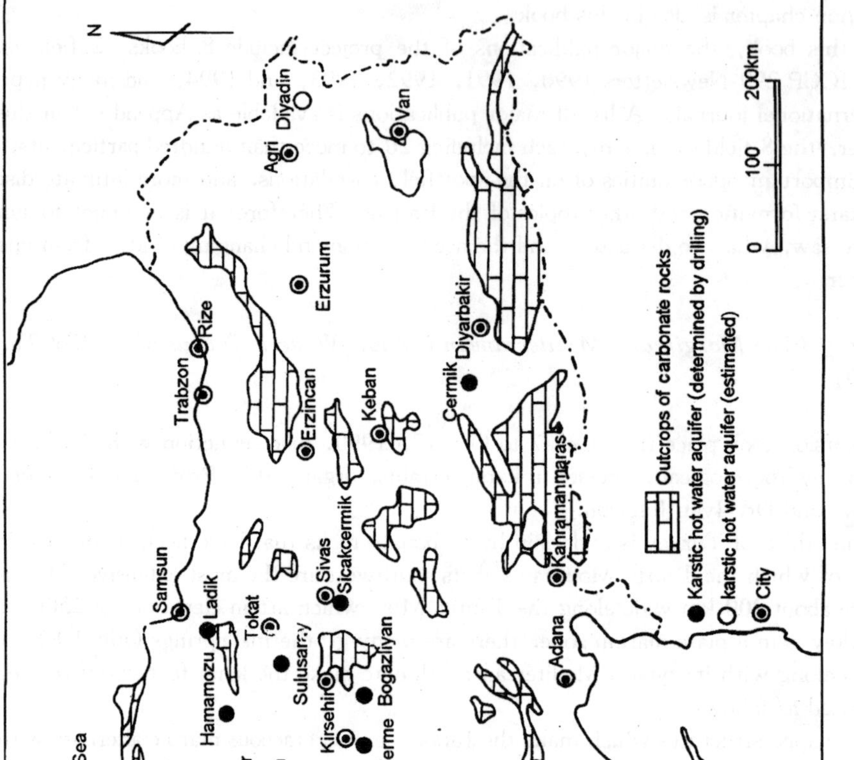

Fig. 1-8 The carbonate rock outcrops and karstic geothermal water of Turkey (Sakir Simsek, 1993)

gion, but also to much wider snow cover in winter, which gives rise to a timber line usually lower than 2000m(Photo 11).

(5) There are many karst records in SW Turkey which are promising for paleoenvironment reconstruction, such as travertine hundred meters deep below sea level; speleothem found 33 meters below modern water table by diving; Tertiary conglomerate hundreds meter thick with majority of well-rounded limestone gravels. Moreover, as a country of long history, Turkey enjoys many karst-related archaeological sites which are very useful for tracing the paleoenvironment of the past 3000 years, such as the Sunken City in the sea, the ancient aqueduct with calcareous tufa encrustation (Photo 12), and the limestone karren on the building stones of Roman theater. In addition, as in Iran and China, multiyear cycles of drought and wet (such as 10 or 20 years) of some karst springs corresponding to relevant meteorological cycles may also be found in Turkey, which will be very useful for studying global environmental change.

1.3.2 *Karst of Intraplate Region with Monsoon Climate-Mainland China* (1991)

The excursion took place in July-August of 1991. 71 persons from 9 countries (Germany, Hungary, Iran, Italy, Japan, Thailand, UK, USA, China) participated in the event. The correlation trip from South China to North China totaling 6700 km passed through the most outstanding types of karst in China, i.e., humid subtropical karst, high mountain karst and semi-arid karst (Fig.9-1). Six typical karst sites were included in the correlation, namely, the Guilin humid subtropical karst with deforestation; the Maolan virgin forest subtropical karst; the Huanglong Ravine high mountain and geothermal karst; the Zhen'an karst at southern slope of Qinling Mt. and northern border of China's subtropical karst; the Tumen and Jinan semiarid karst in Shandong; and Beijing semiarid karst. Detailed data of each point are available in the guidebook of the excursion, which is prepared under the guideline of IGCP 299. In addition, broader and deeper discussions on the characteristics of karst in China are made in the newly published 224 pages hard cover book *Karst of China*, which has 48 colour photos and is a contribution from the Institute of Karst Geology, CAGS to IGCP 299. The major results of correlation are as follows:

1.3.2.1 *International Correlation*

From a global view, the backgrounds for karst development in mainland China are characterized by: hard, compact carbonate rock before Triassic; intraplate region in majority; strong Cenozoic uplift induced by Himalayan Orogeny; monsoon climate; devoid from scouring of great continental ice sheet of the last glaciation; and the effect of allogenic water in many karst regions. Participants were impressed by the unique karst features in China that are quite different from those of other karst regions abroad. For instance, because of the hard, compact carbonate rock, karst aquifers in China are usually extremely heterogeneous and difficult for well sitting, especially in Southern China where karst groundwater quite often appears in the form of underground stream, whereas for the Cretaceous chalk in London Basin, or Tertiary porous carbonate rock in central America, Southeast USA, or Paris Basin, the karst aquifers are more homogeneous. Moreover, many karst hydrological systems in China have a broad expanse because of gentle dipping and thick continuous carbonate rock sequence. Tower karst developed on hard carbonate rock in South China usually shows steep, tall, spectacular stone peaks, whereas those on the porous carbonate rock in Caribbean are low, rounded with gentle slope. As opposed to the Mediterranean region where the first international correlation of this Project took place, and the karst features from mechanical weathering and chemical dissolution enjoy the same importance, the karst feature complex in mainland China under the influence of monsoon climate has sharp contrast between humid subtropical region and semiarid or high mountain region. As a result of strong Cenozoic uplift, and devoid of continental ice sheet in the last glaciation, China has a very old karst archive, composed of plateaus thousands meters in altitude, spectacular high peaks, deep dolinen, and relevant sediments. However, in some of the karst areas abroad, such as the Yucatan Peninsula in Mexico where the Cenozoic uplift has been very weak, or the karst pavement in Ireland where all the previous karst features were scoured away by the last glaciation, the information about the history of karst development is very limited. Because the major karst in mainland China except its Tethys part is in the intraplate regions, there are less geothermal effect on karst development as those occurred near plate collision belt as SW Turkey. However, at its Tethys part, there are many geothermal CO_2 emission, like the Huanglong Ravine calcareous tufa (Photo 17) which has the similar geothermal origin as Pamukale, Turkey.

1.3.2.2 *Correlation between Different Types of Karst in China*

Karst in China enjoys a great environmental coverage. Therefore, karst correlation in China is no less than an international one which may be carried out in some countries each has only one karst type. The achievements from the round China karst excursion are as follows:

(1) The Karst Feature Complex for three major karst types in China are identified. Participants saw that for the humid subtropical karst in south China, it is a combination of tower karst (Photo 3), deep dolinen, red soil, deep sharp karren, surface tufa (Photo 13), big cave system, underground stream, with many corrosional features, and gigantic speleothem. For the semi-arid karst in North China, it is composed of normal-shaped mountain, dry valley, limestone scree with loess cover, tiny karren (Photo 7), small cave system with little speleothem, and big karst springs. For the high mountain karst in western China, the karst feature complex is characterized by frost denudation limestone pinnacles (Photo 14), limestone scree (Photo 15), tiny cave with very few speleothem, and small karst springs.

(2) Sharp boundaries between karst types. The boundaries between the three types are very clear. Participants found sharp contrast between humid subtropical karst of south China and semiarid karst of North China in Qinling Mt. Ridge (Photo 16), and between high mountain karst and other types at the Eastern border of the Tibetan plateau. This is the result of monsoon climate, which is opposed to Mediterranean area and makes the high mountain ridges play important role in the distribution of regional moisture and temperature. This assertion is supported by the data of long term limestone denudation rate observation over China.

1.3.2.3 *Correlation on Karst Hydrology and Environment*

(1) The allogenic water is important in karst development because of its higher chemical aggressivity as well as stronger mechanical erosional effect. In the first day of excursion from Guilin to Jinchengjiang, participants saw its important role in the evolution of tower karst, i.e., the transformation from peak cluster subtype to peak forest subtype. Moreover, the Xiaya underground stream in Tumen area, Shandong province, very rare in semi-arid North China, is another example for the role of allogenic water in karst formation by doubling the effect of rainfall.

(2) A comparison on karst hydrology between North China and South China. Participants learned that karst hydrological features of the two areas are quite different. In the subtropical humid karst region of South China, karst groundwater usually occurs in the form of underground streams with medium to small size recharge area, close relation with surface water, quick response to rainfall and higher amplitude of discharge and water table fluctuation, whereas in the semiarid region of North China, it appears mainly in the form of big karst spring recharged by fissure-karst aquifer with remarkable catchment area and stabler regime. Accordingly, the ways for water resources investigation, estimation, exploitation and protection are also quite different for the two types of karst water.

(3) The environmental impacts of karst hydrology in South China, as originated from numer-

ous underground conduits, are the alternate and interaction of flood, drought, and deforestation. South China karsts are frequented by drought, although most of its territory have an annual precipitation of more than 1000 mm. This is the result of leakage of surface water into underground conduits. However, during the rainstorm, dolinen and poljes are very often inundated where the underground conduits are not wide enough to drain away the excess water. Participants saw that the situation is getting worse because of widespread deforestation process in south China karst. However, in Maolan Karst Nature Preserve, both drought and flood are mitigated remarkably. Moreover, participants are impressed by many skillful small size projects to regulate and exploit water resources in karst conduits, which are summarized in IGCP 299 Newsletter 1991 (p.62 – p.72).

(4) Big karst springs in North China semiarid region are the important sources for local agricultural, industrial or domestic water supply. However, most of them have been declined continuously in both spring discharge and water table of the relevant Ordovician-Cambrian carbonate rock aquifer in the past decades. A lot of them are exhausted. This comes evidently from the over exploitation following the boost of economy. But there are also clear evidences to consider it a result of 20 years dry meteorological cycle after the 1960s. This idea was supported by some participants in the field seminar with some Iranian, Italian and African examples.

(5) Suggestions to improve karst land management. During the field seminar, many helpful suggestions to improve hydrological and environmental study and land management in karst area were given by the participants on the basis of experiences from their own countries, such as to recover vegetation on limestone quarry in Chichibu region, Japan; lessons from improper land reclamation in Nansei Island, Okinawa, Japan; careful use of imported plant species for recovering vegetation on limestone; suggestion to transform farmland on natural slope in southeast Guizhou province into terraced one, so as to mitigate soil erosion in karst area; measures from geochemical considerations to protect tufa as a scenic attraction.

1.3.2.4 *Reconstruct Paleoenvironment with Karst Records*

A lot of Karst records in China are very informative to paleoenvironment. In South China, a sort of widely scattered Cretaceous limestone breccia which contains Atopochara flora in its laminated cementation indicates a dry period but later it was inundated under water. Moreover, it tells the general situation of the area before Cenozoic karstification. In Guangxi Province and southern part of Hunan Province, a boulder clay with prevailing allogenic pebbles (sandstone, vein quartz and etc.) often occurs as low mound 10 – 50m high on karst plain. It suggests a major meteorological event in Middle Pleistocene. This assertion is also supported by many horizontal erosional notches at similar altitudes on limestone peaks. In Tumen area, Shandong, pebbles of metamorphic igneous rock are found in Shanhu Cave 140m higher than local base level. The pebble layer is overlain by flowstone dated back to 208 thousand years by U-series approach. The data indicate the paleohydrological setting in Middle Pleistocene, and the importance of allogenic water in the karstification of the region since long time ago. Also in Tumen, typical Tertiary red clays on limestone are found underlying loess. This evidence for a warm humid Tertiary in the region is also supported by other relic karst features, such as dolinen, cone karst, which are occasionally found in North China.

In both Tumen of Shandong and Xishan mountain karst area of Beijing, a lot of periglacial features were recognized during the field seminar. They include snow gullies on limestone mountain, frost denudation limestone pinnacles (Photo 18) similar to those seen at the modern high mountain karst area on Tibet plateau (Photo 14), and a lot of thick limestone scree, intercalated with loess deposit. All of these findings throw new light into the study on the history of Quaternary climatic change and karst development in North China.

1.3.3 *Trans-Continental Karst Correlation* (*Russia*, *USA*, *Australia*, 1992)

The scientific activities in the third year of this Project are characterized by more extensive trans-continental karst correlation, with a major field excursion across Central Appalachian in USA (organized by G. N. Huppert, P. H. Dougherty, J. Hess), and two others in Central Ural of Russia (organized by V. M. Kutepov, V. N. Andreytchuk and V. N. Kataev), and Southern Australia (organized by D. Gillieson) respectively. 21 persons from 9 countries (Austria, Bulgaria, China, Japan, Germany, France, Romania, Italy and USA) took part in the American excursion (August, 1992); About 130 participants from 7 countries (China, Germany, Japan, Kazakhstan, Lithuania, Russia, and Ukraine) were at the Russian meeting and field trip (July, 1992). 34 persons from 7 countries (Austria, Australia, China, France, Japan, UK, and USA) attended the symposium and field seminar in Australia (December, 1992).

The correlation trip from Washington D. C. to Cave City, Kentucky covered karst of Appalachian Mt., Appalachian Plateau, as well as Central Basin of Kentucky. It passed through Appalachian Mt. twice and totaled about 1600 km. 17 sites were examined, which included 4 points of karst geomorphology and hydrology, 6 caves, 3 points of karst environment and cave utilization, and 4 points of other geological and hydrogeological interest. 7 sites are in the Appalachian Mt. region, and 10 in the Appalachian Plateau and Central Basin region. Geologically, the study area covers both platform region with gentle dip, and folding belt with many thrusts. The modern climate is temperate humid, characterized by annual mean precipitation of 1200 – 1500 mm, and annual mean temperature 8 – 14℃. The Appalachian karst is one of the most well – studied region in the United States and has played important role in the development of American karstology. A symposium entitled " Appalachian Karst " devoted to the 50 Anniversary of National Speleological Society (NSS) was held in Radford, March, 1991. Its 33 paper proceedings was delivered to every participants of the IGCP 299 excursion, giving the up-to-date information on karst research in this region. The field correlation in Russia was in parallel with an International Symposium on Karst Engineering Geology, held in Perm, July, 1992. The week long trip included Berezniki, Solikamsky where the biggest potassium mine of the world locates, ice cave near Kungur, and Ufim Karst Plateau. Russian colleagues provided excellent research results on typical sites of evaporite karst and karst in humid cold temperate area with Taiga and extensive alluvial or periglacial deposits (Photo 19). The two weeks long trip in southern part of Australia totaling 6500 km is another most ambitious excursion of this Project. It started from Canberra and passed through 4 states including New South Wales, Victoria, South Australia and West Australia. Geologically, it covers Tasmania Mobile Zone of eastern mountainous region, and Australia Craton at West. The modern climate en route the trip ranges from Mediterranean type with annual precipitation 700 – 1500 mm which is concentrated in the winter months of June to September, to the arid climate in the west with annual precipitation 200 mm, and annual mean temperature 15 – 16℃. Three major types of karst covering 40 sites in Southern Australia were examined, i. e, humid temperate impounded karst in southeast mountainous region, arid karst on Tertiary carbonate rocks, and syngenetic karst on Quaternary calcarenite. The excursion which combined field discussions with symposiums was well organized. A 115 pages Guidebook was published and given to every participants before the trip began.

1.3.3.1 *International Correlation with Previous Experiences*

In contrast with the Project 's two previous correlation sites in Turkey and China, karsts in Appalachian and Central Basin of Kentucky, or Perm region of Western Ural, are characterized by dense forest and extensive Quaternary cover. Bare carbonate rocks outcrop widespread in China or Mediterranean karst is very few in Perm region or Kentucky. It is believed that periglacial environment during the last glaciation and less Cenozoic uplift are two geological backgrounds that bring about the situation. About 10 thousand years ago, Kentucky was near the southern border of Hudson Bay continental ice sheet, and Perm region near the Baltic and western Siberia ice sheet. It is the moraine that has provided rich source material for the extensive Quaternary deposits of different origin (fluvial, eolian, and etc.) that cover the two karst regions. This geological setting, along with generally low relief, and the dense vegetation has strong influence on karst features. Both areas are recognized as covered karst (karst covered by loose overburden) in majority, characterized by tedious surface feature, without tower karst as in southern China, rare in big solutional basin (polje) as in Mediterranean Karst. Dolinen such as those seen in Sinkhole Plain, Kentucky (Photo 20), or Kungur Plateau, Perm (Photo 21), appear as dish shaped shallow ones covered by loose sediments and pastures. Deep polygonal dolinen of subtropical karst in South China are not available here. Moreover, minor surface features such as karren and kamenitza are also scarcely seen. However, subsurface karst features are well developed under favorable climatic, hydrologic, and geochemical conditions. In Perm region, relatively humid climate is good for cave formation in evaporite. Moreover, there are many bogs under the Taiga (Photo 22). Surface water is usually aggressive with pH6 – 7, and carbonate hardness less than 6 (German degree). So, it is also favorable for cave development in carbonate rock. In the Central Basin of Kentucky, aggressive allogenic water from non-carbonate rock area flows into the gently dipped Mississippi limestone. Besides, there is vertically percolating water from the overlying Pennsylvania sandstone. It is the joint hydrological action of the two type waters that has created the world 's longest cave, the 530 km long Mammoth cave system. The subsurface depositional features of the two regions are characterized by more collapse blocks, fluvial sediments, but less speleothem (Photo 23). Big flowstone or dripstone as those in South China are very rare. It is believed that the aggressive geochemical environment as described before and the slow process in cold temperate region is not favorable for speleothem to grow. The marvellous speleothems in Luray Cave of Virginia (Photo 24) look very old, and are not the product of modern climate. There are some unique speleothem near Perm, such as the salt stalactites in potassium mine (Photo 25), and the permanent ice flowstone, ice dripstone, and ice flakes in Kungur Cave (Photo 26). If we compare the Appalachian and Kentucky karst with those of the North China semi-arid region, then we can find the importance of climate in karst formation. Both areas are under similar latitude, and all have the Paleozoic hard, compact carbonate rocks, but dolinen like the Sinkhole Plain of Kentucky, or gigantic cave like the Mammoth Cave System are not available in North China semiarid karst. In a word, the third year of international karst correlation has provided good examples of humid temperate karst and evaporite karst in gently folding regions with extensive Quaternary cover.

As the only one southern hemisphere correlation excursion for this Project, Southern Australia enjoys many unique karst features, which can make remarkable contribution to our knowledge on karst formation. For example, the Buchan karst in Victoria, is on a latitude of 38℃ S with humid temperate climate, but it is abundant in growing speleothem such as those being seen in Fairy Cave or Royal Cave. This is unique in comparison with other humid temperate karst in Northern Hemisphere. As an "impounded Karst", with carbonate rocks being enclosed by big area of nonsoluble rock, the important role of allogenic water with high aggressivity (carbonate hardness about 1 German degree, pH about 7) in shaping dissolution karst features (big caves, surface dolinen) is the same as other humid temperate karst, but the carbonate hardness in cave water is remarkable (12 – 13 German degree). It explains the abundance of speleothem, but why it becomes high so quickly remains a question. It was found that in some part of Buchan caves the P_{CO_2} is very high (e. g., 2000 ppm as being measured in Royal Cave). Moreover, participants were told that it may be even higher, say 10%, in some Eastern Australian caves. It tells that the carbon cycle in this area of dense forest is very active, and might thus intensify the karst process and speleothem formation. In addition, the climate, although humid temperate in general, but with Mediterranean character, i. e., dry in summer and high evaporation, may also be favourable for speleothem forming. In western part of the Australia Excursion, the exsudation process in Tertiary carbonate rocks caves opens eyes for most of the participants (Photo 27). The fact that the growing of evaporite speleothem can seriously damage the previous calcite speleothem should be taken into account in the whole spectra of karst formation mechanism. Besides, the kilometers long caves in Tertiary carbonate rocks of Nullarbor area; the syngenetic karst on Quaternary calcarenite; the limestone pavement surface inherited from the former sea level, as well as dissolutional features on silicates (Granite Batholith in Wudina) (Photo 28) are all particular features and potential to contribute for our karst knowledge.

1.3.3.2 *Reconstruct Paleoenvironment with Karst Records*

In the Appalachian New York, Paul Rubin tries to use karst features in Clarksville Cave to trace the paleohydrology of the meltwater from the Wisconsinan glaciation. In western part of Virginia, David Hubbord and others take the surface travertine-marl as an "environmental barometer" to tell the increase of runoff resulted by land -use practice, and water pollution. During the field Excursion in Appalachian, Y. Y. Shopov talked about his result from using Laser Luminescent Micro Zonal Analysis on cave minerals to reconstruct environmental change. In Slovenia, Andrej Kranjc and his colleagues try to use the size of flowstone in Skocjanske cave to reconstruct climatic change. In the Ybbstaler Alpen Karst area of Austria, Rudolf Pavuza (Appendix 3 in this book) analyses the hydrodynamic characteristics of karst features, and suggested a phreatic condition before the last glaciation($<$10000a), and vadose one after that. Moreover, he uses the data of Ca/Mg ratio variation to propose a change in the water chemistry and catchment area. In Guilin, China, Lin Yushi and others carried out a thorough study on the feasibility of using speleothem to reconstruct environmental change. They sent stalagmites of different shape and size to a Marble Manufactory to saw out their whole cross section, and investigated the depositional features and the sedimentation history of each stalagmites. It is discovered that the interior sedimentological structure of stalagmites are quite different, some of them are rather simple, but most of them are very complicated. Accordingly, it is inappropriate to take sample from the surface of a stalagmite, or to make an arbitrary drill hole on it for sampling without a clear understanding on its interior sedimentary sequence and history (Fig. 9-7). In some Nullarbor caves, where the calcite speleothems are mixed with evaporite speleothems, Australian colleagues find with Uranium disequilibrium approach, that the age of calcite speleothem are ranging between 300 thousand to more than 530 thousand years, whereas the halite is between 20 to 37 thousand years, or within the period of Holocene. Because the deposition of large amount of calcite speleothem needs a warm wet climate, whereas evaporites usually deposit in dry condition, it is very possible to reconstruct Pleistocene environment with the data from Nullarbor caves.

1.3.4 *Karst in Western Ural of Russia and Environmental Problems* (*July*, 1992)

As a part of IGCP 299 project, 23 karstologists from 18 institutions in the former USSR compiled a karst map series. It is in the scale of 1:2 500 000, and has 16 sheets altogether. The series were shown at the Perm symposium, July, 1992, and included three maps, i. e., map of karst lithologic types (Fig. 1-9); map of karst types (Fig. 1-10); and a map of tectonic division by Yershov. A reduction version in the scale of 1:25 000 000 was prepared as a contribution to IGCP 299.

Western Ural enjoys the world 's typical profile of Permian System, and Perm City is the location where the name of the stratigraphic System comes from. Its upper part is composed of evaporites, underlain by carbonate rock of reef phase. Consequently, evaporite karst with its particular features, such as salt (gypsum) karren, salt (gypsum)dolinen, salt (gypsum)cave, salt stalactite

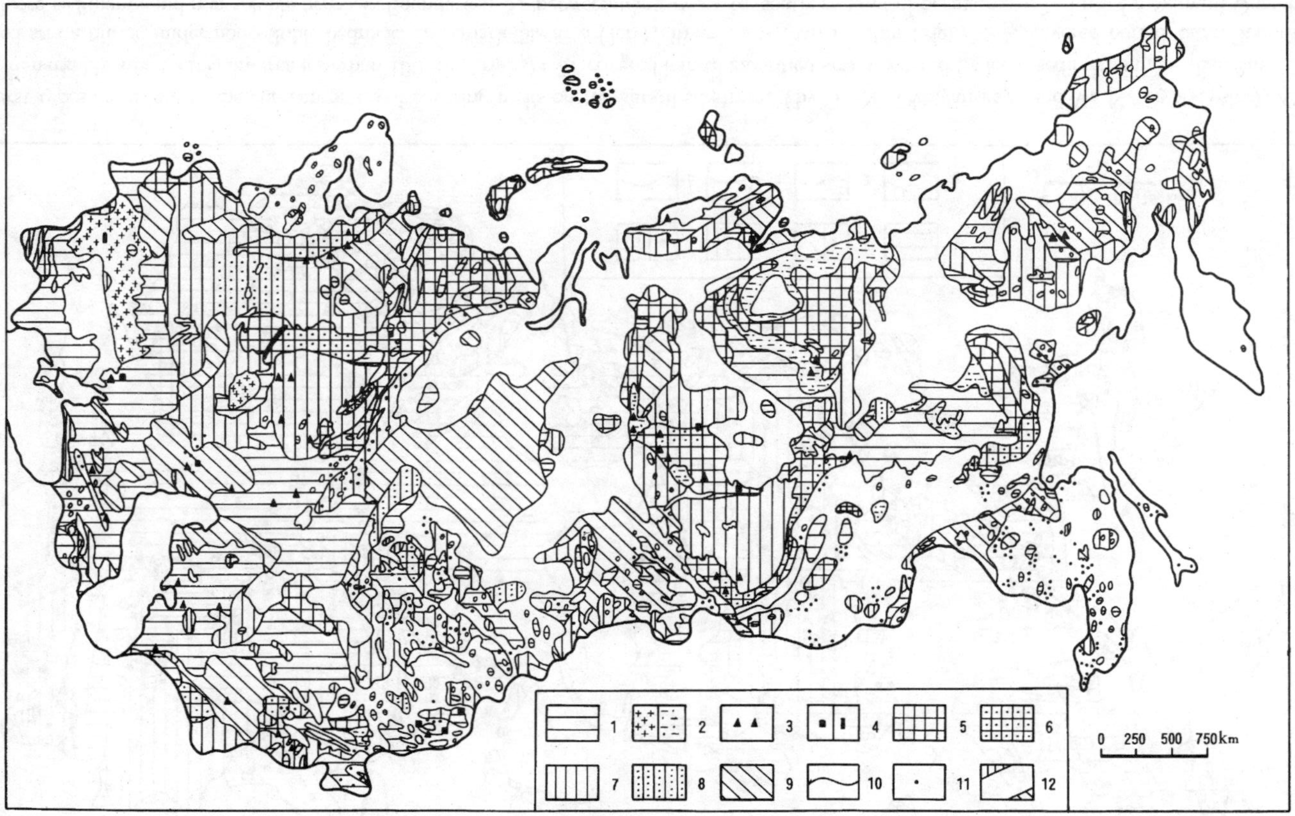

Fig. 1-9 Karst Lithologic Types in the Territory of Former USSR. (by G. N. Dyblyanskaya and V. N. Dyblvansky). Karst Lithologic Types: 1. limestone; 2. chalk and dolomite; 3. sulfates (gypsum and anhydrite); 4. rock salt (sodium and potassium salt); 5, limestone and dolomite mixture; 6. carbonate-sulfate mixture (limestone, dolomite, gypsum. anhydrite); 7. terrigenous carbonate (alternation of limestone, dolomite, marl, siltstone, sandstone, argillaceous, and clay beds); 8. terrigenous sulfates (alternation of gypsum, anhydrite, siltstone, sandstone. argillaceous, and clay beds); 9. intercalation of karstified layer in non-soluble strata (intercalation of limestone, dolomite in siltstone, sandstone, siltstone, and clay). Boundaries: 10. between different types of karstified rocks; 11. small areas of karstified rock, can not be shown as limited by the scale of map (basically carbonate rock); 12. non-soluble rock area

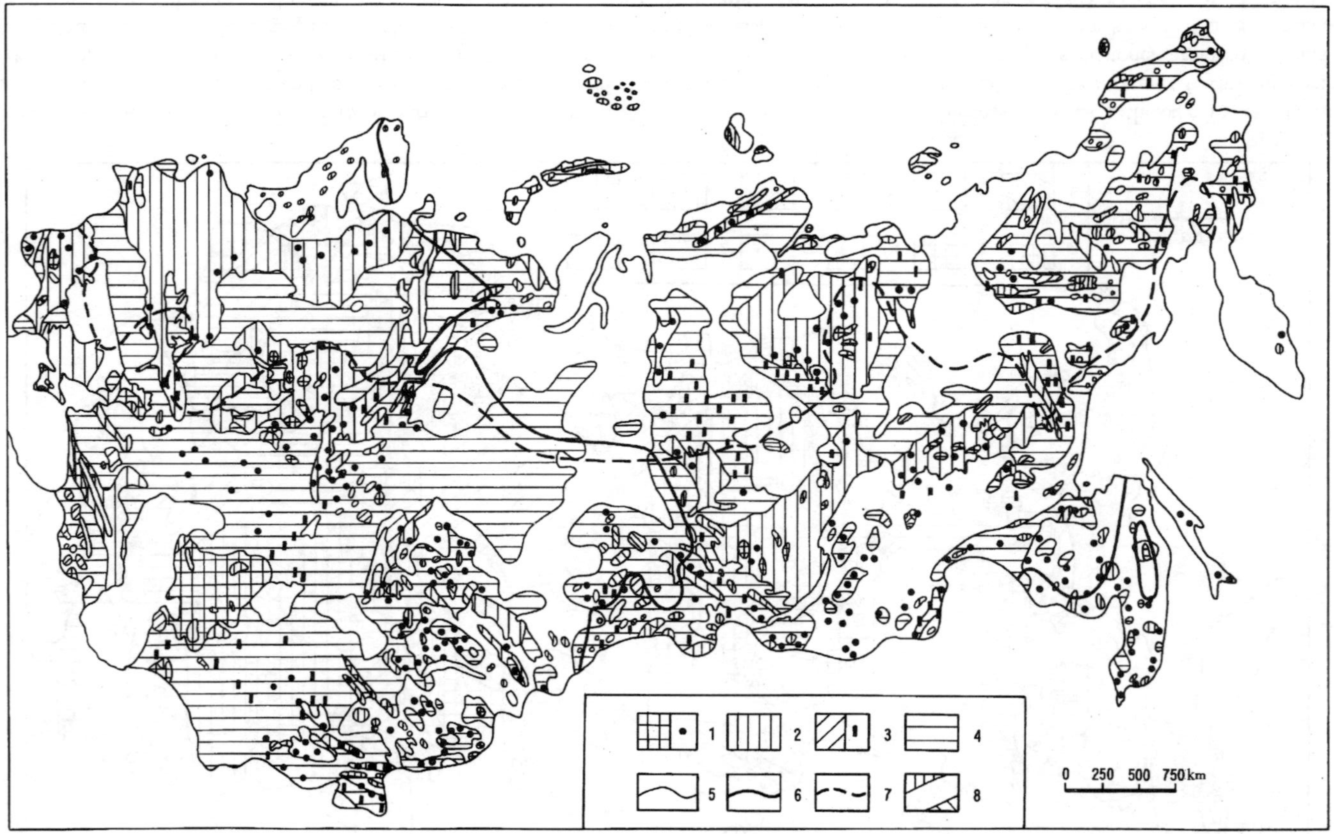

Fig. 1-10 Karst types according to the characteristics of covering rocks on the karstified strata. (by G. N. Dyblyanskaya and V. N. Dyblyansky). Karst types: 1. Bare karst: in remarkable area (left); in area less than 100 km^2(right); 2. covered karst, karstified strata covered by loose sediments more than 2m thick; 3. buried karst, karstified strata buried under non-soluble bedrock, in remarkable area (left), in area less than 100 km^2(right); 4. covered-buried karst, karstified strata underlying both loose sediments and non-soluble bedrock. Boundaries: 5. between karst type; 6. southern limit of permafrost; 7. line of maximum Quaternary Deposit; 8, Non-soluble rock

are unique in the region. Actually, evaporite karst is important for the whole territory of Russian Platform. On the other hand, western Ural provides a good example for humid cold temperate karst.

(1) New ideas on karst ecological system. From humid subtropical experiences, it has been generally considered that the development of underground drainage system is unfavorable for agriculture because it brings about leakage of water, and drought on the surface. However, Russian colleagues find the advantage of underground course for agriculture by draining away excess surface water, as verified by the contrast between Northern and Southern Perm. In its North, agriculture can hard develop in the Taiga and bog regions, but in the South, potato, tomato, and many other crops are growing, following intensive karstification and development of subterranean drainage system (Photo 29).

(2) Water Quality. One problem comes from the waste piles of potassium and other salt mining. Each pile totaling several hundred millions cubic meters is so big that the TDS of water leaching from it is as high as 6 – 120 g/l, which pollutes water resources in a remarkable area (Photo 30). Another source of pollution is from the wells that attract oil from the Permian reef and other lower reservoirs.

(3) Karst collapses. Many incidents of this kind have taken place around Perm region. Some of them are related to salt mining, e.g., a big collapse happened in January, 1986 in the Taiga above Berezniki Potassium Mine. It is elliptical on the plane, with the long axis about 100 m. 1.3 million m^3 of water invaded into the mining tunnel, and caused serious damage (Photo 31). There are also natural karst collapses in carbonate rock. One of them 40m in diameter occurred near the Siberia Railway in June, 1949, which sank a farmer's house, and promoted scientific research on this geological hazard in the former USSR. Karst collapses are very common in the whole area of Russian Platform, some of the modern ones are inherited from paleokarst collapses, dating back even to late Carboniferous, as reported by Russian scientists from detailed works for Moscow Subway and other urban engineering geological investigations.

(4) Permanent ice in cave. On north latitude of 58°, Perm is not in a permafrost region. But there are permanent ice storage in the entrance part of Kungur Cave. It is the result of the special way in heat exchange and storage between surface and different parts of the cave system with chimney effect. Russian colleagues have given the explanation with their data from many years of monitoring and experimental works (Photo 26).

1.3.5 *Karst Correlation between Appalachian Mt. and Central Basin of Kentucky, and Relevant Environmental Problems* (*August*, 1992)

(1) Karst features at Appalachian Mt., Appalachian Plateau, and Central Basin are different, as a result of differences in tectonism and relief. The Appalachian Mt. extends in NE direction at the western border of Virginia State, with a general width of 100 Km. The landscape is characterized by northeast oriented ridges and valleys, with elevation 1000 – 2000m asl. on the ridge, and 300 – 500 m asl at valley. Because of the strong folding, thrusting, and uplifting, and many insoluble formation in Paleozoic Group, the macroscopic landscape of Appalachian Range is normal shape mountain. Karst features, such as natural tunnels (Photo 32), swallet streams are available where streams flow through carbonate rock area. At the Great Valley along the eastern side of Appalachian Mountain, karst features are more concentrated. Underlain by Cambrian and Ordovician dolomite and limestone, there are many small, shallow dolinen, and big caves (Photo 23). The Appalachian plateau lies on the eastern part of West Virginia State. The altitude of the plateau surface is 700 – 1000 m asl. The strata with gentle dip enjoy a two layer structure. The Pennsylvania sandstone on the surface is underlain by the main karstified strata, the Mississippi limestone of lower Carbonifer-

ous. In those parts where the Mississippi limestone exposed following deep dissection, there are a lot of typical karst features, such as deep dolinen, uvala, and sinkhole (Photo 33). However, they never match with cone karst which is widespread in south China subtropical region. The Central Basin of Kentucky State with surface altitude 300 – 400 m asl. has the similar geological background as Appalachian Plateau. The Pennsylvania sandstone covers the highland, but as a result of long time denudation its thickness is limited. The underlying Mississippi limestone exposes in many places, where skylights of subterranean stream, sinkholes, vertical shafts can often be seen. Under the joint action of vertical percolating water and allogenic water, the world's longest cave, the Mammoth Cave System has developed under the highland. On the lowland, numerous shallow, dish-shaped dolinen form the well-known Sinkhole Plain (Photo 20).

(2) Environmental Problems. The ecological system in the Appalachian and Kentucky karst area is good through long time of careful cultivation. Most areas are covered by forest or pasture. Bare carbonate rocks which are widespread in South China or Mediterranean karst are very rare here. Water pollution problems in karst area are getting better after some waste water treatment plants are put into use. Awful smell which used to fill some caves (such as the Horse Cave in Kentucky) has now been improved remarkably. However, local residents still concern about landfill in karst area, e. g., the feasibility of Pulaski landfill is questioned although it has already been put into use for one year. People are not satisfied with the explanation that there is an impermeable bed between the landfill and the underlying caves and karst springs. Another problem is the environmental Radon. Air from some of the Kentucky caves was used for air-conditioning in residence or greenhouse (Photo 34), but is now abandoned because it is found that the Radon concentration in the cave air is too high. The origin of the Radon has been investigated, and some conclusions reached.

1.3.6 *Karst Correlation between Australia Craton and Tasmania Mobile Zone* (*Dec*., 1992)

(1) There are significant differences between karst features at the Australian Craton and those of the Tasmania Mobile Zone, as a result of difference in geology and climate. The Tasmania Mobile Zone distributes at the mountainous regions of eastern part of New South Wales and Victoria states, with a general relief of 1000 m, and a summit of 2234 m at the southern border of NSW. It is generally covered by dense forest predominated by Gondwana flora of Eucalyptus and some others such as Casuarina. Thousands meters of lower Paleozoic marine deposit and volcanic rocks were strongly folded, with a general strike of NS, and medium to vertical dip angle. There are about 100 m of limestone in the Silurian System near Canberra. Whereas in Buchan area of Victoria, there are pure reef limestone and several layers of carbonate rocks with thickness ranging between 40 – 190 m in lower Devonian Series. Cenozoic volcanism was active here, e.g. near Cooma, about 100 km to the South of Canberra. Tertiary basalt is found filling caves in Silurian limestone. In Buchan, basalt dated back 40 millions years by K/Ar approach covers Eocene terrace gravel. This geological background along with humid climate brings about a hydrological setting where aggressive allogenic water flows into limestone area and forms a special type of karst with intensive karstification, which Australia colleagues call as "impounded karst". The karst features of this type include solutional doline, big collapse doline, swallet stream, natural bridge, kilometer long cave passages with many phreatic or vadose dissolutional feature and various types of speleothem. However, micro surface features, such as deep sharp subaerial karren which could usually be seen in humid karst with bare rock, such as in South China, Yorkshire and UK, are rare here although available. Perhaps the dense forest prevents the direct corrosional process of rainfall on limestone surface. The soil cover in this region is dark, and dark brown lime soil in general.

The Australian Craton extends from western part of Victoria through South Australia and West Australia states. It was a part of Gondwana Land which disintegrated after Triassic period. The old land had undergone long time of denudation before Cretaceous when a major transgression covered most part of the Central and Northern Australia. Later, considerable transgression occurred again during Tertiary time in the coastal areas, which deposited 100 – 400 m of Tertiary carbonate rocks. The lithology is porous, with chert concretions in some layers. The bedding planes are usually horizontal except some cross-beddings. After the regression of Late Tertiary, Pleistocene sand dunes 20 – 40 m high accumulated on some beaches, which became calcarenite afterward. There are about 100 Quaternary craters on the border between Victoria and South Australia. The latest eruption was at 4000a BP, but the geothermal impact on karstification is uncertain. The modern surface elevation is 30 – 80 m in general, but there are 200 – 300 m high low hills and knobs on Eyre Peninsula in South Australia State. On the coast lines underlain by Tertiary limestone, there are usually a cliff 70 – 80 m high, with a broad, endless plain behind it. As the modern climate changes from semiarid to arid westwards, the vegetation also changes from Eucalyptus forest at east to xerophile grass in Nullarbor Plain (the Latin word means a treeless plain) gradually. The geological and topographical background, along with a dry climate but still having annual mean rainfall of about 200 mm gives rise to a hydrological setting with considerable hydraulic gradients, which is good for development of karst, especially underground features. The most attractive karst features on the Cenozoic carbonate rocks are the coastal limestone towers (Photo 35), the blowhole and vertical shafts on the Nullarbor Plain, and the long cave system beneath it. Some of the caves are 1 – 4 km long, with great halls, underground streams and lakes, others are decorated with many carbonate and evaporite speleothems. Moreover, following the development of underground drainage system, shallow dish-like dolinen develop around some blowholes, which can swallow surface flood into underground passage. For example, the doline on the surface of Thampanna Cave has a catchment area of 12 km^2. It can be inundated in some wet years, after the 40 m deep cave system was filled up by the flood. The carbonate hardness of the water in cave passage is low (less than 4 in German degree), which shows that this kind of rainfall-recharged water is aggressive. However, dripping water in cave is usually saturated, with carbonate hardness of 11 – 13 degree, and good for speleothem forming. Micro surface features are rare on these Cenozoic porous weak carbonate rocks, but we did see some good karren where there are encrustation of case-hardening. The soil is reddish brown in general, with Fe-Mn concretions being very common. The Australian arid karst on Cenozoic carbonate rocks is different from either arid karst in other part of the world, such as Northwest China, or Yucatan karst on young carbonate rocks, at its bigger underground passages and relevant surface features. It is different from the former because it enjoys more rainfall and weaker rock. It is different from the latter because it has been more uplifted and thence has a favourable hydrological setting.

(2) Karst Environment. The situation is good in general. Natural forests and wildlife are well protected. There are many kangaroos en route the excursion. Moreover, Southern Australia is an area of low geomorphic entropy. Participants were told that natural hazards, such as storm, flood, soil erosion and earthquake are not serious in this region. According to the research with ^{137}Cs, ^{10}Be and some other nuclides, their higher concentration appears on the 5 cm surface soil of highland. In Buchan area, the Eocene terrace alluvium gravel still remains about 200 m above the local base level. However, there are some particular environmental problems in South Australian karst regions.

Salinization. In some areas, water table rises up after changing forest into pasture. It is estimated that one piece of Eucalyptus tree can evaporate 250 liters of water from the aquifer per day. Hence the forest clearing can bring about water table rise and salinization under the climate where evaporation is much higher than precipitation. The remedy measures are to lower down the water table by planting trees on the hills around the pasture, and constructing drainage system on the basin.

Cave Environment. Some of the Australia caves have too high CO_2 content. Moreover, Australian colleagues are aware of the Radon problem, which is now being studied. The conflict between world Heritage Protection in Exit Cave of Tasmania and limestone quarry has been solved recently through negotiation.

Bush Fire. It is found from stalagmite record that Bush Fire is more a natural than a man-made disaster, as some of the events can be dated back to hundreds thousand years. The ecological features of some Eucalyptus forests have fitted this situation, and can survive Bush Fire.

Drinking Water. Because of salinization problem, rainwater is used for domestic water supply in many areas. In general, the hygiene system to accumulate roof water is good. However, the mineralization of rainwater is too low, and there may be a shortage of some trace elements, necessary for human body. Compulsory measures has been taken in some areas to use tablets for compensation.

1.3.7 *Glacial Karst in SE Canada* (*August*, 1993)

Two excursions of IGCP 299 were related to glacial karst. The first was in SE Canada (August, 1993), and the other in UK (September, 1994). Glacial karst is referred to karst developed under a climatic, topographical and hydrological condition controlled by the ice sheet of the last glaciation which took place between 15000 and 12000 years B.P. (the Wisconsinan, Fig. 1-11).

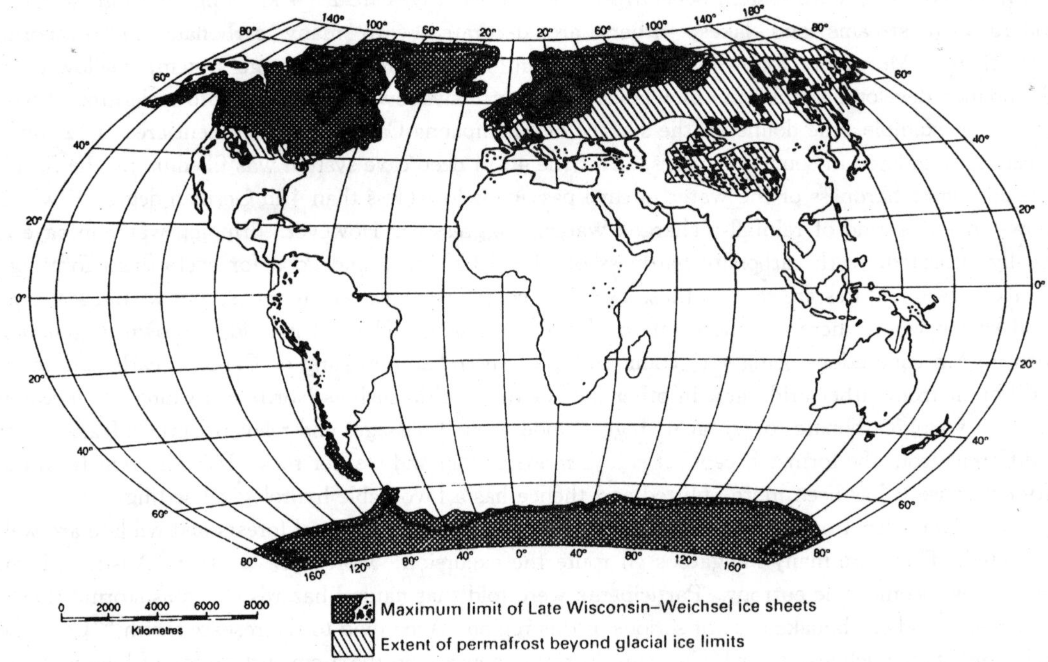

Fig. 1-11 Maximum extent of ice sheets and permafrost at the last glacial maximum (Williams, 1993)

According to D. C. Ford the extension of naked (bare) carbonate karst outcrop in Canada is 900000km^2, the covered karst about 100000 km^2. The approximate number of known caves in carbonate rocks is 500, with a total length of 100 km. Area of gypsum karst is 80000 km^2, number of surveyed caves 50, total length 20 km. The most important Canadian karst areas are shown on Fig. 1-12.

The IGCP 299 excursion organized by Derek Ford took place in SE Canada between Huron Lake and Niagara Fall, covered by ice sheet during the last glaciation. It was from August 23

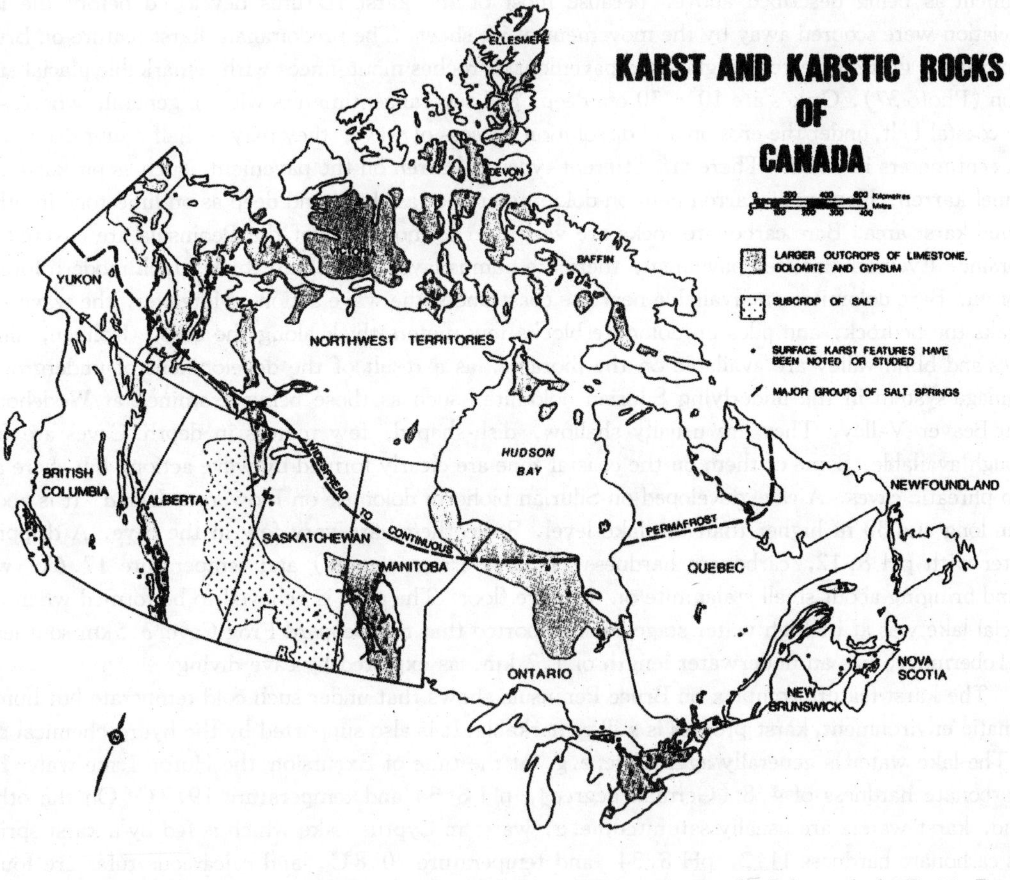

Fig. 1-12 Map of the outcrop of karstic rocks in Canada, plus the subcrop of salt beneath the Prairie Provinces (Ford, 1993)

through Aug. 31, 1993, and started from Hamilton, in conjunction with the 3rd International Geomorphology Conference, and its B_5 excursion on glacial and coastal karst, Bruce Peninsula, Ontario. 61 persons from 21 countries participated the meeting and field trip.

The modern climate of the area is a cold temperate humid one, with annual mean temperature 6.5℃, annual mean precipitation 850 – 1000mm (about 30% falling as snow), and evapotranspiration losses about 50 – 60%. Geologically, the area is underlain by massive dolomite of upper Silurian 50m thick, with intercalation of shaly or cherty beds, and red, green shale of lower Silurian and upper Ordovician more than 100m thick. The geological structure of the region is rather simple, with a general dip of strata southwesterly at 5 – 6m per km. The difference in resistance to weathering between upper Silurian dolomite and the underlying shale, along with the effect of basal ice scour during the last glaciation with a dominant direction of 235° made an escarpment hundred meters high extending 200 km north-westward from Niagara Fall (Photo 36) to Tobermary at the terminal of Bruce Peninsula. The dolomite which forms the caprock of the escarpment is the stage for all the karst features examined during the Excursion. The geological and topographic setting of the dolomite strata provides a favourable hydrological condition for karst formation. The hydraulic gradient could be even more steep 10 220 years ago when the lake surface was about 60 m lower than present.

Participants got a good idea of what karst process can do in ten thousand years under the environment as being described above, because most of the karst features developed before the last glaciation were scoured away by the movement of ice sheet. The predominant karst feature on Bruce Peninsula is grike dissected on glaciated pavement or roches moutonnees with remarkable glacial striation (Photo 37). Grikes are 10 – 30 cm deep, and several centimeters wide in general, whereas in the coastal belt, under the erosion and dissolution process of wave, they may be half meter deep, and ten centimeters in width. There are different types of karren on the pavement, such as pit karren or runnel karren. However, karren here on dolomite are not as sharp and deep as on limestone in other humid karst area. Bare carbonate rocks are very rare as most part of the Peninsula are covered by moraine. Even on glaciated pavement, there are humus layer 20 – 30cm thick which modern forests rely on. Bare dolomites are available near the coast under the wave action. Moreover, the wave also breaks the bedrock, and piles up dolomite blocks few meters thick along the coast. Dolinen, sinkholes and blind valley are available on the moraine, as a result of the development of underground drainage system in the underlying Silurian dolomite, such as those being examined at Wodehouse near Beaver Valley. They are usually shallow, dish-shaped, few meters in depth. Caves are few though available. Some of them on the coastal zone are clearly formed by wave action, but there are also phreatic caves. A cave developed on Silurian bioherm dolomite on Flowerpot Island. It is about 50m long and 30 m higher than the lake level. Speleothems are very few in the cave. A dripping water with pH 8.12, carbonate hardness 11.2 (German degree) and temperature 17.6℃ was found bringing about small stalagmite on the cave floor. The cave is believed to be formed when the glacial lake was at its high water stage. It is reported that the Leopard Frog Cave, 3.5km southeast of Tobermory, has an underwater length of 1.2 km, as explored by cave diving.

The karst feature complex on Bruce Peninsula shows that under such cold temperate but humid climatic environment, karst process is still remarkable. It is also supported by the hydro-chemical data. The lake water is generally aggressive, e.g. at the time of Excursion, the Huron Lake water has a carbonate hardness of 4.8 (German degree), pH 8.34 and temperature 19.7℃. On the other hand, karst waters are usually saturated, e.g. water in Cyprus Lake which is fed by a karst spring has carbonate hardness 11.2, pH 8.34, and temperature 20.8℃, and calcareous tufas are found precipitating on Lake bottom (Photo 38). Perhaps the forest plays some role in intensifying the carbon cycle and the karst process. For instance, the CO_2 content in the humus atmosphere under the forest on Flowerpot Island is 12 000 ppm (at depth of 10 cm) at the time of Excursion. This figure is much higher than that under the forest in some arid region, such as North China. However, it is not as intensive as tropical and subtropical karst, where the carbonate hardness of karst spring in summer time could be much higher and there are big speleothem formation in caves, and thick calcareous tufa on surface stream under the forest.

There were some ecological problems in last century, when most part of Bruce Peninsula was logged for its timber and to settle it for permanent cultivation in the period 1850 – 1900 A.D. The first phase of soil losses might have happened, but is difficult to evaluate now. Since the 1930s, an attempt of farming this area has been abandoned gradually, because of unsuitable karst. Consequently, 60 – 70% of the Peninsula including those areas with bare dolomite pavement or rock blocks are now covered by secondary mixed forest with cedar, balsam fir, jack pine, white pine, birch and hemlock as its major species (photo 39). The trees are 10 – 20 m high. People were told that all of them are 120 years (oldest) to 10 – 20 years in age. Participants from tropical, subtropical or Mediterranean karst, who are facing problems of rock desertification were encouraged from the fact they saw on the Bruce Peninsula.

1.3.8 *Zagros Karst and Other Types of Karst in Iran* (*Oct.*, 1993)

Carbonate rocks of Middle Jurassic to Miocene are remarkable in Iran, especially in Zagros Mt. region at its southwest (Fig. 1-13, E. Raiessi).

The excursion in Zagros Mt. karst organized by A. Afrasiabian concentrated in Kazeron and Maharlu area, and was parallel with the International Symposium on water resources in karst of arid and semiarid zone (Shiraz). 63 persons from 6 countries were at the event.

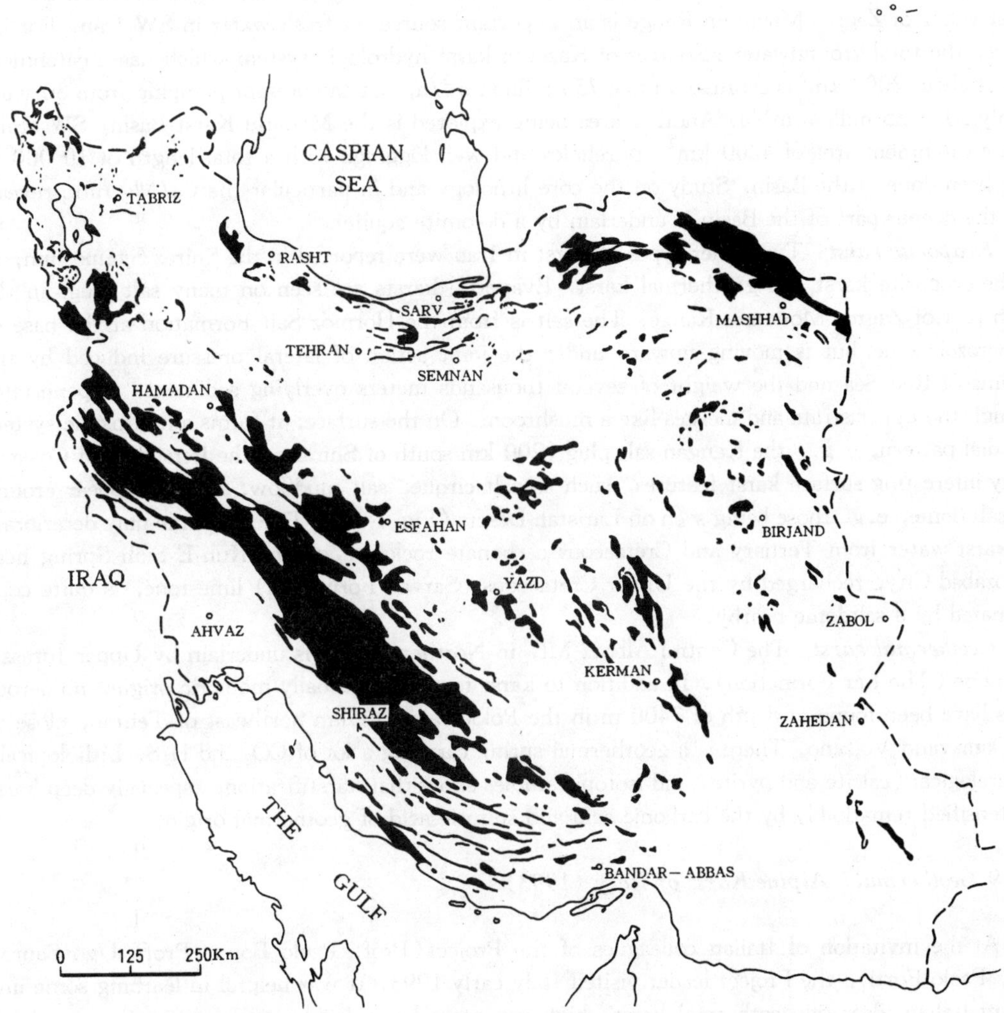

Fig. 1-13 The distribution of carbonate rocks in Iran (E. Raiessi)

People got some ideas about karst in the Zagros Mountain from the excursion around Kazeron City, 160 km to the West of Shiraz. The area is at the southern Part of Zagros Range, 3000 – 4000m asl and about 30°N latitude. It is mainly underlain by carbonate rocks of Oligo - Miocene to upper Cretaceous. The strata has a predominant strike of NW - SE, as a result of tectonic compression induced by the opening of Red Sea. The annual mean temperature is 12℃, with annual precipitation ranging between 142 and 1065mm, so it is considered to be a semiarid to semihumid climate. However, Zagros Mountain is covered by snow for many months each year. The snow melting water plays an important role in karstification. Consequently, Zagros karst is neither like humid subtropical karst as those of South China, nor like semiarid karst as those of North China. In addition to dry valleys and big karst springs (with discharge ranging between 1 to 15 m^3/s), which are very common in North China semiarid karst, there are also remarkable karren, dolines, sinkholes (e.g., near Sepidan, NW Shiraz), caves (e.g., Shapour Cave), even karst lake (e.g., Parishan Lake). Karst water of Zagros Mountain Range is an important source for fresh water in SW Iran. For instance, the total groundwater resources of Kazeron karst hydrologic system which has a catchment area of about 2000 km^2 is estimated to be 750 million m^3/a, but the present pumping from 30 wells is only 20 - 25 million m^3/a. Another area being explored is the Maharlu Karst Basin, SW Iran, with a catchment area of 4200 km^2. Boreholes and well loggings with a total length of 10 000 m have been done in the Basin. Study on the core lithology and in particular the Ca/Mg ratio reveals that the deeper part of the Basin is underlain by a dolomite aquifer.

Evaporite karst. Two other types of karst in Iran were reported in the Shiraz Symposium, i.e. the evaporite karst and geothermal karst. Evaporite karsts are seen on many salt plugs in the south part of Zagros Mountain Range. The salt is from the Hormoz Salt Formation at the base of phanerozoic zone, but is moving upward under the joint action of lateral pressure induced by the opening of Red Sea and the weight of several thousands meters overlying sediment. It penetrates through the upper strata and merges like a mushroom. On the surface, it forms a hydrologic system of radial pattern, e.g., the Kangan salt plug (200 km south of Shiraz on the Persian Gulf Coast). Many interesting surface karst features, such as salt cirque, salt mudflow, salt fall appear around the salt dome, e.g. those being seen on Laristan Desert (Fig.1-14). The salt dome may deteriorate the karst water from Tertiary and Cretaceous carbonate rocks, e.g. the Kuh-E Siah Spring near Firoozabad City, recharged by the Upper Cretaceous (Sarvak Formation) limestone, is quite contaminated by a saltdome nearby.

Geothermal karst. The Central Alborz Mt. in Northern Iran, is underlain by Upper Jurassic limestone (The Lar Formation). In addition to karst features of usually meteoric origin, numerous caves have been found at depth of 7400 m in the Polour area, 85km northeast of Tehran, close to the Damavand Volcano. There is a geothermal spring carrying a lot of CO_2 and H_2S. Lithological, Mineralogical (calcite and pyrite) and isotopic studies show that karstification, especially deep karst is intensified remarkably by the carbonic acid and sulfuric acid of geothermal origin.

1.3.9 *Geothermal, Alpine Karst of Italy* (1993)

At the invitation of Italian colleagues of the Project (Prof. Paolo Bono, Prof. Ugo Sauro, Prof. Paolo Forti), the Project leader visited Italy early 1993. It was helpful in learning some important Italian ideas on geothermal karst, high mountain karst, and gypsum karst from a global view.

Geothermal karst. Being active in modern volcanism and Neotectonism, and widespread in Mesozoic carbonate rocks, Central Italy around Rome is an ideal site for studying karst process of geothermal origin. Under the influence of deep source CO_2, some of the carbonate rock aquifers are natural CO_2 reservoirs, such as the Ferrarelle Mineral Water Field (Photo 40). The CO_2 concentration on the water surface of many karst spring may be more than 6%. The hydrochemistry of the karst water are characterized by very low pH (6 - 7, even less than 4), high carbonate hardness (usually more than 20 in German degree, even more than 80). Moreover, there are widespread tufa

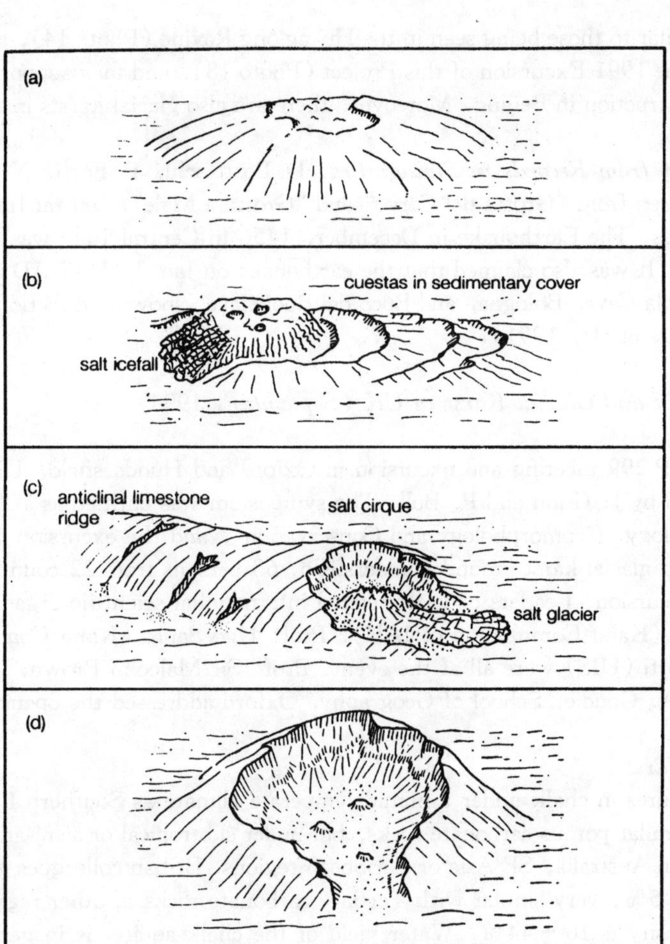

Fig.1-14 Evolution of halite karst: the surface expression of salt domes in Laristan Desert, Iran (Jennings, 1985)

deposits dating back to Pleistocene (Photo 2). All of these show an intensive carbon cycle, and karst process.

Incongruent dissolution. In the Spipola Cave, Bologna, many calcite speleothems are found under this gypsum cave. It tells that under some biogeochemical environment, sulfates can be replaced by carbonates, and the importance of synergetic effect of interaction between lithosphere, hydrosphere, atmosphere and biosphere should be taken into consideration in studying carbon cycle and its relation to karst process (Photo 41).

High Mountain karst. On the pre-Alps mountain near Bossano, small limestone pinnacles of frost denudation origin, matching with limestone scree are found widespread on the slope (Photo

42). It is very similar to those being seen in the Huanglong Ravine (Photo 14), and western suburb of Beijing during the 1991 Excursion of this Project (Photo 18), and may support the idea of paleo-environment reconstruction in Beijing. Moreover, there are also glacial karsts in Alps Mt. of North Italy (Photo 43).

Paleoseismicity from Records in Stalagmites. D. Postpischl, P. Forti, Y. Quinif and others used stalagmites taken from "Grotta del Cervo" and "Grotta a Male", central Italy for tectonic and paleoseismic analyses. The Earthquake in December, 1456 in Central Italy was found recording as stalagmite collapse. It was also claimed that the earthquake on Jan. 3, 1117 AD is expressed in stalagmites from Spipola Cave, Bologna, and Buco dei Buoi Cave, showing direction change in growth axes (Postpischl, D. et al., 1991).

1.3.10 *Chalk Karst and Glacial Karst in UK* (*September*, 1994)

The final IGCP 299 meeting and excursion in Oxford and Huddersfield, UK, Sept. 11 – 23, 1994 was organized by J. Gunn and P. Bull. The symposium was entitled as "Changing Karst Environments: Hydrology, Geomorphology and Conservation", and the excursion was on chalk karst around Oxford, and glacial karst around Huddersfield. 68 persons from 22 countries participated in the meeting and excursion. Leaders of karst-related international scientific organizations, including Prof. Heinz Hoetzl (Karst Commission of IAH), Prof. Ugo Sauro (Karst Commission of IGU), and Prof. Paolo Forti (UIS) were all at the event. Prof. Sir Malcolm Brown, Chairman of IGCP Board, and Prof. A. Goudie, School of Geography, Oxford addressed the opening session.

1.3.10.1 *Chalk Karst*

The karst features in chalk under a humid temperate climate as Southern England were compared to those in similar porous carbonate rocks, but under subtropical or semi-arid climate, such as Nullarbor, Southern Australia, SE Asia or Caribbean regions. British colleagues give the porosity of chalk as 23.5 – 39.5%, very similar with Tertiary carbonate rocks of other region, e.g. in Florida, USA, the porosity is 16 – 44%. Water yield of the chalk aquifer is in general high, for instance, during the experiments at West Berkshire Groundwater Scheme (about 40 km south of Oxford, and 20 km west of Reading) which lasted 87 days in 1976, an average of 85 000 m^3/day was pumped out from 28 boreholes sunk 90 – 195 m deep into Cretaceous chalk aquifer. The results show that the chalk aquifer is more or less homogeneous, in contrast to the great heterogeneity of old phase hard compact carbonate rock. However, Cretaceous chalk in London Basin has little surface or subsurface karst feature, as being shown en route the excursion, or at the deep quarry (Playhatch near Reading, Photo 44) and downhole TV inspection (West Berkshire Groundwater Scheme). Some British colleagues believe that the aquifer media of chalk is a fissure-porosity type rather than a karst-fissure type. This idea is also supported by hydrodynamic and hydrochemical data. Accordingly, karst in chalk of London Basin is quite different with those of the porous carbonate rocks at other parts of the world, where big caves, underground streams, and many surface features, such as dolinen, towers are available, being examined during previous excursions of IGCP 299 Project. The reasons of such contrast are believed to be the consolidation of porous carbonate rocks by calcareous cementation under warmer or arid climate, with higher evaporation or intensive carbon cycle, so waters are easily to be saturated with respect to carbonates. The locally hard, compact lithological features in porous carbonate rocks under arid or tropical condition make some large karst features possible to survive in the generally weak rocks.

1.3.10.2 *Glacial Karst*

The excursions at Yorkshire Dales and Great Asby Scar Nature Reserve, Cumbria provided a chance to compare glacial karst of UK with those of the Bruce Peninsula, Canada. Both areas were covered by ice sheet thousands of meter thick during the last glaciation. Limestone pavement (Photo 45) is the common feature of the two areas and is the background of karstification in the past 12000 years or so. Caves and surface karst features such as dolinen, dissolutional fissures, kamenitza are available in both areas, but there are remarkable differences. In Yorkshire Dales or Great Asby Scar, UK, deep, sharp karren (Photo 46) are widespread on limestone pavement, but it is scarcely seen in Bruce Peninsula, Canada. It is believed that the medium to coarse grained Silurian dolomite in Canada is not as favourable for karren to be preserved as compact Carboniferous limestone of UK. Caves are well developed under the glacial karst of UK. It is reported that there are about 600 km of cave passages surveyed in the Carboniferous limestone of UK, many of them are under glacial karst. But in Bruce Peninsula, caves are very few. The only long cave reported is the 1200 m Leopard Frog Cave near Tobermory, but is, under water level of Georgian Bay and only accessible by divers. It is considered that the Pennine ridge in North England with a relief of several hundreds meters and the acidic water from peat covering limestone have created a favourable hydrological condition for cave formation, whereas the relief in the Great Lake Region of North American is low. Although remarkable caves were developed in the low water stand during glaciation, they are now under the lake water, and difficult for an overall survey.

1.3.10.3 *Environmental Problems of Karst*

Enjoying humid climate, generally covered by grass, with very few bare limestone rock, environmental especially ecological problems in karst of England are not as serious as tropical karst or Mediterranean karst, where rock desertification is usually a great challenge. However, as one of the earliest industrialized countries, with higher population, karst in England is facing more environmental issues than IGCP 299 previously visited correlation sites, e.g., Bruce Peninsula of Canada.

Water pollution. The thin soil on chalk or Jurassic limestone at South England was traditionally used for pasture, but since the late 1940s there has been a change to cereal and oilseed rape cultivation. This more intensive agriculture has been sustained only through increased use of fertilizers and pesticides. Accordingly, in some areas, e.g., Ogbounne and Banbury, nitrate concentrations in ground water are now above the acceptable limit(50 mg/l). Changes in agricultural practice to reduce nitrate concentrations in groundwater is being tested. In Peak District and Yorkshire Dales, animal husbandry and the use of fertilizers and pesticides on the catchment area of karst hydrological systems have caused serious nitrates, phosphates and faecal coliforms pollution to the subterranean streams and karst springs in Carboniferous limestone.

Environmental impact of quarries. Carboniferous limestone is the most quarried in Britain accounting for over 60% of its limestone production. Quarrying has removed some surface karst features and caves in their entirety. Quarrying under water table threatens some interesting karst hydrological features, e.g., turlough, a seasonal lake which is filled and drained by ground water can be permanently drained. Smaller scale extraction for garden rockery stone is a particular threat to pavement in numerous limestone areas of Northern England. For example, on the Orton-Asby escarpment, Cumbria, 17 hectares of unique dissolutional features (karren, kamenitza, etc.) developed after the last glaciation has been removed during the past hundred years especially in the 1960s, 1970s and more recently. Conservation legislation has been enacted in UK to protect such natural beauty, relevant national parks and Sites of Special Scientific Interest(SSSI) have been designated.

Radon problem. In some caves in UK, the Radon concentration is very high and is a new problem for the health of cavers and cave management, e.g. the Castleton Cave, Peak District.

1.3.10.4 *Paleoenvironment Reconstruction with Karst Records*

The Creswell Crags karst area, 20 km to the southeast of Sheffield, is the second richest fossil vertebrate site in the world. More than 190 species of Mammals, birds, reptiles, amphibians and fish have been recorded from the cave deposit. Moreover, there are many Upper and Middle Palaeolithic stone artifacts. Several stages of karstification in the Permian magnesium limestone are distinguished. The earliest one could be dated back to the unconformity between Permian and Triassic. Multidisciplinary study at Robin Hood's Cave on clastic sediments, vertebrate fossils, paleopalynology, karst features(scallops) and flowstone dating (165 ka – 2.2 ka BP) have revealed the history of climate change for the past 500 000 years. Several stages of glaciation and interglacial are identified.

References

AAAS, 1983. Annual meeting program, Detroit, Michigan, 26 – 31 May: 39

Berner, E.K. and R.A. Berner, 1987. The global water cycle, geochemistry and environment. Prentice – Hall, New Jersey, pp. 35 – 43

Bogli, A., 1960. Kalklosung und karstbildung. Z. Geomorph., N.F., Suppl. – Bd.2, Internationale Beitraege Zur Karstmorphologie, pp.4 – 21

Ford, D.C. and P.W. Williams, 1989. Karst Geomorphology and Hydrology. Unwin Hyman, London

Ford, D.C., 1993. Karst and Caves in Canada. Karszt es Barlang, Budapest IGBP, 1992. Reducing Uncertainties: 35

Jennings, J.N., 1985. Karst Geomorphology, Brasil Blackwell, Oxford: 197

Lehmann, H., 1936. Morphologische Studien auf Java. Geog. Abhandl. III, Stuttgart

Liu, Z., U. Svensson, W. Dreybrodt, D. Yuan and D. Buhmann, 1995. Hydrodynamic control of inorganic calcite precipitation in Huanglong Ravine, China: field measurements and theoretical prediction of depositional rate. Geochim. Cosmochim. Acta, Vol. 59, No.15, pp. 3087 – 3097

Mackenzie, F.T. and J.A. Mackenzie, 1995. Our Changing Planet, an Introduction to

Earth System Science and Global Environmental Change. Prentice – Hall, New Jersey: 359

Nature and Resources, 1994. Vol.30, No.3 – 4, UNESCO, Parthenon Publishing: 27

Postpischl, D., S. Agostini, P. Forti and Y. Quinif, 1991. Paleoseismicity from karst sediments: the "Grotta del Cervo" cave case study (central Italy), in M. Stucchi, D. Postpischl and D. Slejko (eds), Investigation of Historical Earthquake in Europe, Tectonophysics, Vol.193, pp.33 – 44

Simsek, S., 1993. Karst hot water aquifers in Turkey. IAHS Publ. no.207, pp.173 – 184

Sweeting, M.M., 1972. Karst landforms. Macmillan, London

Trudgill, S., 1985. Limestone Geomorphology. Longman, London: 17

Williams, M.A.J., D.L. Dunkerley, P. De Deckker, A.P. Kershaw and T. Stokes, 1993. Quaternary Environments. Edward Arnold, London, p.32

Yuan, D. and W. Back, 1991. IGCP project 299: Geology, Climate, Hydrology and Karst Formation. Episodes, Vol.14, No.1, pp. 80 – 81

Global Karst Correlation
Edited by Yuan Daoxian and Liu Zaihua
Science Press and VSP BV, 1998

Chapter 2 Principles of Karst Evolution from Initiation to Maturity and Their Relation to Physics and Chemistry

Wolfgang Dreybrodt
Institute of Experimental Physics,
University of Bremen, D-28334 Bremen, Germany

2.1 Introduction

Karst processes are driven by chemical, physical, and hydrogeological forces. Fig. 2-1 illustrates schematically an uplifted limestone block which is dissected by various primary fractures such as joints and bedding planes at the onset of karstification. Some of these comprise percolating pathways from the upper surface to a valley, through which by the relief surface water present at some input points at the top is driven down to the valley. The solutional attack of this CO_2-containing water widens these fractures by chemical dissolution of the bedrock and underground drainage networks may result. To understand the evolution of karstification on its scales in space and time one has to specify by which parameters these processes are determined.

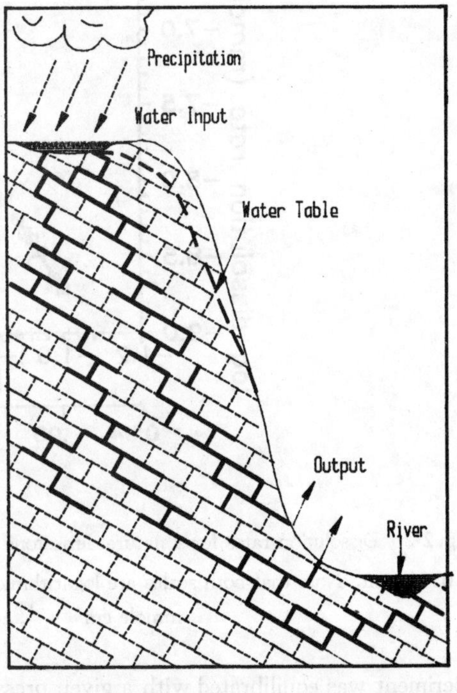

Fig. 2-1 Schematic drawing of a karst aquifer in its initial state. The full lines represent a net of percolating pathways of narrow initial fractures leading water from the water input to the outputs

Karstification proceeds in two steps. During the initiation phase, illustrated in Fig. 2-1, the narrow primary fissures are completely filled with water and consequently the water table is high. The fractures are slowly widened by solutional attack of water close to equilibrium until they have enlarged to such an extent that the flow no longer stays laminar but becomes turbulent and the system is drained effectively. Therefore the water table drops. In the upper vadose zone water now flows in contact to a CO_2-containing atmosphere and by dissolutional action canyons are shaped. In the lower phreatic passages the amount of water is so large and its flow rate so high that it stays far from equilibrium and therefore the second stage of mature karstification exhibits a different evolution, with quick increase of conduit dimensions accompanied by lowering of the water table(Dreybrodts, 1988; Ford and Williams, 1989; White, 1988).

In this chapter we will discuss the basic physical and chemical principles determining karstification in both the initial and the mature state of karst with the aim to understand the reasons why karst does look so different in regions with different climates and geological settings.

2.2 A Basic Model to Specify Parameters

The dissolutional activity of the water flowing through a fracture can be represented by a rate law (Palmer, 1991, Svensson and Dreybrodt, 1992)

$$F(c) = k_n(1 - c/c_{eq})^n = k_n(1 - \hat{c})^n, \hat{c} = c/c_{eq} \tag{1}$$

where k_n is in molecm^{-2}s^{-1} and its numerical value gives the amount of dissolved material per unit area and time if the solution has not yet dissolved calcite, i.e., $c = 0$. Its concentration is equal to the concentration c of the Ca^{2+}-ion (molecm^{-3}). $c_{eq}$is the saturation or equilibrium concentration of calcite.

Fig.2-2 illustrates such a rate law measured in our laboratory for a system closed with respect to CO_2. The experiment was performed as a batch experiment. 3 g of limestone particles of average diameter of 100μm were stirred by a propeller in an aqueous solution of 200 ml, which prior to the

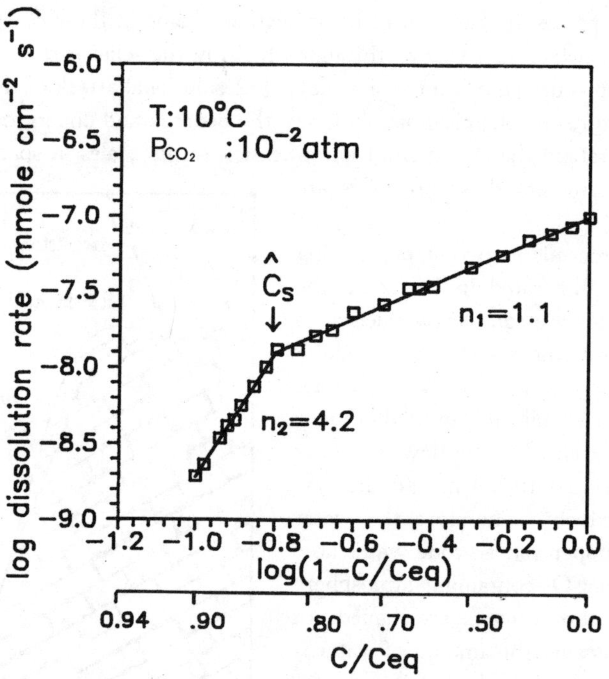

Fig.2-2 Dissolution rates for a natural limestone under closed system conditions at 10℃ with initial P_{CO_2} = 0.01 atm. Note that both scales are logarithmic. $n_1 = 1.1$, $n_2 = 4.2$, $\hat{c}_s = c_s/c_{eq} = 0.84$, $k_1 = 8 \times 10^{-8}$ mmole cm^{-2}s^{-1}, $k_2 = 1.10^{-6}$mmole cm^{-2}s^{-1}

experiment was equilibrated with a given pressure of CO_2(P_{CO_2} = 0.01 atm.). As we will see later such experiments yield the maximal possible dissolution rates, which are controlled by the chemical surface reactions. In nature these rates can be reduced drastically. Since in Fig.2-2 both $F(\hat{c})$ and $(1-\hat{c})$ are plotted logarithmically, a rate law of order n is represented by a straight line with slope n. It is important to note that at the concentration $\hat{c}_s$ there is a change of the slope resulting in a higher order of n.

Therefore the rates must be written as

$$F_1(c) = k_{n_1}(1 - \hat{c})^{n_1} \quad \text{for } \hat{c} < \hat{c}_s; \hat{c}_s = c_s / c_{eq};$$

$$F_2(c) = k_{n_2}(1 - \hat{c})^{n_2} \quad \text{for } \hat{c} \geqslant \hat{c}_s; \tag{2a}$$

where k_{n_2} is related to k_{n_1} by

$$k_{n_2} = k_{n_1} \cdot (1 - \hat{c}_s)^{n_1 - n_2} \tag{2b}$$

and c_s is the concentration where the switch to higher order n_2 occurs. Similar relations have been reported for the open system (Palmer 1991, Svensson and Dreybrodt, 1992).

The basic questions now to be answered are, how do the profiles of the percolating fractures develop in space and time, if a hydraulic head h, assumed to be constant in time, drives a calcite aggressive solution through them. How does the flow rate $Q(t)$ depend on time t? Or more generally, how does a primary fracture evolve from its initial state to a mature karst conduit?

To provide answers we simplify the problem by replacing the irregular real percolating pathway of fractures by one representative fracture of uniform shape along its length l. This shape may be rectangular or ellipsoidal, with an aperture a_0 and a breadth b_0, $b_0 \geqslant a_0$. A part of this fracture is illustrated by Fig. 2-3. At distance x from the input the concentration of calcite is $c(x)$. It increases by the material dissolved from the walls between x and $x + dx$ to a value $c(x + dx) = c(x) + dc$.

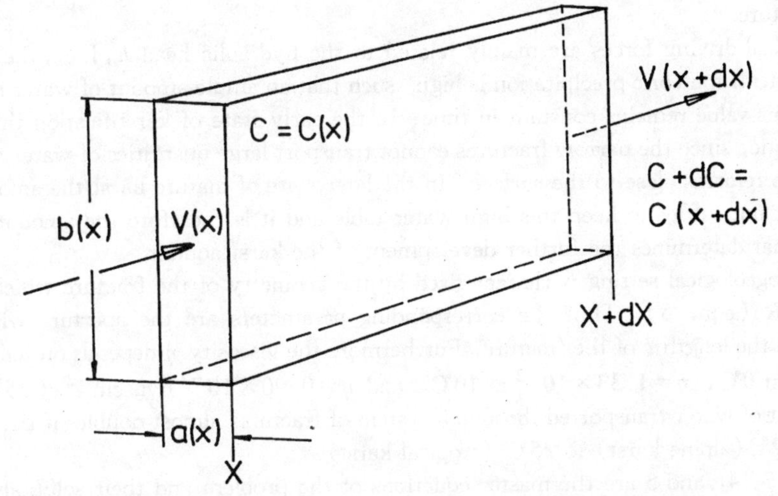

Fig. 2-3 Part of fracture along the percolating pathway at distance x from input between x and $x + dx$. The concentration $c(x)$ increases along the distance dx by dc

The flow velocity of the water is $v(x)$. $A(x)$ is the cross sectional area of the fracture, and $P(x)$ its perimeter at position x. According to the law of continuity the flow rate through the conduit does not depend on the distance x and is given by

$$Q = v(x) \cdot A(x) \tag{3}$$

Now conservation of mass requires that the amount of calcite dissolved per time from the walls between x and $x + dx$ must be equal to the difference of calcite transported by the flow Q out of the fracture at $x + dx$ to that entering it at x. Thus

$$Q \cdot \mathrm{d}c = F(c(x)) \cdot P(x) \cdot \mathrm{d}x; \tag{4a}$$

Integration yields

$$\int_{c_0}^{c} \frac{\mathrm{d}c}{F(c)} = \int_{0}^{x} P(x)\mathrm{d}x / Q$$

c_0 is the concentration at the entrance $x = 0$ of the conduit. During the initial state of speleogenesis flow is laminar and the flow rate $Q(t)$ at time t through the fracture is given by

$$Q(t) = \frac{h}{R}, \quad R = \frac{12\eta}{g\rho}\int_{0}^{l} a^{-3}(x,t) b^{-1}(x,t) M^{-1}(x,t) dx \tag{5}$$

where $a(x,t)$ and $b(x,t)$ are its dimensions, which now vary in space and time. η is the viscosity of the solution, ρ its density, and $M(x,t)$ is a geometrical shape factor with values between 0.3 to 1 (Beek and Mutzall, 1975), g is the earth's gravitational acceleration. Units are [g], [cm], [s], [mole].

Eqns. 2 to 5 specify the parameters which determine karstification in its initial tate. The first group of parameters represents the chemical driving forces. They are k_{n_1}, n_1, k_{n_2}, n_2, c_s, c_0 and the equilibrium concentration c_{eq}. The kinetic constants k_{n_1}, k_{n_2} depend on temperature and on the lithology of the bedrock. The kinetic exponents n_1 and n_2 take values of $1 \leqslant n_1 \leqslant 2$ and $2 \leqslant n_2 \leqslant 6$. The equilibrium concentration c_{eq} is related to temperature and to the amount of carbon dioxide available on the surface of the karst terrain. Finally c_0 is the calcite concentration of the solution entering the fracture.

The physical driving forces are mainly related to the hydraulic head h, i.e., the relief of the fracture system. If meteoric precipitation is high, such that an ample amount of water is available at the surface, this value remains constant in time. In the early state of karstification this can be assumed as realistic, since the narrow fractures cannot transport large quantities of water and therefore the water table remains close to the surface. In the later state of mature karst the amount of water available might not suffice to keep this high water table and it is therefore the amount of meteoric precipitation that determines the further development of the karst aquifer.

The hydrogeological setting is characterized by the geometry of the fracture which determines its resistance R (eqn. 5). Thus the corresponding parameters are the aperture width a_0, the breadth b_0 and the length l of the fracture. Furthermore the viscosity η depends on temperature ($\eta = 1.8 \times 10^{-2}$ at 0℃, $\eta = 1.33 \times 10^{-2}$ at 10℃, and $\eta = 0.90 \times 10^{-2}$ dynscm^{-2} at 25℃). Therefore the amount of water transported through a system of fractures almost doubles if the temperature is raised from 2℃ (alpine karst) to 25℃ (tropical karst).

Eqns. 2, 3, 4, and 5 are the master equations of the problem and their solutions can be obtained numerically (Dreybrodt, 1988, 1990, 1992, 1995; Palmer 1991; Groves and Howard, 1994) or by mathematically analysis of their properties (Dreybrodt, 1995). In the following we will discuss the basic properties of these solutions without going into the mathematical details. As a result of these considerations we will obtain a simple analytic expression, which tells the dependence of the time span from the onset of karstification to the state of first maturity on the parameters discussed above. This time span can be regarded as related to the intensity of karstification, which varies considerably in different geological settings and different climates. It therefore can be used as a key to understand, why in different regions of the world karstic features look so different. In a second step we will then discuss the further evolution of mature karst in its dependence on the parameters introduced above.

2.3 The Initial Phase of the Origin of Conduits

To understand how an initially narrow primary fracture widens into a water leading conduit, it is necessary to know how the dissolution rates change with increasing distance from the input. If dissolution proceeds rapidly, the solution becomes saturated quickly after a penetration distance, short compared to the length of the fracture and therefore loses its solutional power. Only surface denudation could result in this case. On the other hand, if the dissolution rates are low such that the solution can penetrate deeply into the rock without losing dissolutional power, widening must be extremely slow and consequently the evolution of a karst aquifer may take unrealistically long times.

By use of Eqns. 2 – 5 it is possible to obtain the dissolution rates $F(x,0)$ at time $t=0$ for the initial primary fracture as

$$F_n(x,0) = k_n(1-\hat{c}_0)^n\left\{\frac{x}{L_n}+1\right\}^{\frac{-n}{n-1}}$$

$$L_n = \frac{Q(0)}{2(a_0+b_0)}\cdot\frac{c_{eq}}{k_n(1-\hat{c}_s)^{n-1}\cdot(n-1)};\quad n\neq 1 \tag{6a}$$

For linear dissolution kinetics, i.e. $n=1$, the result is

$$F_1(x,0) = k_1(1-\hat{c}_0)\exp\{-x/L_1\};\ L_1 = \frac{Q(0)}{2(a_0+b_0)}\cdot\frac{c_{eq}}{k_1} \tag{6b}$$

The kinetic length L_n gives a measure how quickly the dissolution rates drop as a function of the distance x from the entrance. This is illustrated by Fig. 2-4.

Fig. 2-4a represents the following scenario. Water with a dissolution rate $F(0)$ enters the fracture. Then dissolution proceeds with a linear rate law, i.e., $n_1=1$ (dashed line). After the distance $x=2L_1$ (represented by the perpendicular long-dashed line) the rates switch to a higher order, with either $n_2=2, 4$ or 10 as depicted at the curves (full lines), which represent the dissolution rates in units of the rate $F(0)$ at the entrance. The curve with short dashes gives the rates if linear kinetics are operating along the entire length of the fracture. In this case the rates drop exponentially and for $x=100L_1$ we find $F(x)/F(0)=3.7\times10^{-44}$.

If $\hat{c}=0$ then at $x_1=2L_1$ the concentration has increased to $\hat{c}_s=0.86$ where the switch to higher kinetics occurs. From thereon the dissolution rates drop slowly compared to the first order kinetics. This stresses the importance of high order kinetics. If only linear kinetics would exist the dissolution rates would drop so quickly that for all cases with $l\geqslant 100\ L_1$ (which is realistic in nature) development of karst aquifers would be impossible. If the rates, however, switch to higher order kinetics, with $n_2\geqslant 2$, then the rates drop in such a way that sufficient dissolutional power remains even at the exit, which then is widened slowly.

Fig. 2-4b represents a situation, where a second order ($n_1=2$) rate law is operative along the entire length (short dashes). The solid lines represent the dissolution rates after a switch to higher order, $n_2=4$ or $n_2=10$, at $x=2L_2$. Here in all cases sufficient solutional power at the exit is available.

To translate the data of Fig. 2-4 into real situations, it is necessary to know the values of L_1, L_2 and of $F(0)$. Using $c_{eq}=2\times10^{-6}$ molecm^{-3} and $k_1=5\times10^{-11}$ molecm^{2}s^{-1} we find from eqn. 6.

$$L_1 = k_g\times 2\times 10^9 a_0^3 i\,[\text{cm}] \tag{7}$$

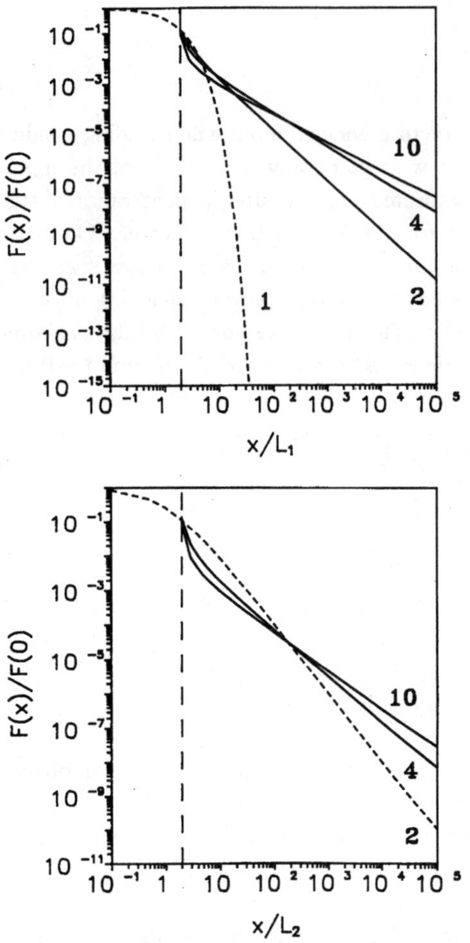

Fig. 2-4 a, upper panel) Dissolution rates in units of the initial rate $F(0)$ as a function of distance measured in units of L_1. The water flows to a distance $2L_1$ and dissolves calcite with linear kinetics, then it switches to kinetics with $n_2 = 2$, 4 or 10 (numbers on full lines). The dashed line shows dissolution with linear kinetics, when no switch occurs.
b, lower panel) Dissolution rates when the first kinetics has $n_1 = 2$ and switches to $n_2 = 4$ or 10 at distance $x = 2L_2$. The dashed line shows dissolution with $n_1 = 2$, when no switch to higher order occurs

where a_0 is in cm. $i = h/l$ is the dimensionless hydraulic gradient driving the solution through the fracture. k_g is a geometrical constant, which is 1 for rectangular joints with $a_0 \ll b_0$, and 0.38 for circular openings with diameter a_0. In natural karst systems the initial hydraulic gradient is in the order of 10^{-2} and the fracture widths are in the order of 10^{-2} cm (Dreybrodt, 1990). Thus first order kinetic lengths are about $L_1 \approx 20$ cm. According to eqns. 6a and 2b the lengths of L_n are $L_n = L_1/(1-n)$. The length scales in Fig. 2-4 therefore extend up to about 10 km. The solutional widening at the entrance in cm/year can be related to $F(0)$ by using a conversion factor $\gamma = 1.17 \times 10^9$ such that $F(0) = 5 \times 10^{-11}$ $molecm^{-2}s^{-1}$ corresponds to 0.05 cm/year (Dreybrodt, 1988).

For a fracture of 10 km length and a width of 10^{-2} cm the dissolution rate at the exit has dropped to about 10^{-8} of its value at the entrance. Therefore to double its width at the exit a time of about 10^7 years is needed. This of course gives an upper limit, since in reality the flow rate $Q(t)$ increases in time due to continuous widening of the fracture. Therefore the kinetic length L_1 increases also enhancing the dissolution rates at the exit. This positive feedback loop finally leads to a steep increase in the flow rates. This is depicted in Fig. 2-5, where the results of a numerical model described elsewhere (Dreybrodt 1988, 1990, 1995) are illustrated. In this special case the parameters used are: $a_0 = 0.02$ cm, $b_0 = 100$ cm, $l = 10^5$ cm, $c_{eq} = 2 \times 10^{-6}$ $molecm^{-3}$, $k_{n_1} = 4 \times 10^{-11}$ $molecm^{-2}s^{-1}$, $n_1 = 1$, $k_{n_2} = 4 \times 10^{-8}$ $molecm^{-2}s^{-1}$, $n_2 = 4$, $\hat{c}_s = 0.9$.

Fig. 2-5a shows the flow rate $Q(t)$ as a function of time. After a long gestation time of about 32000 years, where $Q(t)$ increases by no more than one order of magnitude there is a dramatically steep increase within a very short time span. We call this event breakthrough and the time at which it occurs breakthrough time T.

Fig. 2-5b depicts the profiles of the initially uniform fracture as it evolves in time. Note that the scale of width is logarithmic. At the input of the fracture dissolution rates are high and a funnel like shape is created. Since the rates drop rapidly this shape is restricted close to the input. The rest of the fracture opens up more evenly with a slow widening at the exit which finally accelerates dramatically and within a short time span of hundred years opens up and consequently breakthrough occurs.

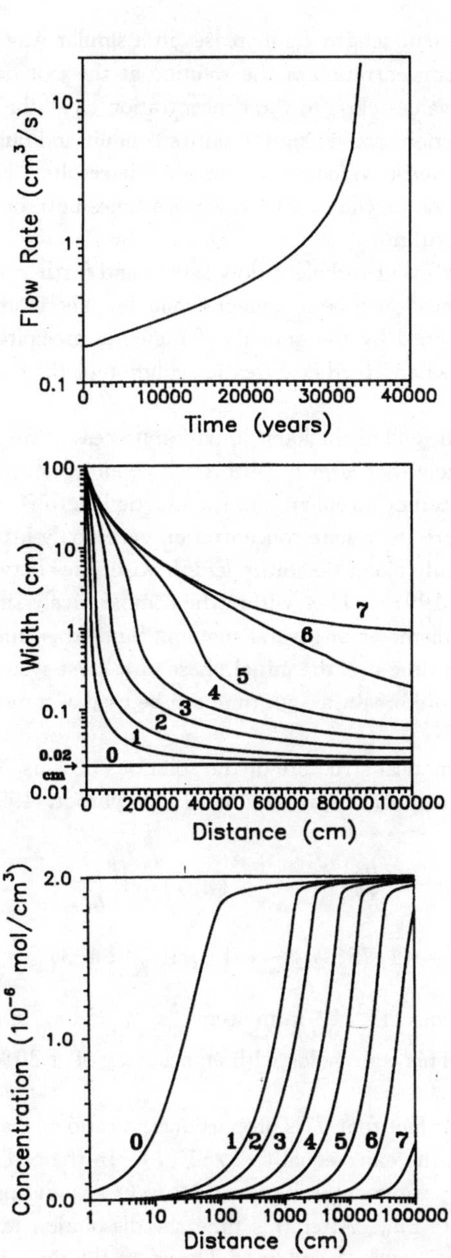

Fig. 2-5 a upper panel) Flow rate $Q(t)$ as a function of time for a conduit with $a_0 = 0.02$ cm, $b_0 = 100$cm, $l = 10^5$cm, $i = 0.05$, $c_{eq} = 2\times10^{-6}$molecm^{-3}, $\tilde{c}_s = 0.9$, $n_1 = 1$, $k_1 = 4\times10^{-11}$ molecm^{-2}s^{-1}, $n_2 = 4$ and $k_{n_2} = 4\times10^{-8}$ molecm^{-2}s^{-1}. The steep increase in flow rate marks the time of breakthrough. Note logarithmic scale of Q. b, middle panel) Profiles of the width along the distancex for increasing times. From bottom to top $T_0 = 0$ years, $T_1 =$ 10 000 years, $T_2 = 20\ 000$ years, $T_3 = 30\ 000$ years, $T_4 =$ 33 000 years, $T_5 = 34\ 000$ years, $T_6 = 34\ 100$ years, $T_7 = 34\ 110$ years. Note the dramatic increase in diameter in the last hundred years. Note also the logarithmic scale of width. (bottom panel) Concentration profiles along the distance x. For the times T_0 to T_7 listed above from left to right. The concentration front, i.e. the steep increase of the curves moves slowly towards the exit as the conduit enlarges slowly. Note that the scale of distance is logarithmic now

During this evolution the kinetic length L_n increases in a similar way as $Q(t)$ (cf. eqn. 6).

As a consequence the concentration of the solution at the exit decreases slowly until at breakthrough it drops rapidly to values close to the concentration c_0 at the input. From then on the fast first kinetics governs dissolution rates along the entire conduit and during this new state of maturity an even and comparatively quick widening of the conduit results. This is illustrated in Fig. 2-5c, which shows the concentration profile $c(x)$ for various times until breakthrough. Note that in Fig. 2-5c the length scale is logarithmic.

After the breakthrough event turbulent flow sets in and furthermore the amount of water needed to sustain the hydraulic head may be no longer available. Therefore the hydraulic head drops to a new value, which is determined by the amount of meteoric precipitation. Consequently the upper entrance parts become vadose and further phreatic evolution of the conduits proceeds below the new watertable.

Breakthrough marks the end of the karst initiation process. Provided a sufficient amount of water is available it is most likely that after breakthrough conduits develop into mature karst channels. After breakthrough flow becomes turbulent and the kinetic length is larger or at least in the order of the conduit length. Therefore the calcite concentration varies only little from the input to the output and dissolution proceeds evenly along the entire length with rates between 0.1 down to 0.01 cm/a. (Dreybrodt and Buhmann, 1991). Thus within the comparatively short time of about ten thousand years a conduit grows to a diameter of several meters. Since this time is mostly shorter or at least comparable to breakthrough time it is the initial phase of a karst system, which determines the evolution of an aquifer. Therefore breakthrough time can be used as a measure of intensity of karstification in a given area.

Analysis of the mathematical structure of the solutions of eqns. 2 − 5 and comparison with the numerical results yield an analytical expression for T (Dreybrodt, 1995)

$$T = C_{n_2} \cdot \frac{(1 + a_0/b_0)^{n_2/(n_2-1)}}{M} \cdot (a_0)^{-\frac{2n_{2+1}}{n_2-1}} \left(\frac{l^2 \eta}{hc_{eq}}\right)^{\frac{n_2}{n_2-1}} \cdot k^{\frac{1}{\frac{n_2}{n_2}-1}} \quad [\text{years}] \tag{8}$$

$$C_{n_2} = (1.75 \cdot n_2 - 4.1) \cdot 10^{-11} \text{ for } 3 \leqslant n_2 \leqslant 4.$$

a_0, b_0, l are in cm, η in dynscm^{-2}, k_{n_2} in molecm^{-2}s^{-1}, and c_{eq} in molecm$^{-3} = 10^6$ mmol/l, h is the hydraulic head in cm. This eqn. holds with an accuracy of ±20% for times between 10^4 to 10^7 years.

Eqn. 8 results from the fact that T is proportional to ratio of the initial width a_0 of the fracture and the rate of widening at the exit, equal to $2\gamma \cdot F(l)$. In the case of a wide fracture this can be understood by the following arguments: $T_0 = a_0/2\gamma F_n(l)$ is an upper limit of the time necessary to widen the exit from a_0 to $2a_0$. After this time the dissolution rate at the exit has increased at least by a factor of eight (cf. eqns. 5 and 6a). Therefore the time needed for a further doubling of the exit width to $4a_0$ is $T_1 = T_0/4$ and with the same argument each further doubling of the exit width ($8a_0, 16a_0, \ldots$) needs $T_2 = T_0/(4)^2$, $T_3 = T_0/(4)^3$ and so on. Thus the total time T to widen the exit to infinity is the sum of this geometric progression $T = 4T_0/3$. This shows clearly that T_0 is a good estimation for the breakthrough time. Note that T_0 is controlled by the dissolution rate at the exit of the conduit.

Consequently, only the rate constant k_{n_2} of the second higher order kinetics determines T. This leads to a most important conclusion. Since the kinetic length of the first kinetics at the entrance is extremely short the concentration increases quickly, in most realistic cases after a distance of about $10^{-3}l$, to c_s, where the higher order kinetics takes over (cf. Fig. 2-5c). Therefore higher order kinetics practically acts along the entire tube, and consequently it does not matter whether the water entering into the fracture has already dissolved limestone from the overlying soil. As long as the concentration c_0 remains below c_s breakthrough times will not be influenced considerably. This is also the result of numerical calculations, which in comparison to $c_0 = 0$ show no more than an increase of about 10% for $c_0 = c_s$, provided c_{eq} is not altered.

From these reasons, in contrast to current opinions, the initiation of karstification is not enhanced, when allogenic water with low hardness enters into a limestone terrain. After breakthrough, however, dissolution rates are determined by the first fast kinetics and are almost even along the entire length. In this stage of mature karst conduits the rate of their enlargement by allogenic water with low concentration is higher than for autigenic water with higher hardness.

Eqn. 8 quantifies the dependence of the intensity of karstification on the various parameters already specified. From eqn. 8 those representing the chemical driving forces are reduced to the kinetic exponent n_2 of the slow kinetics, the kinetic constant k_{n_2} and the equilibrium concentration c_{eq}. The last can be easily obtained by observing the Ca^{2+}-concentrations of local karst springs with diffuse flow which are always very close to equilibrium (Shuster and White, 1971).

c_{eq} is controlled by the CO_2 in the soil in a complex way. Since dissolution of calcite in the soil proceeds under open system conditions, whereas closed system conditions with respect to CO_2 control dissolution in the fracture, the equilibrium value C_{eq} depends on soil P_{CO_2} and on the concentration of the solution entering the fracture. C_{eq} increases with increasing c_0 provided the CO_2-concentration is constant (Dreybrodt, 1995, 1988). Fig. 2-6 shows a diagram from which this can be envisaged. The chemical evolution of water dissolving limestone under closed system conditions is described (Dreybrodt, 1988) by

$$[H_2CO_{3i}^*] - [Ca^{2+}] = [H_2CO_3]^*, [HCO_3]^* = K_H P^i_{CO_2} \qquad (9)$$

$[H_2CO_{3i}^*]$ is the initial concentration of aqueous CO_2 before dissolution starts. $[Ca^{2+}]$ is the concentration of dissolved material. $[H_2CO_{3i}^*]$ is related to $P^i_{CO_2}$ by Henry's law. The straight lines in the $[H_2CO_{3i}^*]$ – $[Ca^{2+}]$ diagram therefore represent dissolution under closed system conditions. In the open system P_{CO_2} remains constant and dissolution proceeds on lines parallel to the $[Ca^{2+}]$-axis (e.g. dashed line AP). If at point P (i.e., $c = c_0$) a solution enters into the fracture and changes from the open to the closed system it dissolves calcite until it intersects the equilibrium curve (lower curve). It is obvious from Fig. 2-6 that this point of intersection, which gives the final concentration c_{eq} is shifted to higher values if either c_0 and/or the initial $P^i_{CO_2}$ are increased.

Little work has been done to obtain the values of n_2 and k_{n_2} in a system closed with respect to CO_2. Measurements on a variety of limestones from South Germany in our laboratory yield values of n_2 between 2 up to 6 and there seems to be a dependence of n_2 on the initial CO_2-concentration. Values of k_{n_2} are in the order 5×10^{-9} molecm^{-2}s^{-1}, varying with initial CO_2-concentration and of course also lithology (cf. Fig. 2-2). More systematic work has to be performed for more reliable data.

The first author to report data for dissolution in the open system was Palmer (1991) who gives values of $n_2 \approx 4$ and $k_{n_2} \approx 3 \times 10^{-9}$ molecm^{-2}s^{-1}. Extensive experimental work on the dissolution rate of natural marbles and limestone in the open system has been performed by Svensson and Dreybrodt (1992). They obtained values of n_2 between 2.5 up to 4.1 and k_{n_2} between 1×10^{-9} and 5×10^{-9} molecm^{-2}s^{-1}. The value of k_{n_2} is of minor influence on breakthrough time. For $n_2 = 3$, ($n_2 = 4$), changes in k_{n_2} by a factor 10 alter the value of T by a factor of about 3, (2). The kinetic exponent n_2, however, is of crucial importance. For a fracture with $a_0 = 10^{-2}$ cm, $b_0 = 100$ cm,

$l = 10^5$ cm, $i = 0.01$, $c_{eq} = 2 \times 10^{-6}$molcm^{-3} and $k_{n_2} = 5 \times 10^{-9}$ molecm^{2}s^{-1}, $T = 10^7$ years for $n_2 = 4$ and $T = 2.5 \times 10^8$ years for $n_2 = 3$.

The hydrogeological forces are reflected by the geometrical parameters a_0, b_0 and l, but they are tied to the physical and chemical driving forces by the parameter group ($l^2 \eta / h\, c_{eq}$). In regions of low temperature as Alpine or Arctic karst one expects low levels of CO_2 with P_{CO_2} from 0.1% up to 1% and consequently low equilibrium concentrations. In tropic karst P_{CO_2} ranges from 0.2% up to 10% (Brook et al., 1983; Ford and Williams, 1989; White, 1988; Yuan Daoxian et al., 1991). Consequently calcite equilibrium concentrations are higher by at least a factor of two in tropic karst. Considering the temperature dependence of the viscosity, breakthrough times, for identical settings else, are lower by about a factor of six in tropic karst compared to low temperature karst.

One interesting feature is the fact that breakthrough times depend critically on l. For $n_2 = 4$ an increase of l by a factor of only two extends the breakthrough time by a factor of six. Therefore in areas of comparable hydraulic head h one expects intensive karstification with many small caves, where geological setting allows comparatively short percolating pathways. In contrast, in regions of large l only few, but long caves will be found.

Karstification times depend most sensitively on the initial fracture width a_0. A variety of investigations using various methods report fracture widths between 5×10^{-3} cm up to 10^{-1} cm with high probabilities in the region between 0.01 to 0.03 cm (Motyka and Wilk, 1984; Wilk et al., 1984; Böcker, 1969; Palliet et al., 1987; Palliet, 1988; Bandis et al., 1985; Johns et al., 1993). For wide fractures with $b_0 \ll a_0$ and $a_0 = 2 \times 10^{-2}$ cm breakthrough times are several 10 thousand years for karst areas where i is high (0.1) and l is of the order of 100 m. Such times are realistic and have been reported by Ford (1988), Mylroie and Carew (1986), and Bakalowicz (1982) as minimum times required for the evolution of a karst aquifer to its maturity. For large systems with $l \approx$ 10 km and $i = 0.01$ correspondingly larger times in the order of ten million years are needed. Still by one order of magnitude, larger times may result if the cross sections of the primary flow paths exhibit a shape of comparable dimensions in a_0 and b_0. This may be the case at intersections of frac-

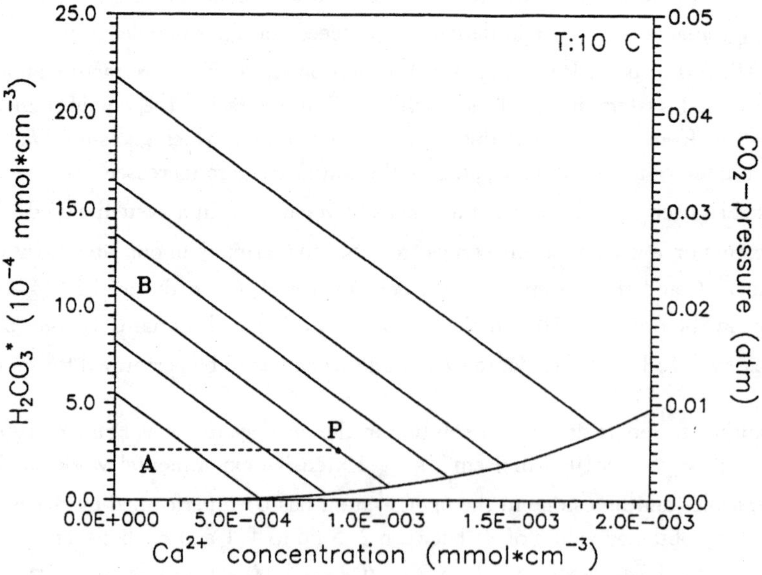

Fig. 2-6 Chemical evolution of a solution dissolving limestone under open system conditions (dashed line AP) and then changes to closed conditions (straight full line PB) until equilibrium is achieved at the lowest curve

tures, or in large discontinuities, such as bedding planes, where fracture apertures vary locally and flow paths develop as a pattern of channels employing all the regions of large apertures where the resistance to flow is small. These phenomena of channelling have been investigated by Brown (1987), Rothmann (1988), and Tsang and Tsang (1989). It is easy to show that such a situation can also be modelled by a two-dimensional network of interconnecting tubes of circular or ellipsoidal cross sections. Caves which have evolved mainly along bedding planes, such as f. i. Mammoth-Flint-Cave in Kentucky, USA may result from such configurations.

Summarising we have found an expression of the time of initiation of karst channels which quantifies the parameters determining karst evolution and which relates the scales of time and space.

2.4 Structural Control of Cave Development by the Geological Setting of Primary Fractures

Real karst systems are three-dimensional or a least two-dimensional. Aquifers leading water to an output can develop only if percolating pathways exist. To give an answer whether such pathways do exist we employ some basic results of percolation theory (Stauffer, 1985; Feder, 1988). Imagine a set of joints to be represented by a square lattice as depicted in Fig. 2-7. Each of the dashed lines represents a possible location of a fracture; but fractures are not evenly distributed. Therefore we assume that the probability that at each of these lines a real fracture is present is $P \leqslant 1$. Fig. 2-7a as an example gives a small net of 10×10 with a probability $P = 1/3$, which means that in average one third of the possible locations carry a real fracture. We further assume that water enters on the top of the grid and leaves at the bottom, whereas the sides of the grid are impermeable. In Fig.

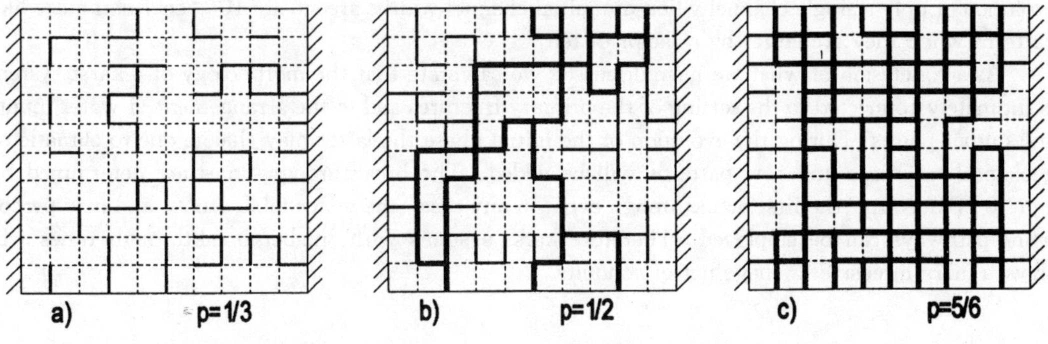

Fig. 2-7 Schematic drawings of a fracture system. Dashed lines denote possible locations of fractures. Full lines mark the locations of existing fractures, fat full lines mark water leading fractures belonging to a percolation pathway. a) occupation probability $P = 1/3$, b) $P = 1/2$, c) $P = 5/6$, $P_c = 1/2$

2-7a we have plotted the real fractures by thick lines. We see that t here are clusters of fractures, which are not connected from the input to the output, and therefore cannot lead water. In such a case an aquifer cannot develop. Fig. 2-7b illustrates the situation for $P = 1/2$. In this case the clusters have merged into each other and percolating pathways appear. All fractures leading water to the output are marked by extra thick lines. From the shape of the percolation cluster we could expect a dentridic cave system. Fig. 2-7c gives the situation with $P = 5/6$. Here we obtain a network and the resulting cave system could be maze like. Percolation pathways only can exist if $P \geqslant P_c$, where P_c is called the critical percolation threshold (Balberg, 1986, Sahimi, 1995). So for each setting of fractures karst development would not be possible for $P < P_c$. For values of $P > P_c$ but still close to

P_c the water is lead through a few pathways which may evolve to large conduits until the water table drops. If P, however, is close to 1 all the many fractures are employed to carry the water away and the water table may drop even though the diameters of the evolving conduits are still small. Therefore in highly fractured geological settings karstification may be intensive but major cave systems are missing. For our examples in Fig. 2-7, $P_c = 1/2$.

The boundary conditions, i. e., the regions of input and output, which are simple, in Fig. 2-7 may be restricted to a few input and output points. Correspondingly, even though a cluster extending over the entire area may exist, it may not lead water to the output. It is obvious therefore that the hydrological setting is of utmost importance to the evolution of a system of conduits.

Furthermore each of the fractures in the network has statistically distributed apertures a_0 and b_0 and lengths l. From all the percolating pathways one will exhibit the shortest breakthrough time, which in average has the smallest resistance, i. e., smallest average length and largest average width and which is subject to the largest hydraulic head (cf. eqn. 8). After breakthrough of this pathway the boundary conditions change due to a dropping water table and only those pathways connecting the new water table to the output will further develop, whereas others will cease to grow.

Little work has been done to simulate the evolution of such two-dimensional systems. Groves and Howard (1995) have performed computer simulations on a small network of 146 pipes with equal lengths and lognormally distributed initial diameters for various input-output configurations. Occupation probability in all those networks is $P = 1$. The simulations were run until a first breakthrough event occurred and the laminar flow switched to turbulence. The results confirm our statements above. Further development of such networks under turbulent flow was investigated in a subsequent paper (Howard and Groves, 1995). Assuming further constant hydraulic head they found evolution of only a single channel when the initial channel widths are small (10^{-2} cm) and maze like patterns when they are larger by a factor of ten.

As a conclusion of what we have discussed we can state that the morphology of a karst system is intimately connected to the setting of the primary fractures and to the arrangement of water input- and output-points. During the evolution of the initial phase the latter may change due to climatic or geological variations and new patterns will be added. The breakthrough times are determined by eqn. 8. Since after the first breakthrough event in any case, the water table drops, and new percolating pathways can be employed. Therefore karst systems with smaller breakthrough times will show a more intensive drainage net of conduits.

2.5 Karstification in Its Mature State

After breakthrough turbulent flow in conduits carries large amounts of water, which in general will be far from equilibrium with respect to calcite. Simultaneously further development of narrow fractures still in the state of initiation will proceed. This leads to the existence of two types of springs in the same karst area: Diffuse flow springs draw their water from narrow fractures, where it has time to come close to equilibrium. These springs vary little in hardness, temperature, and discharge, even in a response to a rain storm. Conduit springs drain water through large channels. Therefore large variations in hardness, temperature and discharge occur upon individual rain storms. The water is far from equilibrium in any case for such type of springs (Schuster and White, 1971).

In the following we will report how fast these conduits will grow. In contrast to the early state, where dissolution proceeds close to equilibrium, we have now to look for dissolution far from saturation, which is mostly determined by the fast first kinetics, $F_1(c)$ in eqn. 2. Fig. 2-8 represents experimental data on dissolution rates for synthetic calcite and a natural limestone for an open system with $P_{CO_2} = 1 \times 10^{-3}$, 5×10^{-3}, and 10^{-2} atm (Svensson and Dreybrodt, 1992). The experiment has been performed as a batch experiment with turbulent flow. The full lines represent the dissolution rates calculated from the equation of Plummer, Wigley and Parkhurst (1978)

$$F = \chi_1 \cdot (H^+) + \chi_2 \cdot (HCO_3^*) + \chi_3 - \chi_4 \cdot (Ca^{2+})(HCO_3^-) \tag{10}$$

where χ_1, χ_2, χ_3, χ_4 denote rate constants. χ_4 is a function of P_{CO_2}. Round brackets stand for activities of the species. It is interesting to note that the PWP-eqn. gives satisfactory agreement to the rates of pure synthetic calcite (upper dashed line) shown also in Fig. 2-8, which exhibit almost linear kinetics. Natural limestone, however, (lower dashed line) has lower rates by an inhibition process of absorption of Ca^{2+} or HCO_3^- – ions to its surface. Details are given by Svensson and Dreybrodt (1992). Fig. 2-9 represents some data of Fig. 2-8 in a logarithmic scale. It is clearly recognised that the rates of natural limestone follow eqn. 2 with $n_1 = 1.7$, $n_2 = 3.4$ and $\hat{c}_s = 0.76$, $k_1 = 1.6 \times 10^{-10}$ molecm^{-2}s^{-1}. Similar results have been obtained for P_{CO_2} of 5×10^{-3} atm and 1×10^{-2} atm. Even though n_1, n_2 and $\hat{c}_s$ vary, depending on lithology the rates in Fig. 2-8 can be used to estimate growth rates of phreatic karst conduits. Note that rates are converted from molecm^{-2}s^{-1} into the rate of solutional wall retreat in cm/year by multiplication with a factor 1.17×10^9 (Dreybrodt, 1988).

For solutions with a Ca-concentration of about $0.5\,c_{eq}$ we obtain rates of about 5×10^{-11} molecm^{-2}s^{-1} corresponding to a wall retreat of 0.06 cm/year. It should be noted here that even though dissolution in phreatic tubes proceeds under closed system conditions the use of the open system data is correct, since after breakthrough the chemical composition of the solution remains almost unchanged on its way from input to the conduit spring. The data are also applicable to solutional entrenchment of canyons in the vadose zone. From these numbers one obtains wall retreats of about 60 cm in thousand years. One has to keep in mind, however, that these are maximal values. In most cases with turbulent flow there is a diffusion boundary layer between the rock surface and the bulk of the solution through which mass transport is affected by molecular diffusion (Dreybrodt and Buhmann, 1991). The thickness of this layer increases with decreasing flow rate and dissolution rates are reduced down to about one fifth of the maximal rates. This has been observed by Lauritzen (1986), who reports increasing dissolution rates in a single conduit with increasing flow rates.

By use of standard limestone tablets, which are inserted into cave streams or conduits for a given time and by measuring weight loss, dissolution rates can be found. Droppa (1986) has reported corrosion intensities between 107 – 145 mm/ka from such experiments in cave streams of the Demänova cave in winter when water temperature was low. In summer values up to 320 mm/ka were observed. This agrees well with the numbers derived from the experimental and theoretical reasons above.

Gascoyne (1981) estimated the entrenchment of vadose cave streams by determining the age of speleothems located at a fixed level relative to the base level of the stream. For caves in moderate climate rates of 20 mm up to 100 mm per thousand years are reported, whereas in tropical climate 130 – 200 mm/ka are found. From an observation by Spöcker(1950), cited in Dreybrodt (1988) one can derive convincing dissolution rates. Spöcker, when repairing a well casted with limestone blocks, found heavily corroded blocks with channels of 2.5 cm diameter. From one of these a spine of a sea urchin was protruding, excluding the evolution of this channel by erosional action. This block had been located fifty years below the water table. P_{CO_2} of the well was about 1×10^{-2} atm and $[Ca^{2+}] \approx 0.27$ mmole/l. There was a continuos discharge of about 4 l/s at a temperature of 10℃. Thus one may assume flow as turbulent. From Fig. 2-8 one finds maximal dissolution rates of 1.4×10^{-10} molecm^{-2}s^{-1} $\triangleq 0.15$ cm/a. The rate calculated from the diameter of the channel corroded into the limestone block is 0.05 cm/year, which again is reasonable regarding the presence of

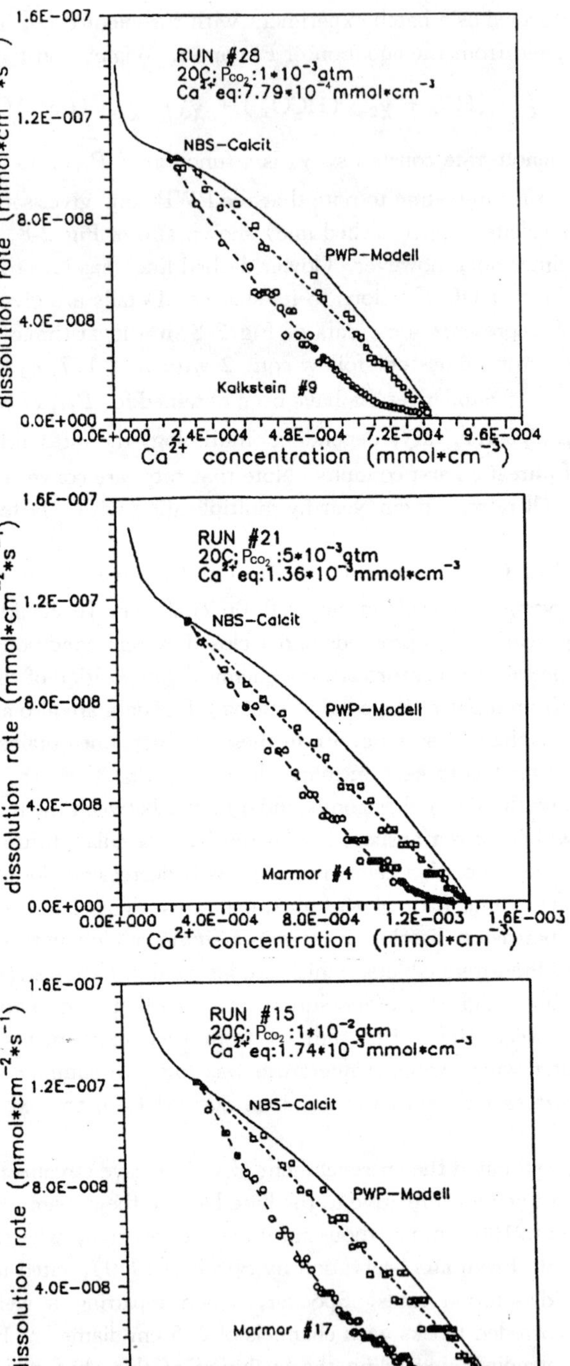

Fig. 2-8 Dissolution rates of limestone, synthetic calcite, and PWP-rates for the open system at 20℃ as a function of calcium-concentration for $P_{CO_2}=1\times10^{-3}$ atm (top), $P_{CO_2}=5\times10^{-3}$ atm (middle) and $P_{CO_2}=1\times10^{-2}$ atm (bottom)

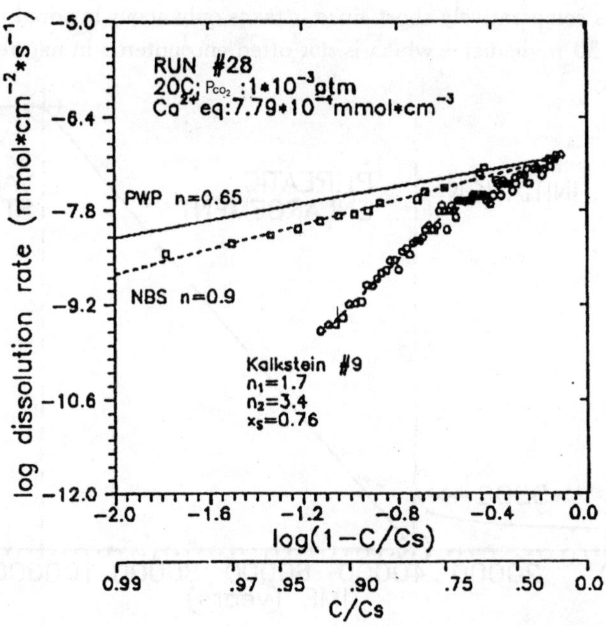

Fig. 2-9 Dissolution rates of Fig. 2-8 for $P_{CO_2}=1\times10^{-3}$ atm plotted logarithmically versus log $(1-c/c_s)$ to show the kinetic switch, $n_1=1.7$ and $n_2=3.4$

boundary layers, which may reduce the maximal possible rates listed in Fig. 2-8.

In summary we can conclude that dissolution rates for karst conduits can be derived from experimental data, provided the chemical composition of the water with respect to pH, $[HCO_3^-]$, and $[Ca^{2+}]$ is known. From Figs. 2-8 and 2-9 one also finds that the PWP-relation (eqn. 10) yields results, which when divided by two are close to the experimental data for $[Ca^{2+}]$ in the region of $0.5\ c_{eq}$. This should be kept in mind, when using the PWP-equation for the estimation of dissolution rates, as is done by many researchers.

2.6 Conclusion

To conclude this work Fig. 2-10 illustrates the history of the formation of a mature conduit taken from the example of Fig. 2-5. Fig. 2-10 shows the conduit width at the exit as a function of time. Since during the initial phase it is in the order of 10^{-2} cm its values are magnified by a factor of 5000 to become visible. During the gestation or initial phase the exit width varies extremely slowly until it has twice the initial width. Then shortly breakthrough sets in and turbulent flow is established. The concentration of Ca^{2+} drops to low values such that an even dissolution rate is active along the entire channel length. The initiation time depends critically on the length and the initial width of the fracture and for realistic cases it covers the range from about ten thousand to ten million years (cf. eqn. 8). After breakthrough enlargement of the conduit proceeds under phreatic conditions at a rate of about 400 mm/ka with variations of about 200 mm/ka. In contrast to the initiation phase the enlargement phase is similar for all phreatic conduits and independent on their former development. Eventually the conduit will become vadose with a river flowing in it. Then entrenchment of canyons with similar rates will occur. Finally the passage becomes completely vadose and growth stops until in a later time by varying external conditions it may become phreatic again and resume growth. The active phreatic phase is comparatively short since it takes only about hundred thousand years to create a passage of about 30 m diameter which is not often encountered in nature.

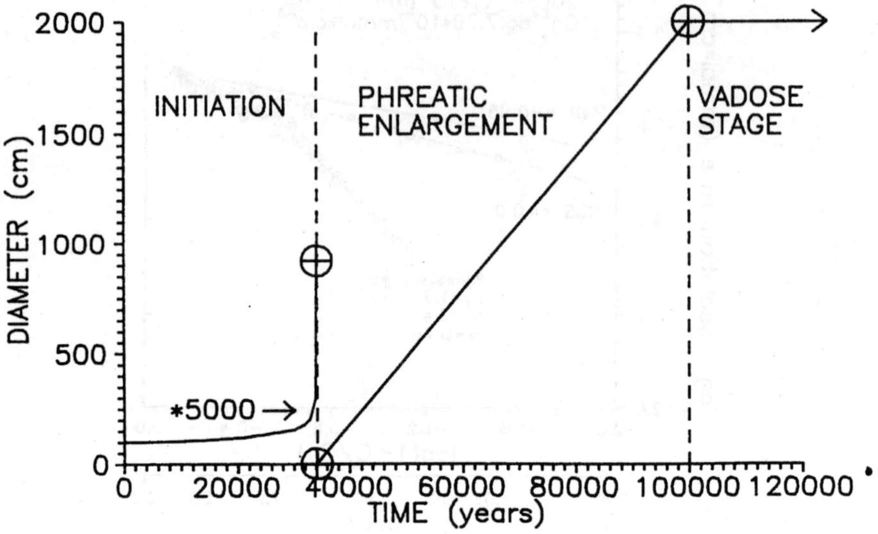

Fig. 2-10 Schematic drawing of the evolution of a conduit from initiation to maturity. The symbols ⊗ mark the transition from initiation to phreatic enlargement and from there to the vadose state

Finally this work shows that evolution of cave systems can be understood only if one considers the dissolution kinetics of limestone. An understanding by only looking for influence of the calcite equilibrium of the system H_2O-CO_2-$CaCO_3$ is not possible. Therefore further research on the dissolution rates of natural limestone under geological relevant conditions is necessary for a deeper understanding.

References

Balberg, I., 1986. Connectivity and Conductivity in 2D and 3D Fracture System. Annals of Israel Physical Society, Vol. 8, pp. 89 – 101

Bakalowicz, M., 1982. La genése de l'aquifer karstique vue par un geochemiste. Reun. Monogr. Sobre Karst – Larra, Vol. 82, pp. 159 – 174

Bandis, S. C., A. Makurat and G. Vik, 1985. Predicted and measured hydraulic conductivity of rock joints. Paper presented at the Int. Symp. on Fundamentals of Rock Joints, Int. Soc. of Rock Mechanics, Björkliden, Sweden

Beek, W. J. and K. M. K. Mutzall, 1975. Transport Phenomena. New York, Wigley

Böcker, T., 1969. Karstic water research in Hungary. Bull. In. Assoc. Sci. Hydrol., Vol. 14, No. 4, pp. 7 – 20

Brown, St. R., 1987. Fluid Flow Through Rock Joints: The Effect of Surface Roughness. Journal of Geophysical Research, Vol. 92 (B2), pp. 1337 – 1347

Brook, G. A., M. E. Folkoff and E. O. Box, 1983. A world model of soil carbon dioxide. Earth Surface Processes and Landforms, Vol. 8, pp. 79 – 88

Dreybrodt, W., 1988. Processes in karst systems – Physics, Chemistry and Geology. Springer Series in Physical Environments 5, Springer Berlin, New York

Dreybrodt, W., 1990. The role of dissolution kinetics in the development of karstification in limestone: A model simulation of karst evolution. Journal of Geology, Vol. 98, pp. 639 – 655

Dreybrodt, W., 1992. Dynamics of Karstification: A Model applied to hydraulic structures in Karst Terranes. Applied Hydrogeology, Vol. 1, pp. 20 – 32

Dreybrodt, W., 1995. Principles of early development of karst conduits under natural and man made conditions revealed by mathematical analysis of numerical models. Water Resources Research

Dreybrodt, W. and D. Buhmann, 1991. A mass transfer model for dissolution and precipitation of calcite from solutions in turbulent motion. Chemical Geology, Vol. 90, pp. 107 – 122

Droppa, A., 1986. L'Influence des saisond de l'ann'ee sur la dénudation karstique. Proc. 9th. Int. Congr. Speleol., 1, pp. 237 – 241

Feder, J., 1988. Fractals. Plenum Press, New York and London

Ford, D. C., 1989. Characteristics of dissolution cave systems in carbonate rocks. In James, N. P.; Choquette, P. W., eds., Paleokarst, Springer, New York

Ford, D. C. and P. W. Williams, 1989. Karst geomorphology and hydrology. Unwin and Hymann

Gascoyne, M., 1981. Rates of cave passage entrendment and valley lowering from speleothem age measurements. Proc. 8th Int. Congr. Speleol., 1, pp. 99 – 101 Bowling Green

Groves, C. G. and A. D. Howard, 1994. Minimum hydrochemical conditions allowing limestone cave development. Water Resources Research, Vol. 30, No. 3, p. 607 – 615

Groves, C. G. and A. D. Howard, 1994a. Early development of karst systems. 1. Preferential flow path enlargement under laminar flow. Water Resources Research, Vol. 30, No. 10, pp. 2837 – 2846

Howard, A. D. and C. G. Groves, 1995. Early development of karst systems. 2. Turbulent flow. Water Resources Research, Vol. 31, No. 1, pp. 19 – 26

Johns, R. A., J. S. Steude, L. M. Castanier and P. V. Robert, 1993. Nondestructive Measurements of Fracture Aperture in Crystalline Rock Cores Using X Ray Computer Tomography. Journ. of Geophys. Res., Vol. 98, No. B2, pp. 1889 – 1900

Lauritzen, S. E., 1986. Hydraulics and dissolution kinetics of a phreatic conduit. Proc. 9th Int. Congr. Speleol. 1, pp. 20 – 22

Motyka, I., and Z. Wilk, 1984. Hydraulic structure of karst – fissured Triassic rocks in the vicinity of Olkusz (Poland). Kras i speleologia, Vol. 14, No. 5, pp. 11 – 24

Mylroie, J. E. and J. L. Carew, 1986. Minimum duration of speleogenesis. 9th Congr. Int. de Espeleol., Barcelona, Vol. 1, pp. 249 – 251

Paillet, F. L., 1988. Fracture Characterization and Fracture – Permeability Estimation at the underground research laboratory in southeastern Manitoba, Canada, U. S. Geol. Survey. Water Resources Investigation, 88 – 4009

Paillet, F. L., A. E. Hess, C. H. Cheng and E. Harding, 1987. Characterization of fracture permeability with high – resolution vertical flow measurements during borehole pumping. Ground Water, Vol. 25, pp. 28 – 40

Palmer, A. N., 1991. The origin and morphology of limestone caves. Geol. Soc. of America Bull. Vol. 103, pp. 1 – 21

Plummer, L. N., T. L. M. Wigley and D. L. Parkhurst, 1978. The kinetics of calcite dissolution in CO_2 – systems at 5℃ to 60℃ and 0.0 to 1.0 atm CO_2. Am. J. Sci., Vol. 278, pp. 179 – 216

Rothmann, D. H., 1988. Cellular – automaton fluids: A model for flow in porous media. Geophysics, Vol. 53, No. 4, pp. 509 – 518

Sahimi, M., 1995. Flow and Transport in Porous Media and Fractured Rock. VCH Verlagsges. Weinheim

Stauffer, D., 1985. Introduction to percolating theory. Taylor and Francis Ltd., London and Philadelphia

Shuster, E. T. and B. White, 1971. Seasonal fluctuations in the chemistry of limestone springs: a possible mean for characterizing carbonate aquifers. J. Hydrol., Vol. 14, pp. 93 – 128

Svensson, U. and W. Dreybrodt, 1992. Dissolution kinetics of natural calcite minerals in CO_2 – water systems approaching calcite equilibrium. Chem. Geol., Vol. 100, pp. 129 – 145

Tsang, Y. W. and C. F. Tsang, 1989. Flow channeling in a single fracture as a two – dimensional strongly heterogeneous permeable medium. Water Resources Research, Vol. 25, pp. 2076 – 2080

White, W. B., 1988. Geomorphology and hydrology of karst terrains. Oxford Univ. Press, New York, Oxford

Wilk, Z., J. Motyka and I. Józefko, 1984. Investigations of some Hydraulic Properties of Karst Solution Openings and Fractures. Annales Societatis Geologorum Poloniae Rocznik Polskiegotowarystwa Gelogicznego, Vol. 43. 1/2, pp. 15 – 43, Krakow

Yuan Daoxian, Zhu Dehao, Weng Jintao, Zhu Xuewen, Han Xingrui, Wang Xunyi, Cai Guihong, Zhu Yuanfeng, Cui Gangzhong, and Deng Ziqiang, 1991. Karst of China. Geological Publishing House, Beijing, China

Global Karst Correlation
Edited by Yuan Daoxian and Liu Zaihua
Science Press and VSP BV, 1998

Chapter 3 Karst Morphogenesis in the Arctic: Examples From Spitsbergen

Stein-Erik Lauritzen
Department of Geology, Bergen University, Alléq aten 41, *N*-5007 *Bergen, Norway*

3.1 Introduction

During late Tertiary and Quaternary periods, large ice sheets and permafrozen ground repeatedly expanded and melted away on the northern and southern hemispheres, during which the characteristic glacial/ interglacial cyclicity of about 100 ka have dominated the last 0.7 Ma (Crowley and North, 1991). Glacial impact on the northern hemisphere can be traced back to the last 5 Ma (Jansen and Sjøholm, 1991). These dramatic changes had a profound and variable impact on karst development, including inhibition, stimulation, erasure or modification, depending on local geomorphic and hydrologic factors. Spitsbergen, Norway and parts of the British Isles display examples of karst areas that have experienced such profound environmental change, as can be seen from their position during the maximum ice extents of the last (Weichselian) glaciation, (Fig. 3-1).

The present landforms of Norway and Spitsbergen are dominated by glacial erosion forms on all scales, like deep fjords, U-shaped valleys, roche moutonnees and glacial striae. In addition, it is in both areas possible to identify a primary, pre-glacial, or "paleic" surface into which the glacial troughs were cut(see review for the Norwegian mainland by Gjessing, 1967). Karst landforms in this setting comprise a melange of morphological elements relative to the glacial landscape (preglacial, sub-glacial or post-glacial) (Ford, 1977; Ford and Williams, 1989), although many of them would be polygenetic. For instance, the Norwegian karst caves may be classified according to their position within these landform elements(Fig. 3-2), (Lauritzen, 1981a). Present-day karstification is dominated by low to moderate pCO_2, cryogenic processes, and relatively large amounts of precipitation, due to the high-latitude climate and the areas' oceanic proximity. Among the areas that were affected by the Pleistocene glaciations (Fig. 3-1), Spitsbergen is still in the high arctic, permafrozen state, while the mainland Norway is presently under a relatively milder, sub-arctic, oceanic climate. In these areas, karst morphogenesis is closely linked to the dynamics of permafrost, glaciers, and not least, the intimate relationship between the glacier aquifer and the karst aquifer. The Spitzbergen karst plays an important role as a model for the conditions that must have prevailed in the karsts of Scandinavia and northern Europe during most of the Pleistocene stadials and interstadials.

3.1.1 *Permafrost, Quaternary Climate and Groundwater*

Permafrost is a thermal condition, where ground temperatures beneath a surficial, seasonally thawed zone (the "active layer") is permanently below 0℃ (Brown, 1970; Price, 1972). Permafrozen areas may be subdivided according to the vertical and lateral extent of frozen zones. In areas of *continuous permafrost*, frozen ground is regionally continuous and may reach a depth of 500 m (Brown, 1970). However, it is not present beneath the sea, freshwater lakes or beneath glaciers that are wider than about 400 m (Werenskiold, 1953). *Discontinuous permafrost* is limited to

Fig. 3-1 Ice extent over northern Europe during the Weichselian maximum (~20 ka B.P.). Most of the north Atlantic ocean was also ice-covered. Ice distribution is from Andersen and Borns (1994)

depths up to tens of meters and occurs in patches, often restricted to frost-susceptible materials. It occurs at lower latitudes than the continuous variant, and may also exist in the high alpine environment in sub-arctic regions.

Taliks are local holes in otherwise continuous permafrost. They may act as sites of groundwater recharge or discharge. Karstification is dependent of flowing, corrosive water, and would therefore be inhibited by permafrost. Exceptions occur in the active layer and in taliks of various kind. Since the age of many karst landforms may be much greater than the duration of specific climatic conditions during the Quaternary, it is necessary to consider permafrost dynamics over longer timespans.

It is useful to distinguish between two different, time-dependent situations of permafrost: a) arctic or subarctic areas where permafrost exists today, and b) more temperate areas where it might have existed in the past, during periods of glacial cooling. In arctic areas, permafrost exists wherev-

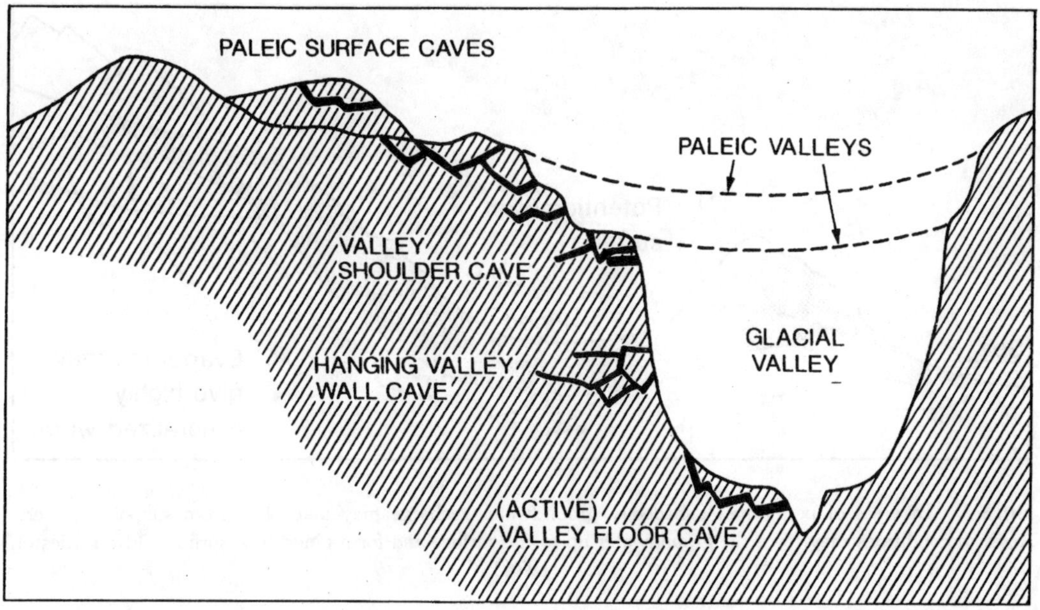

Fig. 3-2 Classification of caves according to their position within pre-glacial (paleic) or glacial valley comp – onents. (after Lauritzen, 1981a)

er sub-polar (i. e., partially warm-based) glaciers are absent, or even exists beneath polar (cold-based) ice. In both cases, the distribution of permafrozen areas would change with ice extents. In the arctic, subglacially thawed ground would expands with expanding subpolar glaciers. In temperate regions, permafrost expand in pace with the periglacial zone in front of continental ice-sheets (i. e., Fig. 3-1), as evidenced by regionally distributed fossil ice-wedges and patterned ground (Ehlers, 1983; Nilsson, 1983).

In a permafrozen area, two principally different aquifers could exist, the seasonal *supra-permafrost* aquifer (within the active layer), and the perennial *sub-permafrost* aquifer that is confined beneath the permafrozen ground. Sub-permafrost groundwater may go very deep, and therefore also transport geothermal heat and brine (Deming et al., 1992). Meteoric recharge of the sub-permafrost system is only possible through taliks of various kind. This makes subpolar glaciers in the upland to the most likely source of groundwater recharge. Artesian conditions may result when glaciers occupy elevated positions in the surrounding landscape, thus giving rise to pingos and springs that are well documented from arctic areas (Fig. 3-3). Subpolar glaciers are only partially cold-based, and frozen only at the lower parts, below the equilibrium line, where it is free from snow. Due to the insulating effect of the glacier ice and snow cover, geothermal heat may cause the upper parts of the glacier to become warm-based, i. e. reach the pressure-melting point of ice. Therefore, this unfrozen zone becomes the most important area of groundwater recharge. Consequently, the extent of warm-based glacier cover would expectedly affect the amount of groundwater recharge and therefore be sensitive to climatic change. Glacial retreat during modern time (for instance, as we have seen on Spitsbergen) may therefore explain numerous historical observations of *decreasing flow* from many springs (Haldorsen and Lauritzen, 1993). Paradoxically, glacier retreat in this climate increases the snow-free ablation area, where the glaciers become cold-based, in turn shrinking the warm-based upper reaches from where aquifer recharge takes place.

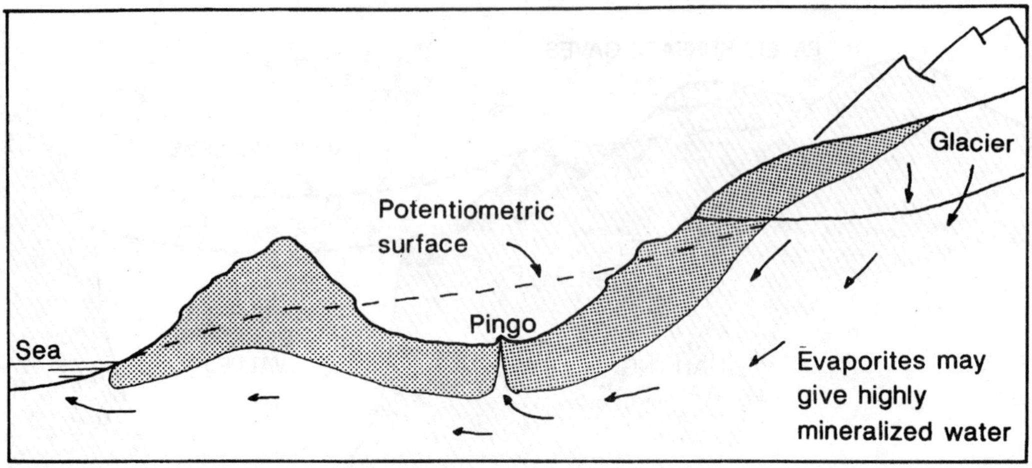

Fig. 3-3 In areas of permafrost (shaded), groundwater recharge may take place from subpolar glaciers. Artesian conditions may force the groundwater up to the surface and form pingo-type springs. (from Liestøl, 1976)

3.1.2 *Cryogenic Effects*

Periodic freezing is common during the commencement and end of the melting season. During freezing, the solutes become concentrated in the liquid phase. The freezing point of aqueous solutions is lowered with increasing ionic strength. The remaining liquid produced by partial freezing of karst waters may both lower the final freezing point, and also become supersaturated with respect to calcite and gypsum. This results in very high mineralization (TDS) of many arctic karst waters (Pulina, 1984a), and in the production of cryogenic precipitates on surfaces and in pore voids of debris and soil (Vogt, 1989, 1991). From a process point of view, these precipitation processes lead to temporary storage of carbonate within catchments.

3.1.3 *Glacier Hydrology and Karst*

Glaciers may be viewed as aquifers which convey water through discrete conduits, and to a lesser extent through the intercrystalline vein system. Under "normal" conditions, we may regard a glacier as a perched aquifer, resting on an impervious bed (aquiclude) (Fig. 3-4A). Water transport is intensified along the aquiclude contact through R-channels (Röthlisberger, 1972) and N-channels (Nye, 1965), or through a more irregular, linked cavity system (Walder and Hallet 1979; Kamb et al., 1985). Basal sliding is largely dictated by water storage and hydrostatic pressures along the aquiclude contact, i. e., the basal water film (Paterson, 1981). Characteristic features of the glacier aquifer are that the water budget is strongly seasonal, and that the interior channel geometry is thought to vary seasonally in concert with the hydrological conditions.

The occurrence of discrete conduits in the englacial and subglacial system allude to a karstic type of drainage. The morphological similarity between ablating glaciers and karst has been known for a considerable time (Horn, 1947; Clayton, 1964; Pulina, 1984b). However, little progress has been made towards quantifying contrasts and similarities between the dynamic behavior of glaciers and karst. So far, the most successful benefit from this avenue of thinking is the adaption of dye tracing techniques (which were originally developed by karst hydrologists) to investigate the move-

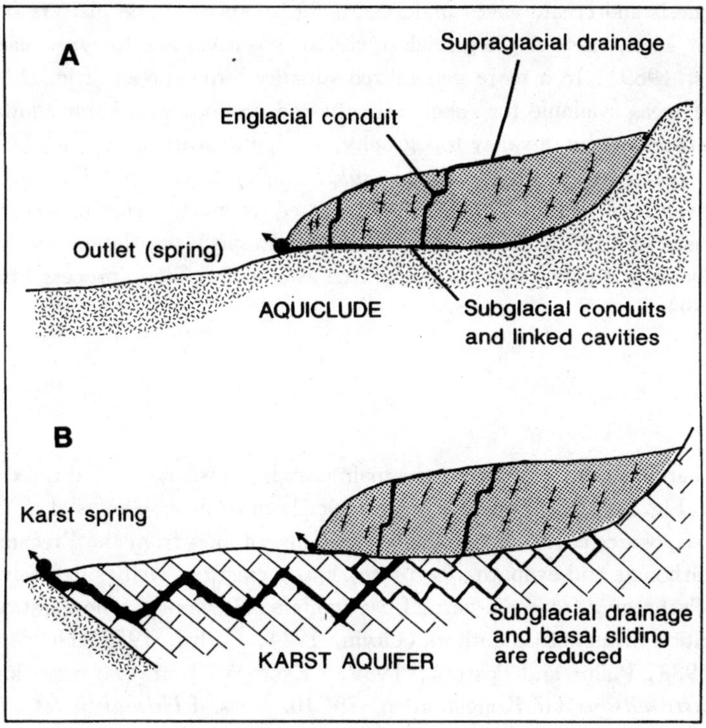

Fig. 3-4 Interaction between glaciers and karst, from Lauritzen (1991). A) "Normal" situation of a glacier (which may be regarded as an aquifer) situated on an impervious bed. Practically all supraglacial and englacial drainage emerges through the spring at the snout of the glacier. The hydrostatic pressure of the subglacial water, which flows through R-, N- channels, linked cavity systems, or is stored in the subglacial regelation film, plays a major factor (as lubricant) for basal sliding in temperate-based glaciers. B) The same glacier situated on a well-developed karst, where subglacial water is pirated into the karst conduits. This may considerably reduce the basal water pressure, thereby impeding basal sliding. See text for further discussion

ment of water through glaciers (Behrens et al., 1971; Lang et al., 1979).

Most interesting and complex cases occur when the glacier aquifer leaks into and interacts with karst aquifers below (Lauritzen, 1991)(Fig. 3-4B). We may expect at least two different effects from this interaction. First, the ice would either erase or even preserve karst forms, depending on their size and permeability prior to glacierization. As mentioned, the sliding velocity of a temperate glacier is directly dependent on the basal water pressure. If the magnitude of leakage from the glacier bed into the karst is large relative to the subglacial water budget, we should therefore expect it to affect the basal sliding velocity of the glacier. Removal of liquid water (i.e., heat), would in turn cause the ice to freeze to its bed. Consequently, plucking and quarrying becomes the prominent erosional effect, as glacial scouring is inhibited. However, if the mechanical strength of the karst forms is greater than the deformation strength of the ice (i.e., larger mogotes or dolines), these landforms may become filled or surrounded with stagnant ice and till. Ice flow is then restricted to take place along zones of deformation higher up into the glacier. The net effect is that *smaller* karst forms tend to become erased by glacier action, whilst *large* forms may, in fact, be preserved and infilled with glacial drift.

Second, superposition of glaciers on karst would enhance karstification by increasing hydraulic gradients, in particular in alpine areas. Such increase in water supply and pressure gradients may stimulate speleogenesis and create caves underneath the snout of alpine glaciers occupying plateaus above deep valleys. Many cases of pro-glacial, invasion-type caves are known (Glazek et al., 1977; Ford and Williams, 1989). In a more generalized situation, the spread of ice-sheets during glacial periods made large areas available for subglacial, thawed ground, and karst aquifers could become activated at any altitude within a valley topography, so that phreatic caves may be formed in apparently "impossible" positions. We may call this *subglacial speleogenesis*. The mechanism was first recognized in Norway by G. Horn (1935, 1947), based on much earlier observations on sub-polar glaciers by Werenskiold (1920, 1953); see also the English translation by McCrady (Horn, 1978). This mechanism is now generally recognized as a speleogenetic process (Ford, 1984; Ford and Williams, 1989).

3.2 Svalbard

The Svalbard archipelago, consists of the main island, Spitsbergen, and three smaller islands to its immediate east(Fig. 3-5). It is one of the geologically most diverse areas of the Norwegian territory. Here, rock exposures cover almost the whole range of ages from the Precambrian to the present time. Both carbonate and evaporite (gypsum) karsts exist, as well as extensive paleokarsts and powerful springs discharging from sub-permafrost aquifers. Previously, the karst of Spitsbergen has attracted the attention of numerous authors (Orvin, 1944; Corbel, 1957; Helldén, 1973; Pulina, 1977; Åerman, 1983; Pulina and Postnov, 1989). Examples from two main karst sites are discussed here, *Blomstrandsøya* (in Kongsfjorden, 79° 10′ N) and *Hilmarfjellet* (76° 40′ N), Fig. 3-5. Blomstrandsøya is an island of 31 km^2, consisting entirely of karst rocks and reaching an altitude of 370 m a.s.l. (Fig. 3-6). The area was earlier described by Corbel (1957), but the present discussion is supplied by numerous new observations and interpretations. Hilmarfjellet (Fig. 3-7) forms a large karst massif that is almost completely surrounded by an ice-field, and deeply incised by valley glaciers. On the shore-side, the karst is dissected into several extensive raised marine abrasion platforms ("strandflats") at various levels up to about 300 m a.s.l. (Szczesny et al., 1987). The summit of Hilmarfjellet reaches 800 m a.s.l. The area is famous for its powerful, thermoglacial karst springs (Orvin, 1944; Liestøl, 1976).

3.2.1 *Climate*

Svalbard, at 76° 30′ - 80° 30′ N latitude (Fig. 3-5), is situated farther north than any point on the Siberian or north American mainland. It belongs to the high arctic environment, only comparable to northern Greenland and Ellesmere Island. However, due to the North Atlantic Current, Spitsbergen experiences a much milder and humid climate than should be expected for the latitude. Along the west coast, where one finds several settlements, among those, 3 Norwegian and 2 Russian coal mining communities, the mean annual temperature is −4 to −5°C with about 400 mm precipitation per year(Fig. 3-8). Sub-zero temperatures prevail for most of the year. Hence, surface runoff is restricted to the short summer melting season (4 months). The whole region is within a zone of continuous permafrost, with variable depth estimated to be 200 − 450 m thick (Liestøl, 1976, 1980). In spite of large surface outcrops of some aquifers, the permafrozen ground would make them into the confined type, and artesian conditions (Fig. 3-3) have produced numerous pingos, icings and springs (Liestøl, 1976).

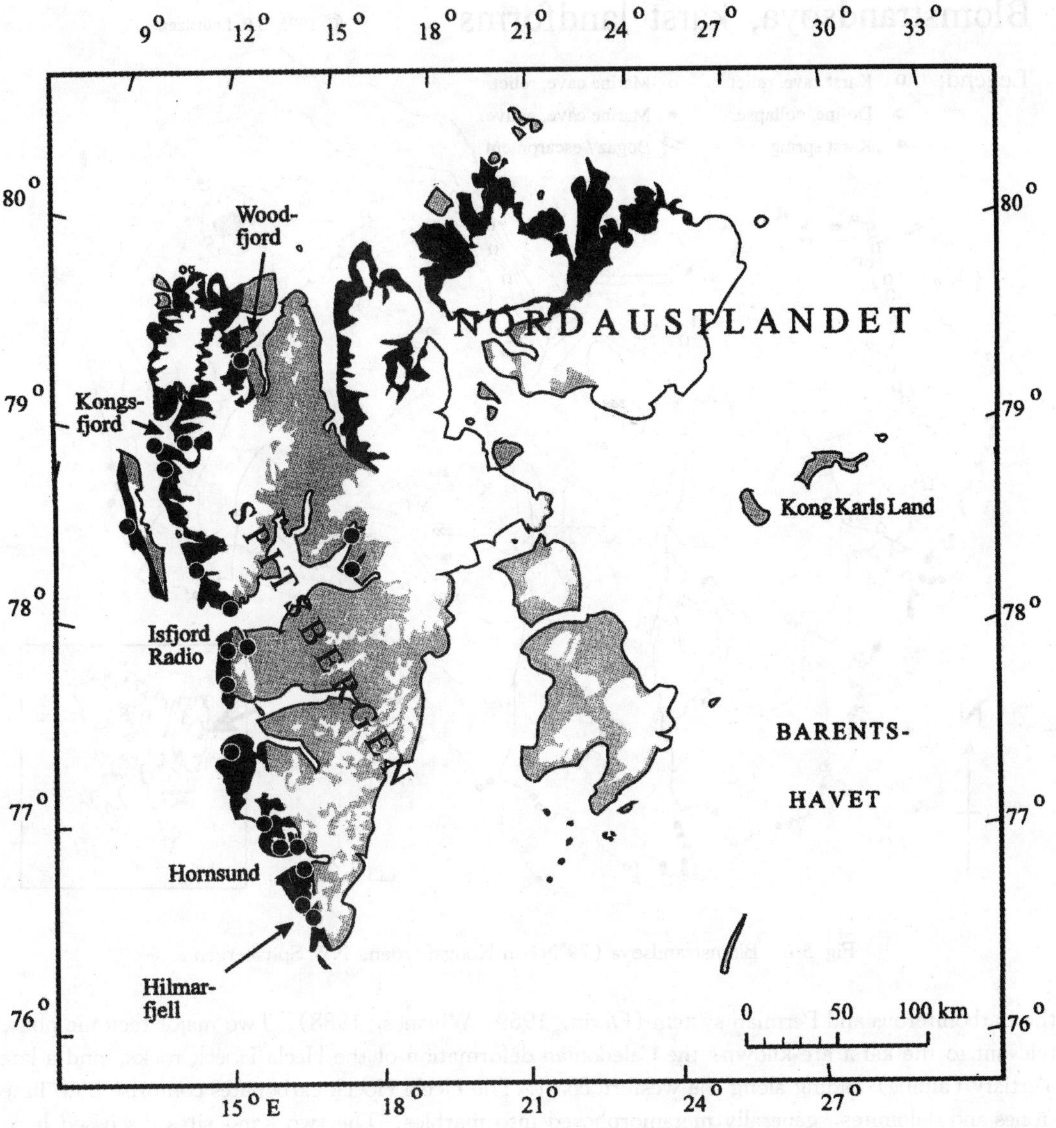

Fig. 3-5 Distribution of major springs and karst phenomena in western Spitsbergen, Dark shade: Rocks of the Hecla-Hoeck complex (late Precambrian to Silurian), containing limestones and marbles. Light shade: Younger (Mesozoic and Cenozoic) rocks, including Permian evaporites. White areas: Glaciers and icefields. Black dots: Karst springs. Geology adapted from Winsnes (1988)

3.2.2 *Lithology, Tectonic Setting*

This discussion is restricted to formations containing karst-bearing rocks; for an excellent, wider review, see Worsley and Aga (1986). Most of the carbonate rocks are limestones, dolomites and marbles of the so-called Hecla Hoeck complex (Winsnes, 1988). This is a suite of pre-Caledonian, metamorphosed and strongly tectonized rocks that is outcropping along the western and north-eastern part of Svalbard (Fig. 3-5). In addition, evaporites (gypsum and anhydrite) occur within

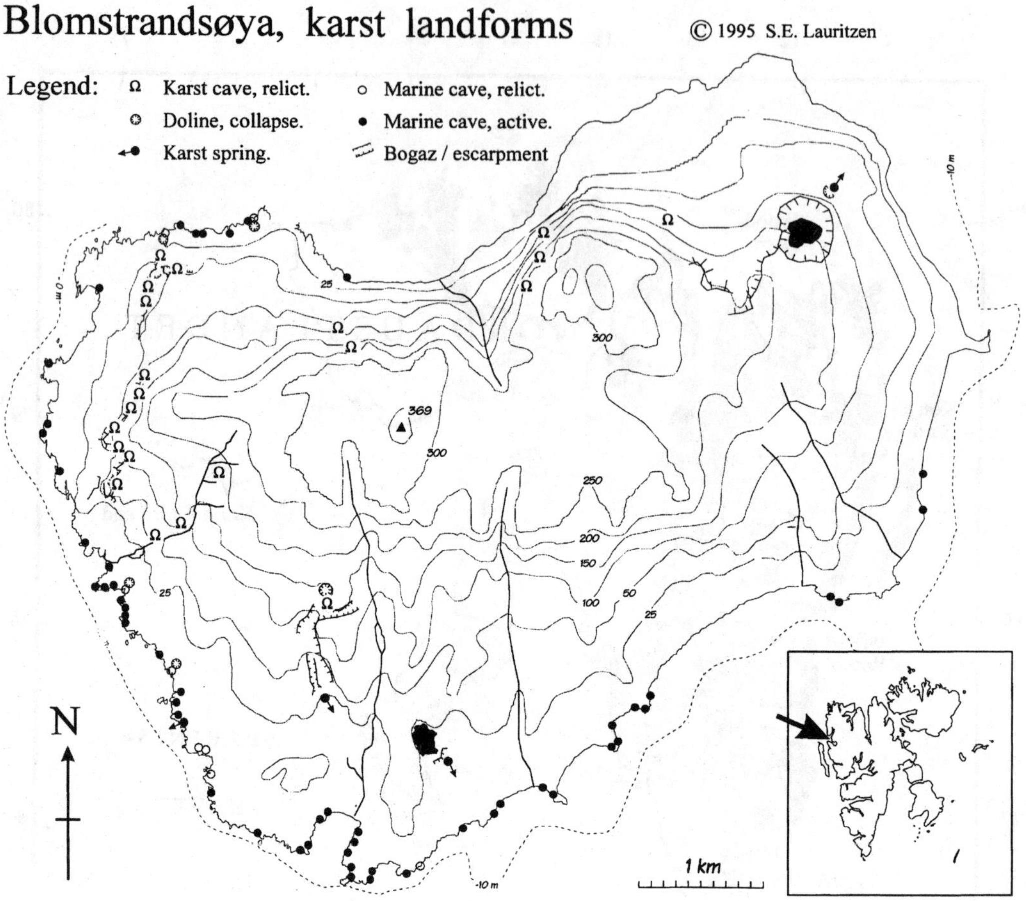

Fig. 3-6 Blomstrandsøya (79°N) in Kongsfjorden, NW Spitsbergen

the Carboniferous and Permian system (Orvin, 1969; Winsnes, 1988). Two major tectonic phases relevant to the karst are known: the Caledonian deformation of the Hecla Hoeck rocks, and a later Tertiary (alpine) folding along the western coast. The Hecla Hoeck carbonates comprise both limestones and dolomites, generally metamorphosed into marbles. The two karst sites discussed here, *Blomstrandsøya* and *Hilmarfjellet* are both situated in metamorphic Hecla Hoeck marbles.

3.2.3 *Hydrothermal Karstification*.

During the Caledonian and later tectonism, a large number of fractures formed, which became filled with sparry, hydrothermal calcite. In several cases, like in Blomstrandsøya, the calcite spar lines the walls of rounded and tubular dissolution cavities (Photo 49). This indicates corrosive liquid flow (i.e., karstification) prior to or contemporaneous with the deposition of the calcite. A similar situation of calcite spar fillings within corrogenic cavities has been described from the Hornsund area, where the homogenization temperature of fluid inclusions was determined in the range of 100 – 180℃. Isotopically, the calcite was lighter ($\delta^{13}C = -0.07$ to -0.45 ‰ (PDB); $\delta^{18}O = -15.03$ to -15.64 ‰ SMOW) than the marble wallrock ($\delta^{13}C = 0.79$ ‰; $\delta^{18}O = -9.81$ ‰) (Karwowski and Kozik, 1982). This would suggest a relatively cool, low pressure hydrother-

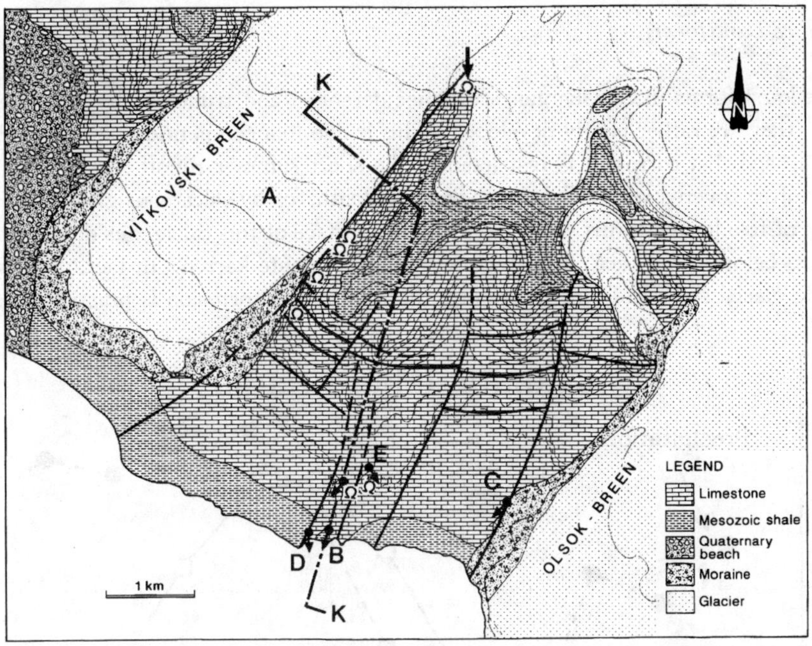

Fig. 3-7 The Hilmarfjellet karst, SW Spitsbergen, situated between the two glaciers, Vitkovskibreen and Olsok-breen. A: Area of subglacial piracy on Vitkovskibreen; B: Trollosen spring, C: Olsok springs; D: Fisosen springs; E: Small supra- permafrost springs emerging from the active layer. Ω: Relict caves. K-K: approximate position of cross-section depicted in Fig. 3-11

mal regime that is comparable to the conditions of present-day hot springs in the vicinity (*vide infra*). Quite frequently, the influence on paleokarstic inheritance on later karstification routes can be seen by numerous cave passages that are guided by hydrothermal calcite veins.

Present-day thermal activity is well documented on Spitsbergen. Numerous hot springs occur along the west coast (Orvin, 1944), displaying temperatures up to 28℃. The hottest springs are associated with Tertiary volcanism on the extreme NW summit of Spitsbergen (Hoel and Holtedahl, 1911). The geothermal heat flux associated with these "hot spots" play an important role in the karstification processes, not least because they create and sustain numerous taliks through which water flow and corrosion processes may act.

3.2.4. *Paleokarst*

Paleokarst is well developed in deposits of various geologic periods in Spitsbergen and reported by numerous workers. *Lower Carboniferous* (Culm) paleokarst channels and cavities of at least 10 – 15 m subaerial relief are described from West Spitsbergen (Flood, 1966). Also, extensive paleokarst breccia fans and fills with *Early Devonian* ("Old Red") sediments have been mapped on Blomstrandsøya. The radial distribution of these fans suggests that the present surface of the island was at or near the surface when the redbeds were accumulating (Thiedig and Manby, 1992). Parts of the present karst surfaces of Blomstrandsøya are therefore an exhumed post-Devonian landscape.

3.2.5 *Surface Landforms*.

Surface karst forms in Spitsbergen are either deranged and truncated by glacial erosion, or if post-glacial, they are rather poorly developed. This is due to a competition between gelifraction and karstification, and that corrosion is restricted to the short summer runoff season(Fig. 3-8). Karst outcrops are often covered with a flaky cryoclastic regolith, or by calcareous glacial till, masking the development of free karren forms. The large specific surface of this calcareous debris would consume aggressiveness before it may act on bedrock surfaces and create karren. In fact, beneath only 1 – 2 cm thick till, glacial striae are intact, proving that postglacial corrosion is practically zero.

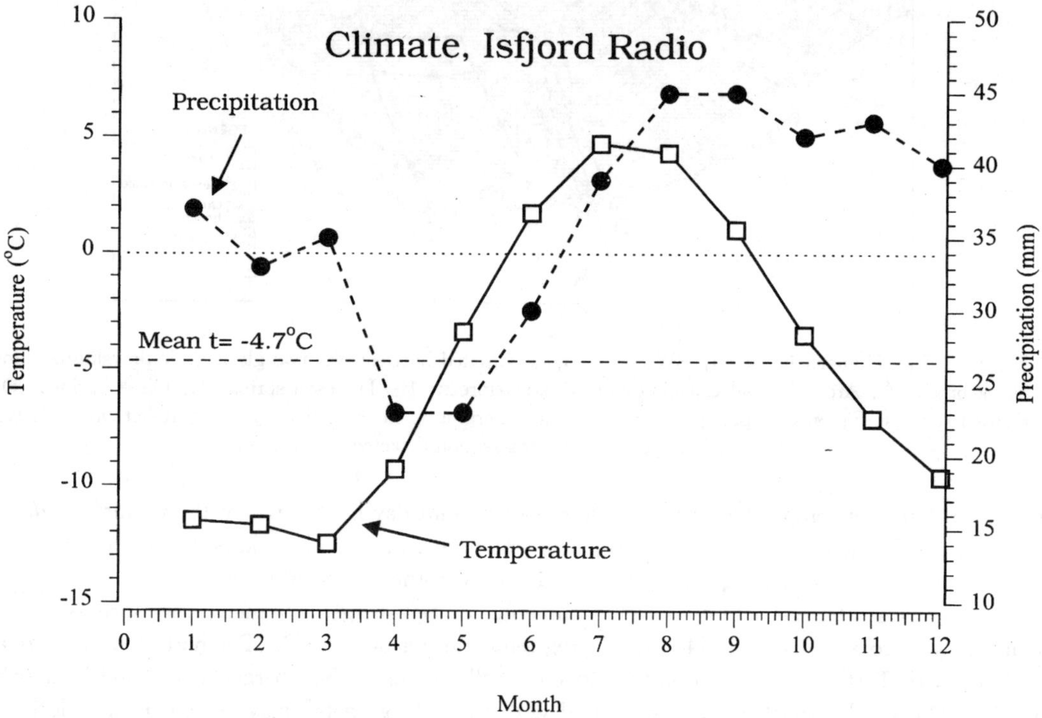

Fig. 3-8 Climate characteristics of Isfjord Radio, western Spitsbergen (Hanssen-Bauer et al., 1990). Due to the warm water of the Atlantic Current, the climate on Svalbard is anomalously mild and humid for its high latitude (76° 30′ – 80° 30′ N)

3.2.5.1. *Dolines and Bogaz Forms*

Doline and grike formation by normal processes is inhibited by the permafrost. Dolines of moderate sizes (i.e., up to about 10 m diameter) are only found where the permafrost is interrupted by marine and geothermal taliks. Marine taliks are found along the sea shoreline, where collapse and suffosion dolines may develop in conjunction with sea caves and their blowholes (Photo 50). Geothermal taliks exist where underlying, active caves carry hot water, causing the thawed cryoclastic regolith to form suffosion dolines(Photo 51). Geothermal talik dolines are often aligned with underlying fault-lines, which are the carriers of geothermal heat and also provide thawed subsurface voids (caves) to absorb the suffosion products. Talik dolines are also found in shingle beds on elevated beach deposits (Salvigsen and Elgersmaa, 1985). In other cases, dolines appear to be relict, as they may form ponds and lakes. The inundation of dolines, due to permafrost, is commonly encountered on Spitsbergen (Salvigsen et al., 1983; Salvigsen and Elgersmaa, 1985; Pulina and Postnov, 1989).

Other larger and possibly much older forms are occasionally found. One example is the lake on the NW *summit* of Irgensfjellet on Blomstrandsøya (Photo 52), forming a large closed depression, some 500 m in diameter, Fig. 3-6. The topographic position of this landform excludes any origin through glacial erosional processes, karstification remains as the only plausible explanation. The large size and the fact that it supports a lake today indicate its relict nature and high age. The present lake drains underground through a shallow, supra-permafrost system to a small spring about one hundred meters to the north, Fig. 3-6. We may interpret the depression as a relict (i.e., infiltration inhibited by permafrost) and pre- or interglacial karst form (i.e., it is too large to have been formed by post-glacial karstification).

Bogaz-forms (i.e., "karst streets" or "corridors") may become up to some tens of meters wide and some hundred meters long. On Blomstrandsøya, bogaz forms are abundant on SW slopes. This position (i.e., oriented down-ice) is compatible with the widely-held view that Bogaz-like forms ('shallow corridor karst') may have been formed by subglacial drainage underneath the Pleistocene ice cover (Ford, 1984; Ford and Williams, 1989).

3.2.5.2 *Karren*

All bare rock surfaces are pitted and rough, with a relief up to a few centimeters. The tips of spiky protrusions on the millimeter and centimeter scale are often covered with a tiny deposit of secondary carbonate precipitate, probably produced by evaporation or freezing out of solutions from these exposed surfaces. Cryogenic precipitates (Vogt, 1989, 1991) are very common on the underside of the cryoclastic debris, under boulders and in cracks (Woo and Marsh, 1977; Pulina, 1990).

On bare roche moutonnees or other sloping rock surfaces, shallow rundkarren may exist. They are typically 3 centimeters deep, 12 – 15 cm wide and 1 – 3 m long, and may form braided patterns(Photo 53). One exception was found on a SW facing slope on Blomstrandsøya, where the melt runoff from underneath a large snowpatch created deep decantation runnels of the *rinnenkarren* type(Photo 54). The snowpatch is sufficiently large to last all through the summer season, creating a continuous water supply that is virtually independent on rainfall. This gives a tremendous advantage over other rock surfaces which only receive water during snowmelt and occasional showers. A long-lasting, ablating snow cover also stabilize the subnival temperature above zero, which impede gelifraction. We may therefore suggest that the generally poor karren development observed in Spitsbergen may be a result of the limited amount and duration of surface runoff and competitive destruction by gelifraction on exposed surfaces.

3.2.6 *Subsurface Landforms*

3.2.6.1 *Caves*

Albeit numerous cave entrances are exposed in almost every limestone cliff face, exploration is quickly halted by permafrozen sediment chokes and plugs of ground ice. The relict caves above sealevel are blocked after a short distance; the deepest exploration so far, is 17 m in a cave in Blomstrandsøya. Based on cave morphology and various fills, the caves may be subdivided into 3 groups: pre-glacial or paleokarst caves, subglacial caves and post-glacial (marine abrasion) caves. This classification only refers to the most obvious genetic mode of a cave and do not exclude the possibility of a polygenetic origin, which is certainly the case for several of them. In fact, many caves that bear signs of significant subglacial development may have developed along pre-existing paleokarst voids.

(1) *Pre-glacial caves*

The previously mentioned hydrothermal cavities also belong to this group. Thiedig & Manby (1992) described paleokarst channels of sub-Devonian origin. In addition, numerous paleokarst caves can be observed in section along the SW cliffs of Blomstrandsøya. Additional evidence of cave fills may be seen on the cliff faces below numerous relict cave entrances where the rock surface is stained red as clays are washed out from their interior. This means either that the material originates from Devonian paleokarst fills within the karst, or that the caves have received 'Old Red'-derived fills sourced from the glaciated upland during the Pleistocene glaciations. Cave conduits that are exposed in gullies at Hilmarfjellet are filled with white, kaolinitic sediments that may place them into the pre-glacial category.

(2) *Sub-glacial caves*

In addition to the paleokarst caves and fissure fills, several relict phreatic caves are exposed in cliff faces and gully walls at various altitudes. Tubular passages, roof pockets, anastomoses and ceiling half-tubes provide ample evidence for a phreatic origin (Fig. 3-9 and Photo 55). Some passages

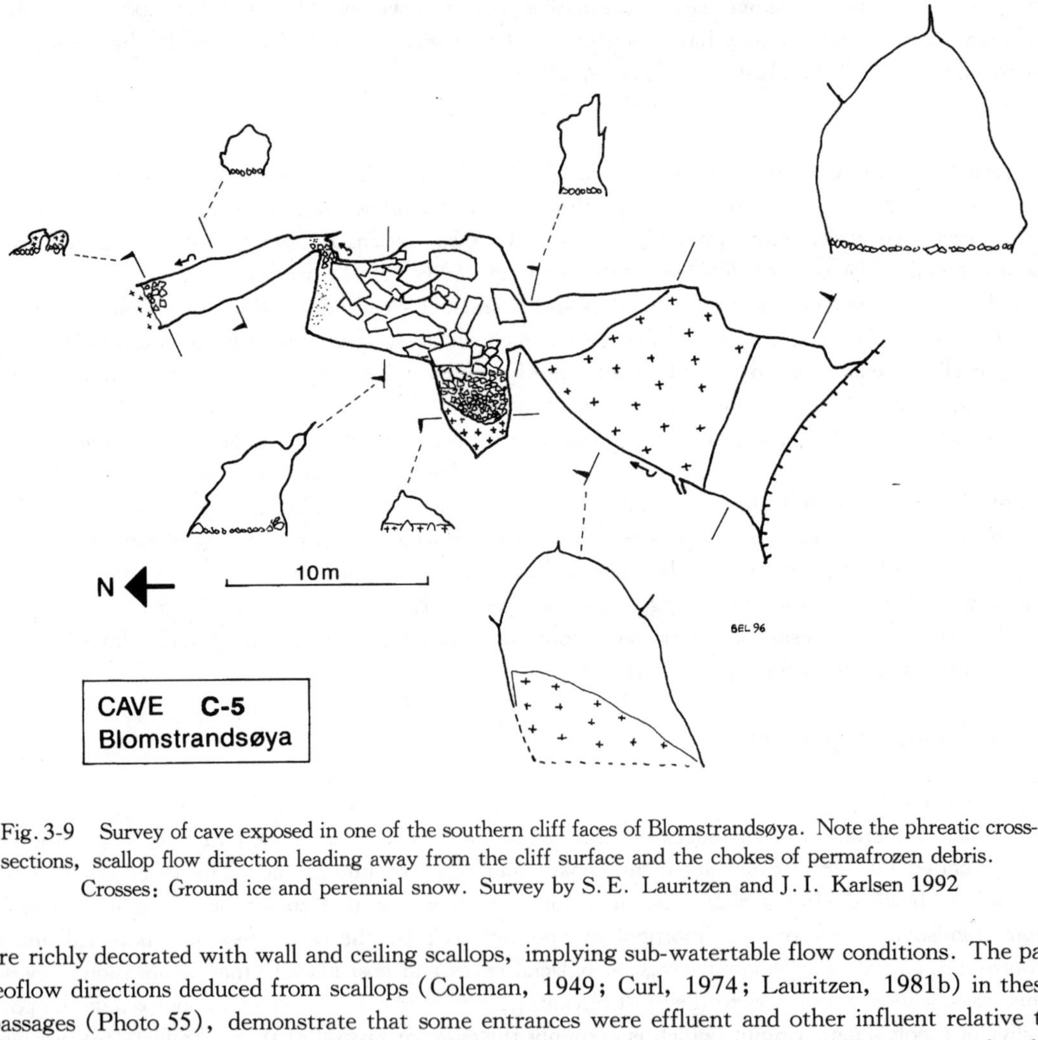

Fig. 3-9 Survey of cave exposed in one of the southern cliff faces of Blomstrandsøya. Note the phreatic cross-sections, scallop flow direction leading away from the cliff surface and the chokes of permafrozen debris. Crosses: Ground ice and perennial snow. Survey by S. E. Lauritzen and J. I. Karlsen 1992

are richly decorated with wall and ceiling scallops, implying sub-watertable flow conditions. The paleoflow directions deduced from scallops (Coleman, 1949; Curl, 1974; Lauritzen, 1981b) in these passages (Photo 55), demonstrate that some entrances were effluent and other influent relative to the surface. This pattern coincides with the Weichselian subglacial hydraulic gradients, i. e. the observed paleoflow indicates water influx (paleoponors) on cliff entrances facing up-ice, and effluent flow (paleosprings) from entrances facing down-ice. The phreatic conditions implied from ceiling scallops require a complete cover of glaciers, like the situation depicted in Fig. 3-1. This is evident both in Blomstrandsøya and Hilmarfjellet karst, demonstrating that the hydraulic morphology of many Spitsbergen caves may be explained by subglacial, phreatic karstification.

(3) *Post-glacial caves (sea caves)*

Sea-caves are common on exposed, coastal cliffs. For instance, more than 60 individual sea caves were mapped along 10 km shoreline on Blomstrandsøya, Fig. 3-6. The caves may reach a depth of more than 15 m and become 5 – 10 m wide, and they typically exploit pre-existing fissures and faults. The entrances form tall rifts or wide arches, depending on the aspect of the guiding fracture. In spite of that sea cliffs are exposed almost all around the island, seacaves are concentrated along the most exposed SW-facing shore-line (i.e. out through the fiord, Fig. 3-6), indicating that wave abrasion and cavitation are perhaps the most important agents for their formation. Additional agents may be the corrosional efflux of both shallow suprapermafrost karst water and, perhaps more important, sub-permafrost groundwater that is confined between the permafrost and the deeper halocline. The latter situation is analogous with speleogenesis in coastal aquifers in warmer regions (Mylroie and Carew 1988). Therefore, the combination of corrosion, induced by the mixing of "fresh" karst water and seawater (Dreybrodt, 1988) and seasonal gelifraction, accommodated by tidal wrenching effects of sea ice, seem like feasible agents that would act synergistically with classical wave abrasion. The fact that freshwater springs emerge in some seacaves support this synergistic view, which is summarized in Fig. 3-10.

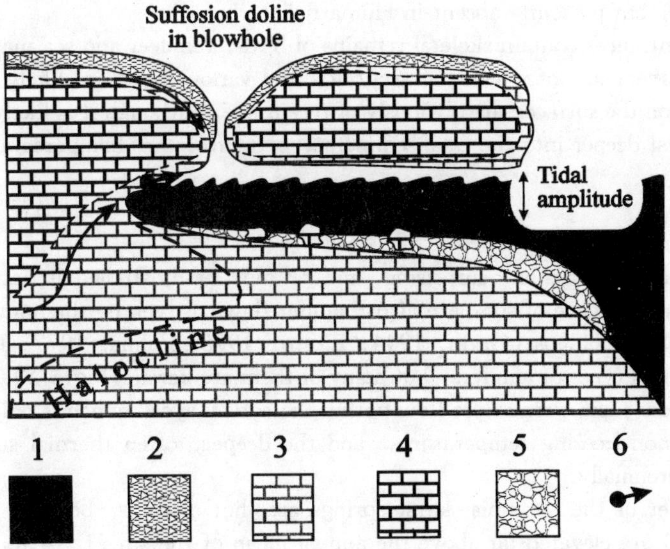

Fig. 3-10 Conceptual cross-section through sea cave in permafrozen karst. Three different agents seem to be active in speleogenesis, a) wave abrasion and cavitation, b) Corrosion by sub- and suprapermafrost groundwater emerging at the halocline contact, c) Sea-ice quarrying during tidal cycles. 1. Seawater; 2. Cryoclastic regolith; 3. Unfrozen karst rock; 4. Permafrozen karst rock; 5. Beach gravel and rockfall; 6. karst spring

3.2.6.2 *Speleothems*

Due to the permafrost and inhibited vadose percolation, speleothems are almost absent and poorly developed in Spitsbergen. Modest flowstones and crusts have been found in caves running underneath south-facing cliffs and under surfaces beneath bird colonies (also often in a sun-catching aspect), where the guanos have stimulated a rich soil with thick grass cover, presumably producing excess CO_2 and organic acids to trigger speleothem deposition. Secondary calcareous cementation of cave sediments is also known. Stalactite- forms are small and rare; the most common speleothems are porous crusts of hardened, calcitic moonmilk that can attain 1 – 2 cm thickness. They are most commonly found as ceiling and wall deposits.

Uranium-series dating of samples revealed Holocene ages, in some cases heavily contaminated with detrital Th ($^{230}Th/^{232}Th \leqslant 20$), (Ivanovich and Harmon, 1992). In two cases, ages of 30 ka was determined by isochron dating on calcite- cemented cave sediments, indicating that the climatic conditions were sufficiently mild to allow precipitation of these cements.

3.2.6.3 *Cave Fills and Paleontology*

Because of the permafrozen condition, which makes excavations impossible without using heavy mining equipment, cave sediments are difficult to study in section. However, judging from exposed surfaces and rare cross-sections, the most common cave fill is cryoclastic debris deposited by mass movement. In a few cases, carbonate-cemented fluvial quartz sandstone and gravel conglomerate have been detected (cement dated to 30 ka, see above), and one case of a sandy, kaolinite-rich clay fill is known from the Hilmarfjellet karst. Production of kaolinite may indicate weathering under warm and humid conditions, which prevailed in Spitsbergen during the Tertiary. The cave may therefore be of that age, or the fill was derived by erosion of Tertiary sediments that are abundant in central Spitsbergen, but presently absent in Hilmarfjellet.

Often, cave entrances contain skeletal remains of birds, reindeer and sea mammals, brought in there by various scavengers, of which the arctic fox and various birds are likely candidates. These bones, as exposed on the surface, are obviously of recent age. Although it is likely that similar, older deposits may exist deeper into the cave sediments, permafrost has hampered any further investigations.

3.2.6.4 *Springs and Active Aquifers*

Perhaps the most spectacular, surprising, and yet most easily studied aspect of the Spitsbergen karst is the abundant evidence of sub-permafrost aquifer flow, as seen by the numerous icings, karst springs and open-system pingos (Orvin, 1944; Liestøl, 1976; Pulina, 1977; Lauritzen, 1991). These springs drain all types of aquifers, but many of them are karstic(Fig. 3-5). Karst aquifers are of two types, shallow supra-permafrost flow within the active layer, which is only active during the summer season at non-freezing temperatures, and the deeper, often thermal sub-permafrost flow which may flow perennially.

A large number of the perennial karst springs are 'hot' springs, because their temperatures (+3℃ to +15℃) are elevated far above the annual mean of the sites (−4 to −5℃). Extreme temperatures up to 27℃ have been reported for the Woodfjorden springs, Fig. 3-5. These springs drain through limestones, deposit large tufa dams, and their high temperature may be attributed to young volcanism (Hoel and Holtedahl, 1911). The main recharge area is underneath glaciers nearby, and evidence of that the discharge and temperature have decreased since they were first described (1910), may be attributed to a similar decrease in glaciers in the upland (*vide supra*) (Haldorsen and Lauritzen, 1993). Several other thermal springs have been studied in the Hornsund area (Krawczyk, 1989), displaying a range of temperatures from 8 to 12℃, depending on the mixing ratio of glacial and thermal water.

The largest and most impressive karst aquifer in Spitsbergen is the one underlying Hilmarfjellet (Fig. 3-7), where springs vary in discharge from ~1 l/s up to 70 m^3/s and 15 to 3℃ in temperature (Lauritzen, 1993). Except for small *supra*-permafrost springs, that display 'normal' solute contents and P_{CO_2}, all other springs display very high specific conductivity due to a high brine content. They also carry H_2S and contain deposits of a whitish organic slime. Trollosen, the largest spring, discharges turbid, glacial water and displays large seasonal variations of discharge and temperature(Photo 56). In addition, upon changes in discharge, the spring ejects spontaneous pulses of warm, saline water. Dye tracing tests have proven that part of the water is sourced from the Vitkovski glacier (moulin A, Fig. 3-7). The isotopic composition of SO_4^{2-} / S^{2-} and deviant $[Cl^-]/[SO_4^{2-}]$ indicate that the sulphide may be of bacterial origin, and that the salinity is not a result of simple dilution of modern seawater with glacial water. Detection of bacteriomorphs and spherules of FeS_x support this hypothesis, and it is most likely that the salt component is sourced from deep, thermal brine or connate water (Lauritzen, 1994; Lauritzen and Bottrell, 1994). The combination of these observations leads to a conceptual, geometric model of the Hilmarfjellet karst aquifer(Fig. 3-11).

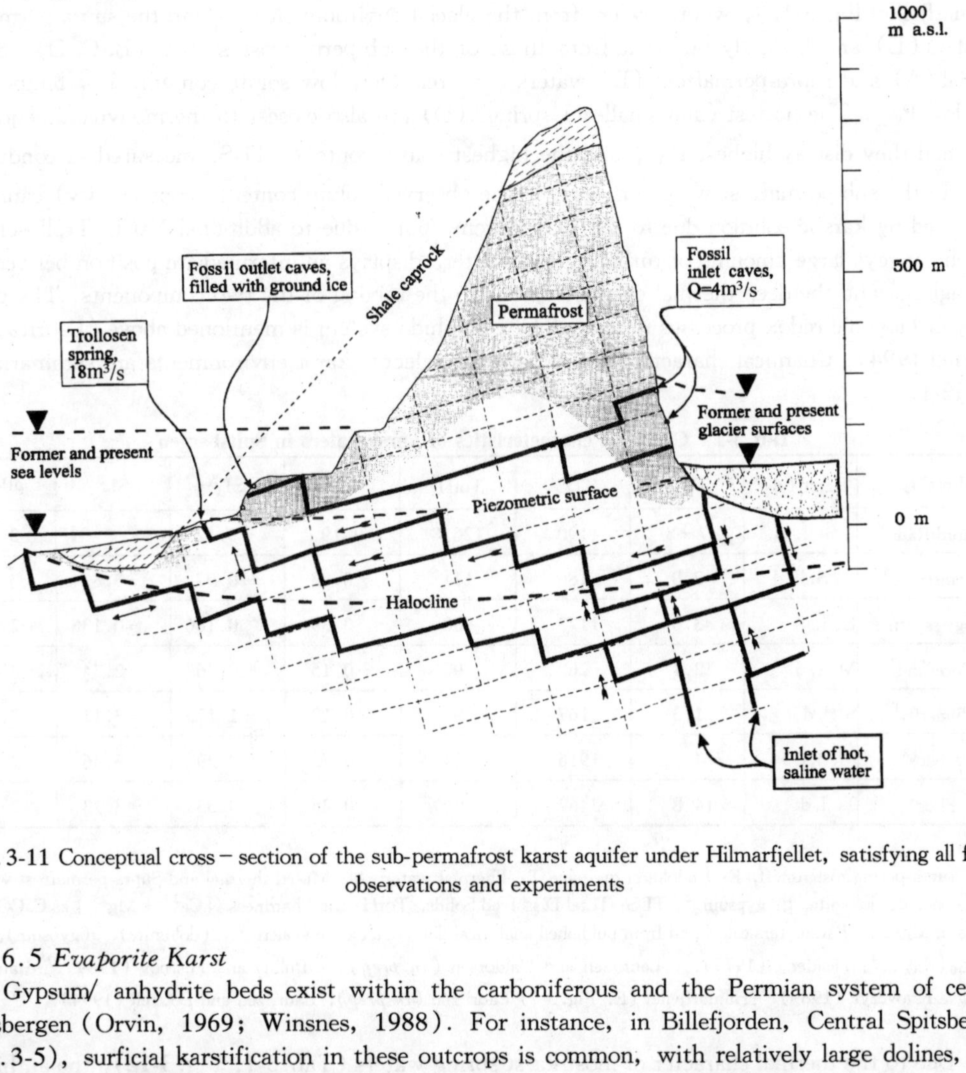

Fig. 3-11 Conceptual cross-section of the sub-permafrost karst aquifer under Hilmarfjellet, satisfying all field observations and experiments

3.2.6.5 *Evaporite Karst*

Gypsum/ anhydrite beds exist within the carboniferous and the Permian system of central Spitsbergen (Orvin, 1969; Winsnes, 1988). For instance, in Billefjorden, Central Spitsbergen (Fig. 3-5), surficial karstification in these outcrops is common, with relatively large dolines, collapsed caves, streamsinks and springs (Salvigsen et al., 1983). Perhaps the best studied evaporite karst is the Kongressvatnet karst, close to Isfjord Radio (Pulina and Postnov, 1989)(Fig. 3-5). Large, waterfilled dolines are common in this area (Salvigsen and Elgersmaa, 1985). The Kongressvatnet lake (a karst doline in part developed in gypsum beds) drains underground through a cave system, and also receives water from numerous gypsum springs. Water balance studies suggest that a nearby glacier in the upland, some 5 km away, is the main recharge area, functioning largely after the scheme depicted in Fig. 3-3 and 3-8. Another characteristic feature is cryogenic gypsum crusts found on snow and ice (Pulina and Postnov, 1989).

3.2.7 *Processes*

3.2.7.1 *Water Chemistry*

The carbonate karst component in the chemical composition in most sub-permafrost karst springs is obscured by mixing with thermal brine (which may be viewed as allogenic) and dissolved evaporites. This is illustrated by the chemical composition of various aquatic environments at Hilmarfjellet (Fig. 3-12), where waters from the glacial environment (A) and the supra-permafrost aquifers (E) are distinctly different from those of the sub-permafrost system (B, C, D). Supra-glacial (A) and supra-permafrost (E) waters have relatively low solute content, low temperature and low P_{CO_2}. The hottest (and smallest) springs (D) are also closest to thermodynamic equilibrium, and they display highest P_{CO_2}, and the highest solute content (TDS, measured as conductivity). In the sub-permafrost water (B, C, D), the observed solute content (conductivity) cannot be explained by karstic solution due to the CO_2 system, but is due to additional NaCl. Trollosen (B) which conveys large amounts of turbid, glacial water, displays an intermediate position between the supraglacial and the deep thermal chemistry, due to the mixing of the two components. The probability of biogenic redox processes in the sulphate-sulphide system is mentioned above (Lauritzen and Bottrell 1994). Chemical characteristics of various, selected karst environments are summarized in Tab. 3-1.

Tab. 3-1 Chemical characteristics of karst waters in Spitsbergen

Locality	Karst type[1]	T, ℃	TDS[2]	TotH[2]	SI_c[3]	SI_d[3]	SI_g[3]	pP_{CO_2}[3]
Isfjord Radio[4]	S. l. d.	7-8	190	126.8	0.19	-0.42	-	3.04
Blomstrand[5]	S. l, d	2.0	186	111	-0.03	-0.97	-3.83	3.02
Kongressvatn I[6]	E. l, g	3.0	1173	900	0.39	0.146	-0.138	2.61
Hornsund[7]	M. l, d	12.1	260	90	-0.15	-0.36	-2.34	3.46
Hilmarfj.[8]	S. l, d	1.3	167	92	-0.126	-1.175	-3.11	3.24
Trollos[8]	M. l, d	4.1	1916	114	-0.73	-2.29	-3.46	2.23
Fisos[8]	T. l, d	14.8	3467	201	0.35	0.33	-3.13	2.28

[1]: S: supra-permafrost runoff, E: Endokarst drainage T: Thermal water, M: Mixed thermal and Supra-permafrost water l: Limestone, d: dolomite, g: gypsum.[2]: TDS: Total Dissolved Solids, TotH: total hardness ($[Ca^{2+} + Mg^{2+}]$ as $CaCO_3$), all values in Mg/L.[3]: Parameters calculated from published analytical data, SI_x (x = c (calcite), d(dolomite), g(gypsum), pP_{CO_2} $-\log_{10}(P_{CO_2})$.[4]: Hellden, (1973).[5]: Lauritzen and Haldorsen (*in prep*).[6]: Pulina and Postnov (1989).[7]: Raudfjellet springs, Krawczyk (1989).[8]: Hilmarfjellet (E, Fig. 3-7) Lauritzen (*in prep*), Lauritzen and Bottrell (1994).

Due to the thermal character of most karst spring waters (Tab. 3-1, Fig. 3-12), the authigenic chemical processes that are *climatically* controlled and relevant to surface karstification at this high latitude are better studied in surficial waters and in supra-permafrost systems. Numerous studies of runoff from such sites have revealed a relatively low solute content and P_{CO_2} (Helldén, 1973, 1974)

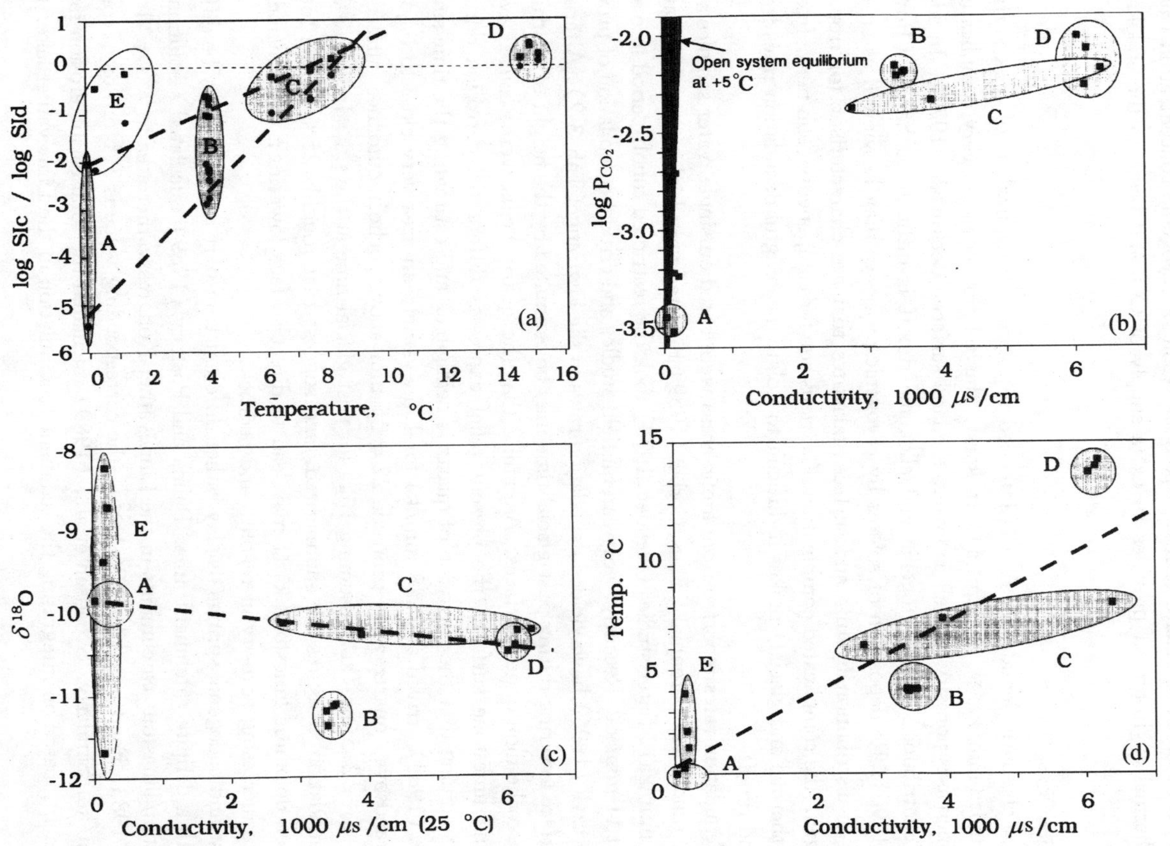

Fig. 3-12 Characteristics of water chemistry of the Himarfjellet karst (Lauritzen 1993). Capital letters refer to various sub-environments, depicted and explained in Fig. 3-7. a) Relationship between temperature and the saturation index of. calcite (SI_c, squares) and dolomite (SI_d, black dots). b) Conductivity vs log P_{CO_2}, the shaded wedge along the y-axis represents the amount of conductivity that can be explained by mineralization from the $CO_2/H_2O/CaCO_3$ system. Only the supra-permafrost and supraglacial water plot here. c) Conductivity against stable isotope composition of the water. d) Conductivity vs temperature. See text for further discus sion

(Lauritzen and Haldorsen, in preparation). These results are in general agreement with similar studies in other arctic regions (Cogley, 1972; Smith, 1972; Woo and Marsh, 1977); the differences may in part be due to vegetational contrasts (Woo and Marsh, 1977) and biogenic CO_2. Most areas that have been studied in Spitsbergen are dominated by cryoclastic regolith, almost devoid of vegetation. Isfjord Radio displays supersaturated waters with a P_{CO_2} very close to that of air, similar to the supra-glacial and supra-permafrost waters of Hilmarfjellet, Fig. 3-12. The surficial waters are close to saturation with respect to calcite (SIc), a possible result of cryogenic concentration (*vide supra*). The geothermal environment provides an extra supply of CO_2 and brine to the endokarst waters, see Fig. 3-12b.

3.2.7.2 *Denudation Rates*

The concept of chemical denudation rate is intended to express an equivalent of rock surface lowering per time unit (mm/ka = m^3/km^2 a). In karst, this relation becomes very complicated, because corrosion increases porosity as well as lowers the land surface (Beckinsale, 1972). In addition, the relative contribution from autogenic and allogenic runoff is difficult to handle (Pitty, 1968; Lauritzen, 1990). Re-deposition of solutes by cryogenic processes may be viewed as analogous to the similar re-distribution by tufa and surface stalactites that are characteristic for tropical karst. In Spitsbergen, the complicated combination of various aquifer components (sub-permafrost, supra-permafrost, thermal and glacial) makes it difficult to isolate meaningful denudation rates from water chemistry and runoff.

The earliest denudation rates reported from arctic areas were based on single water samples and an assumption that runoff was perennial. Thus, Corbel (1959) reported very high values for Spitsbergen (40 and 15 mm/ka). Later studies (Helldén, 1973) took the restricted runoff period into account and arrived at 11 mm/ka. Recently, very careful field studies and critical compilation of previous results by Krawczyk (1995) have yielded denudation rates in the low range(Tab. 3-2). Alternatively, the total surface lowering during post-glacial time may be estimated by the height of protruding quartz veins on roche-moutonnee surfaces. Assuming that the quartz veins were scoured even with the surrounding limestone surface, the present relief expresses differential corrosion during post-glacial time. Assuming that the corrosion of quartz is negligible, and estimating the time since exposure, Åkerman (1983) arrived at 2.48 mm/ka for Linnévatnet, an area very close to Isfjord Radio. On Blomstrandsøya, quartz veins protrude 22 – 25 mm above roche moutonnee surfaces, which convert to 2.2 – 2.5 mm/ka, assuming 10ka for post-glacial time at the site. In Tab. 3-2, the two types of denudation measures are summarized, and suggest that roughly 25% of the total chemical corrosion on dolomitic limestone karst may lead to direct surface lowering; the remainder may be attributed to increasing porosity in regolith and bedrock.

Evaporite karst and endogenic springs display rather different transport rates that may be difficult to associate with a definite catchment area. Pulina and Postnov (1989) calculated a solutional loss in various gypsum/limestone catchments in the Linnévatnet-Kongressvatnet area to 7.3 – 1.7 m^3/day for August 1983. For Linnédalen (36 km^2), the corresponding value is 3.1 m^3/day, converting to 10.3 mm/ka. Similarly, Svendsen et al., (1989) calculated the total clastic erosion rate for the same catchment, based on integrating the sediment accumulation in the Linnévatnet lake, to 15 mm/ka.

As an example of solute transport from the sub-permafrost karst, which cannot easily be associated with neither catchment area nor aquifer volume, Trollosen at Hilmarfjellet yields a total transport of roughly 11 m^3 $CaCO_3$, 0.3 m^3 gypsum ($CaSO_4 2H_2O$), and 215 m^3 NaCl in one year. Since a substantial amount of the recharge is subglacial water (~ 0℃), which is being heated up during transit, the thermal transport of Trollosen at average annual discharge (8 m^3/s) amounts to 177 mW.

Tab. 3-2 Denudation rates in Spitsbergen and Canadian arctic karst

Site	Karst type	Reference	Rate (mm/ka)	Type of determination
"Spitsbergen"	Limest. dol.	Corbel (1957)	5 – 50	Chemical
Kongsfjord	Limest. dol	Corbel (1964)	16	Chemical
Isfjord radio	Limest. dol.	Hellden(1973)	11.4	Chemical
Hornsund	Limest. dol	Pulina (1977)	5 – 20	Chemical
Fugleberget, hornsund	Limest. dol	Krawczyk (1994)	6 – 7	Chemical
Central Spitsbergen	Limest. dol	Kostrzevski et al. (1988)	3.4 ± 0.17	Chemical
Calypsostranda SW Spitsbergen	Limest. dol	Krawczyk (1995)[1]	7.3 – 13.1	Chemical
Linnédalen	Mixed limest. dol. gypsum	Pulina and Postnov (1989)	10.3[2]	Chemical
Blomstrand	Limest. dol.	Lauritzen (unpubl.)	2.2 – 2.5	Quartz veins
Linnedalen	Limest. dol.	Åkerman(1983)	2.48	Quartz veins
Somerset island, Canada	Limest.	Smith (1969)	2	Chemical
Cornwallis island, Canada	Limest.	Cogley (1975)	7.5	Chemical
Ellesmere island, Canada	Limest.	Woo and Marsh (1977)	3.3 ± 0.6	Chemical
North Sascatchewan River, Canada	Limest.	Ford and Drake (1982)	11	Chemical

[1]: Several authors, cited in Krawczyk (1995). [2]: Calculated from Pulina and Postnov's data, using 36 km^2 catchment area and assuming 4 month's of runoff.

3.3 Conclusions

(1) Spitsbergen is still in a high-arctic, permafrozen state that may serve as an important *in situ* model for other karst areas that have suffered similar conditions in the past.

(2) There is ample evidence of paleokarst activity, ranging from early, deep corrosion by thermal water to subaerial karst developed under a warm, low latitude climate in the Devonian. The sub-Devonian karst landscape is partially exhumed, as seen on Blomstrandsøya. There is also good evidence for *inheritance* during later stages of Pleistocene (subglacial speleogenesis). Many of the relatively young cave fragments "bleed" redbed clastics, indicating that speleogenesis has in part been dictated by paleokarst voids.

(3) *Subglacial speleogenesis* is in an active state in Spitsbergen, as exemplified by the Hilmarfjellet karst. Aquifer activity increases in pace with expansion of subpolar glaciers. There is an intimate interaction between the glacier aquifer and *sub-permafrost aquifers*. The system is perennial. "Hot" springs are common, where biogeochemical processes, like sulphate reduction, are active.

(4) During the Pleistocene glaciations, subglacial speleogenesis was much more extensive, as revealed by numerous phreatic, scalloped cave fragments hanging high up in valley walls. They are relict and plugged with ground ice after a few meters.

(5) A separate, *supra-permafrost* aquifer and runoff system exist within the active layer. This system is strongly seasonal and only active in the summer season. There is little or no mixing between the supra- and sub-permafrost karst aquifers, as seen from the distinct chemical differences

between the two.

(6) The present- day denudation rates on bare limestone and dolomite surfaces in Spitsbergen as measured by hydrochemical integration in small, supra-permafrost catchments amount to 10 mm/ka or less. Of this, only 25% results from direct surface lowering on exposed karst surfaces (2.2 – 2.5 mm/ka).

References

Åkerman, J. H., 1983. Notes on chemical weathering, Kapp Linne, Spitsbergen. International Permafrost Conference, Proceedings, Vol. 4, pp. 10 – 15

Andersen, B. G. and H. W. Borns, 1994. The Ice Age World 208 pp. Scandinavian University Press, Oslo.

Beckinsale, R. P., 1972. The limestone Boogaboo: surface lowering or denudation or amount of solution? Transactions of the Cave Research Group of Great Britain, Vol. 14, pp. 55 – 58.

Behrens, H., H. Bergman, H. Moser, W. Rauert, W. Stichler, W. Ambach, and H. Eisner, 1971. Study of the discharge of alpine glaciers by means of environmental isotopes and dye tracers. Zeitschrift für Gletscherkunde und Glacialgeologie, Vol. 7, pp. 79 – 102.

Brown, R. J. E., 1970. Permafrost in canada. University of Toronto Press, Toronto.

Clayton, L., 1964. Karst topography on stagnant glaciers. Journal of Glaciology, Vol. 5, pp. 107 – 112.

Cogley, J. G., 1972. Processes of solution in an Arctic limestone terrain. Institute of British Geographers, Special Publication, Vol. 4, pp. 201 – 211.

Coleman, J. F., 1949. An indicator of water – flow in caves. University of Bristol Speleological Society, Proceedings, Vol. 6, pp. 57 – 67.

Corbel, J., 1957. Les karts du Nord – oest de l'Europe et de quelques regions de comparison. Institute des Etudes Rhodanniennes. Memoires, Vol. 12, pp. 1 – 541.

Corbel, J., 1959. Vitesse de l'Erosion. Zeitschrift für Geomorphologie, Vol. 3, pp. 1 – 28.

Crowley, T. J. and G.R. North, 1991. Paleoclimtatology. Oxford University Press, New York.

Curl, R. L., 1974. Deducing flow velocity in cave conduits from scallops. National Speleological Society, Bulletin, Vol. 36, 1 – 5.

Deming, D., J.H. Sass, A.H. Lachenbruch and R.F. De Rito, 1992. Heat flow and subsurface temperature as evidence for basin – scale groundwater flow, North Slope of Alaska. Geological Society of America Bulletin, Vol. 104, pp. 528 – 542.

Dreybrodt, W., 1988. Processes in karst systems. Physics, Chemistry and Geology, 288pp., Springer Verlag, Berlin.

Ehlers, J., 1983. Glacial Deposits of North – west Europe, 470 pp. A. A. Balkema, Rotterdam.

Flood, B., 1966. On the contact between the Hecla Hoeck and the Culm, Vestspitsbergen. Norsk Polarinstitutt Årbok, 7 – 11.

Ford, D. C., 1977. Karst and Glaciation in Canada. Proceedings, 7th. International Speleological Congress, Sheffield 1, pp. 188 – 189.

Ford, D. C., 1984. Karst groundwater activity and landform genesis in modern permafrost regions of Canada. In : LaFleur, R. G. (eds.): Groundwater as a Geomorphic Agent 340 – 350. Allen and Unwin, New York.

Ford, D. C. and P.W. Williams, 1989. Karst Geomorphology and Hydrology, 601 pp. Unwin Hyman, London.

Gjessing, J., 1967. Norway's Paleic Surface. Vol. 21, pp. 69 – 132.

Glazek, J., J. Rudnicki and A. Szynkiewicz, 1977. Proglacial caves – a special genetic type of cave in glaciated areas. Proceedings, 7th. International Speleological Congress, Sheffield 1, 215 – 217.

Haldorsen, S. and S. E. Lauritzen, 1993. Subpermafrost groundwater in Svalbard. Hydrogeology of Hard Rocks. 26th Congress of the International Association of Hydrogeologists 2, 940 – 949.

Hanssen – Bauer, I., Kristensen Solås, M. and Steffensen, E. L., 1990. The Climate of Spitsbergen, 40 pp. Det Norske meteorologiske Institutt, Oslo.

Helldén, U., 1973. Some calculations of the denudation rate in a dolomitic limestone area at Isfjord Radio, West Spitzbergen. Transactions of the Cave Research Group of Great Britain, Vol. 15, pp. 81 – 87.

Helldén, U., 1974. Karst. En studie av Artfjälets karstområde med jämförande korrosionsanalyser från Västspetsbergen och Tjeckoslovakien pp. Lunds Universtet Geografiska Institutionen, Lund.

Hoel, A. and O. Holtedahl, 1911. Les nappes de lave. les volcans et les sources thermales dans les environment de la Baie Wood au Spitsberg. Det Norske Vitenskapsakådemi. Skrifter. Matematisk – naturvitenskapelig Klasse Vol. 9, pp. 1 – 20.

Horn, G., 1935. Über die Bildung von Karsthöhlen unter einem Gletcher. Norsk Geografisk Tidsskrift Vol. 5, pp. 494 – 498.

Horn, G., 1947. Karsthuler i Nordland. Norges Geologiske Undersøkelse, Vol. 165, pp. 1 – 77.

Horn, G., 1978. Limestone Caves in Nordland. Cave Geology, Vol. 1, pp. 124 – 138.

Ivanovich, M. and R.S. Harmon, 1992. Uranium – series Disequilibrium: Applications to Earth, marine, and Environmental Sciences, 910 pp. Clarendon Press, Oxford.

Jansen, E. and J. Sjøholm, 1991. Reconstruction of glaciation over the past 6 Myr from ice – borne deposits in the Norwegian Sea. Nature, Vol. 349, pp. 600 – 603.

Kamb, B., C. F. Raymond, W. D. Harrison, H. Engelhardt, K. A. Echelmeyer, N. Humphrey, M. M. Brugman and T. Pfeffer, 1985. Glacier surge mechanism: 1982 – 1983 surge of variegated Glacier, Alaska. Science, Vol. 227, pp. 469 – 479.

Karwowski, L. and A. Kozik, 1982. The occurrence and origin of coarse crystalline calcite in the carbonate massifs of Sørkappland (South Spitzbergen). Wyprawy Polarne Uniwersytetu Slaskiego 1977 – 1980. Uniwersytet Slaski, Katowice, Poland 1, 47 – 59.

Krawczyk, W. E., 1989. Thermal springs below Raudfjellet, South – West Spitsbergen. Acta Universitatis Wratislaviensis, Vol. 1069, pp. 67 – 74.

Krawczyk, W. E., 1995. Denudacja chemiczna w wybranych zlewniach SW Spitsbergenu (Chemical denudation in selected catchments of SW Spitsbergen). Ph. D., Uniwersytet Slaski, Sosnowiec, Poland, 233 pp.

Lang, H., C. Leibundgut and E. Festel, 1979. Results from tracer experiments on the water flow through the Aletchgletcher. Zeitschrift für Gletscherkunde und Glacialgeologie, Vol. 15, pp. 209 – 218.

Lauritzen, S. E., 1981a. Glaciated karst in Norway. Proceedings, 8th. International Speleological Congress. Bowling Green, Vol. 8, pp. 410 – 411.

Lauritzen, S. E., 1981b. Statistical symmetry analysis of scallops. National Speleological Society, Bulletin, Vol. 43, pp. 52 – 55.

Lauritzen, S. E., 1990. Autogenic and Allogenic Denudation in Carbonate Karst by the Multiple Basin Method: an example from Svartisen, North Norway. Earth Surface Processes and Landforms, Vol. 15, pp. 157 – 167.

Lauritzen, S. E., 1991. Groundwater in Cold Climates: Interaction Between Glacier and Karst Aquifers. In: Gjessing, Y., Hagen, J. O., Hassel, K. A. and Wold, B. (eds.): Arctic Hydrology. Present and Future Tasks, Hydrology of Svalbard – Hydrological problems in cold climates, pp. 139 – 146. Norwegian National Committee for Hydrology, Oslo.

Lauritzen, S. E., 1993. Interaction between glacier and karst aquifers: Preliminary results from Hilmarfjellet, South Spitsbergen. Kras i Speleologia, Vol. 8(XVII).

Lauritzen, S. E., 1994. Microbial activity in thermoglacial karst springs in Spitsbergen. In: Sasowsky, I. D. and Palmer, M. V. (eds.): Breakthroughs in Karst Geomicrobiology and Redox Geochemistry. Abstracts and Field – Trip Guide for the Symposium held February 16 through 19. 1994. Colorado Springs, Colorado 44. Karst Water Institute, Charles Town, WVa.

Lauritzen, S. E. and S. H. Bottrell, 1994. Microbiological activity in thermo – glacial karst springs, south Spitsbergen. Geomicrobiology Journal, Vol. 12, pp. 161 – 173.

Liestøl, O., 1976. Pingos, springs and permafrost in Spitsbergen. Norsk Polarinstitutt Årbok, Vol. 1975, pp. 7 – 29.

Liestøl, O., 1980. Permafrost Conditions in Spitsbergen, Oslo.

Mylroie, J. E. and J. L. Carew, 1988. Solution conduits as indicators of late Quaternary sea level position. Quaternary Science Reviews Vol. 7, pp. 55 – 64.

Nilsson, T., 1983. The Pleistocene 651 pp. Reidl Publishing Company, Dordrecht.

Nye, J. F., 1965. The flow of a glacier in a channel of rectangular, elliptic or parabolic cross section. Journal of Glaciology, Vol. 5, pp. 661 – 690.

Orvin, A. K., 1944. Litt om Kilder på Svalbard. Norsk Geografisk Tidsskrift, Vol. 10, pp. 16 – 38.

Orvin, A. K., 1969. Outline of the geological history of Spitsbergen. Skrifter om Svalbard og Ishavet, Vol. 78, pp. 1 – 57.

Paterson, W. S. B., 1981. The Physics of Glaciers, 380 pp. Pergamon Press, London.

Pitty, A. F., 1968. The scale and significance of solutional loss from the limestone tract of the southern Pennines. Proceedings of the Geological Association of London, Vol. 79, pp. 153 – 177.

Price, L. W., 1972. The Periglacial Environment, Permafrost, and Man, 88 pp. Association of American Geographers, Washington, D.C.

Pulina, M., 1977. On karst phenomena occurring in the southern part of Spitsbergen (Uwagi o zjawiskach krasowych w poludniowej czesci Spitsbergenu). Kras i Speleologia, Vol. 1, pp. 104 – 129.

Pulina, M., 1984a. The effects of cryochemical processes in the glaciers and the permafrost in Spitsbergen. Polish Polar Research, Vol. 5, pp. 137 – 163.

Pulina, M., 1984b. Glacierkarst phenomena in Spitzbergen. Norsk Geografisk Tidsskrift, Vol. 38, pp. 163 – 168.

Pulina, M., 1990. Geomorphological effects of the cryochemical process. Quaestion Geographicae, Vol. 13/14, pp. 99 – 112.

Pulina, M. and I. Postnov, 1989. Gypsum karst in the NW part of the Nordenskiold Land – West Spitsbergen. Kras i Speleologia, Vol. 6(XV), pp. 40 – 57.

Röthlisberger, H., 1972. Water pressure in intra – and subglacial channels. Journal of Glaciology, Vol. 11, pp. 177 – 203.

Salvigsen, O. and A. Elgersmaa, 1985. Large scale karst features and open taliks at Vardeborgsletta, outer Isfjorden, Svalbard. Polar Research, Vol. 3, pp. 145 – 153.

Salvigsen, O., Ø.. Lauritzen and J. Mangerud, 1983. Karst and karstification in gypsiferous beds in Mathiesondalen, Central Spitsbergen, Svalbard. Polar Research, Vol. 1, pp. 83 – 88.

Smith, D. I., 1972. The solution of limestone in an Arctic environment. Institute of British Geographers, Special Publication, Vol. 4, pp. 187 – 200.

Svendsen, J. I., J. Mangerud and G. H. Miller, 1989. Denudation rates in the arctic estimated from lake sediments on

Spitsbergen, Svalbard. Palaeogeography Palaeoclimatology Palaeoecology, Vol. 76, pp. 153 – 168.
Szczesny, R., L. Lindner and L. Marks, 1987. Photogeological map of the Hilmarfjellet region (Sörkapp Land, Spitsbergen) (1:10 000), Institute of Geology, Warsaw University.
Thiedig, F. and G. M. Manby, 1992. Origins and deformation of Post – Caledonian sediments on Blomstrandhalvøya and Lovénøyane, northwest Spitsbergen. Norsk Geologisk Tidsskrift, Vol. 72, pp. 27 – 33.
Vogt, T., 1989. Croûtes calcaires d'origine cryogénique. Zeitschrift für Geomorphologie, pp. 115 – 135.
Vogt, T., 1991. Cryogenic Physico – chemical Precipitations: Iron, Silica, Calcium Carbonate. Permafrost and Periglacial Processes, Vol. 1, pp. 283 – 293.
Walder, J. and B. Hallet, 1979. geometry of former subglacial water channels and cavities. Journal of Glaciology, Vol. 23, pp. 335 – 346.
Werenskiold, W., 1920. Svalbards fysiske geografi. Naturen, Vol. 44, pp. 1 – 1234.
Werenskiold, W., 1953. The extent of frozen ground under the sea bottom and glacier beds. Journal of Glaciology, Vol. 2, pp. 197 – 200.
Winsnes, T. S., 1988. Bedrock Map of Svalbard and Jan Mayen (1:1000 000), Norsk Polarinstitutt.
Woo, M. K. and P. Marsh, 1977. Effect of vegetation on limestone solution in a small High Arctic basin. Canadian Journal of Earth Sciences, Vol. 14, pp. 571 – 581.
Worsley, D. and O. J. Aga, 1986. Evolution of an arctic archipelago: The Geological History of Svalbard 121 pp. Den Norske Stats Oljeselskap (STATOIL), Stavanger.

Global Karst Correlation
Edited by Yuan Daoxian and Liu Zaihua
Science Press and VSP BV, 1998

Chapter 4 Karst of Urals

V.N. Andreichuk, I.A. Lavrov
Kungur Karst Station, Academy of Science of Russia

"Urals" is a Turkish word meaning "belt". Really, Ural mountains are like a narrow belt cutting plains of Northern Eurasia from the cold seas of the Arctic Ocean to hot steppes of Kazakhstan (Fig. 4-1). Urals stretch for 2000 km from the North to the South. The mountainous New Land (Novaja Zemlja) islands are the prolongation of Urals in the North and Mugodzary mountains — in the South. It was accepted for a long time that Ural ridge is a border-line between two parts of the world— Europe and Asia. There are many karst phenomena in the Urals. Its exploration has a big scientific and practical importance.

Fig. 4-1 The Urals on the map of former USSR

4.1 Geological and Orographical Peculiarities of the Urals

In tectonic aspect the Urals are a large megaanticlinorium consisting of anticlinoriums and synclinoriums systems which are separated by deep faults (Fig. 4-2). In the kernels of anticlinoriums the oldest rocks crop out to the surface: crystalline shales, quarzites and granites of Proterozoic and Cambrian. Synclinoriums are filled with thick lithological complexes of Palaeozoic sedimentary and volcanic rocks containing many karstic rocks (limestones, marbles). Foredeeps are also filled with sedimentary rocks, in particular, evaporate formation (gypsum, anhydrite, dolomite, salt).

Ural mountains were formed as a result of Caledonian and Hercynian orogenic cycles. In the East Slope of the Urals folding processes began earlier than in the West Slope. They were more intensive and led to formation of folded and scaly structures complicated by faults and thick intrusions. In the West Slope Paleozoic rocks (including upper Paleozoic rocks absent in the East Slope) are folded in simple folds rarely with faults and intrusions. The tectonic pressure making a folding was

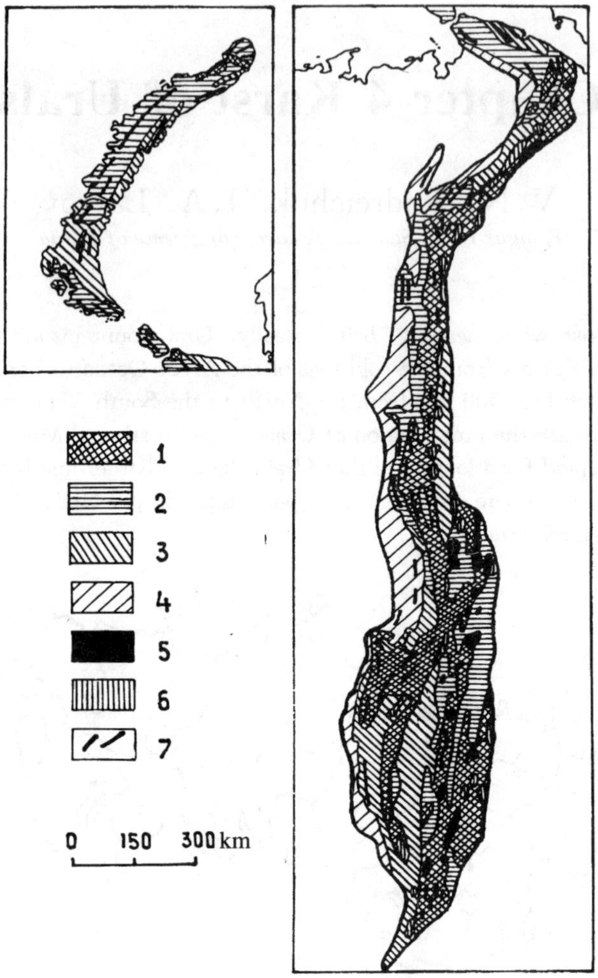

Fig. 4-2 The general tectonic scheme of the Urals. 1. Old kernels (metamorphic rocks). Hercynian folding; 2. Anticlinal zones; 3. Synclinal zones; 4. Pre-Urals foredeep. Large intrusions; 5. Granites and granitoides; 6. Gabbro, dunites, peridotites; 7. Directions (axes) of folds

from east to west.

Major denudation of mountains, planation (and weathering crusts formation) took place during Mesozoic and Kainozoic time. Tectonic movements were characterized by blocky uplifts and subsidences accompanied by folding and faulting locally. During Quaternary period differential low-amplitude tectonic movements prevailed.

Orography of the Urals reflects their tectonic features. Ridges and hills correspond to the anticlinal zones, and depressions to the synclinal zones. Ridges and depressions stretch meridionally and submeridionally reflecting change in large tectonism from the west to the east. According to the relief and landscapes, 5 geographical areas in Urals could be distinguished: Polar Urals (and Pai-Choy ridge), Pre-Polar Urals, Northern Urals, Middle Urals and Southern Urals. The highest peaks of the Urals are situated in the Pre-Polar area (Narodnaja M., 1894 m). The Middle Urals is the lowest (400 – 800 m high).

4.2 Karstic Rocks

Different types of karstic rocks are widespread in the Urals and in the eastern outlying of Russian platform (Fig. 4-3). Lithologically they include different kinds of carbonate (limestones, marbles, dolomites, siderites, magnesites), sulfate (gypsums, anhydrites) and salt (rock salt, potash salt) rocks. Moreover, there are also marls, sandstone and conglomerates with calcareous and gypseous cement, and freshwater calcareous tufa, which are liable to karstic process too. Stratigraphically, the mentioned rocks range between Riphean (lower Proterozoic) and Quaternary (Tab. 4-1). In Zauralje region, karst phenomena (dolines) are also developed in Paleogenic siliceous rocks (silicilithes) in a remarkable area.

The basic characteristics of karstic rock distribution in the Urals region is their extension in the meridional direction according to the tectonic features. It is shown especially in the folded zone of the Urals. Karstic rocks here lie between terrigenous rocks. They are shown on the surface on the wings of synclinal structures. In the folded Urals area karstic and non-karstic rocks alternate with stripes 1 – 20 km wide, and tens and hundreds of kilometers in length.

The crystalline rocks lie in mountain part of the Urals at the depth of 1.5 – 3.6 km. They appear on the surface in the axial part of mountains and in some anticlines. The rocks of basement are Proterozoic sediments (sandstones, argillites, conglomerates, dolomites, limestones, marls) and their metamorphic varieties: quartzites, phyllites, and marbles.

The most widespread karstic rocks are in Paleozoic strata. Ordovician marbles and metamorphic limestone are spread as narrow stripes in the axial part of the Urals. Silurian rocks (dolomites, dolomitic limestone, limestone) appear in western folds of the Urals. Carbonate rocks are also typical for all Devonian, especially its upper (Eifelian and Givetian units) part (Western and Eastern Slopes). Carboniferous limestones (250 – 1300 m in thickness) are the major karstic rocks distributed in folded zone of the Urals. They comprise the most spectacular and large-scale karst phenomena in the Urals. Permian system rocks developed mainly in the platform and Pre-Urals foredeep areas. The lower part of Lower Permian is mainly limestones and dolomites (the Asselian, Sakmarian and Artinskian units). On the border between platform and foredeep Artinskian reef massives are spread.

The Kungurian layer of the upper part of Lower Permian is divided usually into Filippovsky (lower) and Irensky (upper) formations in the area. The first of them is mainly carbonate rocks (limestones, dolomites) and the second sulfate rocks (gypsums, anhydrites with dolomites strata). The thickness of Irensky formation changes from 30 – 50 m (platform) to 370 m (foredeep). For the Pre-Urals foredeep depressions it is also typical for its potash salt sediments (400 – 700m thick).

Sulfate rocks area in Pre-Urals region is remarkable (from Komy Republic in the North to Orenburg district in the South). But in dependence on tectonic situation, they show themselves on the surface usually as a stripe 15 – 30 km wide (in the case of monoclinal bedding) along the platform-foredeep border or as ring areas (stripes) in the brachyanticline structures. Salt rocks lie at the depth of 80 – 500 m.

Thus, karstic rocks are widely spread in the Urals region. Their total area can be estimated according to different approaches, but is approximately 300000 km^2 in general.

Some particular groups of rock are made up by siderites and magnesites in Southern Urals where karst phenomena and caves were also found (Andreichuk et al., 1989).

Tab. 4-1 Position of karstic rocks in the stratigraphical section of the Urals

System	Series	Layer, horizon	Index	Typical rocks
Quaternary		Pleistocene	Q	Travertine
Neogene	Pliocene	(Karst breccia horizons)	N_2	Breccia
Neogene			N	Clay
Permian	Upper	Tatarian	P_2t	Sandstone
		Kazanian	P_2kz	Conglomerate
		Ufimian	P_2u	Argilite
		Šešminsky	$P_2š$	Aleurolite
		Solikamsky	P_2si	Marl
	Lower	Kungurian	P_1k	Gypsum
		Irensky	P_1i	Anhydrite
				Salt
		Filippovsky	P_1f	
		Artinskian	P_1ar	Limestone
		Sakmarian	P_1s	Dolomite
		Accelian	P_1a	
Carboniferous		Upper	C_3	
		Middle	C_2	
	Lower	Serpukhovian	C_1s	
		Visean	C_1v	
		Tournasian	C_1t	
Devonian		Upper	D_3	
		Middle	D_2	
		Lower	D_1	
Silurian		Upper	S_1	
		Lower	S_1	
Ordovician		Upper	O_3	
		Middle	O_2	Marble
		Lower	O_1	
Proterozoic		Vendian	V	
		Riphean	R	

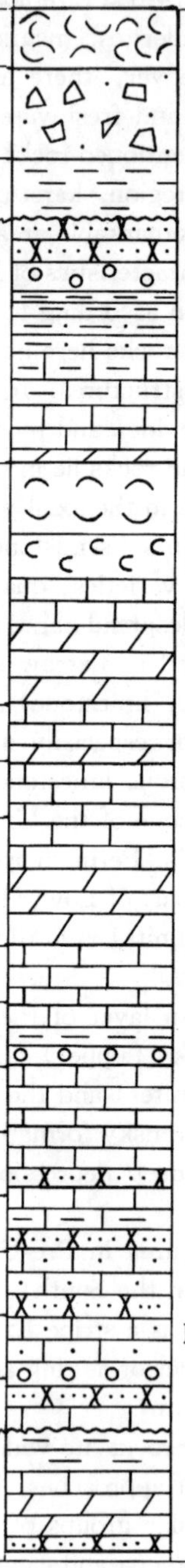

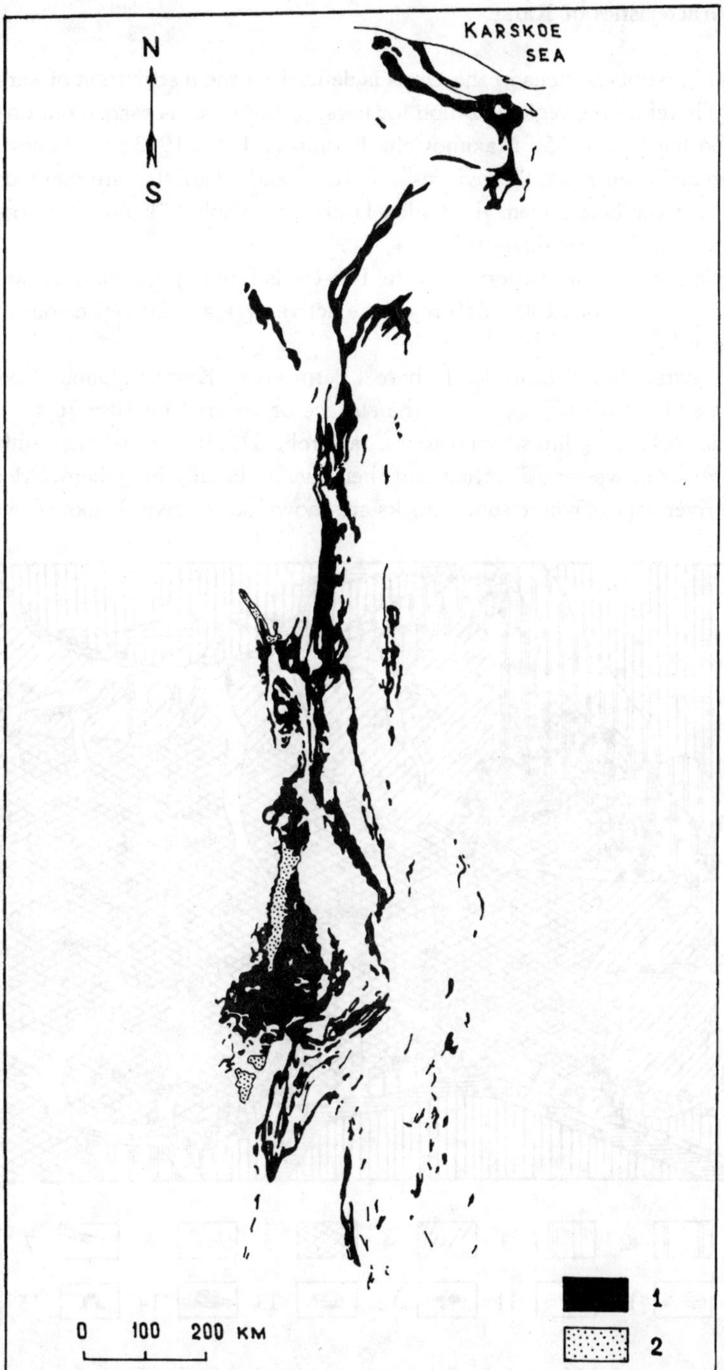

Fig. 4-3 The distribution of karst rocks in the Urals. 1. Carbonate rocks (limestones, marbles, dolomites); 2. Sulphate rocks (gypsums and anhydrites)

4.3 General Characteristics of Karst

Spreading of karst phenomena in the Urals is defined by the distribution of karstic rocks following tectonisms. Therefore the regionalization for karst of the Urals is carried out on the tectonic base (Maximovich, Gorbunova, 1965; Maximovich, Kostarev, 1968, 1973; Gorbunova, Andreichuk et al., 1992). Karstic "countries", "provinces", "areas" and "districts" are marked out according to the scales of the tectonic units: from the folded Urals as a whole ("karstic country") to the minor geological structures as "karstic districts".

In the outlying of Russian platform and the Pre-Urals foredeep, karst develops in the near-surface conditions — at the depth 100 – 250 m in the active drainage influence zones along the 150 – 200 m deep river valleys.

Most sulfate karst shows itself clearly here (Perm area, Komy Republic, Bashkortostan Republic). Gypsum and anhydrites appear on the surface or covered by 10 – 70 m or more of particoloured terrigenic rocks (argillites, sandstones, alevrolites). It is usual that sulfate rocks plunge under terrigenic rocks in western direction and then change facially into them. Most active karst is developed in the river valleys where sulfate rocks are shown on the river banks. Covering rocks there

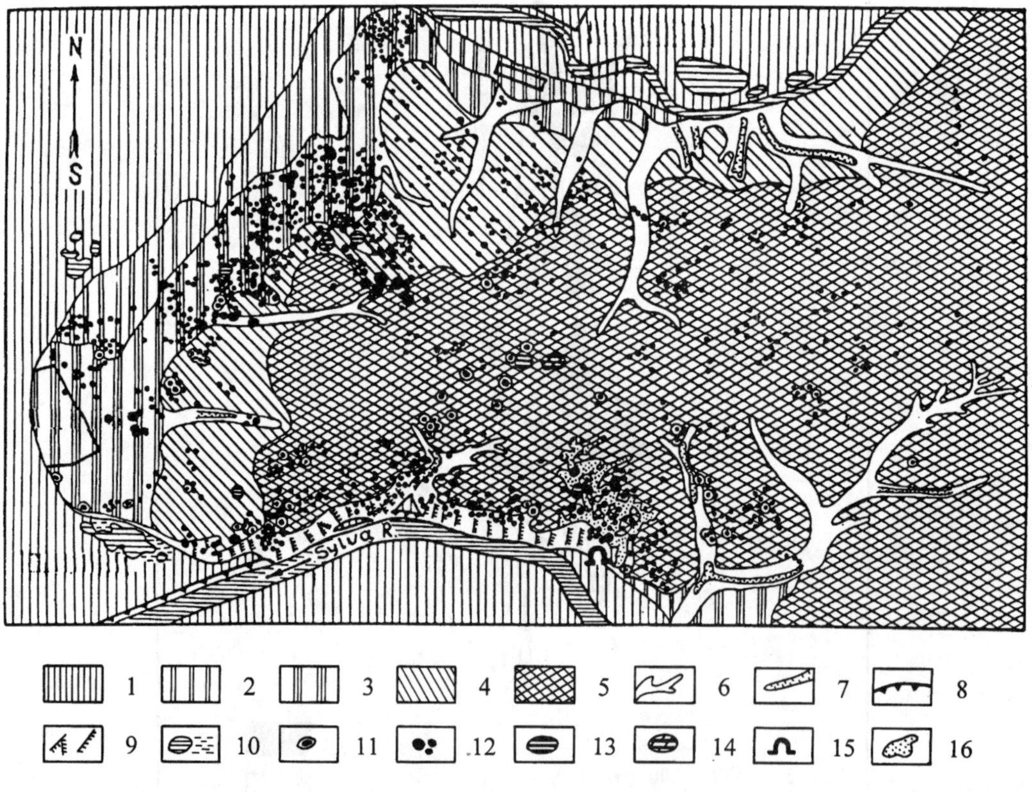

Fig. 4-4 Ledjanogorsky (Ice Mountain) sulphate massive (typical for Pre-Urals area) with its famous Ice Cave. Terraces: 1. I Terrace (4 – 12m); 2. II Terrace (15 – 25m); 3. III Terrace (30 – 40m); 4. IV Terrace (55 – 60m); 5. High terraces(>75m high). Erosion forms: 6. Large ravines; 7. Erosion ditches; 8. River bench; 9. Steep slope with outcrops of gypsums and anhydrites; 10. Former river-bed (lakes).
Karst forms: 11. Sinks; 12. Swamped dolines; 13. lakes; 14. outcrops; 15. Caves; 16. Cave area

have a small thickness (0 – 15 m) with loose structure (Quaternary deposits) and sulfate rocks are very fractured (tectonic, unloading and weathering fractures). Karst doline density here is so high that near-river places are often as badlands. The Aurgaza River (Bashkortostan) is a very good example in this aspect. There are hundreds of dolines from river valleys to watersheds that is possible to see in example of Ledjanogorsky (Ice-Mountain) massive (near Kungur town) which is typical for Perm Pre-Urals area (Fig. 4-4). Besides dolines, there are also karst-and karst-erosional depressions, karst lakes, and sinking rivers etc. The output of the karst springs is generally 10 – 100 liters per second.

Carbonate rocks appear on the platform outlying area too. The most classic limestone karst area is the Ufimskoje plateau (12000 km^2) stretching from Sylva River (Perm area) to Sim River (Bashkortostan). The plateau elevates 50 – 100 m above surrounding hilly plains. It is covered with mixed forests and intrenched by net of shallow dry valleys. Watersheds of plateau are dotted with karst dolines, but there are no deep shafts and pits. It is a result of the covering of limestone with thick (10 – 100 m and more) argillaceous-calcareous rocks, a sort of karst breccia. They present themselves terrigenic (clay, dolomite, limestone) material, derived from sulfate rocks in strata earlier (in Pliocene). In present time the frontal part of the cover is situated in extreme western part of the Plateau (Fig. 4-5). Because of the thick karst-eluvial cover, the majority of karst dolines have a karst-suffosion genesis and conical shape.

Their density on the plateau changes from 305 to 10 – 15 dolines per km^2 (Gorbunova, Andreichuk et al., 1992).

In hydrogeological aspect Ufimskoje plateau presents itself a large basin of fracture-karstic water flowing to the plateau periphery — major river valleys, where many karst springs flow out with discharges ranging between 50 and 500 liters per second. Krasny Kljuch (Red Spring) in Bashkirian part of the Plateau is the largest in Russia (55 m^3 per second, average annual output – 12.6 m^3 per second).

Pre-Urals foredeep consists of a series of depressions (Fig. 4-6). Some of them contain thick saliniferous and gypsum rock formations of Kungurian lying under the calcareous and terrigenic rocks of Ufimian (Verhnepechorskaja, Solikamskaja, Jurjusano-Sylvenskaja depressions etc.).

Sediments lie as cupola-shaped structures and depressions. On the wings of the structure where gypsums appear on the surface sulfatic karst develops locally. There are no salt rocks on the surface but saline springs in river valleys indicate salt karst at the depth. In the places where salty underground water mix with sulfatic water their aggressivity increases for gypsum rocks. As a result of sulfatic rocks solution large sink or vast depressions develop on the surface (Orljankin, 1941; Shestov and Shurubor, 1963). The processes of subsidence depression formation are particularly wide above the salt layers. In a process of salt rocks solution, and subsidence of covering rocks in top-parts of salt bodies (anticlines), wide (1.5 – 200 km^2) depressions (15 – 50 m deep) with hydrographic-net develop (Fig. 4-6; Shestov and Shurubor, 1963; Gorbunova et al., 1992). Many of them are filled with water and become lakes with running-water (Dorofeev, Lukin, 1969). It was estimated that the Chusovskoje Lake, for example, with a subsidence-erosion depression of 40 km long, 5 km wide, and 30 m deep needed 110000 years for its development, because Visherka-River takes out from the lake about 100 thousand tons of salt per year (Orljankin, 1941). The thickness of sediments in dissolution depressions could be 60 m and only 3 – 5 m on periphery. As a result of uneven subsidence, the covering rocks (marls, sandstones, limestones) on slat become more fractured and permeable to water. Karst denudation on the tops of salt structure remained an argillaceous gypsum caps. In the salt and gypsum karst areas, the mineralization of some springs and lakes water is 5 – 34 g/l because of high dissolution of ground water (Gorbunova et al, 1992).

In some places of foredeep, karst develops in gypsiferous sandstones and conglomerates with calcareous cement (Shimanovsky, 1964, 1968).

In the folded part of the Urals karst processes develop in Ordovician-Permian limestones, dolomites, marbles with total thickness more than 2000 m. Karstic rocks are parted with terrigenic deposits which divided Paleozoic carbonate complex into 3 parts (Gydrogeologia, 1972). In dependence on concrete geological structures carbonate rocks appear on the surface, mainly, in their wings.

Hydrographic-net cuts carbonate rocks of different parts to the depth of 50 – 200 m. The basic

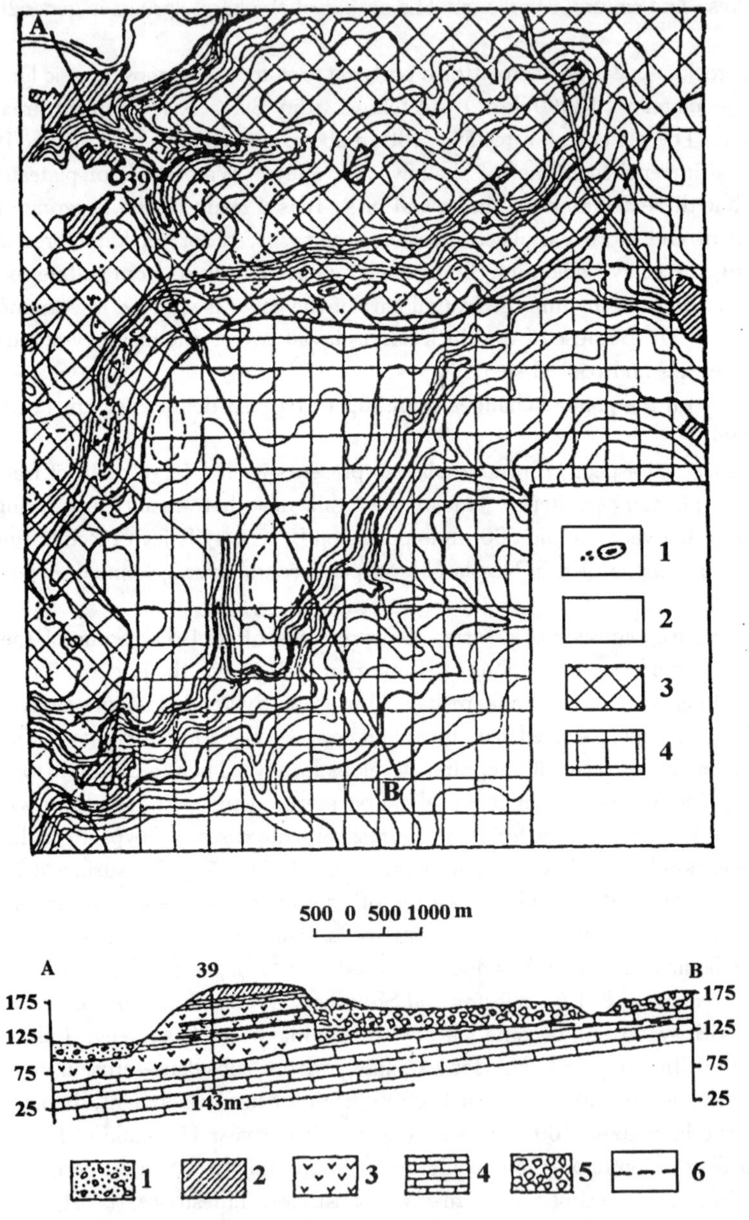

Fig. 4-5 The frontal part of the sulphate rock covering the western part of Ufimskoje plateau (Kungur town area). Plan: 1. Dolines; 2. Alluvial sediments; 3. Sulphate rocks; 4. Carbonate rocks. Section: 1. Alluvial deposits; 2. Loam; 3. Gypsums and anhydrites; 4. Limestones and dolomites; 5. Karst breccia; 6. Underground water table

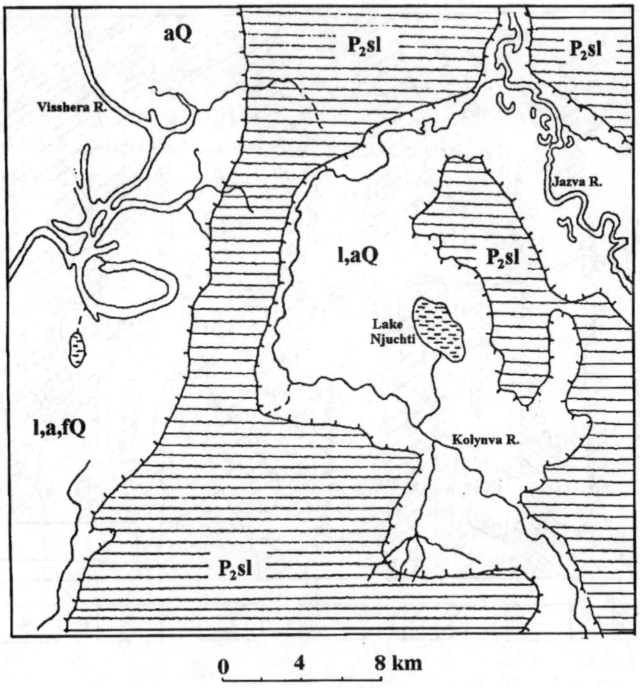

Fig. 4-6 Solution subsidence depression in Kolynva River valley (Gorbunova et. al. 1992)

feature is that meridional folds with their carbonate strata were cut by large rivers which drain karst aquifers. But tributary valleys of those large "latitudinal" rivers are formed meridionally along the folds and take up often synclinal depressions and their wings, and more rarely take up the cap rocks of structures. The level of karstic water are lower than their river-beds because karst aquifer is connected hydrodynamically with bottom of the major draining rivers. Therefore in valleys of tributaries, leakage of river water through the ponors and fractures often take place. They move under surface to main draining river and appear in the large valley as springs ($0.5 - 3.0$ m^3 per second). Usually the courses of underground river are along the bottom of dry valleys with chains of dolines. Entrances into the caves are also here. They are ponors for modern or old underground drainage system along the dry valley. On the watersheds between valleys, karstic dolines are less than in tributary valleys. They are very often karst-suffosion in origin. One of the typical areas with the above mentioned features are shown in Fig. 4-7.

In carbonate rocks of active water circulation zone (to the depth of $150 - 350$ m from the surface) karstic water has hydrocarbonate-calcic composition, and their mineralization is generally $0.45 - 0.60$ g/l. Most cavities are in this zone.

The described scenario are typical for the majority of karst districts of the folded Urals. There are hundreds of small dry valleys with modern and old ponors, cave-ponor systems in the alternate ridges and depressions. They played and play now an important role in the karst evolution depth across the river valleys. Their deepening was caused earlier and is caused in present time by the position of water saturated zone in carbonate rocks and also the conditions of leakage of suspended flow in meridional valleys of tributaries.

Side by side with typical limestone karst, there are also (in folded part of the Urals) some unique examples of karst development, in particular, marble karst in pre-polar Urals area (Andre-

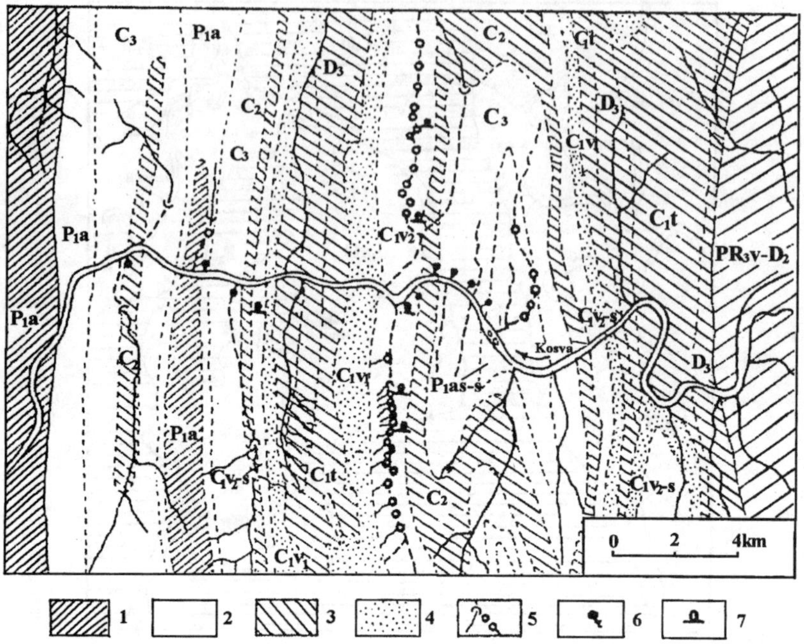

Fig. 4-7 One of the typical limestone karst areas on the Western Slope of the Middle Urals (Kizelovsky coal basin). 1. Non-karst rocks; 2. Karst rocks (limestones); 3. Intercalation of non-karst and karst rocks; 4. Coal measures; 5. dolines; 6. Large karst springs; 7. Caves

ichuk and Lavrov, 1992), siderite and magnesitic karst in the Southern Urals. In the first case, it is a peculiar paragenesis of carbonate and siliceous hydrothermokarst when alkaline solutions, circulating along the contact of marbles with quartz vein bodies dissolved carbonate and siliceous rocks at the same time. This phenomenon was established not long ago (Andreichuk and Lavrov, 1992) and it needs more studying.

In the second case (karst of siderite) we also have some interesting data about originality of karst. As it is known, siderite dissolves in the water rather well. Its solubility reaches 720 mg/l ($T = 18℃$, $P_{CO_2} = 1$ atm.), which is not much less than for calcite (1100 mg/l, Maximovich, 1975). Especially their dissolution proceeds actively in near-surface conditions — in the zone of siderite rocks oxidation. Under such water condition, the dissolution of siderites is dominantly a hypergene process. But if drainage of water filled fractures is bad, siderite will transform "in situ" into limonite filling up fractures. In the time of erosion washing or suffosion carrying-out the loose limonite, fractures and cavities will become an empty cavity. Sometimes they have considerable sizes. One of the discoveries is in the Bakal siderite deposit, where the cave is 26 m long and 500 m^3 in volume (Andreichuk et al., 1989). Karst of siderites and magnesites is not well studied yet.

In some places of the Urals, especially in the Middle and Southern Urals, we find karstic-shaped formations in other types of rocks: serpentinites, quartzites, granites.

The peculiar interest-provoking phenomena is typical at Zauralje area. There, on the vast area, a number of siliceous Paleogenic rocks (silicilithes) karst relief is developed on the surface (dolines, small dry valleys, etc.; Kovalchuk, 1988). There are many springs in the valleys and the ground water contains much (30 – 120 mg/l) SiO_2. It is established that the high solubility of siliceous rocks was caused by their permeability and its amorphous state. The friability of rocks also promotes the carrying out of the smallest particles from rock. As a result of joint action of dissolution and suffosion, non-compact zones are formed inside the rocks and on the surface-small depressions.

4.4 Caves

Widespread karstic rocks, long term development of Urals area in continental conditions has made remarkable quantity of caves in the region. Difference in geological history, tectonism, relief, climate and other factors of environment has caused the variations in the conditions of speleogenesis.

Some particular geochemical backgrounds promote also the development of caves in non- karstic rocks.

Up to now, Urals is studied very unevenly in the speleological aspect. Karst of Northern Urals is poorly investigated and areas of Pre-Polar and Polar Ural, Paj- Choj ridge and New Land islands are quite unexplored. Till today 1784 caves are known in the Urals(LavroV, Andreichuk, 1992, 1993). Their total length is about 180 km. 36 caves have length more than 1 km (Tab.4-2). 1525 caves(86%) are explored in carbonate rocks, 218 (12%) in sulfatic rocks, 4 in granites, 3 in dolomites, 8 in quartzites, 2 in conglomerates, 5 in marls, 2 in miascites, 3 in marbles, 4 in sandstones, 1 in siderites, 10 in shales and other rocks. Caves with length to 10 m make up 30% of the total number of caves, 10 – 100 m – 54%, 100 – 1000 m – 14%, 1000 – 10000 m – 2%. The most caves explored are in the Middle and Southern Urals: in Perm area (574), in Bashkortostan Republic (571), in Cheljabinsk area (268), in Ekaterinburg area (243); less in Komy Republic (110), Orenburg (12) and Tjumen (6) areas. The largest caves are concentrated in Bashkortostan.

On the bases of numerous literature sources and results of personal investigation, we made a scheme for speleological division of the Ural region (Lavrov, Andreichuk, 1992, 1993). Speleological countries, provinces, areas and districts are defined according to the tectonic principle. 2 countries (Eastern- European and Ural), 8 provinces, 21 areas and 54 districts are mapped.

Urals caves are rather various in lithology, morphology, genesis, chronology, climatic peculiarities, fauna, and archaeological remains.

The majority of gypsum caves developed in Pre-Ural have a young age (Pleistocene, Holocene), and are situated inside the river banks and formed in the zone of fluctuation of underground water table brought about by periodical high river water. The largest gypsum cave is the Kungurskaja Ledjanaja (Kungur Ice Cave) – 5700m long. Gypsum caves of the region are good object for studying karst collapses. Two mechanisms of collapse are investigated in details:

infiltrational and gravitational (Andreichuk, Dorofeev, Lukin, 1990). Estimation methods for karstic risk were also worked out. Gypsum caves are also interesting for paleo-karst investigations. Karst breccia zones, filling the caves, mark earlier stages of karst development and allow to paleogeographical reconstructions. Very often seen in caves are also different results of hydration of anhydrites: ceiling deformations, filling of fractures etc..

Caves in carbonate rocks are more diverse in their morphology, deposits, genesis than gypsum caves. The majority of caves are old (Pliocene- Pleistocene). Genetically they are as fragments (with different degree of preservation) of karst systems, which were formed in vadose conditions (caves-ponors). In some largest caves (Pobjeda, Sumgan etc.) there are morphological elements of phreatic stage in their development. A lot of caves are in water and are developing in phreatic conditions now. Karst channels of Shumiha Cave, for example, are situated 70 m below the local drainage river and Goluboje Ozero (Blue Lake) Spring 56 m.

Limestone caves of the region are interesting for different Paleoenvironment-reconstructions and as excursion objects.

Urals caves are very interesting also in paleozoological and archaeological aspects. Numerous remains of Pleistocene and Holocene fauna are discovered in tens of caves. In some caves(Medvedzja, Kizelovskaja, Tain etc.) burial sites of bear skeletons (Ursus speleo)have a mass nature. Many of them decorate geologic museums of Russia. The most ancient cave site of man are Paleolithic age, especially in caves of Southern Urals. In two caves (Kapova and Ignatjevskaja) Paleolithic cave - paintings are remained. There are many mammoths, woolly rhinoceroses and other animals painted on the walls. The results of archeological investigations in Northern Urals caves prove that man appeared in that area in Paleolithic and they have big importance for the elucidation of the question about settling of people in Northern Eurasia.

The living fauna of Ural caves is relatively poor and not so specific (Martin et al., 1993). There are few troglobionts in caves(Pl. baschiricus Skorikov, Sch. baschkirica Kniss, Crangonix Chlebnikow) but troglophiles are very various (more than 60 species). Tens of caves are populated by bats but their specific composition is studied insufficiently.

Very typical phenomenon for Ural caves is their glaciation. Ice is formed and accumulated in winter time in overwhelming majority of caves.

More than 50 of them keep ice during all the year. The most famous caves with underground glaciers are Askinskaja, Kungurskaja Ledjanaja, Pobjeda etc. Usually underground glaciers occupy no more than 1000 m^2(Askinskaja – 5000 m^2), their thickness is 6 – 10 m, volume 2000 – 10000 m^3.

Ice is accumulated in near-entrance parts of caves or in pocket-shape caves. Cave ice is usually from some tens to some thousands of years old.

Many of Ural caves are very attractive and are often visited by tourists. But only one cave-Kungurskaja, is equipped for mass visit. About 200000 people visit the Cave in separate years. More than 80 caves(5%) are taken under the state of protection as geological and archaeological monuments. But because of the ineffective law it is very difficult to stop their destruction by unorganized visitors. Series of caves are destroyed in limestone quarries.

Some of Ural caves are unique in genetical aspect. These are Saveljev Grot formed in miascite as a result of solution of calcite vein, Pujvinskaja Cave in Pre-Polar Urals. The later cave presents itself the example of ancient hydrothermokarst cave developed along the contact between quartz vein and marbles (Andreichuk and Lavrov, 1992). The carbonate and the siliceous rocks have the tracts of solution. The age of quartz mineralization (crystals) on the cave walls was defined as 270 million years. It is possible that cave is a relic cavity of Permian epoch when active folding took place on the Western Slope of the Urals! (the Cave is situated on the Eastern Slope). Pujvinskaja Cave is a good object for studying siliceous hydrothermokarst.

4.5 Practical Importance of Urals Karst

Practical importance of karst of the Urals is determined by its variation and wide spreading in the region, from one side, and by intensive industrial activity of man, to another. Urals, especially Middle and Southern, are during some centuries a main districts of Russian industry which is based on different kinds of ores (iron, copper, nickel, chrome, titanium, gold etc.) and other minerals (coal, oil, gas, asbestos, building materials, decorative and precious stones). The whole series of minerals are connected immediately with karst and karstic rocks. In many places of folded Urals, limestones, dolomites, marbles are quarried for building and facing material, raw materials for metallurgy. The Bacal siderite deposit, the world's largest of this kind is mined as iron-ore and magnesites of Satka deposit as refractories, in cement production. In pre-Urals area, gypsum from some quarries is used not only for the Urals. The largest potash deposit in Russian (2nd in the world) is situated in pre- Urals foredeep (Solikamsk depression), extracting to the surface from mines. In all

Tab 4-2 Largest cave of Urals and Pre-Urals (data till 01.01.1995)

N	Cave	Length (m)	Area (m^2)	Volume (m^3)	Depth (m)	Relief* (m)	Lithology and age of rocks
1	Sumgan	9860	55260	350000	130	130	lm C_1V
2	Divja	9750	–	–	–	28	lm P1
3	Pobjeda	8000	40000	230000	103	233	lm D_3fm
4	Kizelovskaja	7600	–	–	43	45	lm C_1V_{2-s}
5	Kungurskaja	5700	52000	100000	12	30	g – a P_1k
6	Hlebodarovskaja	3550	18000	42000	48	48	lm C_2
7	Geologov-2	3400	12000	34000	125	130	lm C_1V_{2-s}
8	Propaschaja Jama	3218	8700	37500	90	90	lm D_1
9	Kapova	2640	20200	105000	30	103	lm C_1V
10	Zigzag	2500	9500	37900	120	120	lm D_3f
11	Maximovicha	2217	6800	30600	13	25	lm PR_2mn
12	Sukhaja Atja	2130	10000	50000	75	85	lm D_3
13	Kutuk – 2	2050	9000	28000	110	110	lm D_3f
14	Novomuradymov – skaja	2000	6800	18600	108	108	lm D_1
15	Kutuk – 4	1869	6700	90000	155	155	lm C_1v
16	Geologov – 3	1700	–	–	55	52	lm C_1v_2 – s
17	Shemakhinskaja – 1	1660	5800	–	8	20	lm D_1 – D_2
18	Octjabrskaja	1523	8400	71200	98	98	lm D_3fm
19	Shemakhinskaja – 2	1510	5700	6800	40	40	lm D_1
20	Rossijskaja	1450	3500	20000	80	80	lm C_1v_{2-s}
21	Zujatskaja	1410	–	–	20	20	g – a P_1k
22	Nignemihailov – skaja	1400	–	–	1	9	g – a P_1k
23	Olimpija	1380	10300	106600	101	101	lm C_1v
24	Tjomnaja	1300	–	–	144	144	lm C_1v_{2-s}
25	Kiselovskaja	1260	–	–	37	37	lm D_3
26	Kalkaman – Tishek	1200	1600	4100	10	74	lm D_2e_2 + Zv
27	Solomennaja	1168	–	–	18	18	lm D_3
28	Skazka	1160	2000	4000	18	35	lm D_1
29	Grjoz	1154	2800	8400	85	91	lm D_2e_2 + zv
30	Shumiha	1120	–	–	74	74	lm D_3
31	Ischeevskaja	1002	4600	9600	26	26	g – a P_1k
32	Malaja Divja	1000	–	–	–	6	g – a P_1k
33	Mariinskaja	1000	–	–	47	47	lm C_1v_{2-s}
34	Novaja Podkamenskaja	1000	–	–	–	–	g – a P_1k
35	Shalnaja	1000	–	–	–	–	g – a P_1k
36	Urnjak	1000	–	–	–	–	g – a P_1k

lm: limestone; g – a: gypsum and anhydrite; * The distance between highest and lowest points of cave

of the cases karst is a serious factor that is necessary to be taken into account when estimating the raw resources, for reasonable management of mine and for safe exploitation of deposits (to tackle problems, such as water- inflows into mines and quarries, technogenic karst and activation of collapse and subsidence processes). The karstic water inflows are generally main concern in bauxite and coal deposit areas.

Some of the mineral deposits of the Urals are related to karst process genetically. These are, in first line, karstic bauxite of the Eastern Slope (Northern Urals Bauxite area) and in the South (Southern Urals bauxite area), nickel and other ores of limestone weathering crusts, and fault zones.

Exceptionally important practical significance have oil and gas reservoirs in Permian oil-bearing limestones and dolomites. Their extraction is made in many districts adjacent to the Urals (outlying of platform, foredeep: Pre-Urals, Bashkortostan and Komy Republics, Orenburg and Permian areas). Carbonate rock reservoirs lie at the depth of 1.5 – 2.0 km. Top parts of brachyanticlinal structures, salt dome and large fault are old traps there.

In the Northern Urals gold-, diamond-, platinum- and gems- placers are related to karstic traps. In the major cases, their formation were affected by the uneven surface of karstic limestones, with presence of "pockets", trap- cavities accumulating loose sediments. Usually placers gravitate to modern or ancient buried river valleys which cross limestone zones. Large karstic dolines of Pre-Urals are also as traps for brown coal, peat, fresh-water calcareous tufa deposits.

The most important thing for the Urals industry and population is the karstic water. In spite of humid climate and remarkable water resources the problem of shortage of clean fresh water stands very sharply. The majority of surface rivers, especially around the towns, settlements are very polluted from sewage water of plants. Therefore it is naturally that underground water, in particular karstic water, are used more and more. The significance of karstic water uninterruptedly grows because the water capacity of karstic rocks is higher than non- karstic rocks. In the Middle Urals the problem of clean water is so urgent that construction of large water-plants from non-polluted karstic areas are planned, for example, from Ufimskoje Plateau, which is a gigantic reservoir of high-quality fresh water. In karstic districts of Pre-Urals karst does everything the wrong way round: it makes the water-supply problems more sharp because karstic water of sulfatic and carbonate rocks are not good for the use owing to their high mineralization(1 – 5g/l and more). Mixing with surface water they salt down them making worse their quality.

The Urals karst is also very important from the engineering-geological point of view. Occupying wide areas, especially in the Pre-Urals, it makes big difficulties when building different objects (houses, roads, dams, pipelines etc.). Because of karst it was often necessary to give up a series of alluring projects which were important for economic and social development of the region. Considerable problems happen in some old Urals towns which were built earlier without taking into account the karst. In last years this problem became more difficult owing to karst activation caused by man's activity.

4.6 The Influence of Human's Activity on Karst

It is difficult to find in Russia and probably in the world a region where the human influence in karstic area is so multiple, so big and the side-effects are so serious as Urals.

The various types of man's impact, from one side, and conditions of karstgenesis (lithologic, geomorphologic, climatic, hydrologic etc.), from the other, caused diversity in types of anthropogenic karst. We shall note briefly the major ones according to basic directions of human activity in karst areas of the Urals (Andreichuk, 1988).

Mining activity. Karst develops when: working of gold-, diamond-, and platinum placers (river basin of Vishera, Ivdel, Is etc.); extraction with boreholes of oil, gas (treatment of carbonate reservoirs with acids), underground water, salt; open extraction (with quarries) of limestones, dolomites, gypsums, siderites, magnesites; mine extraction of coal (lying among limestones), bauxite, potash; underground nuclear explosions(Pre-Urals) in order to increase the output of oil- bearing rocks; placing of industrial sewages in the deep-buried permeable rocks and so on.

The most disastrous technogenic karst phenomena are: surface deformations (sinks, subsidences) as a result of underground water pumping (collapses are induced by carrying-out of sediments from filling cavities); giant collapses above the salt mines (Sol-Ilezk, Berezniki towns), caused by fresh water breaking into mines and dissolving salt. One of such sink is showed in the

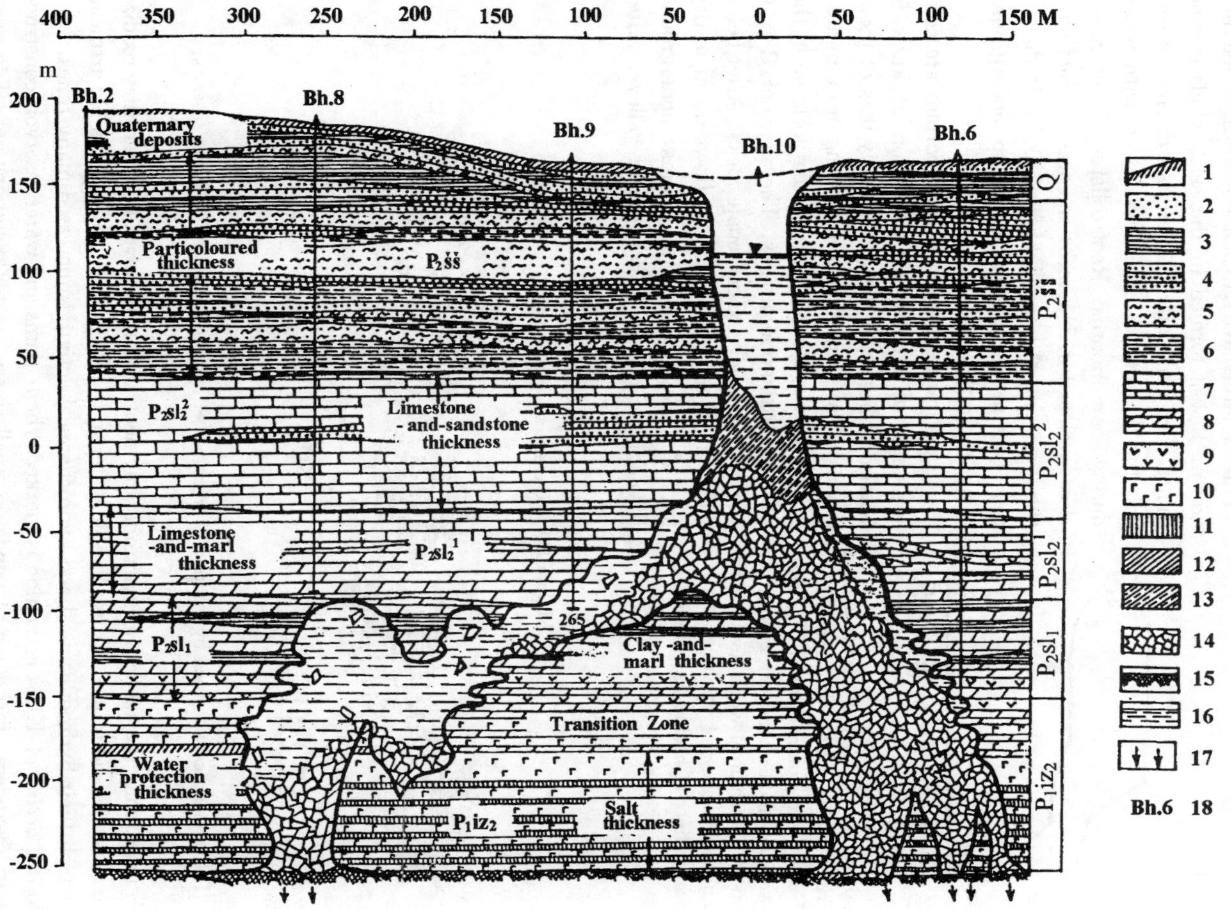

Fig. 4-8 The giant sink above the salt mine (the Pre- Urals foredeep, Verchnekamsky potash salt deposit, Berezniki town, Photo 31). 1. Soil; 2. Sand; 3. Clay; 4. Sandstone; 5. Aleurolite; 6. Argillite; 7. Limestone; 8. Marl; 9. Gypsum; 10 Halite; 11. Carnallite; 12. Sylvinite; 13. Loam, sandy loam; 14. Limestone, Sandstone(collapsed material); 15. Mines; 16. water; 17. Places of brines filtration(January 1986); 18. Borehole and its number

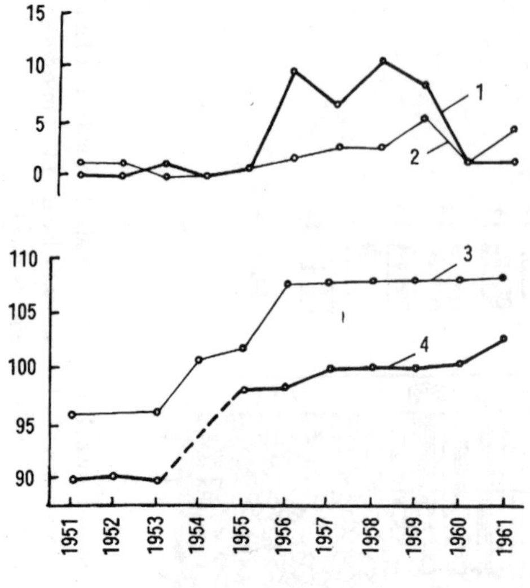

Fig. 4-9 The dynamics of collapse process in near-bank zone of Kama-reservoir after dam construction and water level rise (see Lukinet, et al.) 1. sinkholes on the lower and middle terraces; 2. sinkholes on the high terraces; 3. maximal water levels of Kama River (Chochlovka village); 4. minimum water levels of Kama River (Chochlovka village)

Fig. 4-8. It is formed in 1986 above the world's largest potash mine near Berezniki town (Andreichuk and Lukin, 1986). Owing to penetration of aggressive water along the ancient fracture in salt (when it was widened under technogenic strains), large cavity (volume more than one million m^3) was formed in the salt. Underground mines (>15 million m^2) were as a draining reservoir for flowing water. It was filled with water during some months. Roof collapse of salt cavity also developed in 3 months and was finished with the formation of large sinkhole (100 m in diametre, 140 m deep; total depth to underground mines more than 400 m).

Less impressive but very important are consequences of technogenic activation of karst in Kizel coal basin. It pumps out daily tens of thousands m^3 of karstic water flowing into mines. Mine water contains sulphuric acid forming in the sulphides oxidation process. They have pH 2 – 4 and are aggressive to carbonate rocks. After being pumped out on the surface, it flows down to dry karstic valleys where they sink underground through the ponors in bottoms of valleys. After

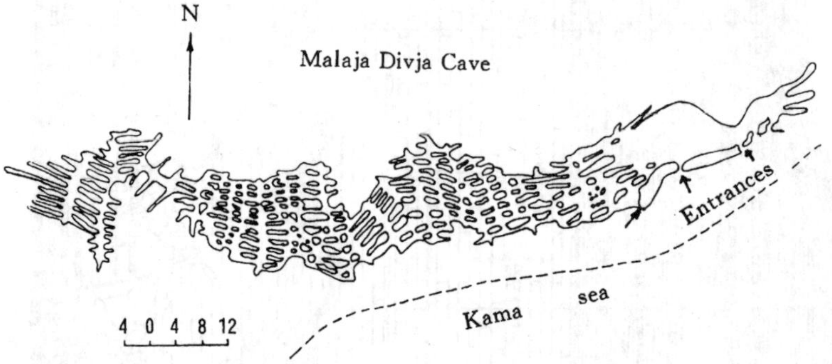

Fig. 4-10 The gypsum cave formed by solution of fracture net in near-bank zone of Kama reservoir

interaction with limestone, the acidic water considerably neutralise themselves but then they oxidize again near the coal seams and mines. Thus, karstic water in coal basin are involved in a big artificial circulation, in which their hydrodynamical and hydrochemical activities increased many times.

Hydrotechnical activity. Karst activation is marked when: dams and water reservoir construction, cutting short meanders, formation of ponds on small rivers, water pollutions etc. The most spectacular example of hydrotechnical influence to karst is Kama sea (reservoir) (Pecherkin, 1969; Pecherkin and Zakoptelov, 1982). The Southern banks of the reservoir consist of gypsums and anhydrites. As a result of the rise of karstic water level the processes of solution and suffosion activated collapse processes and sink formation on the surface (Photo 19, Fig. 4-9). As a result of solution it began intensive degradation of sulfatic banks. Owing to corrosion broadening of fracture it began to form caves which were called by I.A. Pecherkin as "ephemeral" (because the time of their existence is no more than some years or two-three dozens of years). In some cases solution of fracture nets in near bank zone led to the formation of "net caves" (Gorbunova et al., 1992; Fig. 4-9 and Fig. 4-10).

Populated areas. On the built-up territories an activation of collapse processes (Lukin, 1972, 1992) was marked. It is related to the change in the filtration properties of soils and rocks when building, leakages of water out of conduits and sewage systems took place, and increased the static and dynamical pressures to grounds. Moreover, it may also be induced by dehydration as a result of water pumping and other causes. It is necessary to take notice that the majority of karst collapse are suffosional and they are caused by processes in loose sediments covering karstic rocks. This conclusion is very important for estimation of karst risk and avoiding unjustified expenses for countermeasures against karst disasters.

Very considerable in the region are the consequences of other types of technogenic impact on karst: road-building, pipeline construction, clearance of forests etc. One of the most interesting examples of technogenic karst is karst of artificial salt massives (Pre-Urals, Berezniki town), where potash is extracted for potash fertilizers production.

The waste-heaps are as high as 50 to 80 m with the area of tens hectares and tens and hundreds of millions m^3 in volume (Photo 30). The material of the waste heaps consist of salt rock crumble, clay flakes and various inclusions contained in the primary halite and potash salt mass. Due to the natural compaction the waste heaps material is cemented and turns from a loose and wet mass into a dense polymineral salt rock. The porosity of fresh material is 40 to 50%, whereas those of the old ones at the heap foundation is reduced to 0 to 2%. High permeability and solubility of the material, presence of insoluble admixtures and the heterogeneous density of the waste heaps predetermine the conditions of the atmospheric precipitation penetration and of the formation therein of a peculiar hydrodynamic zonality. Within the waste heaps, surface and underground karstic features are formed. The surface forms are mainly brought about by the water movement along the surface in the aeration zone. They are representative with negative (karren, swallow holes, shafts, trenches, tunnel-shaped holes) and positive (ridges, protrusions and outliers) features.

Technogenic activation of karst in the Urals and its consequences are a very good object for comprehensive investigations.

In this review we limited ourselves by very general information about karst of such a large but insufficiently explored region as Urals. From the given examples it is possible to retrace a great number of geomorphologic, climatic (from polar to southern deserts!), geological and landscape backgrounds and laws of karst development. Taking into account the great size of region, variety of karstogenesis, important practical, scientific and aesthetic significance, uneven exploration and many other factors, karst of the Urals must be recognized as phenomenon of global significance. Its study needs cooperation of specialists from all disciplines.

References

Andreichuk, V.N. and I. A. Lavrov, 1992. Pujvinskaja peschera i problema gidrotermalnogo karsta Rutilovogo plato (Pripoljarny Ural), Izuchenie uralskych pescher. Kungur

Andreichuk, V.N., A.I. Kovaltchuk and I.A. Belokrys, 1989. Cave in siderite, Proceeding of 10 – th International Congress of Speleology. Budapest

Andreichuk, V.N. and V.S. Lukin, 1988. Bolshoi Bereznikovsky proval, Problemy izuchenija technogenogo karsta. Kungur

Andreichuk, V.N., E.P. Dorofeev and V.S. Lukin, 1990. Organnye truby vcarbonatno- sulfatnoj krovle pescher, Peschery. Perm

Gydrogeologia SSR. M.: Nedra, 1972. T. 14 (Ural).

Gorbunova, K. A., V. N Andreichuk, V. P. Kosarev and N. G. Maximovinch, 1992. Karst i peschery Permskoj oblasty, Perm

Gorofeev, E. P. and V. S. Lukin, 1969. Karstovye muldy osedanija v severnoj chasty Solikamskoj depressii, Voprosy karstovedenija. Perm

Kovalchuk, A. I., 1988. Projavlenija suffosii i Karsta v kremnystych osagkach Zayralja, Problemy izuchenija technogennogo karsta. Kungur

Kostarev, V. P., 1990. Karst Urala i Priuraja. Dis.... kand. geol-mineral. nauk. Perm

Lavrov, I. A., and V. N. Andreichuk, 1992. Peschery Urala i Priuralja. Kungur

Lavrov, I. A., and V. N. Andreichuk, 1993. Peschery Urala i Priuralja, Peschery. Itogy issledovanij. Perm

Lukin, V. S., 1972. Usilenie provalnogo processa na zastroennych uchastkach, Voprosy ingenernogo karstovedenija. Kungur

Lunkin, V. S., N. Ch. Laptiev, U. I. Shangin, 1963. Issledovanijeprovalnych javlenij na zakarstovannych poberezjach Kamskogo Vodochranilischa, Razvedka i Ochrana nedr. N 12. 14.

Lukin, V. S., 1992. Provaly na zastroennych territorijach v SrednemPreduralje, Problema psevdokarsta. Perm

Maximovich, G. A., 1975. Karst traverinov, izvestkovych tyfov, magnestovi sideritov, Gydrogeologia karstivedenije. Vyp. 7. Perm

Maximovich, G. A. and K. A. Gorbunova, 1958. Karst Permskoj oblasty. Perm

Maximovich, G. A., and K. A. Gorbunova, 1965. Tipy karsta Urala, Tr. Mosc. ob- vaispytat. prirody. T. 15.

Maximovich, G. A. and V. P. Kostarev, 1968. karst skladchatogo Urala, KarstUrala i Preuralja. Perm

Maximovich, G. A. and V. P. Kostarev, 1973. Karstovye rajony Urala i Priuralja, Uch. zap. Perm. un-ta. Perm, N 308.

Martin, V. I., A. I. Smirnov and U. V. Sokolov, 1993. Peschery Bashkyrii, Peschery. Itogy issledovanij. Perm

Orljankin, S. M., 1941. Geologia, gidrogeologia i solenosnost Kolvo-Visherskoj vodorazdelnoj oblasty i granichaschych sney uchastkov, Zap. Vseros. miner. ob- va. Ch. 70, vyp. 1.

Pecherkin, A. I. and V. E. Zakoptelov, 1982. Karst i suffosija na beregach vodochranilisch. Perm

Pecherkin, I. A., 1969. Geodinamika poberezgij Kamskych vodochranilisch. T. 2. Perm

Pecherkin, I. A., G. I. Karzenkov and I. K. Mackevich, 1965. Efemernye peschery, Peschery. Perm, Vyp. 5(6).

Shestov, I. N. and A. B. Shurubor, 1963. Chusovskoje ozero i jego proischozgdenie, Chim. geografia i hydrogeochemija. Perm, Vyp. 2(3).

Shimanovsky, L. A., 1964. Klastokarst Jurjuzano- Sylvenskoy depressii, IZV. AN SSSR. Ser. Geogr. N 2.

Shimanovsky, L. A. and V. Z. K. Chursik, 1968. Charakterisike karsta Jurjuzano- Sylvenskoj depressii, Karst Urala i Priyralja. Perm

Global Karst Correlation
Edited by Yuan Daoxian and Liu Zaihua
Science Press and VSP BV, 1998

Chapter 5 Karst in the Baltic Republics

Paukstys Bernardas[1], Karise Velo[2]
[1] *Geological Survey of Lithuania*
[2] *Institute of Geology, Estonian Academy of Sciences*

5.1 Introduction

Karst — a process of complicated hydrodynamic, chemical and mechanical interactions between water and rocks is developing when four main natural conditions are met: (i) availability of soluble sediments in geological cross-section; (ii) permeability of the soluble sediments, (iii) availability of water, which is (iv) capable to dissolve rocks (Sokolov, 1962).

The three Baltic Republics of Estonia, Latvia and Lithuania with total area of 175000 km^2, is underlain by karst rocks of different age and type: Ordovician, Silurian and Devonian, Carboniferous and Permian limestones, dolomites, gypsum, which are outcropping on the land surface or covered by thin strata of Quaternary sediments. Most of karst in the Baltic States is the so called covered type of karst. On the land surface it is expressed by sinkholes, ponors, land subsidences, and karst lakes. Subsurface caves, cavities and fractures are also available but not as abundant as surface karst forms. The areas of karstified territories, density and type of karst forms and investigation level differ in all three Republics.

In the Northern part of the area, Republic of Estonia, Ordovician and Silurian limestones and dolomites are the main series outcropping to the land surface or are covered by glacial Quaternary sediments, while in Southern part of the territory, in Latvia and Lithuania, the younger Upper Devonian soluble rocks are exposed to atmospheric impact or exogenic geological processes. Not only age of karst rocks but also karst types and forms are different in Northern and Southern parts of the Baltics. In Estonia karst is expressed on the land surface by scarce and shallow sinkholes, karst springs, karren, dry valleys and niches. Main subsurface forms are caves and caverns. Karst features are mainly concentrated in Central and Northern parts of the country, where Ordovician and Silurian limestones and dolomites are covered by thin strata of Quaternary deposits.

In southern part of the Baltic states (Southern Latvia and Northern Lithuania) Upper Devonian dolomites and gypsum are outcropping on the land surface. The density of surface karst forms (sinkholes, collapses, shafts) is very high here, and reaches 200 sinkholes per km^2 in Lithuania, and 140 per km^2 in Latvia, while caves and other subsurface features are less known. Exception is river Daugava in Latvia, where caves prevail.

5.2 History of Studies

The first written reference to karst phenomena in Estonia dates from the 18th century, when A. Hupel (1774), J. Fischer (1784) and several other amateur scientists mentioned water-swallowing depressions (sinkholes) and subterranean rivers. In the second half of the 19th century, karst attracted the attention of geologists, who outlined the connection of karst phenomena with tectonic and other kind of faults in rocks (Eichwald, 1852; Schmidt, 1858). In the first half of the

20th century the foundation was laid for detailed studies of larger karst areas. The first work was completed on the Uhaku karst field, NE Estonia. (Orviku, 1929). In the middle of the century, attention focused on the deep karst in oil shale mines (Gatalskii, 1957; Gazizov, 1958). Systematic and detailed research into surface karst was initiated in the whole carbonate rock area of Estonian. The first generalizing summary was completed in 1959 (Heinsalu, 1959). In the succeeding 35 years a major contribution was made by Ü. Heinsalu (23.09.1928 – 27.01. 1994), whose numerous works dealt with the main karst areas, karst springs, subterranean rivers and karst lakes in Estonia. He also outlined the significance of karst phenomena in ground water development (Heinsalu, 1961 a, b; 1967a, b; 1976; 1978; 1991; 1993). The present survey of Estonian karst is based primarily on Ü. Heinsalu's data.

Lithuanian karst region is also well investigated from the geological point of view. First scientific observations related with mineral water of Likenai health resort, situated in the centre of karst region, were initiated by the Lithuanian geochemist T. Grothus at the middle of the 19th century (Grothus, 1886). After that investigations of stratigraphy, lithology and useful minerals of the region followed. Fundamental geological research of Devonian sediments in the 20th century was carried out by outstanding Lithuanian scientists J. Dalinkevicius (1932), M. Kaveckis (1961), V. Narbutas (1958, 1985). Important knowledge to the body of karst research was contributed by V. Ignatavicius (1981), J. Paltanavicius (1986), V. Marcinkevicius (1981, 1986), A. Klimas (1981, 1990). Valuable data on geology and hydrogeology of karst region has been obtained in a course of geological mapping of the area in a scale 1:200 000, but most significant information was collected during the large scale mapping of the region and adjacent areas in the scale 1:50 000 carried out in 1977 – 1991. On the basis of this information evaluation of human impact to the development of gypsum karst was made by B. Paukstys (1991).

5.3 Natural Conditions of Karst Development — Geography, Climate and Geomorphology

Karst development depends very much on climatic-geomorphologic conditions of the area. All three Baltic States of Lithuania, Latvia and Estonia are located in the area with surplus humidity. Lithuanian karst region is situated on the Middle Lithuanian Lowland, characterized by positive balance of effective precipitation. The annual amount of total precipitation, according to the data of Birzai meteorological station in a course of last 15 years, differs from 434 to 592 mm, the average being 570 mm. Climate of Northern Lithuania and Southern Lavia is transitional between maritime and continental. Distinctive feature of it is often changes of the weather, frequent fallout of precipitation, high cloudiness and humidity, and short duration of snow cover. 75% of precipitation in a form of rain is falling in warm season, which lasts about 200 days from April to October. Mean monthly amount of precipitation is changing from 11 – 20mm to 134 – 157mm (Basalykas, 1958). Specific humidity of the air is flucutating between 76 – 82%. Chemical composition of precipitation is represented in Tab. 5-1.

Tab. 5-1 Average concentration of main ions (in mg/l) in precipitation of karst region (data of Kemeri meteorological station, Latvia)

SO_4^{2-}	Cl^-	HCO_3^-	NO_3^-	NH_4^+	Ca^{2+}	Mg^{2+}	Na^+	K^+	pH
5.1	1.3	1.8	0.9	0.4	1.0	0.2	1.1	0.4	5.4

Snow appears at the end of November and melts at the end of March. Thickness of a snow cover reaches 15 – 18 cm. Soil, depending on it's composition, thickness and duration of snow cover, landscape type, etc. is frozen to the depth varying from 0.6 to 1.0 m. Melting of the snow and soil frost starts at the end of April and lasts 10 – 20 days. Duration of cold period is ca. 120 days. The coldest month of the year is January with mean monthly temperature of – 5℃. The warmest months are June – July with mean monthly temperature + 15℃. Mean annual temperature is + 4.8℃.

The development of karst is also favoured by Estonia's moist climate (the amount of precipitation received is twice as much as evaporation), moderately mild winters and relatively warm summers: average annual precipitation is in the range 550 – 650 (in uplands 700) mm/year, evaporation 320 – 350 mm/year, mean annual air temperature +4.5 – +5.5℃. The mean air temperature of February, the coldest month of the year, is –5.5 – 7℃, and July, the warmest month, is +16.5℃ – +17℃.

Lithuanian karst region is characterized by the flat, slightly hilly landscape with absolute altitudes differing from 25m in a valley of river Musa to 65m and more above the sea level in the eastern part of the territory (Basalykas, 1958). The North-Western side of karst region is a zone of Middle Lithuanian marginal moraine with absolute height of land surface reaching 40 – 60m. Relative changes of landscape altitudes reach 12 m. But the main feature of the landscape of the region are karst sinkholes located separately and in groups. Sinkholes and karst shafts with a depth differing from 2 to 12 meters and diameter from several to 40m represent a characteristic landscape of North Lithuanian karst region (Marcinkevicius and Buceviciute, 1986).

Surplus humidity and positive balance of effective precipitation form surface runoff and streams. Mean annual karst river specific discharge varies from 4.9 to 5.5 $l/(s \cdot km^2)$. Rivers are recharged mainly by precipitation. Low part of recharge (5%) is formed by karst groundwater. Most of rivers in the region cut upper part of karst rocks and aquifers. Then karst groundwater has recharging and also discharging influence to the rivers of the region (Paukstys & Taminskas 1992), Tab. 5-2.

Tab. 5-2 Karst influence to river discharge

River	Catchment area, km^2	Length, km	Gauging station	Karst influence:	
				$l/(s \cdot km^2)$	%
Musa	5318.0	284.0	Ustukiai	–0.41*	–7
Ystras	43.5	199.3	Talackoniai	–0.01	0
Levuo	1587.5	148.0	Pasvalys	+0.05	+1
Pyvesa	500.4	95.4	Zadeikiai	–1.05	+19
Tatula	504.1	66.2	Trecioniai	+0.69	+13
Roveja	216.4	34.8	Paroveja	+0.04	0
Agluona	86.9	19.7	Dirvonakiai	–0.02	0
Apascia	892	87.5	Simpeliskiai	+0.01	0

* (–) river is recharging karst aquifer, (+) groundwater is discharging into the river.

Rivers of karst region belong to the basin of Lielupe which brings it's waters to the Baltic Sea. Biggest tributary of Lielupe is river Musa (148 km long) with it's own stream Levuo being 145 km long. Other rivers of the region are smaller. Mean annual discharge of the rivers varies from 0.3 to 26.0 m^3/s, the width of the streams is changing from 5 to 50 meters, average depth do not exceed 1m (Marcinkevicius and Buceviciute, 1986). Floods occur in autumn and spring. They are formed by enhanced amount of precipitation. Spring floods start at the end of March and lasts about 20 days. Low summer level is formed from the end of May to October. After the autumn rains the autumn floods start. From the middle of December till the end of March surface streams are covered by ice. In dry time of summer and winter low water rivers are recharged by karst groundwater.

5.4 Geology and Hydrogeology

5.4.1 *Estonia*

Estonia is situated on the southeastern slope of the Fennoscandian Shield. The crystalline basement consists of Proterozoic rocks which are overlain by Vendian and Cambrian sand and siltstones and clays, followed by Ordovician sedimentary rocks (in Tremadoc - sandstones and black shales, higher carbonate rocks, mostly limestones). Then come Silurian carbonate rocks (limestones, dolomites, marls), which from Middle Estonia southwards are discordantly overlain by Devonian terrigenous rocks (mainly Old Red), in the extreme southeastern part of the area also by Devonian

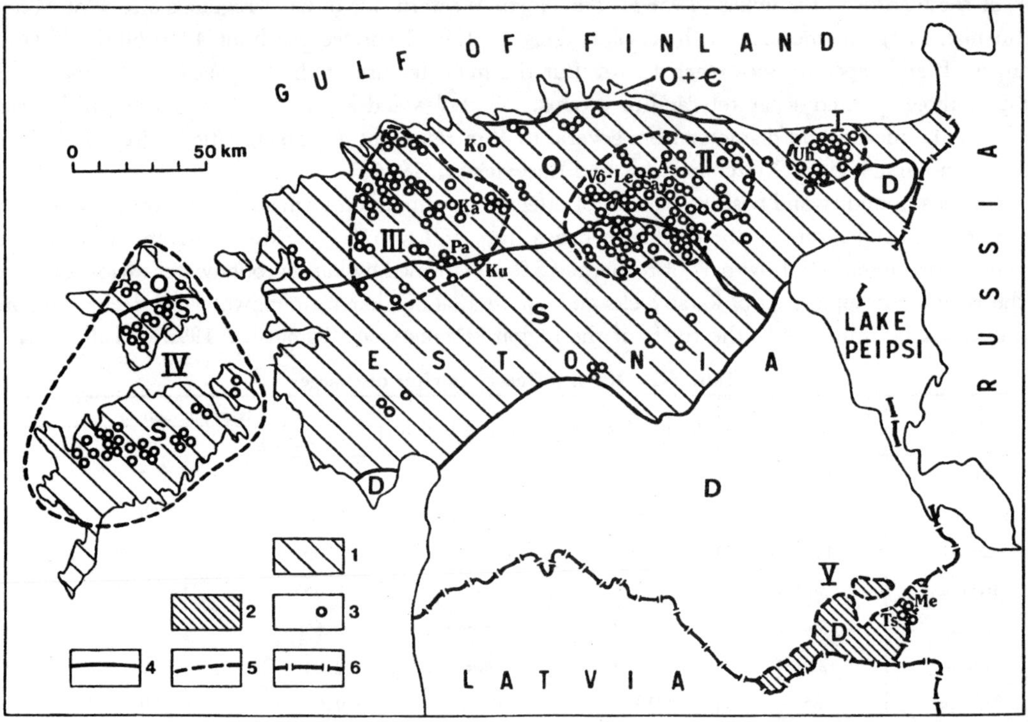

Fig. 5-1 Karst phenomena in Estonia: 1 – North Estonian karst province; 2 – South – East Estonian karst area ; 3 – karst field or large sink hole; 4 – stratigraphical boundary; 5 – boundary of karst area; 6 – frontier. I – Jôhvi karst area (Jôhvi Upland): Uh – Uhaku karst field; II - Pandivere karst area (Pandivere Upland): As - Assamalla karst field, Sa - Savalduma karst field, Vô-Le - Vôhmetu-Lemküla karst field; III - Kohila karst area, Ka - Kata karst area, Ku - Kuimetsa karst area, Pa - Pae karst area; Ko - Kostivere karst area (situated separately); IV - karst area of West Estonian islands; V - South-East Estonian karst area: Ts - Tsiistre karst field, Me - Meremäesink hole

carbonate rocks (Fig. 5-1). The bedrock's strata have a gentle southward dipping (3 – 4 m/ km). The thickness of carbonate rocks ranges from 5 – 20 metres on the northern boundary of the outcrop area to 250 metres on its southern boundary. Carbonate rocks crop out in an area of ca 30 600 km^2, which accounts for 68% of Estonia's territory. Upper Palaeozoic, Mesozoic and Lower Cenozoic sediments are not found in the republic, because at that time Estonia was dry land and relevant deposits have not been preserved here. In Estonia, the Quaternary cover consists of Pleistocene and Holocene deposits, which prevailingly are thin (up to 10 m). Occasionally, on the so-called "alvars" it is entirely lacking. Quaternary sediments are at their thickest (more than 200 metres) in the ancient buried valleys.

Conditions, favourable for the development of karst, formed first after the regression of the Silurian sea. The first stage of karst development (early Devonian) lasted some 10 million years. The second stage, about 340 million years, embraced the period from the late Devonian up to the first Quaternary glaciation. Of that long period, the Neogene and Paleogene (total duration 50 million years) seemed to have been most favourable for karst development. At that time the earth's crust was subject to intensive rebound, as a result of which the sea level was more than 100 metres lower than nowadays. Evidence is derived from deep buried valleys. Hence, the local base level must have been much deeper as well, which promoted the development of karst phenomena. In the Quaternary period, Estonia was repeatedly covered with glaciers. The advancing ice scoured the bedrock, broke and pulverized the dislodged rocks and destroyed surficial karst forms. South-East Estonia was freed from the ice sheet some 13000 years ago, and North-West Estonia about 11000 years ago (Raukas, 1986). Large areas were inundated by big ice-dammed lakes and the waters of the Baltic Sea. Karst could develop in those areas not until the withdrawal of water. The most favourable conditions for karst development occurred in North and Central Estonia and on western islands, where the Ordovician and Silurian carbonate rocks are extremely fissured and the Quaternary cover is thin. In southern Estonia, carbonate rocks are overlain by Devonian sandstones and thick Quaternary cover. Currently, there are no conditions promoting the development of karst in this part of the republic. Only in the extreme southeasternmost corner of Estonia, karst phenomena occur in Upper Devonian carbonate rocks. In view of the above, the North-Estonian karstprovince with four prominent karst areas (Jõhvi, Pandivere, Kohila and West-Estonian islands), and South-East Estonian karst area are distinguished (Heinsalu, 1977; Fig. 5-1).

Despite the great thickness of the carbonate rock layer, only its topmost 5 – 10 m have karstified. Deeper the karst is weakly developed due to the presence of clayey interlayers (marl) in carbonate rocks, which is a serious obstacle to the development of deep karst. Besides, downwards carbonate rocks are less fissured. As a result, the velocity of water movement decreases furnishing basis for the conditions unfavourable for karst development. Areas, where the Quaternary cover is thin and consists of deposits high in water permeability (sand, gravel), provide the best conditions for the development of karst. In areas with clayey tills the development of karst is hampered.

5.4.2 *Lithuania*

Investigated area is located on the East-European old platform, Eastern side of the Baltic synclinorium. From a hydrogeological point of view the region is a part of the Baltic Artesian Basin (Juodkazis, 1979) (Fig. 5-2). Lithuania and Latvia are situated on the central part of the basin, where the crystalline basement is overlain by different kinds of karst rocks. The sedimentary cover on the crystalline basement in Northern Lithuania comprises a sequence of deposits of Palaeozoic and Cenozoic age. It is known that karst is developing only to the depth of active water exchange. Geological section of active water exchange zone starts from the regional aquiclude-Narva clayey formations of the Middle Devonian age. The aquiclude is overlaid by a thick formation (up to 200 m) of Middle -Upper Devonian Upninkai-Sventoji sands, sandstones and clays ($D_2up - D_3sv$). Terrigenic sands and sandstones contain a large amount of fresh groundwater which is being abstracted and used as a main source of drinking water not only in karst region but in all Eastern Lithuania. Upninkai - Sventoji sediments are covered by a thin strata (2 – 9 m) of Jara clayey marls (D_3j) which are considered to be a local aquiclude in an area. The named aquiclude is overlain by dolomites, marls and

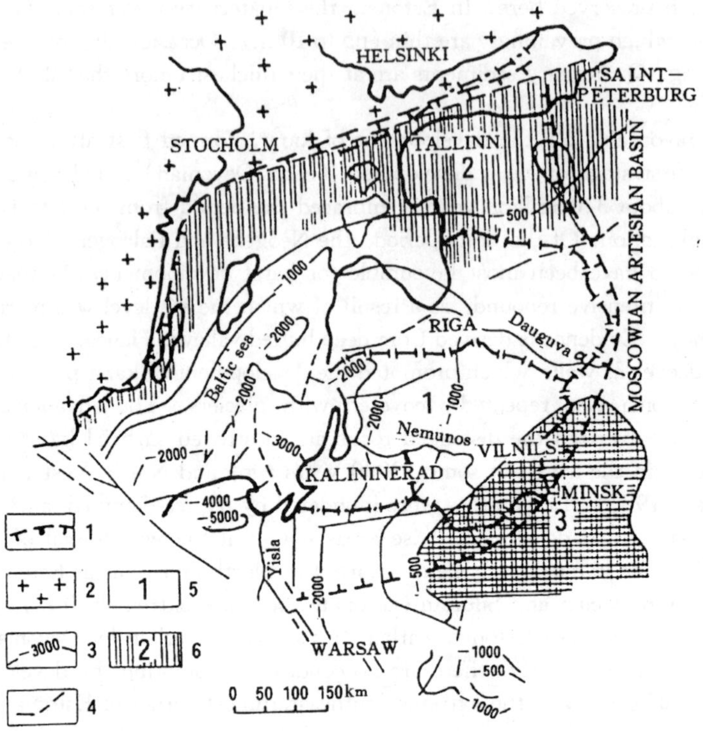

Fig. 5-2 Sketch map of the Baltic Artesian Basin: 1. The boundaries of the basin; 2. outcrop of crystalline and metamorphic rocks; 3. isolines of the depth to basement; 4. faults and joints; 5. the central part of the basin; 6. the northern slope of the basin

clays of Suosa and Kupiskis (D_3s, D_3kp) with a rather constant thickness (40m)(Marcinkevicius & Buceviciute 1986). Upper Devonian gypsic dolomites and gypsum of Tatula formation lay above Kupiskis dolomites (Fig. 5-3). Old and modern karst process is being developed in Tatula sediments. The thickness of karst rocks is not uniform along the territory and varies from 5 to 48 m. Two gypsic layers could be distinguished in Tatula sediments — the lower one with a thickness of 13 – 24 m and upper, 11 – 15m thick. Gypsum layers are separated by interlayer of marl of 3 – 7m thick. Gypsic sediments are composed by 70% of gypsum mineral intercalating with dolomite and marl. On local sites of the region karstified gypsum is covered by Ystra dolomites (D_3ys) with a thickness of up to 5 m (Narbutas, 1979). But the main part of karst rocks are covered only by glacial sediments. Devonian and Quaternary formations are water-bearing and form a united interconnected hydraulic system consisting of 3 confined and one unconfined aquifers: Sventoji -Upninkai (D_2up-D_3sv), Suosa-Kupiskis (D_3s-kp), Ystra -Tatula (D_3ys-t) and Quaternary (Q).

All aquifers are being exploited with different extent for drinking and domestic purposes by population and industrial units of the region. Water quality in the aquifers is different. Quaternary glacial sand and loam contain mainly fresh water (total dissolved solids (TDS) 0.5 – 0.8 g/l), with bicarbonate-calcium composition. Water is often heavily polluted by nitrogen and organic compounds. In karst aquifer (D_3 ys-t) slightly mineralized (TDS 1.5 – 2.4 g/l), very hard (total hardness up to 35meq/l) water prevails. Sulphate and calcium are the main ions forming chemical composition of the waters. The aquifer is not protected from human impact therefore amount of anthropogenic contaminants (nitrogen and organics) often exceeds requirements of drinking water standard.

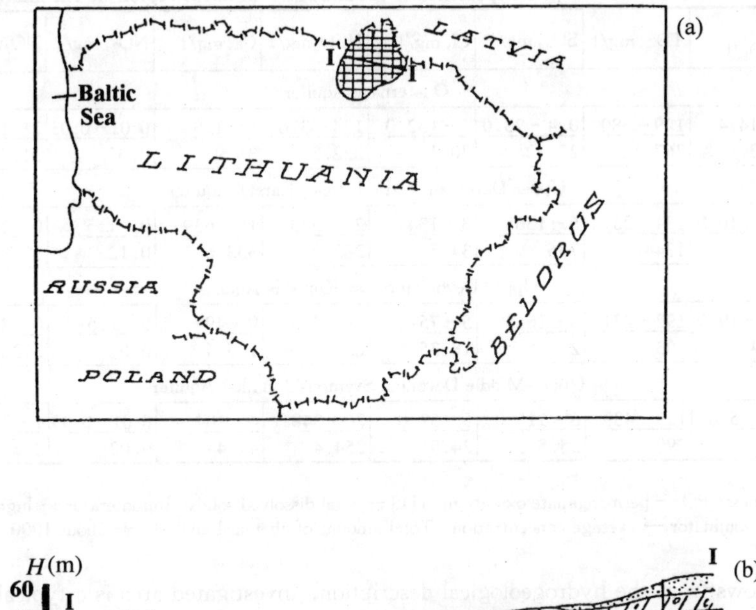

Fig. 5-3 Location of karst region of Lithuania (a) and geological cross-section of an area (b). 1. Karst region; 2. Line of cross-section; 3. sand; 4. moraine till; 5. limestone; 6. marl; 7. sandstone; 8. clay; 9. gypsum

D_3kp-s aquifer contains mainly fresh, bicarbonate-calcium-magnesium groundwater with TDS of 0.5 – 0.8 g/l and total hardness reaching 10 meq/l. But due to hydraulic connections with mineralized karst waters in places of downward filtration sulphate-calcium water with TDS of 1 – 2 g/l are met. Traces of pollution are being observed in some monitoring wells.

The lowest D_{3-2}sv-up aquifer contains groundwater of high quality (TDS 0.2 – 0.6 g/l, total hardness 5 – 7 meq/l.). Sulphate concentrations at some places reaching 100 mg/l and traces of nitrogen compounds show that the aquifer has connection with upper water- bearing horizons (Paukstys 1991). Summarized data on chemical composition of groundwater in karst region are presented in Tab. 5-3.

Tab. 5-3 Chemical composition of groundwater in karst region of Lithuania

TH, meq/l	P O, mgO_2/l	TDS, mg/l	SO_4, mg/l	Cl, mg/l	HCO_3mg/l	Ca, mg/l	NO_2, mg/l	NO_3, mg/l	NH_4mg/l
Quaternary Aquifer									
1.4 – 11.0	1 – 14.4	129 – 680	0.4 – 73.0	6 – 132.0	134 – 396	6 – 129	0.01 – 0.03	2 – 180	0.1 – 5.0
3.71	4.53	267	22.42	30.1	222.5	36.9	0.02	31.7	0.58
Upper Devonian Ystra Tatula (Karst) Aquifer									
2.7 – 34.4	0.8 – 10.9	234 – 2314	6 – 1565	3 – 134	29 – 543	11 – 639	0 – 1.5	0 – 200	0 – 112
20.8	4.9	1344	756	34.5	283	333.6	0.12	19.35	18.3
Upper Devonian Suosa Kupiskis Aquifer									
2.7 – 27.7	0.4 – 10.9	192 – 2711	4 – 1655	5 – 75	29 – 375	9 – 494	0 – 1.5	0 – 35.0	0 – 60.0
7.7	2.94	503.3	271.6	18.35	233.9	105.4	0.07	3.32	5.69
Upper-Middle Devonian Sventoji-Upninkai Aquifer									
0.28 – 5.8	0.8 – 5.6	129 – 439	6 – 115.0	5 – 52.0	76 – 348	4 – 104	0.01 – 0.03	1 – 3.0	0.1 – 4.5
3.44	2.6	290	35.5	24.0	254.4	44.4	0.02	2.6	0.68

TH — total hardness; PO — permanganate oxidation, TDS — total dissolved solids. Innumerator — highest and lowest concentrations, in denominator — average concentration. Total amount of chemical analyses — about 1000.

As it follows from the hydrogeological description, investigated area is a typical example of inverse hydrochemical zonality: upper aquifers contain mineralized groundwater while in lower ones fresh water of good quality is determined.

Covered karst is characteristic for the territory. The main surface karst form is sinkhole. Sometimes several sinkholes join and make poljes. At the vicinities of Kirkilai village about 300 karst lakes, different in size and shape are recorded (Kilkus, 1977).

Density of karst sinkholes is not uniform in the region. The areas with major amount of sinkholes are related with the valleys of rivers Musa, Levuo, Pyvesa and also with waterdivides of mentioned rivers. The density of sinkholes on such areas transcends 20 units/km^2.

The highest amount of sinkholes — 200 units/km^2— was counted in Kirkilai geological reserve. Density of sinkholes has inverse correlation with a thickness of covering deposits. Mostly karstified areas are covered by Quaternary till, loam and sand with a thickness of up to 5 m. The depth of the sinkholes vary from 2 to 12 m, diameter — from several to 40m (Marcinkevicius and Buceviciute 1986).

There are not many data about the origin, location and density of fractures in karst deposits. According to available data vertical fractures usually have North and North - East direction. Results of detailed geological mapping of the area show that 25% of fractures have direction of 300° – 320°, 23% of fractures are dipping at 0 – 20°, and 20% have direction of 40° – 60°. Located at a distance of 0.5 – 5.0 m and intersecting each other the fractures form blocks in monolithic rocks. The blocks on their own in a course of exogenic geological processes are cut by horizontal voids. Availability on the walls of the cracks of iron hydroxides show that groundwater is circulating through them.

The fractures and voids in karst rocks are very significant for karst development. Correlation between the prevailing direction of fractures and long axes of sinkkholes was noticed. On the investigated territories long axes of sinkholes are perpendicular to each other, with dominant direction to North - East, North and East (Marcinkevicius and Buceviciute, 1986).

The detailed data which was collected during the large scale mapping of the region and adjacent areas, scale 1:50 000 carried out in 1977 – 1991 point out the complicated geological-hydrogeological composition of the region. Thin cover of Quaternary moraine tills and sands (0 – 10m), is interfered by a dense network of sinkholes and stipulate infiltration or direct runoff of precipitation and surface waters into karst aquifers. Besides sinkholes, the old karst is also developed in the region. It is characterized by subsurface cavities scattered in all section of karst sediments. The cavities are filled by drift material and dolomitic flour. This makes the region sensitive to all changes of hydrodynamic and hydrochemical equilibrium in karst aquifers. Changes of groundwater pressure or flow velocity can cause the removal of filling debris material from the cavities and influence the appearance of new sinkholes on the land surface. In spite of this human activity in the region for years was carried out without any restrictions.

5.5 Karst Morphology and Karstification Density

5.5.1 *Karst Development in Estonia*

In the carbonate rocks of the North-Estonian karst province the following five hydrodynamic zones are distinguished (Heinsalu 1977):

1. Zone of surficial circulation occurs in the areas, where the Quaternary cover is missing. Water flows on the ground dissolving and eroding rocks. Frequently, this zone is lacking.

2. Zone of vertical circulation (aeration zone). In this zone water moves periodically downwards along vertical joints. This takes place in spring during and after the melting of snow, and after heavy rains. The thickness of this zone in Estonia ranges from 0.5 – 1 m in lower areas to 10 m in elevated areas. In the central part of the Pandivere Upland it is up to 15 m thick. Sometimes, particularly in small karst fields, the aeration zone is lacking, because the zone of periodical fluctuations reaches often straight to the ground. In some occasions the water may rise higher the earth's surface, and temporary karst lakelets are formed.

3. Zone of seasonal karst water fluctuations. The zone is characterized by the alteration of vertical and horizontal circulation of karst water. The thickness of the zone is usually 3 – 4 metres, in the Pandivere Upland it occasionally attains 13 metres, in low-lying areas it is less than 1 metre.

4. Near-surface zone of horizontal circulation. In this zone unconfined ground water flows towards rivers. It is also known as the zone of saturation where water occurs permanently.

5. Zone of deep circulation is related to karstified rocks, permanently saturated with water. The water flows at a very slow rate towards the sea. Contemporary rivers have no direct impact on the zone of deep circulation.

5.5.2 *Karst Zonation in Lithuania*

According to geological composition and conditions of karst development karst region of Lithuania is divided into 5 zones.

First zone -territory of active modern gypsum karst is characterized by often appearance of new sinkholes and land subsidences. The second zone is an area of underground gypsum karst. On the surface of this area rare but large sinkholes and surface collapses are formed. This is related with thicker gypsum layers and overlaying sediments (up to 15 m). Third zone is the territory of development of glacial and pre-glacial karst. It is characterized by a dense network of fractures and voids in Devonian dolomites and evaporites. Here one can often observe a set of so called karst deposits: dolomitic flour, calcitized marl, dedolomites, etc. Fourth and fifth zones occupy territories where Devonian and Permian carbonatic rocks (dolomites and limestones) are covered by thin strata of glacial deposits. Ancient carbonate karst is outgrowing in those rocks and modern karst is presented by dissolution of old fractures and voids.

Upper Devonian Tatula gypsic sediments are dipping at the angles changing from 10′ – 15′ to 2°. Due to such dipping upper layers of elevated (eastern) part of the sequence were cut by glacier and gypsum is outcropping at preglacial on skylight on a narrow strip (5 – 10km wide) stretching to south west and south direction. This strip is covered by thin strata of Quaternary sediments and modern karst is most active at this zone.

5.5.3 *Karst Morphology in Lithuania*

Karst in North Lithuania is developed on the land surface and also in the subsurface. Surface karst forms are represented by sinkholes, karst shafts, land subsidences, lakes, dolines, etc. Subsurface forms are enlarged solution voids, cavities and caves.

More than 8500 sinkholes different in size and shape are counted in region of active gypsum karst, with an area of 4000 km^2. According to number of sinkholes on an area unit karst terrain is divided into four zones : slightly karstified territories (0 – 20 sinkholes /km^2), medium karstified (20 – 50 units/km^2), strongly karstified (50 – 80 units/km^2) and extremely karstified (> 80 units/km^2) areas. Such division was proposed by the Russian scientist G. Maksimovich (1969). Shape, diameter and depth of sinkholes vary greatly. Oval-shaped sinkholes of medium size are prevailing in the region (Tab. 5 – 4). Summarized data of 676 sinkholes are presented in the table.

Tab. 5-4 Morphologic and morphometric data of sinkholes (Buceviciute and Marcinkevicius, 1992)

Shape			Diameter			Depth	
Circle	Oval	Irreg – ular	to 10m	10 – 50m	>50m	Shallow (to 5m)	Middle (5 – 10m)
18%	61%	21%	10%	87%	3%	93%	7%

A lot of sinkholes were destroyed during the land reclamation. This is obvious from retrospective analyses of aerial mapping. Although those sinkholes are filled with soil, stones, bushes and other rubbish material and could not be observed on the surface, in reality they serve as paths of surface water and pollution infiltration into karst aquifers.

The main part of shallow sinkholes are dry, only those with impermeable layer of peat at the bottoms are filled by water. Deeper sinkholes reach unconfined groundwater, sometimes the level of the confined, artesian water. In such case, in favourable geomorphologic conditions springs are outleting on the land surface. Such springs occur in the valleys of river Levuo, in Pasvalys town, Orija, near Berklainiai village, Apascia in Draseikiai village, etc. Some springs are sources for starting rivers. In Likenai resort from the shallow sinkhole with a diameter of 13 meters discharging spring creates Smardone river which is the tributary of Tatula river. But also opposite picture can be observed, when 8 km long stream Pozemis disappears in former cave, which was destroyed by land reclamation and quarrying of gypsum deposits. Several joined sinkholes form poljes. Most of poljes are located around Kirkilai village. They are filled with water and often form small lakes with a depth to 10 and more meters. The lake named Ilgasis (Long Lake) is composed of 30 different sinkholes and has length of 1100 m, width 200 m (Kilkus, 1976). A lot of small pits and land subsidences could be observed on arable lands. Many of them are filled with soil during the land cultivation, but each year they become deeper and wider and after some time they are left in the field because the land close to them could not be used for agriculture any more.

Underground karst forms are less investigated. From observations of natural and artificial outcrops it is known that Upper Devonian Tatula gypsic formations are cut by vertical and horizontal fractures and voids, which sometimes are transformed into channels by seeping water. During the drilling process it was found out that cavities with a depth of 10 and more meters are formed in Tatula sediments. Often they are filled with dolomitic debris material (so called dolomitic flour), moraine till, sometimes sand, gravel and marl. Amount of cavities is decreasing with depth. The deepest hollow filled with water was found at a depth of 96.4m in Radviliskis region (Buceviciute and Marcinkevicius, 1992). About existence of big underground emptities one can judge from sudden collapses of holes with a diameter of 40 and more meters and depth about 10 meters. It have been calculated by Russian scientists that cavity underground is 3 times bigger than karst collapse on the surface. Density of fractures and voids in karst sediments is uneven in a cross section. It is obvious from the conductivity of karst rocks which is very different and changing from 1 – 2 to 124 m/day (Buceviciute and Marcinkevicius, 1992).

Among the big number of surface karst forms only one karst cave is known today in the karst region of Lithuania. Although not being very large and exotic the cave was awarded the status of geological monument as a sole representative of underground karst form in the country. It is formed in the same gypsiferous geological formations as surface karst forms. The entrance to the cave appears at the bottom of karst shaft at a depth of 9.5 meters. It is narrow and watered and that protects the cave from casual visitors. The cave consists of main cavity filled by water and 3 narrow passages. According to the data of Lithuanian speleologists the height of the main cave is 3.1 m, total length of passages 46 m, area of the cave is 42 m^2 and volume 28 m^3. Depth of the lake which fills the main cavity varies from 1 m to 1.8 m, the bottom is covered by 0.5 m thick mud mainly composed of dolomitic flour. Walls of the cave are made of karren and scallops, cut by fissures and cracks which serves as paths for surface water seepage. Although an underground lake in the cave is hydraulically connected with karst aquifer, dynamic, chemical and thermal heterogeneities are characteristic to it.

6 monitoring wells are installed into karst aquifer at the vicinities of the cave in a distance of 0.2 – 1.5 km from it. According to regime observations groundwater level fluctuations in them reach 0.14 – 2.29 m per year. But the level of cave lake is constant all the year instead of spring and autumn floods, when water level rises by 0.5 – 1.0m. Tracer measurements in the lake show that water movement in it is very slow: dyed water disappeared from the lake only after 2 weeks. Chemical composition of groundwater in the lake and monitoring wells is also different. In the wells sulphate calcium water is prevailing with total dissolved solids of 0.5 – 2.2 g/l and total hardness of 8.5 – 33.5 meq/l. In the lake also sulphate calcium water is being contained but it's salinity reaches 1.5 – 2.2 g/l and total hardness 23 – 29 meq/l. Groundwater temperature in the observation points also differs. Water in the cave do not exceed +5℃ even in the hottest time of the year, while temperature of groundwater in the observation wells fluctuates from 6 to 10℃. Such heterogeneities are typical features for groundwater systems of karst regions.

Judging from geological composition of the territory it is clear that there should be more caves in the area. Some of the caves were destroyed by human activity. Local people remember another cave which existed near Birzai with a high entrance and about 30m long (Narbutas, 1958), but after development of gypsum quarry and later land reclamation the cave has been destroyed. Now at the place of former cave one can find a big void to which small river Pozemis disappears.

Besides mentioned karst forms in a zone of active gypsum karst on the roof of Tatula layers a lot of karren are developed. Karren and pits are filled by residual material of dolomites, marls of Devonian and Silurian age and also by glacial till and sand. Between them in some places relics of gypsum and dolomites are met. Shape, size and distribution of karren are very uneven. Their size is related with a thickness of gypsum layer and reach 2 – 3 meters in width and 3 – 6 meters in depth. This type of karst is characteristic for third and fourth zones of karst region. When investigating karst sediments and forecasting development of karst process in Lithuania one should keep in mind that many karst forms (karren, pits, sinkholes, etc.) are covered by glacial sediments and could not be observed on the land surface. But any disturbance of natural equilibrium in such areas can easily cause appearance of karst forms on the land surface.

Since 1960 three geological reserves: Kirkilai, Karajimiskis and Kirdoniu-Tatulos have been established on the area. Territories on which karst is being protected were also established in Latvia (Tab. 5-5)

Tab. 5-5 Karst reserves in Lithuania and Latvia

Name of reserve	Area, hectares	Date of establishment	Protected objects
	Lithuania		
Karajimiskis, Birzai district	72	1960	Sinkholes, cave, river, discharging into ponor
Kirdoniu-Tatulos	90	1960	Sinkholes
Kirkilai	382	1960	Sinkholes
	Latvia		
Kazugrava, Cesis district	1.5	1974	Group of caves
Zanderi, Cesis district	1.5	1974	Dolomitic caves
Auksniupe, Auksnes district	5.5	1974	Sinkholes, dry valley
Skaistkalne, Bauska district	42	1977	Sinkholes
Ezernieki, Riga district	60.4	1977	Sinkholes
Klintaine, Stuckas district	13.6	1977	Sinkholes, dry valley
Ritere, Stuckas district	2.3	1977	Sinkholes, dry valley

5.5.4 *Surficial Karst Forms and Phenomena of Estonia*

Karren are small holes, depressions and grooves, which usually develop in the areas where the Quaternary cover is lacking. The hollows are small, usually only 0.5 to 2 cm in diameter, and their depth does not exceed 5 cm. Karren abound in the Pae karst field and in the small rocky Vaika islands, where sea water has also affected their development.

Open joints occur on the alvars, where the Quaternary cover is very thin or lacking. Generally, they are 0.5 – 1.0 m wide, and several metres deep. The length of the joints may amount to several tens of metres. Open joints are abundant in the Kostivere and Savalduma karst fields.

Sinkholes are the most wide-spread karst phenomena in Estonia. They frequently occur in closed hollows into which meltwaters tend to accumulate in spring. Sinkholes are found also on the margins of boggy areas where the rock is covered with thin soil high in water permeability, but also in the beds of brooks and rivulets. Often a subterranean river or brook begins from a sinkhole. Most frequently, sinkholes are oval-shaped, sometimes also cone-like or irregular in shape. Large sinkholes are 5 – 30 metres wide, up to 60 metres (occasionally 100 m) long and 3 metres (in the areas with thick Quaternary cover up to 6 m) deep. Sinkholes are found in all Estonian karst fields (Kostivere, Uhaku, Kuimetsa, Kata, Savalduma, Pae). A sinkhole may swallow up to 800 – 900 litres of water per second (usually 20 – 100 l/sec). There are more than 50 sinkholes in Estonia, through which a river or brook enters the ground and passes along an subterranean course. The remaining sinkholes, exact number of which is not yet known, swallow water periodically — in spring when the snow melts or in autumn during heavy rains. Otherwise they are dry.

Karst hollows and valleys above subterranean rivers. Karst hollows develop above the course of subterranean karst waters. According to the data available, in Estonia subterranean rivers and brooks flow along karst cavities at a length of 0.3 – 0.5 to 2 – 3 kilometres. Five large karst areas have been identified above subterranean rivers and brooks (Fig. 5-1):

1. Kostivere karst area (above the subterranean stretch of the Jõelähtme River);
2. Uhaku karst area (above the subterranean stretch of the Erra River);
3. Kata karst area (above the subterranean stretch of the Tuhala River);

4. Kuimetsa karst area (above the subterranean stretch of the Vaopere brook);
5. Pae karst area (above the subterranean stretch of the earlier existed nameless brook).

The Kostivere karst area occupies the territory of more than 100 hectares and is largest in Estonia. The Jõelähtme River flows at a length of 2.5 kilometres underground. There are many karst hollows along its underground course, which in places have joined to form long (up to 450 m) chains. There are also several 200 – 300 m long and 2 – 3 metres deep karst hollows. One can find interesting relict forms, for instance, the "Stone Board "(or "karst mushroom", Photo 57). The water table in the subterranean Jõelähtme River fluctuates in the range of 5 metres: every spring when the snow melts, sometimes also in summer and autumn during heavy rains, the karst hollows fill with water and turn into temporary karst lakelets.

In **the Uhaku karst area** the Erra River flows for about 0.4 km underground. The water disappears within a stretch of 1 km, where the river bed abounds in sinkholes. Above the subterranean course of the river there have developed large sink depressions, up to 65 metres in diameter and 6 metres in depth. On the bottom of the deepest holes there is always some water, marking the level of the underground water. In spring, when the snow melts, karst hollows are filled with water (the water table is 1 m from the earth's surface). During ice ages the surficial karst forms were buried under sediments, in the Holocene karst revived again.

In **the Kata karst area** the Tuhala River flows at a length of 2.5 kilometres underground. There are more than 30 karst depressions above the subterranean course of the river. Above a stretch of the river, a more than 500 m long, 100 m wide and 3 m deep karst valley has developed. During the melting of snow in spring, sometimes also during heavy autumn rains, the water level in the subterranean river rises so high that a well in one of the karst hollows starts to pour over. This well is popularly known as the "Witch Well" (Photo 58). The capacity of the well is 100 l/sec.

The Kuimetsa karst area occupies the territory of 12 hectares. The Vaopere brook flows underground for 2.5 kilometres. Karst depressions, up to 100 metres in length, up to 40 metres in width and with a depth of up to 3.5 metres have formed along the subterranean watercourse. The field abounds in small karst hollows. In the 1950's, the spring meltwaters caused extensive floods, to date these are rare, because most of the water which earlier used to flow into the karst field has been directed elsewhere.

The Pae karst area is located on an area of 2 hectares. It displays a variety of karst forms, including caves which are among the largest in Estonia (width 5 – 6 m, height 1 m). Karren occur in great numbers. The karst forms have developed above a nameless subterranean brook which existed here in past centuries.

KARST SPRINGS. Estonia has thousands of karst springs, which form the prevailing part of Estonian springs. On the basis of the groundwater outflow, descending and ascending springs are distinguished. In the case of the former, the water flows out from the cracks of carbonate rocks or from between the layers. In ascending springs, hydrostatic pressure makes the water move upwards along the cracks. It appears on the ground through the spring funnel on the bottom of which one can see the "boiling" of water. The funnels are 0.5 – 30 m in diameter and 0.3 – 1.5 m deep. The bodies of water which are located above very large spring funnels or groups of funnels are termed spring lakes. The diameter of the largest spring lakes amounts to several hundred metres. Karst springs frequently form groups (up to 10 springs in one group). There is a great number of temporary karst springs which function only during the spring high-water period and 2 – 8 weeks after it. Such springs derive water from the zone of seasonal karst water fluctuation. Permanent karst springs are fed by the zone of horizontal karst water circulation. The water temperature in karst springs is +4 – +6℃ throughout the year, on the outflow of subterranean rivers it often exceeds +10℃. The maximum capacity of large karst springs is 1000 – 3000 l/sec (usually 150 – 400 l/sec), and the minimum yield 100 – 130 l/sec (usually 30 – 60 l/sec). Generally, the ratio of minimum and maximum yields ranges from 1:30 up to 1:100. Only in rare cases, it is 1:1 up to 1:10. Like the near-surface groundwater, the water in karst springs is of HCO_3 – Ca – Mg – type, the dissolved salt content is 0.3 – 0.4 g/l. Under the conditions of state socialistic system large-scale agriculture (particularly in 1960 – 1990), when mineral fertilizers were excessively used, the concentration of NO_3 in the water of karst springs constantly increased. Against the natural background of 10 mg/l, it was often 30 – 40 mg/l, in some places even more. Since 1990, owing to the reduction of mineral fertilizer use, the NO_3 concentration in karst spring water has been declining.

On the slopes of the Pandivere Upland, the numerous karst springs occur at three levels. The abundance of springs is due to the circumstance, that in the center of the Upland there is an area (1375 km^2) where no rivers or brooks occur, and precipitation water enters the ground through karst cavities. Numerous rivers begin from the karst springs of the Pandivere Upland.

WET KARST HOLES AND TEMPORARY LAKELETS. The North-Estonian karst province is rich in karst hollows, which in spring after the melting of snow turn into lakelets. They dry in the second half of the summer. In spring, such a hollow is usually filled with snow melt water, which after some time percolates into the ground. In spring, when the ground water table rises, the hollow is again filled with water through its bottom which stays there till June or July. There is a lot of temporary karst lakelets in the Savalduma karst field. Noteworthy are also Assamalla, Võhmetu-Lehmküla a.o. karst lakelets.

The South-East Estonian karst area (ca 700 km^2) is rich in karst springs. Deep karst hollows occur in the Tsiistre karst field. In spring they turn into temporary karst lakelets. The largest sinkhole is situated at Meremäe.

5.5.5 *Subterranean Karst Phenomena of Estonia*

BURIED KARST. Karst, buried under the Quaternary cover, has developed before the last (Weichselian) glaciation or even earlier, partially undoubtedly before the Pleistocene. Subterranean karst forms are represented by caves, cracks, caverns and subterranean rivers, encountered in limestone quarries, ditches and foundation trenches. Large bedrock hollows of karst origin under the Quaternary cover occur in the Pandivere Upland and elsewhere. The depth of those hollows may be 5 – 15 m, diameter in places several hundred metres and length 1 km.

KARST CAVES AND CAVERNS. In Estonia karst caves are rare. Due to the high clay content of carbonate rocks, they have rather modest dimensions. The advancing ice sheet destroyed the near-surface caves or they were filled with meltwater sediments. There are altogether 24 karst caves in 11 karst fields in Estonia. In eight karst fields they have developed in subterranean water courses. Most frequently these are single very small karst tunnels or their expansions, termed suffosion caves (grottos). All karst caves occur at a depth of 1 – 7 metres from the earth's surface and have a horizontal floor. The height of caves ranges from 0.5 to 1.5 m (max. 4 m), width from 0.5 to 12 m. Estonian karst caves are situated in the zone of seasonal karst water fluctuations, and are entirely or partially filled with water in spring. Therefore, stalactites, stalagmites or travertine are not found in these caves. As a matter of fact, even if they form somewhere, they would dissolve during the high water period entirely.

Smaller karst cavities - caverns are abundant in karstified rocks. They are displayed in the walls of limestone quarries, in the walls and ceiling of oil shale mines. They have also been observed when drilling wells. Caverns are numerous at a depth of 10 – 30 metres, within tectonic fault zones they may occur down to the depth of 100 m.

Frequently, older karst cavities are filled with sediments. Depending on the time of development, they may contain Devonian, pre-Pleistocene deluvial or Pleistocene sediments.

From time to time crystals of dolomite and calcite, less frequently pyrite, galenite and other sulphites have been found in karst caverns.

5.6 Anthropogenic Factors of Karst Activation

It was already mentioned that the major human activity in Lithuanian karst region having influence on karst development is groundwater extraction and agriculture. Minor impact is caused by land reclamation, civil and hydrotechnic construction, mining, waste water discharge, etc.

Interconnected system of aquifers is being exploited for drinking water supply by digging and drilling wells. About 600 drilling wells installed into different aquifers are registered on the karstified terrain. The average water consumption from a single well differs from 10 to 50 m^3/day.

Besides separate wells two waterworks in Birzai and Pasvalys towns consume correspondingly 2.0 and 3.6 thousand m^3/day of groundwater. It was planned that in 2010 water consumption will increase to 9 thousand m^3/day in Birzai and 14 thousand m^3/day in Pasvalys(Paukstys, 1991), but due to recent political- economical changes in the country and decrease of industrial production these figures may change. Nevertheless in a course of groundwater abstraction it's level in the main production aquifer (D_{2-3} sv-up) of Pasvalys waterwork from 1970 decreased by 7.5 m, while the drawdown in Birzai reached 8 m since 1961. It was evaluated by mathematical modeling that significant influence to the development of depression cone will cover Panevezys town which is 40 – 60 km to the South of karst territory with groundwater consumption of 110 thousand m^3/day.

Due to the development of drawdown in the aquifers hydraulic relations between them become even more complicated: vertical flow velocity is increasing, groundwater head in the aquifers is diminished and redistributed, and that increases infiltration of fresh precipitation and polluted surface waters into karst aquifer. Groundwater abstraction enlarges gypsum solubility and accelerates removal of dolomite flour from subsurface cavities to the rivers and (or) adjacent cavities.

The other anthropogenic factor influencing karst development on a regional scale is agriculture. Farming is highly developed in karst region as well as in other parts of the country. Almost all karstified area except of the territories of geological reserves is occupied by arable lands. For the enlargement of harvests chemical and organic fertilizers, herbicides and pesticides are widely used. The sortiment of fertilizers is represented by nitrogen, phosphorus, potassium compounds and microelements. For the mitigation of acidity of soils the liming is used. Liquid and solid manure are also widely applied. In 1974 on the karstified lands of Birzai and Pasvalys regions 60 thousand tons of mineral and about the same amount of organic fertilizers were introduced, while in 1990 their amount increased correspondingly to 94 thousand tons and 160 thousand tons, respectively.

Implemented measures elevated fertility of the soils but also became the regional source of groundwater pollution. In the unconfined water in some of dug wells concentration of nitrates reaches 400 mg/l (highest permitted concentration (HPC) for drinking water is 45 mg/l), nitrites – 7.5 mg/l (HPC – 3.3mg/l), ammonium – 100 mg/l (HPC – 2.0 mg/l), permanganate oxidation – 19 mg/l (HPC – 2 mg/l). Karst waters are also heavily polluted on some areas (Klimas and Paukstys, 1993).

5.7 Karst Protection Measures in Lithuania

After investigations of natural and anthropogenic conditions of karst development measures for karst protection were worked out.

One of the main tasks is planning of groundwater abstraction in karst region. In order to diminish development of drawdown in karst aquifers it was proposed to prohibit exploitation of groundwater from gypsum-dolomitic aquifers. Today all water supply is planned from the Upper Devonian sandstones (D_3 sv). For the same purpose concentrated water abstraction should be stopped. Alternative waterworks were prospected and should be constructed for Birzai drinking water supply.

For mitigation of adverse impact of dispersed agricultural pollution it is necessary to limit agricultural activity in the region. It has been done in 1977 and 1982 by Governmental resolutions. But these measures did not give positive results because environmental protection measures were only declarations, but the requirements for larger crops from the unit of arable land were still in action. In 1991 on the initiative of geological and agricultural institutions a new governmental resolution was accepted which is practically limiting agricultural activity in the region. The main achievement of new resolution is that it is planned to change the specialization of agricultural activity in the region limiting it at the vulnerable karstified lands. According to vulnerability criteria: degree of rock karstification, density of sinkholes and groundwater pollution extent karstified land has been divided lands into the groups with different extent of limitation of agricultural activity. Besides them protection zone of karst territory was implemented (Fig. 5-4).

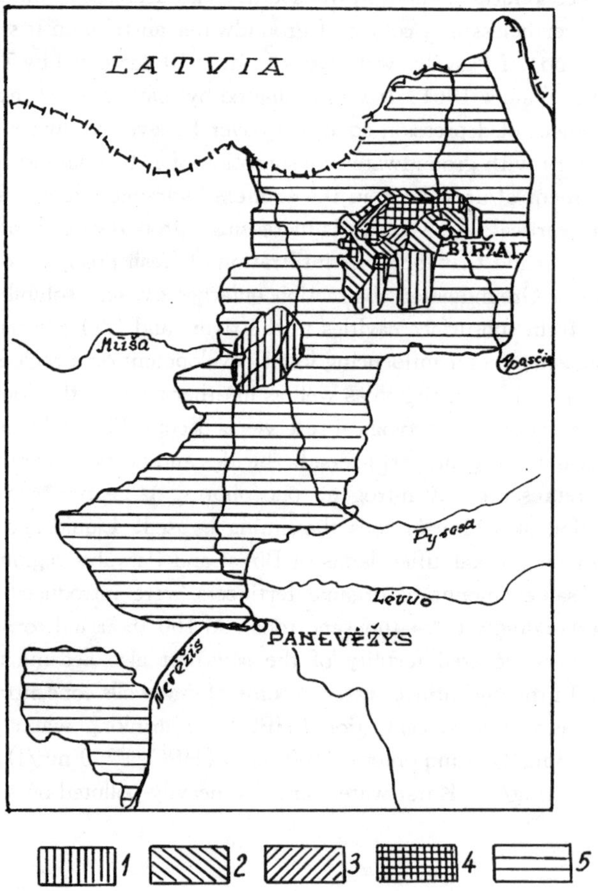

Fig. 5-4 Limitation of agricultural activity on karstified lands of Lithuania. 1. first land group; 2. second land group; 3. third land group; 4. fourth land group; 5. protection zone of karst area

According to governmental resolution the following protection measures for karst lands were proposed and now are implemented.

1. On the first group of lands (to 20 sinkholes/100hectares) grain crops should compose at least 50% of arable lands, perennial grasses - 40% and potatoes and sugar beet species not more that 10%. Fertilizer loadings should not exceed 90 kg/hectare of nitrogen, phosphorus and potassium fertilizers (active material) and 80t/hectare of manure. The application of triazinic herbicides and clororganic insecticsides is prohibited.

2. On the lands of second group (20 - 50sinkholes /100hectares) cultivation of potatoes and sugar beet is prohibited, as is the establishment of new orchards and gardens. 43% of arable lands should be used for grain and 57% occupied by perennial grasses. No more than 60kg/hectare of nitrogen, phosphorus and potassium fertilizer and 60 tons/hectare of manure may be applied. There is a prohibition on herbicides, retardants and insecticides on these lands.

3. On the lands of third group (50 - 80 sinkholes /100 hectares) perennial grasses and pastures should prevail. No more than 60 kg/hectare of mineral phosphorus and potassium fertilizers may be applied. The use of mineral nitrogen fertilizers and pesticides (except fungicides) is prohibited.

4. On the lands of fourth group (more than 80 sinkholes /100 hectares) only meadows and forests are permitted, although it is allowed to cultivate curative plants. All sorts of fertilizers and chemical protection agents are prohibited

5. All groups — in a zone of radius 25 m around each sinkhole a protection zone should be established. Within this zone only grass without any fertilizers and chemicals may be cultivated. These lands should be excluded from land use.

It is prohibited on all land groups:

—to apply liquid ammonia and ammoniac water;

—to use aircrafts for application of fertilizers;

—to destroy or damage sinkholes, to use them for discharge of drainage water, to dump waste materials, to exploit peat from the bottoms of sinkholes, to build settlements, landfills, land reclamation and hydrotechnical facilities and other objects influencing environment only after the thorough assessment of geotechnical conditions of the building site and agreement of the projects with Ministry of Environment and Geological Survey.;

—to construct underground oil storages, filtration fields, build enterprises with hazardous production, to build new and reconstruct old chemical stores.

The area of actively protected karstified lands compose 27.6 thousand hectares. and karst protection zone is occupying 166 thousand hectares (Fig. 5-4).

Protection zone includes sporadically scattered sinkholes and basins of main karst rivers. Human activity in this area should not affect natural environmental equilibrium and pollute surface and groundwater.

For each land group plans for development of ecologically sound agriculture are designed. Biological agriculture, without chemical fertilizers, is being introduced in the region. A governmental programme for protection of karst water from pollution and mitigation of human impact to vulnerable karst hydrosphere was prepared and is being introduced in the region. Financing from national budget is allocated for implementation of protection measures (construction of waste water treatment plants, manure storage, etc.).

Design and implementation of protection measures will hopefully stabilize karst development.

References

Basalykas, A., 1958. Physical Geography of Lithuania. Vilnius, 504pp. [in Lithuanian].

Buceviciute, S. and V. Marcinkevicius, 1992. Karst morphology. Proceedings of the Lithuanian High Schools. Geologija. 49 - 58. [in Lithuanian].

Dublianskij, V. N., V. I. Klimenko and A. N. Michailov, 1990. Main factors of karst development and evaluation of its activity by grade scale. Engineering Geology, Vol. 2, pp. 52 – 58 [in Russian].

Eichwald, E., 1852. Dritter Nachtrag zur Infusorienkunde Russlands. - Bull. Soc. Nat. Moscou, XXV, 11, 388 – 536.

Fischer, J. B., 1784. Zusätze zu seinem Versuch einer Naturgeschichte von Livland, nebst einigen Anmerkungen zur Physischen Erdbeschreibung von Kurland von J. J. Feber. Riga, 305.

Gazizov, M. S., 1958. On morphology and origin of deep karst in the Baltic oil-shale basin. - Trudy inst. geol. AN ESSR, II, 133 – 162 (in Russian).

Gatalskii M. A., 1959. Microdislocation and jointing of rocks in the Baltic region and their significance in the migration and distribution of fluids. - Trudy VNIGRI, 131, pp. 65 – 77 (in Russian).

Grothus, T., 1886. Untersuchung des quelwassers zu Schmordan. Beitr. Chem. und Phys. B. 18 H. 1. 83 – 114

Heinsalu, Ü. J., 1959. Karst phenomena of the Quaternary period in Estonian SSR. Tallinn, 27 pp. (in Russian).

Heinsalu, Ü., 1961a. Karsti arengutingimustest Eestis (Conditions of the development of karst in Estonia). Geoloogiline kogumik. Tartu, 106 – 115 (in Estonian, summary in English).

Heinsalu, Ü., 1961b. Karstinähtuste levik ja omapära Eestis (Distribution and peculiarities of karst phenomena in Estonia). - Antropogeeni geoloogia. Eesti NSV Geoloogia Instituudi Uurimused, VII, 159 – 166 (in Estonian, summary in German)

Heinsalu, Ü., 1967a. Karst Eestis (Karst phenomena in Estonia). – Eesti Loodus, 9, 542 – 547 (in Estonian, summary in English).

Heinsalu, Ü., 1967b. Karst Pandivere kõrgustikul (Karst in the Pandivere Upland). – Rakvere rajoonis. Kodu-uurijate seminar-kokkutulek. Tallinn, 37 – 44 (in Estonian).

Heinsalu, Ü., 1976. Karstiallikate ja -vormide teadusliku uurimise ja kaitse olukord Eesti NSV (Research into solution springs and karst phenomena and their protection in Estonian SSR). Eesti NSV maapõue kaitsest. Tallinn, Valgus, 53 – 67 (in Estonian, summary in English).

Heinsalu, Ü., 1977. Karst jalooduskeskkond Eesti NSV-s (Karst phenomena and natural environment in Estonian SSR). Tallinn, Valgus. 95 lk. (in Estonian).

Heinsalu, Ü., 1978. Karsti tähtsusest põhjaveevaru täienemisel Eestis (The importance of karst formations in replenishing Estonian ground water reserves). – Põhjavee kasutamisest ja kaitsest Eesti NSV-s. Tallinn, 44 – 53 (in Estonian, summary in English).

Heinsalu, Ü., 1991. Karstiga seotud loodusmälestiste kaitsest Lahkme-Eestis (Protection of karst-related natural monuments in Estonian Water Shed). - Lahkme- Eesti looduskasutus ja -kaitse. Tallinn, 46 – 59 (in Estonian, summary in English).

Heinsalu, Ü., 1993. Karst and springs. - The Pandivere State Water Protection Area, Jyväskyla, 15 – 18.

Hupel, A. W., 1774. Topographische Nachrichten von Liv- und Estland, Bd. I. Riga, 590.

Juodkazis, V. J., 1979. Principles of hydrogeology of the Baltic States. Vilnius, 144 pp. [in Lithuanian].

Kilkus, K. I., 1977. Karst of North Lithuania. Karst lakes. (Proceed. of Academy of Science of Lithuania) B 6(103) 125 – 133. [in Russian].

Klimas, A. J. and B. Paukstys, 1990. Organization of lithomonitoring in karst region of Northern Lithuania. Engineering geology 4, 75 – 80 [in Russian].

Klimas, A. and B. Paukstys, 1993. Nitrate contamination of groundwater in the Republic of Lithuania. Bulletin of Geological Survey of Norway 424, 75 – 85.

Krainov, S. R. and V. M. Svec, 1980. Principles of groundwater geochemistry. Moscow, 288 pp. [in Russian].

Krainov, S. R. and V. M. Svec, 1987. Geochemistry of groundwater for drinking- domestic use. Moscow, 237 pp. [in Russian].

Marcinkevicius, V. and S. Buceviciute, 1986. Geological and hydrogeological conditions of sulphate karst development in Northern Lithuania. Geologija (Lithuanian high school scientific papers), Vol. 7, pp. 104 – 119 [in Russian].

Narbutas, V., 1979. Geological peculiarities of Lithuanian karst region and problems of its protection. Annual proceedings of geography, Vol. 17, pp. 155 – 166 [in Lithuanian].

Orviku, K., 1929. Uhaku. Kirde-Eesti karstiala stratigraafiast ja geomorfoloogiast (Uhaku. About the stratigraphy and geomorphology of the karst area of North-East Estonia). - Tartu Ülikooli Geoloogia Instituudi Toimetised, 14. Tartu, 36 lk. (in Estonian, summary in German).

Paukstys, B., 1992. The risk of karst activization and limitation of economic activity. Proceedings of the Lithuanian High Schools. Geologija. 13, 131 – 140 [in Lithuanian].

Paukstys, B. and Taminskas, 1992. Surface and groundwater regime. Proceedings of the Lithuanian High Schools. Geologija. 13, 58 – 86 [in Lithuanian].

Paukstys, B., 1991. Influence of anthropogenic activity to evolution of gypsum karst in North Lithuania. Doct. thesis, VSEGINGEO, Moscow, 25 pp. [in Russian].

Raukas, A., 1986. Deglaciation of the Gulf of Finland and adjoining areas. Bull. Geol. Soc. Finland, Vol. 58, No. 2, pp. 21 – 33.

Schmidt, F., 1858. Untersuchungen über die Silurische Formation von Estland, Nord- Livland und Oesel. - Arch. Naturk. Liv-, Est- und Kurlands, Ser. I, Bd. 2, Lief 1, 248 S.

Sokolov, D. S., 1962. Main conditions for karst development. Moscow, 320 pp. [in Russian].

Zakutin, V. P. and B. P. Paukstys, 1993: Effects geochimiques de la pollution agricole des eaux souterraines dans la region karstique de la Lituanie. Hydrogeologie.

Global Karst Correlation
Edited by Yuan Daoxian and Liu Zaihua
Science Press and VSP BV, 1998

Chapter 6 The Karst Geomorphology and Hydrogeology of Great Britain

John Gunn[1], David Lowe[1], Tony Waltham[2]

[1] *Limestone Research Group, Department of Geographical and Environmental Sciences, Huddersfield University, Queensgate, Huddersfield, England.*

[2] *Civil Engineering Department, Nottingham Trent University, Burton street, Nottingham, England*

6.1 Introduction

Great Britain, comprising England, Scotland and Wales, is a relatively small island with an area of about 229 000 km^2, a maximum length (north-south) of 1000 km and a maximum width (east-west) of 450 km. Beds of dominantly carbonate rock, many of which may be referred to as limestone, are present throughout the geological column in Great Britain and within the island there is probably a greater range of karst landforms than in any area of comparable size in the world(Fig. 6-1, Tab.6-1). The aim of this chapter is to describe these landforms briefly, placing them in their hydrogeological context, and to account for some of the differences between them. Carbonate rocks, on which the majority of karst is developed, are considered in detail, with brief discussion of evaporite karst. The various pseudokarst landforms, principally caves of tectonic origin, are outside the remit of this account.

Major carbonate or limestone units now at outcrop in England and Wales were deposited during the Carboniferous, Jurassic and Cretaceous periods and underlie areas that are sufficiently large and contiguous to constitute significant aquifers. Less extensive carbonate outcrops in England, with minor significance in the context of cave and karst development, were deposited during the Permian and Devonian periods; minor outcrops in northern Scotland were deposited from late Precambrian to early Ordovician times. Of these only the Permian carbonates of northern England have been significantly developed for water supply. Various carbonate lithologies, including marble, cornstone, and true limestone or dolomitic limestone, form relatively insignificant parts of the Proterozoic (late Precambrian) basement, the Ordovician, Silurian and Triassic systems, and the more recent systems within the Cainozoic. Most are relatively impure, thin or discontinuous and many lie within sequences that are either highly tectonised and metamorphosed or are dominantly well indurated and effectively impermeable. Consequently they have few surface karst landforms or caves and at best are sources of domestic water.

Hydrogeologically, the carbonates may be arranged along a continuum from the Cretaceous Chalk, which has a largely diffuse storage and non-turbulent flow system with isolated conduits, through to the Durness carbonates in which the majority of flow is through dissolutionally-enlarged conduits with relatively little non-conduit flow or storage (Fig. 6-2; Atkinson and Smart, 1981; Gunn, 1992). Geomorphologically, there is a marked distinction between the younger carbonates, particularly those of Cretaceous and Jurassic age, which are essentially non-cavernous, and the older carbonates, particularly the Carboniferous Limestone, in which there is extensive cave development. This distinction is also apparent in the relative abundance and variety of surface landforms.

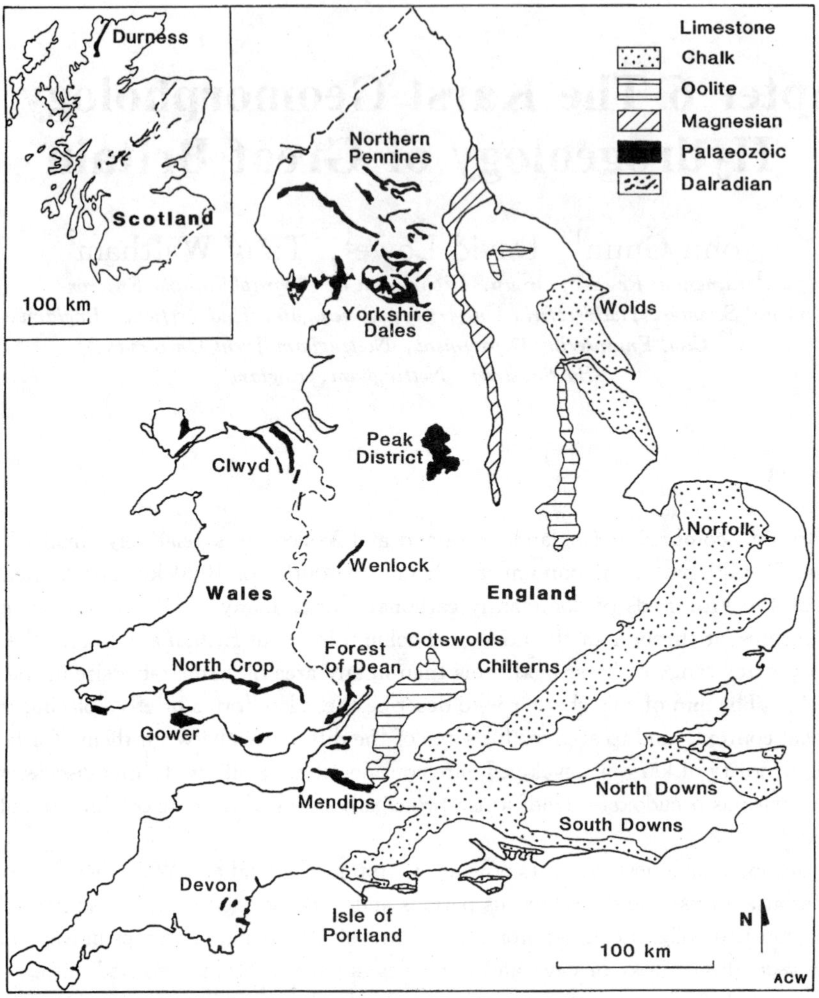

Fig. 6-1 Outline map of the main areas of karst in Great Britain. The Paleozoic limestones are of Lower Carboniferous age, except for the Devonian limestone in Devon, and the Cambrian-Ordovician limestone in Durness; the Dalradian limestones are only across central Scotland

6.2 Cavernous Karsts

6.2.1 *The Carboniferous Limestone*

The most extensive cavernous carbonate outcrops in Great Britain are the limestones (and less common dolomites) of Dinantian age, commonly referred to as the Carboniferous Limestone. They contain over 600 km of cave passage, some 95% of Great Britain's cave resources. Deposition of the Carboniferous Limestone sequence occurred during a series of major transgressive/regressive cycles (Ramsbottom, 1973), within which superimposed minor cyclicity led to depositional facies variation, producing a wide variety of carbonate and subordinate non-carbonate rock types. The initial Carboniferous transgression was not uniform across Great Britain, such that early Dinantian beds are

Tab. 6-1 The karst regions of Great Britain. A comparison of the major features which give the individual character to each main karst region (from Waltham et al., 1996)

Region	Yorkshire Dales[1]	Northern Pennines[2]	Peak District	Mendip Hills	South Wales	Rest of Great Britain[3]
Geology						
Karst area[4]	320 km²	220 km²	420 km²	110 km²	220 km²	9000 km² (mostly chalk)
Karst relief[5]	270 m	70 m	260 m	260 m	330 m	200 m (chalk)
Limestone thickness[6]	200 m	40 m	400 m	700 m	150 m	200 m (chalk)
Typical dip	1°	1°	5°	30°	10°	Varies between areas
Last glaciation	Devensian	Devensian	Anglian[7]	None	Devensian	Varies between areas
Karst[8]						
Glaciokarst	●●●	●●			●	● (Scotland)[9]
Fluviokarst			●●	●●		●● (chalk)
Interstratal karst			●		●●	
Pavement area[10]	677 ha	613 ha	0	0	8 ha	28 ha (Scotland, North Wales)
Dry valleys	●		●●●	●	●	●● (chalk)
Karst gorges	●●	●	●	●●		
Collapse features	●		●			
Doline fields	●●				●●	●● (covered chalk)
Ephemeral lakes					●	● (chalk)
Polygonal karst	●			●		
Famous Sites	Malham Cove Gaping Gill	Hutton Roof Crags	Dove Dale Peak Cavern	Cheddar Gorge Wookey Hole	Dan-yr-Ogof Porth yr Ogof	
Caves						
Major passage types	Vadose joint shafts, phreatic on bedding	Joint mazes	Phreatic on veins and bedding	Downdip phreatic loops	Downdip vadose, strike phreatic	Varies between areas
Number of caves[11]	1420	620	210	220	270	410
Total cave length[11]	325 km	65 km	50 km	55 km	175 km	45 km
Caves over 1km long	50	9	9	10	12	6
Longest caves[12] km	Ease Gill System 68	Goyden Pot 6	Peak-Speedwell System 14	Swildon's Hole 9	Ogof Ffynnon Ddu 50	Slaughter Cave 11 (Forest of Dean)
	Kingsdale System 24	Knock Fell Caverns 5	Giants Hole 5	St Cuthbert's Swallet 7	Ogof Agen Allwedd 33	Ogof Llyn Parc 4 (North Wales)
	Gaping Gill System 18	Fairy Hole 4	Bagshaw Cavern 4	Wookey Hole 4	Ogof Draenen 28	Uamh an Claonaite 3 (Scotland)
	Ireby-Notts System 12	Devis Hole 2	Carlswark Cavern 2	Gough's Cave 2	Ogof Daren Cilau 28	Ogof Llyn Du 2 (North Wales)
Deepest caves[12] m	Ease Gill System 211	Goyden Pot 61	Giants Hole 214	Eastwater Cavern 180	Ogof Ffynnon Ddu 308	Ogof Llyn Parc 115 (North Wales)
	Gingling Hole 210	Scrafton Pot 44	Masson Cavern 190	Longwood Swallet 175	Ogof Daren Cilau 217	Slaughter Cave 99 (Forest of Dean)
	Meregill Hole 205	Pate Hole 33	Peak-Speedwell System 182	Swildon's Hole 167	Ogof Agen Allwedd 177	Cnoc nan Uamh 90 (Scotland)
	Penyghent Pot 196	Ayleburn Mine Cave 30	Nettle Pot 180	Manor Farm 151	Dan-yr-Ogof 140	Ogof Hesp Alyn 90 (North Wales)

1 The main karst area of the southern Yorkshire Dales, on the Askrigg Block. 2 Including the karst east of Morecambe Bay and round the eastern fringe of the Lake District. 3 Mostly the weakly cavernous karst of the Chalk and Jurassic limestones; also including the cavernous karst of Devon, Forest of Dean, North Wales and Scotland. 4 Approximate area of karstic landscapes; does not include all the limestone outcrops. 5 Approximate values for the local relief within the limestone, which dictates the maximum descent from sink to rising, added to any depth of caves beneath the resurgence level. 6 Geological data is generalised for purposes of comparison. 7 Or possibly Wolstonian. 8 Most karst features are found to some extent in all the main karst regions, but their importance is assessed in relative terms: ● = significant, but minor; ●● = important and widespread; ●●● = internationally important. 9 Location of the major features noted in brackets. 10 From Ward and Evans (1976). 11 Recorded cave longer or deeper than 5m; figures rounded to nearest 10 caves and 5km of passage; from unpublished database of Limestone Research Group, University of Huddersfield. 12 Subject to continuous revision.

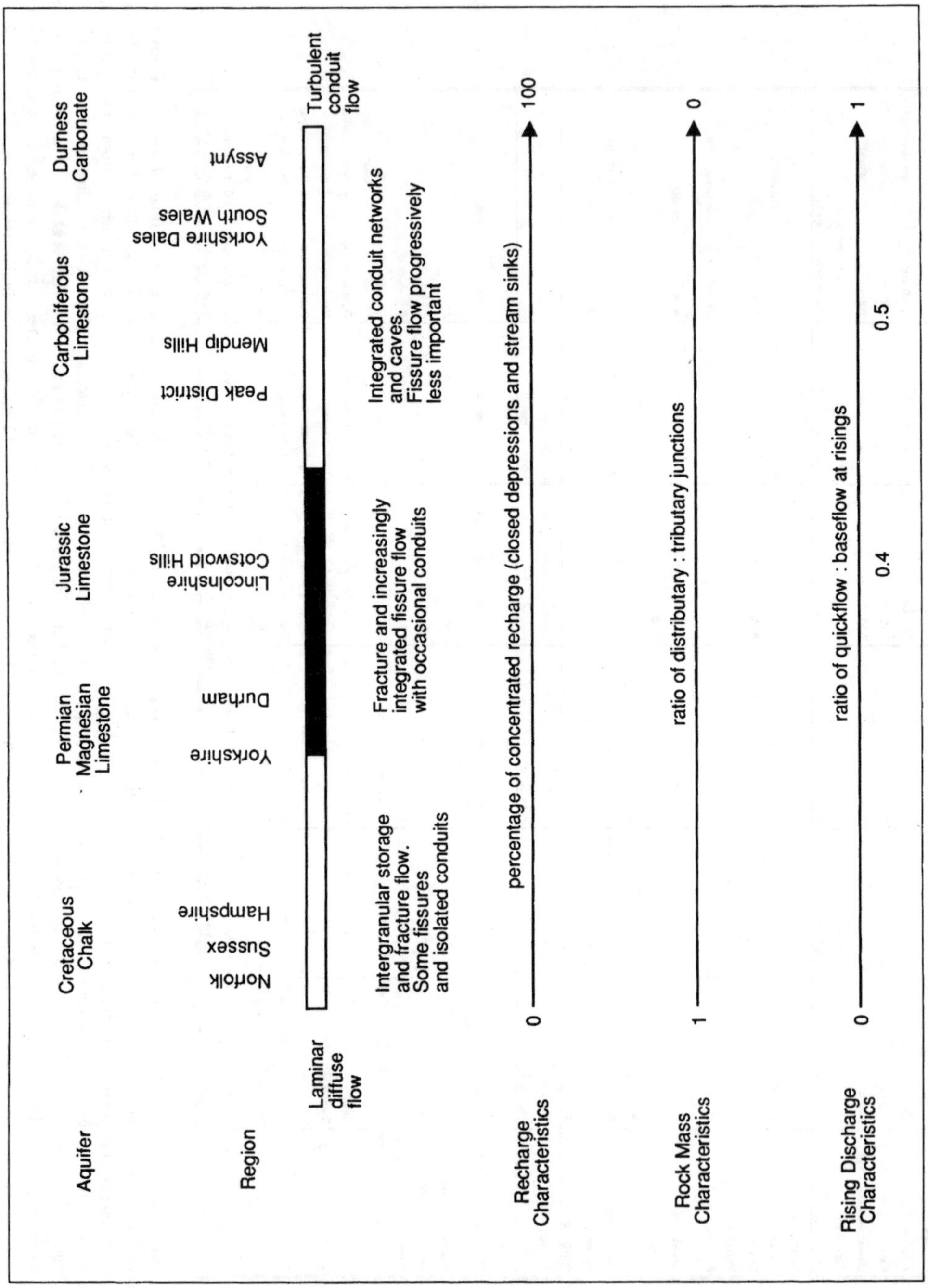

Fig. 6-2 The hydrological spectrum, wherein the British karst aquifers cover the full range of hydrological properties

absent in some areas. Similarly, parts of later major cycles may also be absent locally, reflecting the irregularity of transgressions and regressions against uneven pre-Carboniferous and intra-Dinantian erosion surfaces.

From the point of view of this review, the more important beds within the Carboniferous Limestone sequence are massive shelf deposits. These were laid down in relatively shallow water, and include rocks with a spectrum of grain sizes and locally variable chemistry, as a reflection of changes in conditions associated with the major and minor cyclicity. Also important in some areas are marginal deposits, broadly termed reefs, which generally mark a transition between the shelf and basinal depositional environments. These reefal limestones stand out, within the Carboniferous Limestone as a whole, as possessing a locally significant primary porosity and permeability.

The massive beds of high purity carbonate within the Carboniferous Limestone have long been renowned for the extensive systems of cave passages, commonly of great size, that they contain. Relatively recently, it has become apparent that many of these passages owe their origin, nature and location not just to the limestones which form the bulk of the sequence, but also to thinner interbeds of non-carbonate rock types, to less pure carbonate beds of several types, and to zones within the succession that underwent pene-contemporaneous (palaeo-)karstification (Lowe, 1992). Such aberrant beds or zones include sandstones, shales (sensu lato), coals and seatearths, a variety of volcanic rocks (particularly air-fall material) and evaporitic rocks, as well as the so-called palaeo-karstic surfaces that may be regionally extensive. Most, if not all, such rock types or horizons are commonly related to breaks between major cycles of deposition, reflecting episodes when conditions were temporarily sub-aerial, or when carbonate deposition was minimal and/or in a hypersaline environment. These and related beds appear to influence cave development(speleogenesis) physically and chemically. Their physical role has traditionally been related to non-carbonates acting as aquicludes within a succession where the carbonates are assumed to be aquifers. Though valid up to a point, this view may not be totally correct and it is clear that theoretically, prior to the establishment of dissolutional (cavernous) permeability, many non-carbonates present more viable aquifers than the dominant carbonates. Their chemical role, in providing a potential source of strong acids and/or physically soluble components to allow dissolution in rocks beyond the reach of meteoric carbonic acid, is of particular importance to the earliest, inception, phase of speleogenesis. Hence, these typical beds and zones within the carbonate succession have been termed inception horizons(Lowe, 1992).

Excluding the imposed cavernous permeability, the primary porosity (0.001 to 1.0%) and primary permeability (0.001 to 0.01m/day) of most of the pure carbonates are very low. The specific yield of the main body of the rock is therefore negligible. Groundwater flow within these beds is almost entirely along dissolutionally widened fissures (joints, faults and bedding planes). These enlarged fissures are mostly water-filled and only a small proportion of those above the water table are large enough for human examination. The initial fissures guided the establishment of complex, branching conduit systems that are unlike the fracture and conduit systems in British Permian and Mesozoic limestone in terms of their size, frequency, number of tributaries (common) and number of distributaries (much less common). Hence the conduits are more obviously karstic and in some cases they are analogous to "a surface stream with a roof". In most conduits, flow velocities are high (100 – 500 m/h) and vary with the nature of the underground drainage system and the hydrological state. Velocities usually increase with output discharge, the rate of increase being a function of the relative amounts of vadose and phreatic passage in the system. Vertical flow velocities through the unsaturated zone are much more variable but generally increase with the physical size of the route followed. Water flowing along fractures and discharging as vadose seeps in caves may take several months to travel from the surface whereas vadose fissure flow and shaft flow have velocities approaching those of underground streams.

Deep circulation of meteoric water in hydrothermal convection systems, that are thought to be primarily within the carbonate sequence, is thought to be responsible for the warm springs that issue through the Carboniferous Limestone in the Peak District (most notably at Buxton and Matlock) and at Bath (the highest temperature at 46℃), Bristol, and Taffs Well (near Cardiff). These are the only surface manifestations of geothermal energy in Great Britain.

Although Dinantian limestones crop out widely, many of the outcrops are scattered and broken and this has inhibited the development of large integrated underground drainage systems. The most important areas for both surface and underground karst landforms are the Yorkshire Dales, the Peak District, the Mendip Hills, South Wales (including the Forest of Dean) and North Wales. The five areas have similar climates and roughly comparable altitudes. However, they differ in their hydrogeology and hydrogeochemistry and in the development of cave systems as a result of different environments of deposition, tectonic history and the resulting geological structure, cover deposits and the local Pleistocene history of fluvial, periglacial and glacial stages. They have also had their drainage modified in differing ways and to differing degrees by human activities over the last 500 years. Detailed accounts of the limestone and caves of each area have been published (Smith, 1975; Ford, 1977, 1989; Waltham, 1974), the hydrogeological contrasts between them have been examined by Gunn (1992), and all the main caves and karst sites are included in a national review (Walthm et al., 1996). The present account draws on these to provide a brief summary of the contrasting karst environments.

6.2.1.1 *The Yorkshire Dales and Northern Pennines Karsts*

The Dinantian carbonate sequence in the region generally known as the Yorkshire Dales is bounded to the west by the Dent Fault, to the south and south-west by the Craven Fault system and to the east by overlying clastic rocks of Namurian age (Fig. 6-3). The southern watershed of Wensleydale is usually taken as the northern boundary as this marks the limit of the main outcrops of massive carbonates of Great Scar facies, the major limestone unit. The outcrop of this limestone has an irregular shape, broadly along the flanks of the major river valleys (the Dales) and wrapped around several inliers and outliers of impermeable rocks (Fig. 6-3). The region is situated on the south-west section of the Askrigg Block, an uplifted area that is largely fault bounded. The geological structure is relatively simple with a gentle dip to the north, interrupted by several very gentle folds with east-west axes, and a gentle easterly dip off the Pennine Anticline along the eastern outcrops. A 100 – 200 m thick sequence of massive limestones (the Great Scar facies) overlies an undulating impermeable basement of Lower Palaeozoic rocks, the surface of which has a relative relief of about 100 m. The limestones are succeeded by Yoredale facies rocks, up to 300 m thick and comprising cyclic repetitions (cyclothems) of limestone, sandstone and mudstone, with some thin coal seams. This sequence is in turn overlain by Namurian sandstones and shales of Millstone Grit facies. The limestone beds within the Yoredale sequence are generally thin and some are impure. Though they may locally contain large and significant underground drainage lines and complex network maze caves, the more important karst aquifers and major caves are developed within rocks of Great Scar facies.

Over 1400 known caves contain more than 300 km of mapped passages (Brook et al., 1988 – 1994). Most cave systems are a combination of active stream passages intersecting abandoned phreatic tunnels. The vadose stream caves descend vertical, fracture-guided shafts which link sub-horizontal canyon passages initiated along bedding planes and shale beds (Waltham, 1970; Waltham et al, 1981). Most streamways drain into active phreatic conduits, which drain partly up-dip to flooded resurgences. The high-level phreatic passages were abandoned following Pleistocene rejuvenations of the karst due to glacial deepening of the Dales. The Ease Gill Cave System has over 70 km of flooded conduits beneath the valley floor, taking drainage from sinks on the fells both sides of the Dale.

Ice sheets scoured the entire Yorkshire Dales karst, during probably four of the Pleistocene cold

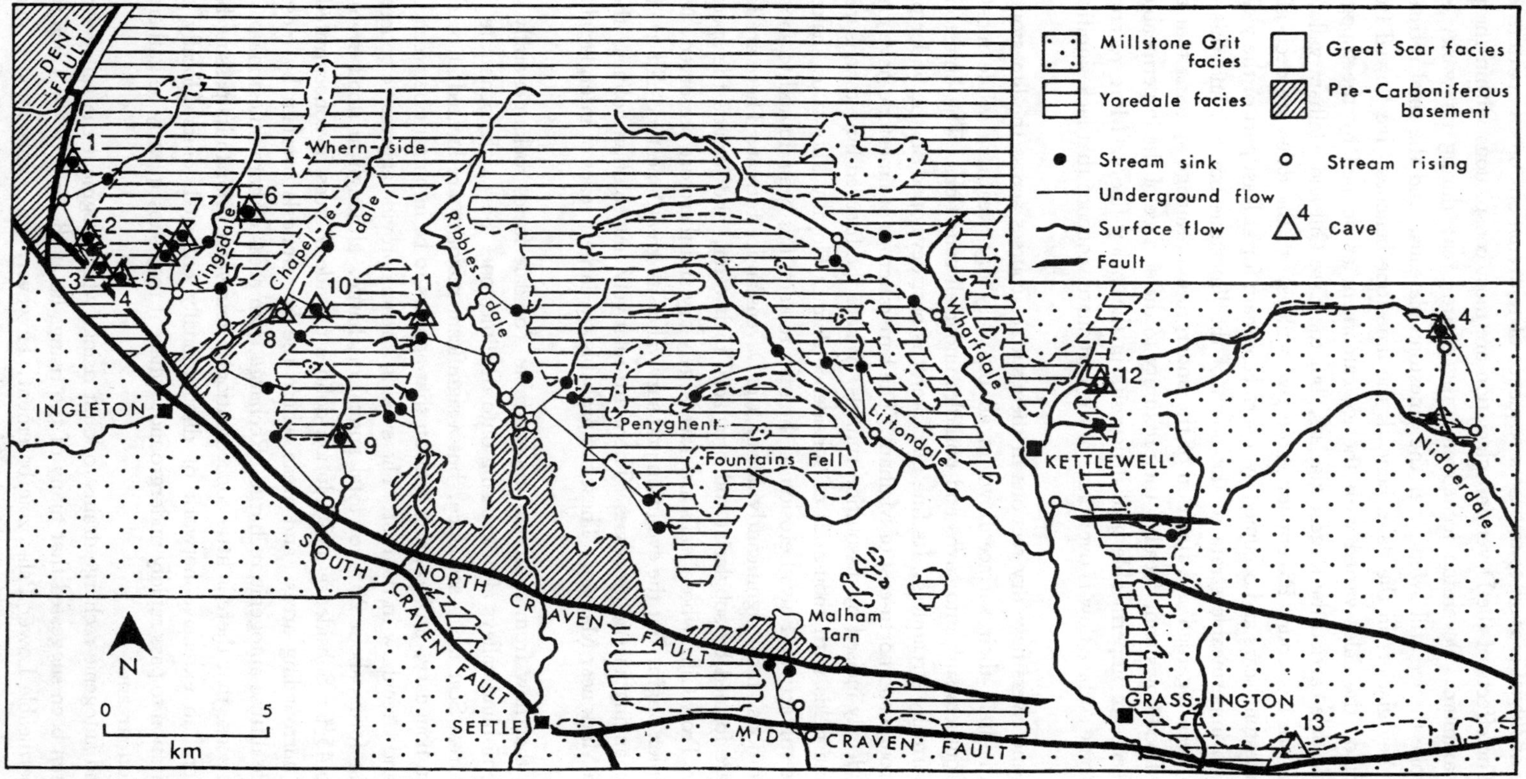

Fig. 6-3 The Yorkshire Dales karst. Only a few of the major caves are marked and numbered: 1 = Ease Gill Cave System; 2 = Lost Johns Cave; 3 = Ireby-Notts Pot; 4 = Marble Steps Pot; 5 = Keld Head; 6 = King Pot; 7 = West Kingsdale Cave System; 8 = God's Bridge; 9 Gaping Gill; 10 = Meregill Hole; 11 = Alum Pot; 12 = Dow cave

stages. They interrupted the karstic processes of warmer climates, and their phases of glacial erosion alternated with those of fluvial erosion to impose a sequence of rejuvenations on the pattern of geomorphic evolution. The effects of the Devensian glaciation are most conspicuous within the present landforms. At its maximum, Devensian ice covered the entire area; during its wane, summit nunataks appeared while the ice still swept over the limestone plateaus, and the final retreat stage saw only shrinking valley glaciers in the dales beneath the limestone benches. Ice flowed from the north, and its impact on the dales varied with the ice catchment as defined by the topography; Wharfedale and Ribblesdale carried the largest glaciers, but the Ease Gill and Malham valleys were both sheltered from major ice scour. Except for those two valleys, all the dales are deep glaciated troughs flanked by limestone scars and occupied by a surface stream for at least part of the year. The streams all originate on impermeable strata to the north of the limestone outcrop and this surface flow has traditionally been regarded as a function of the underground drainage systems that are unable to accommodate flood flows and, locally, the proximity to the surface of the impermeable basement and/or the presence of impermeable glacial deposits in the valley floors. More recent views suggest that at least some surface flow is over parts of the carbonate sequence that lack significant inception horizons.

All the streams and rivers have dry sections in their surface courses across the limestone. The Ribble and Wharfe maintain their surface flows in all but very dry weather, while most small streams off the shale outliers sink into caves and potholes under all conditions. The limestone high ground is therefore normally streamless. Its fine glaciokarst is best developed on the wider plateaus south-east of Ingleborough and north-east of Malham. The bare outcrops of limestone have great expanses of pavement, deeply incised by dissolution runnels. Where the fissured limestone is veneered with glacial till, doline fields with thousands of subsidence dolines (locally known as shakeholes) have formed, and are still active. Fluvial erosion of the mature karst has been limited to short periods of periglacial conditions, most significantly during the Devensian ice retreat. There are few dry valleys, but some were formed by subglacial and proglacial meltwater, and include the spectacular gorges of Gordale and Trow Gill, whose walls are now largely dry and therefore preserved. Malham Cove has a more complex origin, but the evolution and survival of its great limestone cliff are further consequences of the changing karstic processes. There are relatively few solution dolines, the most notable being at High Mark near Malham. These are probably the largest relics of interglacial karstic development.

Surface streams that flow from overlying impermeable Yoredale facies rocks generally sink at the end of blind or semi-blind valleys after crossing onto the limestone. Few sinks penetrate the uppermost beds of the Great Scar facies sequence, but a significant majority are located at or close to the Brigantian/Asbian boundary, an inception horizon that appears to be important between Casterton Fell in the west and Greenhow in the east. The sinking streams provide aggressive concentrated allogenic recharge that forms about 20% of total annual discharge, although in flood events they may contribute up to 45%. Subsidence and solution dolines provide sources of concentrated autogenic recharge. The surrounding areas, and areas where the limestone is overlain by mesotropic brown earths, provide diffuse autogenic recharge. Recharge from areas of bare limestone pavement is also diffuse, in the sense that there is little concentration of rainwater prior to its passing beneath the surface. However, an extensive network of dissolutionally enlarged joints (locally termed grikes) allows precipitation to pass rapidly underground, where it may subsequently be gathered into fast-flowing percolation streams.

The allogenic and autogenic recharge drains to karst risings which augment the valley-streams. Previously, it has often been suggested that many of the risings lie at the base of the Dinantian sequence upon the impermeable Lower Palaeozoic basement. However, this explanation is generally inadequate as several major risings are associated with widespread inception horizons. For example,

Leck Beck Head and Keld and Malham Cave risings lie close to the boundary between the Malham Formation and the underlying Kilnsey Formation. In addition, cave passages visible at risings such as White Scar Cave and at the Brants Gill Head and Douk Ghyll risings in Ribblesdale appear to have been conceived upon inception horizons above the basement level before cutting down to, and locally into, the impermeable beds.

The chemistry of water emerging from karst risings in the Yorkshire Dales reflects the mode of recharge and the nature of the flow route followed. Concentrated allogenic recharge from streams which originate on rocks of Yoredale and Millstone Grit facies is usually aggressive, with a low calcium concentration. As the streams move through the limestone, calcium concentrations increase rapidly and vary directly with flow-through (and hence rock-contact) times. As the limestones are largely free-draining, these times are generally short and this is one reason why the mean calcium concentrations at major risings in the Dales (8 – 27 mg/l) are less than at risings in the other main Carboniferous Limestone karsts. Where the allogenic catchment includes Yoredale facies limestones the calcium concentrations of the sinking streams are higher and there is proportionately less increase along cave streams. The soils developed on glacial drift deposits are poorly drained, acidic, and probably have low soil carbon dioxide concentrations due to restricted biological activity.

The Yorkshire Dales karst owes its spectacular geomorphology to the combination of so many landforms: the sinks that take all the drainage, the expanses of pavement, the long scars, the deep gorges and the innumerable dolines. The area is strictly a glaciokarst, but Ingleborough and Malham provide the finest limestone landscapes in Great Britain.

Thinner limestones within a mixed Yoredale facies sequence extend to the north, but have distinctly different styles of geomorphology and hydrogeology within the karst of the Northern Pennines. Low white scars, plucked clean by the glaciers, fringe narrow rock terraces which almost trace the contours in most of the northern Dales. Many of the limestone pavements are truly dramatic, and form huge expanses of bare rock wherever the stronger limestone beds were exposed in the right attitudes to be stripped clean by the Pleistocene glaciers. Within the Northern Pennines, the morphologies of the caves are a function of the thin limestones which house them. These limestones are interbedded with clastic sedimentary rocks of low permeability, and therefore formed confined or artesian aquifers, before they were drained and rejuvenated as valley floors were excavated through them. Under these conditions of slow phreatic flow, the systems of tectonic joints were opened by solution to form networks of fissure caves. Developed to maturity, these form spectacular maze systems, and Knock Fell Caverns is Britain's largest known maze cave. The Northern Pennines karst also has many vadose stream caves, beneath the hillsides, beneath some valley floors, and passing beneath some interfluves.

6.2.1.2 *The Peak District Karst*

In contrast to the other British Carboniferous Limestone regions 450 km^2 limestone outcrop in the Peak District forms a compact area some 40km long (north-south) and up to 20km wide, surrounded by lithologies that support significant surface drainage, Triassic sandstones to the south and Namurian Millstone Grit facies rocks elsewhere (Fig. 6-4). Further contrasts with other regions are provided by the variable thickness of the limestone sequence, which ranges from around 200 to over 1800m and by the geological structure. The limestones have been folded such that dips of up to 20° are common in shelf facies rocks, with much steeper dips in rocks of reef facies. They are highly varied lithologically, and show evidence of rapid vertical and lateral facies changes. Within the Dinantian succession, a number of potential inception horizons are presented by palaeokarsts and regressive beds at cycle boundaries, some of which are marked by tuff or lava horizons, and thinner volcaniclastic clay beds known locally as 'wayboards'.

The majority of the Peak District karst is devoid of surface drainage, and the Dove and the

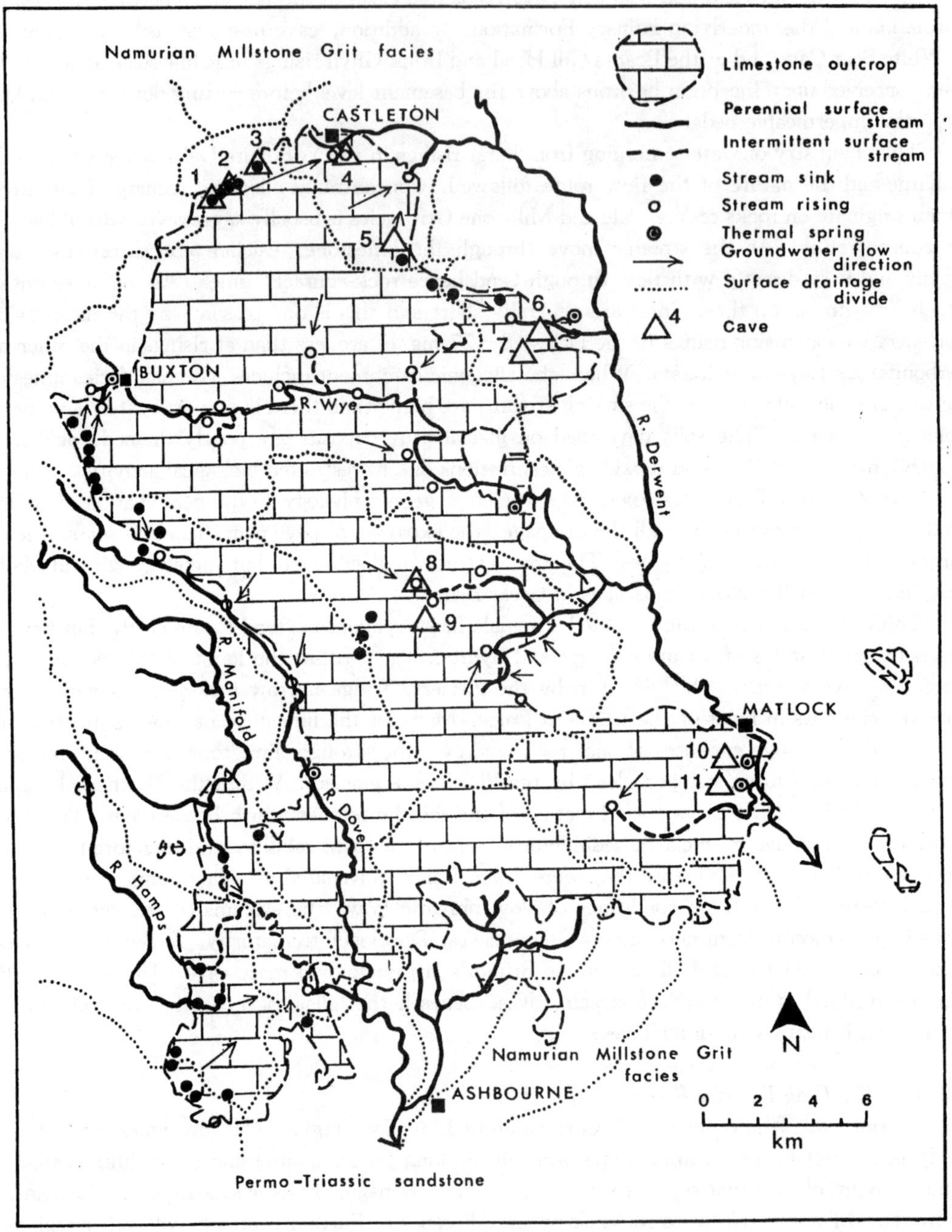

Fig. 6-4 The Peak District karst. The main caves are marked and numbered: 1 = Perryfoot Swallet; 2 = P8 Cave; 3 = Giants Hole; 4 = Peak Cavern; 5 = Bagshaw Cavern; 6 = Carlswark Cave; 7 = Waterfall Swallet; 8 = Lathkill Head Cave; 9 = Cales Dale Caves; 10 = Masson Hill Cavern; 11 = Devonshire Cavern

Wye are the only perennial rivers that flow on limestone for a significant distance. Despite the absence of present day surface drainage the limestone massif is essentially a fluviokarst dissected by a complex network of normally dry valleys. These are thought to have originated on an impermeable cover and been superimposed onto the limestone. Their desiccation was probably a result of a gradual karstification of drainage, aided by lowering of the regional water table as a consequence of downcutting by major rivers. Although the entire karst was probably overrun by ice during at least one glacial advance. Quaternary glaciations are not thought to have played a significant part in the incision of major river valleys. However, the smaller dry valleys would have been reactivated when the ground was frozen under periglacial conditions during the Pleistocene cold periods. The limestone surface is pitted by closed depressions, some of which were either modified or created by lead miners. The most common natural depressions are solution dolines and subsidence dolines that occur mainly where the limestone is overlain by thick superficial loess and other drift deposits. The average size and density of depressions is less than in most other major British Carboniferous Limestone karsts and they are generally only details within the fluviokarst landscape.

Limestone pavements are rare in the Peak District; those that originated from the Anglian glaciation have either been destroyed by later frost action or have been buried beneath younger soils. Many of the deeper dry valleys are lined by rock scars marking the outcrops of the stronger limestone beds and especially the massive reef units. Rocky tors have formed due to Pleistocene frost action in some of the dolomite outcrops (Ford, 1963). Most of the karst lies under a veneer of soil, derived from frost action and loess accumulation, both largely during the Devensian periglacial conditions. Superficial material on the steeper valley sides is commonly solifluncted, and soil creep has initiated the formation of extensive areas of terracettes. Only isolated patches of an initially widespread Anglian glacial till have survived the erosional regime that has prevailed in the area since the ice cover decayed.

Most of the limestone outcrop stands topographically higher than the surrounding outcrops of younger shales, which are more easily eroded. Surface drainage is therefore predominantly towards the shale, and allogenic waters draining onto the limestone are limited in extent. Only where escarpments of Namurian Millstone Grit strata are close enough to the karst and high enough, do surface streams cross the shale and sink into the limestone. The best example is Rushup Edge, from where thirteen streams drain mainly via sinks in marginal reef limestones into the Peak-Speedwell Cave System, which is characterised by large and mature conduits (Gunn, 1991). Eight of the stream sinks are associated with accessible influent caves including the 240m deep Giant-Oxlow system. The influent caves drain to flooded conduits (sumps), the deepest of which are at a similar altitude to the input sumps in Speedwell Cavern. Cave divers have explored these flooded conduits from both their up and downstream ends to depths of up to 45m. Despite the flooded sections, flow-through times for at least part of the drainage are rapid, and this is the only basin in the Peak District that is similar hydrologically to those in the Yorkshire Dales.

The Bradwell, Stoney Middleton and Wye basins also border on higher impermeable strata from which streams of aggressive water flow and sink soon after crossing onto the limestone. However, diffuse recharge through the cover of soil and superficial deposits dominates across most of the limestone outcrop and consequently, there are relatively few open sinkhole caves in the Peak District karst. With no basement rocks exposed, many of the resurgences are vauclusian, offering only difficult access to submerged passages, and open cave passages at resurgences are few in number. Over much of the Peak District, the underground drainage pattern is less well known than in the other Carboniferous Limestone regions, because water tracing experiments cannot easily be undertaken in an area largely devoid of surface drainage. In addition, the natural drainage of much of the central area has been altered substantially since the Eighteenth Century by the driving of mine levels (soughs) to de-water the limestones and facilitate the extraction of lead and zinc ores. In some cases this has resulted in the drying up of surface streams for all or part of the year.

A special feature of the Peak District caves is their relationship to the hydrothermal mineral deposits in the limestone. Some palaeokarst features pre-date the Permo-Triassic mineralisation, which has subsequently influenced the Tertiary and Pleistocene development of the modern caves and karst; large dissolutional rifts lie along the mineral veins (the rakes) in many cave systems. In the Matlock area, caves intersect and follow some of the mineral ore bodies, where mining has reexposed some of the palaeokarst features (Ford, 1984). Containing sediment sequences that include fluvioglacial material more than 730 000 years old (Noel, 1987), the Masson Hill caves offer fragmentary evidence covering an exceptionally long timespan of karst evolution. A second equally long record of Pleistocene events is provided by the relict caves and sediment fills exposed by limestone quarrying in Eldon Hill.

The geochemistry of limestone groundwaters in the Peak District has been studied by Edmunds (1971) and by Christopher and Wilcock(1981). Solute concentrations at risings are generally higher than those measured in Yorkshire, due to the greater importance of autogenic inputs; greater water-rock contact times and greater soil CO_2 concentrations resulting from higher soil microbiological activity.

6.2.1.3 *The Mendip Hills Karst*

South of Bristol, Dinantian age limestones crop out along a 48km strip that extends from the inliers of Brean Down and Bleadon Hill, through the Mendip Hills proper to the Frome inlier (Fig. 6-5). The main outcrop is a compact plateau that is thought to be largely a subaerial erosion surface of late Pliocene age. The plateau is up to 10km wide and rises abruptly to 225 – 255m above sea level from flatter areas, at 0 – 30m, floored by less resistant Mesozoic strata. The structure of the region is complex, as Hercynian folding has produced four periclines arranged en echelon from WNW to ESE. The oldest rocks (Silurian shales and volcanic rocks, and Devonian Old Red Sandstone) crop out in the fold cores, forming low, whale-backed hills that rise to 60m above the limestone plateau surface. The limestones dip away from the fold cores at angles between 20° and 40° on the south limbs to more than 70° on the north limbs, which are overturned locally.

Like the Peak District, the Mendip Hills are dominantly fluviokarstic. The limestone plateau is devoid of surface streams, but dissected by a network of dry valleys that are active only under extreme flood conditions and are thought to have been superimposed from an impermeable cover, followed by gradual karstification of drainage, with re-activation under Pleistocene periglacial conditions. However, unlike the Peak District, the valleys drain into deep gorges that may represent overdeepened rejuvenated sections of the drainage network formed under periglacial conditions. The valleys are also distinguished from those in other British karst areas by the large numbers of closed depressions located in their floors. Another similarity between the Peak District and Mendip karsts is that lead mining has created anthropogenic depressions and modified natural depressions, making it difficult to discern their origin. However, most appear to have been formed by the concentration of dissolutional activity at the junctions of lines of structural weakness. Lead mining activity did not modify the underground drainage but a more recent anthropogenic activity, limestone quarrying, has already produced some changes and will have an even greater impact in the future if more limestone is extracted from beneath the water table. In common with the Peak District, the majority of the annual recharge to the Mendip karst aquifers is from autogenic recharge which occurs via closed depressions and by infiltration through the cover of soil and superficial materials. it accounts for about 95% of the annual discharge from risings for the Mendip Hills as a whole. Allogenic recharge is provided by streams that originate on the Devonian and Silurian rocks, and sink after crossing onto the limestone. Stanton and Smart(1981) reported that by 1980, some 90 streams had been proved by water tracing to feed to one or more of the 51 risings which emerge from the limestone. The tracing experiments have revealed straight line flow velocities from stream-sinks to risings of 0.5 – 21 km/d with a mean of 6.3 km/d, providing ample evidence of a turbulent flow regime in conduits. Repeated tracing experiments have also shown that velocities vary in proportion to discharge at the ris-

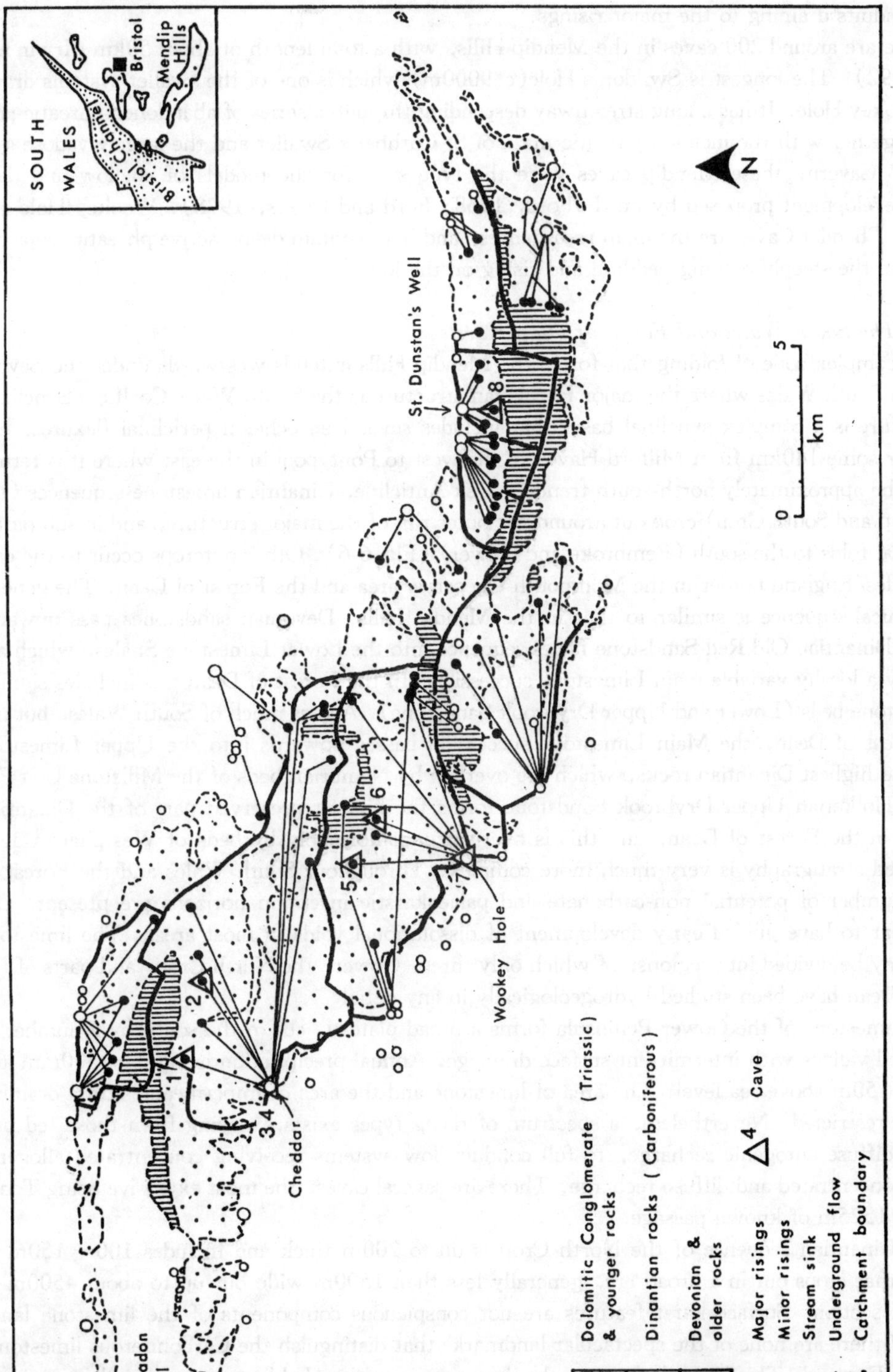

Fig 6-5 The Mendip Hills karst. The main caves are marked and numbered: 1 = GB Cavern; 2 = Longwood Swallet; 3 = Gough's Cave; 4 = Cheddar Rising; 5 Swildon's Hole; 6 = St Cuthbert's Swallet; 7 = Wookey Hole; 8 = Withybrook Slocker and Shatter Cave

ing. Hence, the general pattern is of sinking streams feeding into conduits that converge to form master conduits draining to the major risings.

There are around 200 caves in the Mendip Hills, with a total length of about 50km (Irwin and Jarrat, 1992). The longest is Swildon's Hole(c.9000m) which is one of the swallet systems draining to Wookey Hole. It has a long streamway descending through a series of abandoned phreatic passages. Together with the inclined phreatic maze of St Cuthber's Swallet and the largely vadose system of GB Cavern, these Mendip caves were the type sites for the models of shallow and deep phreatic development proposed by Ford (Ford, 1968; Ford and Ewers, 1978). Wookey Hole and the nearby Cheddar Caves are the main resurgences, and both contain deep, active phreatic loops descending on the steeply dipping bedding and rising on the joint.

6.2.1.4 *The South Wales and Forest of Dean Karsts*

The complex zone of folding that forms the Mendip Hills extends westwards under the Severn Estuary to South Wales where the major Hercynian structure is the South Wales Coalfield Syncline. The structure is a complex synclinal basin that includes several en echelon periclinal flexures, extending for some 140km from Milford Haven in the west to Pontypool in the east where it is terminated by the approximately north-south trending Usk Anticline. Dinantian limestone sequences (the North Crop and South Crop) crop out around the outer rim of the major structure, and in sub-parallel periclinal folds to the south (Pembroke and Gower) (Fig.6-6). Other outcrops occur to the east on the Wales/England border in the Monmouth-Chepstow area and the Forest of Dean. The general stratigraphical sequence is similar to that in the Mendip Hills. Devonian sandstones pass upwards through a Dinantian Old Red Sandstone facies sequence into the Lower Limestone Shales, which are overlain by a locally variable main Limestone succession. In the Forest of Dean this includes significant sandstone beds (Lower and Upper Drybrook Sandstone). Across much of South Wales, but not in the Forest of Dean, the Main Limestone succession passes upwards into the Upper Limestone Shales, the highest Dinantian rocks, which are overlain by Namurian beds of the Millstone Grit Facies. The Holkerian Upper Drybrook Sandstone forms the highest preserved part of the Dinantian succession in the Forest of Dean, and this is overlain unconformably by beds of Westphalian age. The detailed stratigraphy is very much more complex. Throughout South Wales and the Forest of Dean, a number of potential non-carbonate and palaeokarstic inception horizons are present, and these appear to have guided early development of dissolutional voids in most areas. The limestone outcrop may be divided into regions, of which only three: Gower, the North Crop, and parts of the Forest of Dean have been studied hydrogeologically in any detail.

The limestone of the Gower Peninsula forms a broad plateau, cut in the south by a number of well defined valleys with intermittent surface drainage. Annual precipitation is 1000 – 1500mm and altitude <150m above sea level. The area of limestone and the area of impermeable strata draining onto it are restricted. Nevertheless, a spectrum of rising types exists, varying from those fed primarily by diffuse autogenic recharge, to full conduit flow systems receiving concentrated allogenic and both concentrated and diffuse recharge. There are several caves, the most extensive being Tooth Cave with 1525m of known passage.

The Dinantian sequence of the North Crop is up to 200m thick and includes 100 – 150m of limestone that crops out in a broad arc, generally less than 1500m wide but up to about 4500m in the central section. Surface karst features are not conspicuous components of the limestone landscape, and there are none of the spectacular landmarks that distinguish the Carboniferous limestones in much of England. This is partly because the limestone is surrounded by topographically prominent sandstones that lie stratigraphically both above and below. Much of the limestone outcrop is little more than a line of scars backed by a narrow dip-slope and overlooked by the scarp face of the strong Namurian Basal Grit. The limestone outcrops were subjected to glaciation during the Devensian, but

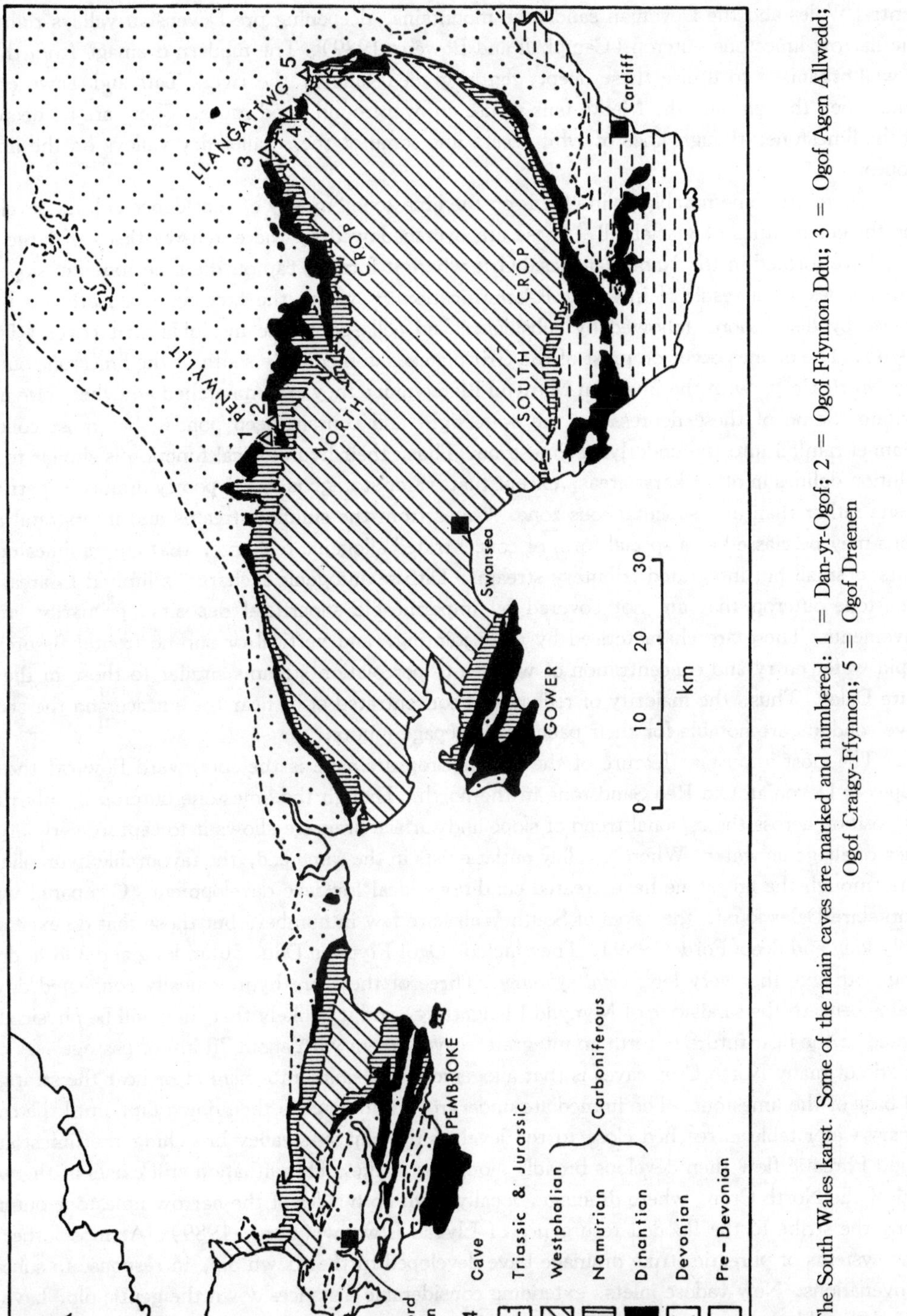

Fig. 6-6 The South Wales karst. Some of the main caves are marked and numbered: 1 = Dan-yr-Ogof; 2 = Ogof Ffynnon Ddu; 3 = Ogof Agen Allwedd; 4 = Ogof Craig-y-Ffynnon; 5 = Ogof Draenen

limestone pavements are developed on only a few of the interfluves where the dip is low; much of the karst is now veneered with till, and limestone pavements are not extensive. Ice moved south from central Wales and the Devonian sandstone mountains, deepening pre-Devensian valleys right across the narrow limestone outcrop (Campbell and Bowen, 1989). The modern drainage from the north is well organised to utilise these deep, gently graded valleys; the rivers Taff and Tawe cross the limestone, though only the Mellte fails to use an overground flood route. There are no deep gorges in the limestone, though lines of white scars line some of the smaller dry valleys on the limestone slopes.

There are some notable doline fields on the limestone, mostly of subsidence dolines developed in the thicker mantles of glacial till. These are overshadowed by the extensive fields of large dolines that have formed in the Namurian Basal Grit where it forms a cap on the limestone dip slopes. The Grit dolines are a result of interstratal karstification — where the limestone beneath has been removed by dissolution, followed by subsidence and collapse of the insoluble Grit cover (Thomas, 1974). The dolines occur on most of the Grit plateaus immediately south of the limestone outcrop of the North Crop, with the finest on Mynydd Llangynidr; they are unmatched anywhere else in Great Britain. Some of these depressions are watertight and contain deep ponds, but most collect and channel rainfall into the underlying limestone. Thus, their hydrological function is similar to that of solution dolines in other karst areas, except that water storage is in the poorly drained superficial deposits rather than in a subcutaneous zone. Water from the sinking streams and interstratal depressions may be classed as a special form of concentrated allogenic recharge, that enters limestone conduits as small but integrated tributary streams. Diffuse autogenic recharge is limited to areas of the limestone outcrop that are not covered by impermeable superficial deposits, primarily limestone pavements. These are characterised by close jointing, and vertical or sub-horizontal fissures allow rapid water entry and concentration of water into percolation streams similar to those in the Yorkshire Dales. Thus, the majority of recharge is concentrated at or near the surface and the accessible cave conduits are notable for their paucity of seepage inputs.

The most important feature of the North Crop drainage is the southward flow off the higher slopes of Devonian Old Red Sandstone in the north. Though the limestone outcrop is only narrow, its position across the regional trend of slope and surface drainage allows it to capture very large supplies of allogenic water. Where a valley outlet exists in the same bed, the favourable hydraulic gradients through the limestone have created conditions ideal for cave development. Compared with the Yorkshire Dales karst, the caves of South Wales are few in number, but those that do exist are notably long and deep(Ford, 1989). They include Ogof Ffynnon Ddu, 50km long and 308 m deep, along with six other very long cave systems. Three of these are hydrologically connected down dip drains beneath the sandstone of Mynydd Llangattwg, and it is likely that they will be physically connected in the near future to form an integrated cave system with about 70 km of passages. A characteristic of many North Crop caves is that allogenic water sinks into them at or near the stratigraphical base of the limestone. The immediate underground drainage is then down dip, until the contemporary water table is reached close to the level of the adjacent valley breaching the limestone outcrop. Phreatic flow then develops broadly along the strike. This situation still exists at the western end of the North Crop, where drainage, locally from both sides of the narrow limestone outcrop, is along the strike to the flooded resurgence of Llygad Llwchwr(Ford, 1989). At most other sites, new systems of phreatic strike drainage have developed further down dip, in response to subsequent rejuvenations. New vadose inlets, extending considerable distances down the gentle dip, have intersected the old phreatic trunk caves, creating the very extensive passage networks which give these Welsh caves their great length.

Most of the North Crop caves can be ascribed to one of three broad types, which are characterised according to the relationship between the narrow limestone outcrop and the local topography.

Valley floor sites with major stream sinks include the caves of Porth-yr-Ogof and the Little Neath River where large passages are developed beneath or close to the normally dry surface valleys. Where streams sink into the limestone outcrops high on the major interfluves, caves develop down the hydraulic gradient and obliquely to the adjacent valley floor; the caves of the Swansea Valley are of this type, and the contrasting patterns of Ogof Ffynnon Ddu and Dan-yr-Ogof reflect a relationship between geological structure and valley orientation. The third cave type underlies the gently sloping Grit plateaus, and carries drainage from sinks in the marginal limestone outcrop on the higher, up-dip side through to risings in the lower side; the caves of Llangattwg have this pattern, where the lower edge of the gentle dipslope has been trimmed by recession of the Clydach Gorge. The sheer size of the North Crop caves give them a special place in any review of Great Britain's karst. They also have an exceptional diversity of passage morphology and depositional detail, and their long Pleistocene histories are recorded in their complex passage networks.

Though similar stratigraphically to the main South Wales karst, the Forest of Dean is a distinct structural unit. Most of the area is an asymmetrical synclinal basin, formed by the superimposition of folds generated during mid-Carboniferous and Hercynian tectonic episodes. The centre of the basin contains effectively impermeable Westphalian Coal Measures, which lie unconformably upon the Dinantian Upper Drybrook Sandstone. Towards the south the main basinal structure breaks down into several component north-south folds. Dips here and on the western side of the basin are relatively gentle, contrasting with the very steep dips along much of the eastern edge of the area. The 'Main Limestone' (comprising Lower Dolomite, Crease Limestone and Whitehead Limestone) sequence crop out around the rim of the basin. Its maximum thickness is about 150m, and it includes at least three significant inception horizons, one within the Lower Dolomite, one at the base of the Crease Limestone and the third at the top of the same formation. The latter two correspond to non-sequences at major cycle boundaries. Much of the underground drainage within the Main Limestone of the western area flows via an integrated multi-branched conduit system to emerge at the Slaughter Rising, on the east bank of the River Wye. About 11 km of passages have been explored in the associated cave system. South of Symonds Yat the Wye has incised a deep gorge, cutting the full Dinantian sequence in the core of Worcester Syncline. The Slaughter Rising lies on the fold axis and it is possible that at times of high discharge underground flow emerges in the river bed. In drought leakage from the river into synclinal core conduits within the Lower dolomite is equally probable. No significant karstification has been found on the steeply-dipping eastern rim of the basin, though once-extensive bodies of iron ore within the carbonate succession are believed to have been emplaced at least partly within an ancient pre-existing cavern network guided by the Crease Limestone inception horizons.

South of the main basin, the major cave system which drains to the Otter Hole resurgence lies on the west side of the Wye near Chepstow. Otter Hole appears to be the present downstream end of an integrated cave system partially analogous to the Slaughter system to the north. Much of the Otter Hole main drain is guided essentially by a single inception horizon within the Lower Dolomite, as are the main drains in the Slaughter System, and both drainage networks are partially related to the axial zones of plunging synclines.

6.2.1.5 *The North Wales Karsts*

Outcrops of Dinantian carbonate rocks extend across North Wales from Anglesey, in the west, to the eastern side of the Vale of Clwyd, and thence southwards towards Shropshire (Fig. 6-1). As in South Wales, sequences vary in detail and thickness from area to area. A traditional sub-division on the basis of gross lithology comprises Basement Beds, overlain in order by Lower Brown Limestone, Middle White Limestone, Upper Grey Limestone and Sandy Limestone. Generally the beds dip gently, though locally moderately steeply, on the limbs of major regional folds. Large scale faulting has led to the off-setting and separation of once continuous outcrops, and many lesser faults, joints and mineral veins are present.

Except where contacts are faulted, the carbonate sequences lie unconformably upon impermeable Lower Palaeozoic rocks and pass upwards into clastic-dominated late Brigantian to Namurian rocks. Palaeokarstic surfaces (including major neptunian infills) and beds of non-carbonate rock occur throughout the succession, and some appear to have functioned as inception horizons. The entire extent of the Dinantian outcrops was glaciated at least once during the Pleistocene. Thick deposits of till and gravelly drift, commonly with younger peat deposits filling hollows, overlie much of the limestone. The carbonate sequences are heavily mineralised locally and there has been much mining of lead, zinc, copper and iron. As in the Forest of Dean, it appears that some mineral emplacement, particularly that of the iron ore deposits near Dyserth, was into pre-existing(palaeo-) karstic cavities. Some mine workings encountered extensive natural caverns, and deep drainage tunnels have permanently dewatered large, naturally phreatic, cave systems. Ogof Hesp Alyn and Ogof Hen Ffynhonau are spectacular phreatic caves whose passages are accessible since they were totally drained less than 100 years ago (Appleton, 1989). At Minera, north of Llangollen, the rejuvenated drainage system including the caves of Ogof Llyn Parc and Ogof Llyn Du has a fine sequence of abandoned phreatic strike passages and downdip canyons in a dipping limestone sequence.

The types and extent of surface karst features are variable, depending upon the level within the carbonate sequence that is exposed, the local lithology and structure and the nature of the overlying superficial deposits. Between Minera and Llangollen, where the carbonates are within a classic escarpment feature locally complicated by faults and mineral veins, lines of solution dolines mark the outcrop of clastic beds within the sequence. Many such dolines extend downwards as narrow dissolutional shafts, almost certainly reflecting an enhanced, strong acid, aggressiveness of the drainage from the overlying 'shales' acting down joint fissure intersections. More rarely in this and other areas, relatively small surface streams are swallowed by similar joint guided holes, but only a relatively small amount of insurgence cave passage has been explored.

Dry and blind valleys are common landforms in most areas. Some are greatly overdeepened and 'straightened' by the effects of late Devensian glacial meltwater. Other valleys maintain surface flows throughout the year, even across bare and seemingly well-fissured limestone. This probably reflects the erosional immaturity of valley floors that were scoured and exposed only at the end of the last glaciation. A corollary to the drainage of previously flooded phreatic cavities by mine workings is that several formerly major natural resurgences have been effectively abandoned by normal flow. Modern drainage is captured and channelled via man-made routes such as the Park and Deep day levels in the Minera area and the Sea Level Tunnel of the Halkyn area. The latter drainage level captured water that formerly emerged at St Winifride's holy well. A flow of around 300l/s in 'average' conditions can grow to several times that amount in wet weather as can the combined normal flow of the Minera levels at about 150 l/s (Appleton, 1989).

Although there are some sinking streams, autogenic recharge dominates in most areas and as a result solute concentrations at risings are generally high(c. 300 mg/l $CaCO_3$). Tufa is deposited downstream of a rising at Dyserth Falls, Clwyd and at Caerwys extensive relict tufa deposits up to 6m thick have been partially removed by quarrying.

6.2.2 *Permian Magnesian Limestone of Northern England*

Carbonate rocks of Permian age, interbeded with evaporite rich beds and mudstones, crop out in a narrow strip to the east of the Pennine Hills from Nottinghamshire to County Durham (Fig. 6-1). The sequence, commonly referred to as the magnesian Limestone, lies unconformably upon a peneplain of Carboniferous rocks and passes eastwards, in the direction of dip, beneath thick sandstones and mudstones of Triassic age. Much of the Permian outcrop is covered by glacial deposits of variable thickness. The hydrogeology of the magnesian Limestone is uniform along its outcrop. Groundwater yields are a function of the degree of fissuring and faulting, and recharge varies with the thickness of the superficial deposits. In County Durham it is a productive aquifer as there is an extensive fissure permeability and the yields from some individual fissures are comparable with those of conduit flow risings in the Carboniferous Limestone. Over the limited area where the limestone is unconfined it receives recharge from closed depressions and by leakage from stream beds. Water table conditions prevail in this area, but elsewhere the aquifer is confined and commonly artesian. Transmissivities are generally around 300 m^2/d but can exceed 1500 m^2/d.

Many small caves are known within the Cadeby and Brotherton formations (Lower and Upper Magnesian Limestones), but most are tectonic rather than karstic in origin. However, some, such as Farnham Cave near Knaresborough(Lowe, 1978), are undergoing dissolutional modification and a few are entirely dissolutional, though their location is clearly guided by fissure weaknesses associated with gentle folding. A shallow gorge through Creswell Crags, on the Nottinghamshire/Derbyshire border, has five caves exposed in its walls, all of which are truncated fragments of phreatic rifts and mazes. The gorge is a palaeofracture that seems to pre-date mid-Permian Marls and the caves may be part of a Permian intraformational karst. Stalagmite layers within them have been dated back as far as 300 ka(Rowe et al., 1989), and the clastic sediments have yielded important Devensian and earlier animal and human remains (Jenkinson, 1984, 1989). The site is best known as the type locality of the Cresswellian culture, which occupied the cave in the late Devensian interstadial.

Surface karst features are to be found along the entire Permian outcrop and are generally limited to closed depressions and dry valleys. Lines of depressions crossing the Brotherton Formation outcrop south-east of Ledsham in Yorkshire were reported to indicate the course of underground streams fed from swallow holes. Water-worn passages were visible in one such depression. Elsewhere in this general area, karst features have been reported affecting the exposed succession, and palaeokarstic features that may influence underground water movement are also known within the rocks. The Knaresborough Gorge contains some large active tufa screens.

6.2.3 *Devonian Carbonates of Southwest-England*

Massive, highly fossiliferous mid Devonian limestones are present across part of South Devon (Fig. 6-1). Relatively thin, but laterally persistent beds of limestone within the Ilfracombe Beds of North Devon and Somerset probably correlate with the thicker limestones to the south. All these Devonian rocks are lightly metamorphosed, and some of the limestones are known commercially as marbles, though their scale of recrystallisation has not been enough to destroy their fossil shell structures. Surface karst landforms are insignificant in the fluvial landscapes, even on the largest outcrops that form large coastal headlands. However, over 50 caves have been explored in the South Devon limestones and the Baker's Pit System and Pridhamsleigh Cavern are of significant length and size. Berry Head has many small caves formed at the marine/freshwater interface during high interglacial sea levels of the Pleistocene (Proctor, 1988; Proctor and Smart, 1991). Kent's Cavern at Torquay has about 400m of large, relict, phreatic passages forming a maze now truncated in the wall of the Ilsham Valley (Proctor and Smart, 1989). These contain thick clastic sequences interbedded with stalagmite floors, of which the lower one is over 350000 years old. The faunal remains are extremely important (Campbell and Sampson, 1971), including an abundance of pre-Anglian cave bear bones in the lower sediments and Devensian mammoth, rhinoceros and deer in the middle layer. Few caves are recorded in the thinner and less pure limestones to the north, but some development has occurred in the Devonian limestone of the Quantock Hills.

6.2.4 *Carbonates of the Durness Group of Scotland*

Formerly referred to as the Durness Limestone, the 1000m-thick Durness Group of northern Scotland includes up to seven distinct formations that are essentially dolomitic. The oldest rocks within the Group were deposited during the early Cambrian and the youngest part of the sequence is of early Ordovician age. A major break in deposition stretching through the mid to late Cambrian is generally accepted (Palmer et al., 1980), with the plane of unconformity separating the early Cambrian Sailmhor Formation from the overlying, early Ordovician Sangomore Formation. However, the situation may have been more complex, with several cycles of deposition and erosion represented within the preserved succession. The top of the Sailmhor Formation is a well-marked palaeokarstic surface that reflects intense dissolutional activity prior to the deposition of the Sangomore Formation. Dissolutionally enlarged joints up to 4m wide and 150m in vertical extent, now containing neptunian fill of Sangomore Formation type, penetrate the Sailmhor Formation, which also contains bedding-parallel zones of brecciation, deduced to have been formed by collapse following dissolution of interbedded evaporites. These and similar indicators higher in the sequence (Young, 1979) suggest that karstification was active periodically during the full extent of Durness Group deposition. Rather than there being only one major gap in the succession, it is not unreasonable to assume that greater thicknesses of carbonate and clastic sediment may have been deposited and that much was subsequently removed by surface and subsurface dissolution of carbonate and evaporite or subaerial erosion by other agents. In context it is equally reasonable to deduce that during the karstification phases there was some degree of underground water flow and associated cave development.

The limited and poorly exposed Durness Group outcrops are penetrated by several active and abandoned caves, notably in the areas around Inchnadamph and Knockan. Many of the caves are formed on the planes of thrusts and faults, and groundwater flow is also constrained by a number of igneous intrusions. Each Pleistocene glaciation covered the area with ice and largely removed earlier karstic landforms. Glacial till, glaciofluvial debris and blanket peat bogs mask much of the carbonate outcrop, and periglacial weathering during the Loch Lomond stadial created areas of frost-shattered debris and solifluction flows. A few rocky gorges expose the carbonates and there are a few high crags, but there are no extensive doline fields or limestone pavements. Sinks, dry valleys and risings are the most conspicuous features of the karst. Allogenic drainage is from the higher ground of Breabag and Conival in the east, and most of it sinks where it crosses onto the dolomite. Both the Traligill River and the stream of Allt nan Uamh flow entirely underground, except in very wet weather, though some streams maintain surface courses over the dolomite, mainly supported on mantles of glacial till. The associated caves water in post-glacial stream trenches and flooded passages, and they also contain many passages which predate the last glaciation (Atkinson et al., 1995).

Along the northern coast, where the palaeokarstic features mentioned above are best exposed, a number of supposed sea caves, including Smoo Cave and the Balnakeil Gloup, may be at least partially true karst features.

6.2.5 *Limestones within the Dalradian Supergroup of Scotland*

A thick sequence of sedimentary rocks deposited during Neoproterozoic (late Precambrian) to Cambrian times was subsequently deformed and metamorphosed to form the rocks now referred to as the Dalradian Supergroup. Rocks of similar type are found in several parts of northern Scotland, as well as in Northern Ireland and Connemara, and include dolomitic, graphitic, and serpentinous marbles as well as beds of impure limestone. Some of the higher beds within this sequence, including carbonates, may be the metamorphosed equivalents of relatively undeformed rocks of Cambrian to Ordovician age that are discussed below. Occurring as relatively thin units within a complexly deformed succession, the several limestone units within the Dalradian Supergroup are of no significance as aquifers and of only passing interest as a potential focus of karst landscape development. Nonetheless, in areas such as Argyllshire, relatively thin limestone units, including the Ballachulish Limestone, have played a prominent local role in the shaping of the landscape. Across such areas, minor streams, that gather on impermeable solid rocks and glacial drift deposits, sink into limestone outcrops. Study of these small, scattered and commonly remote outcrops, and the karst drainage systems that they support, has been limited, but a number of minor caves have been explored. These include Uamh nan Uachdar (Cave of the High Ground), the highest limestone cave in Great Britain at an altitude of 895m (Young, 1992).

6.3 Weakly Cavernous Karsts

6.3.1 *The Cretaceous Chalk*

The Chalk is the name given to the group of formations, preserved over much of Great Britain, that were deposited during the late Cretaceous Period. It is a pure, white, relatively weak, friable, poorly lithified, porous limestone. Its matrix is composed largely of crystals, fragments and skeletons of coccoliths; most particles are <0.002mm across, and it is poorly recrystallised as it is largely composed of low-magnesium calcite which was stable at the low burial depths (Hancock, 1975, 1993). Through much of its thickness (c. 300m) it is remarkably pure, with about 98% calcium carbonate. The main impurities are sporadic marl seams and flint, a siliceous deposit of biological origin, which occurs in concentrated form as discrete nodules, or continuous sheets that tend to follow the bedding.

At the present day, the Chalk of Great Britain is confined almost entirely to south-east England, where a gently-dipping sequence of Mesozoic and Cainozoic sedimentary rocks dominates the surface geology (Fig. 6-1). In this area the landforms and underground drainage are completely different from those of the older cavernous carbonates and some hydrogeologists have argued that the Chalk should not be considered to be karstic, particularly as the characteristics are a function of the mechanical properties of the chalk rock. However, it is equally clear that carbonate dissolution processes have played a major part both in the geomorphological and the hydrogeological evolution of the Chalk, and to this extent it is no less karstic than the other British limestones.

Chalk is generally fairly weak, but surface flow is rare on the permeable rock and the outcrops are surrounded by even weaker clays and sands. Consequently, the Chalk generally forms relatively high ground, commonly as a series of escarpments, and the distinctive landscape of Chalk karst is a softly contoured grassy upland known as downland or downs. Devensian ice covered little of the Chalk, but earlier glaciations reached to the Chilterns and glacial till masks some of the eastern outcrops. The rounded landforms are the product of periglacial weathering. The top 10m of most Chalk outcrops have been so frost shattered that they now form a rubble weak Chalk or a thixotropic putty Chalk (Higginbottom, 1966). Solifluction was widespread during the Devensian cold stages, and combe rock is a Chalk head common on valley floors. Chalk outcrops were covered by woodland until the clearances between Mesolithic and mediaeval times, and the subsequent sheep grazing has maintained the short turf of the modern downland.

Dry valleys are common on the Chalk karst escarpments-largely the result of solifluction and snowmelt erosion during the Devensian. They form steep combes on the scarp faces and large dendritic systems on the dip slopes. Springs are common at their lower ends, and winter rises of the water table create many seasonal surface streams, known as bournes. Diffuse input of rainfall creates very few dolines on the main chalk karst. Along the margin of the Tertiary cover, on the very gentle dip slopes, allogenic drainage creates active sinkholes, deep subsidence dolines and dissolutional fissures that are now largely clay-filled. Most of these features fringe, breach or underlie the feather-edge of the Tertiary cover in the London basin, but large dolines also punctuate the Quaternary cover in the East Anglian Brecklands and the Dorset Heaths.

East of the main outcrop the Chalk is present beneath cover, and thus underlies most of eastern and southern England, except where it has been removed by erosion from the Weald Anticline. It underlies much of the driest but most densely-populated part of the country and is the most important aquifer in Great Britain, yielding about half of the country's pumped supplies. Full descriptions of the hydrogeology are given in Downing et al. (1993) and the following account draws heavily on Price (1994).

The matrix porosity of the Chalk is commonly very high. It must have exceeded 80% on deposition as even after burial and compaction it is normally in excess of 30% and locally 50%. There is a difference between the Chalk of southern England and that farther north, which has undergone greater recrystallisation and thus commonly has a lower porosity. The processes of burial, compaction, diagenesis, and subsequent uplift, have led to the Chalk being extensively fractured. These fractures generally occur in three sets, one being more or less parallel to the bedding, while the other two form a conjugate set orthogonal to the bedding. The fracture spacings range from a few millimetres to several metres apart, thinner beds having more fractures. At depth, the fractures may be more or less closed or, at best, open fractures may be widely spaced. These basic tectonic fractures may impart a bulk hydraulic conductivity to the rock that is one or two orders of magnitude greater than the hydraulic conductivity of the matrix. In common with most limestones under a soil cover, weathering is concentrated in the topmost few metres of the Chalk (the subcutaneous zone). The resultant widening of apertures and reduction in fissure separations leads to high permeabilities and to a lack of structure. However, in some localities, there is a layer of putty chalk of low permeability, probably a result of permafrost during the Devensian. Within the upper few tens of metres of the aquifer, some fractures are enlarged by dissolution to form features with significant openings, commonly developed along near-horizontal (bedding-plane) joints. Many take the form of flattened tubes, and may be expected to divide and rejoin, in the manner of a braided stream, thus imparting significant anisotropy to the aquifer.

The presence of a porous matrix intersected by fissures leads theoretically to double-porosity behaviour, but because some fissures are enlarged, there is the possibility of a second degree of double-porosity behaviour. For example, in response to pumping, water may flow from the network of smaller fissures to fissures that have been developed by dissolution of calcium carbonate. In addition, it is possible that flow towards a well may occur within the less-developed fissure system so that flow takes place in the same direction through two systems of differing permeabilities. Such behaviour is referred to as double-permeability behaviour. The enlarged fissures generally show the same orientation as undeveloped fissures. It is therefore generally accepted that they developed from the tectonically-controlled fractures by dissolution. This implies that there must be a continuous gradation from tectonic features with minimal openings to the well-developed or karstic features. In some ways this makes any division into classes of fissures, based on size of fissure opening, arbitrary and rather meaningless. Nevertheless it is convenient when describing the Chalk to have some terminology for distinguishing between the almost ubiquitous joints with small openings and the rarer, but hydraulically very important, larger fissures. Price(1994) suggests that the basic tectonic fractures be referred to as *primary fissure*, and the enlarged fissures as *secondary fissures*. Secondary fissures appear generally absent from Chalk beneath interfluves and remote from valleys, and the primary fissures appear tightly closed. The transmissivity of the Chalk in such localities is commonly only in the range 10 – 100 m^2/day. However, beneath valleys, whether dry or containing streams, transmissivities are much higher and can be in excess of 2000 m^2/day. Transmissivity is not distributed uniformly with depth but is generally concentrated at a few horizons. In particular the water table commonly occurs within a highly permeable zone, which probably developed as a result of concentrated flow towards a discharge area; once such a zone has developed, the water table will tend to stay within it. In most cases these enlarged openings are probably a few millimetres to a few tens of millimetres in aperture, but they can become karstic or near-karstic with dimensions of more than a metre.

Dissolutional enlargement to the scale of explorable caves is relatively unusual in south-east England and most so-called caves in the Chalk are man-made tunnels. However, there are active caves beneath the Water End sinkholes that can absorb up to 1 m^3/s of surface drainage before overflowing. Recorded flow through times average 5500m/d and clearly indicate presence of open, dissolutionally widened, fissure systems. At Beachy Head, Sussex retreating sea cliffs have intersected some 370m of passage that ends inland at a water-filled section (Reeve, 1981). Shorter passages have been explored in sea cliffs around Beer, in Devon, and Flamborough Head, Yorkshire. Elsewhere, velocities in excess of 1km/d have been recorded for the Chalk (Atkinson and Smith, 1974; Price et al., 1992) and it is possible that many dissolution conduits are partly or completely filled by sediment. There are reported examples of wells, drilled and cased through Tertiary beds into the Chalk, producing sand, and a record of at least one well dug through chalk encountering seams of gravel; these are probably derived from infilled dissolution features. Many of the best-developed dissolution features have been reported from near the edge of the Tertiary beds that overlie parts of the Chalk. The increased runoff, which is commonly acidic, generated by rainfall on the Tertiary deposits, leads to the presence of these enhanced dissolution features and hence to some of the highest transmissivities recorded from the Chalk.

6.3.2 *Jurassic Limestones*

Limestones of variable thickness occur throughout the Jurassic, but only three areas provide aquifers of regional significance: the Corallian Group of the Upper Jurassic in north-east Yorkshire, the Lincolnshire Limestone Formation, and the Great and Inferior Oolite groups of the Cotswold Hills. Part of the storage in these limestones is in the form of extensive interconnected fissure systems and consequently there can be considerable variation of groundwater levels between winter and summer and both during and following individual periods of rain. The outcrops have been deeply dissected by valleys that locally penetrate into underlying impermeable beds. This allows rapid drainage through the fissure systems. In many cases the relationship between rivers and the aquifers is complex (Rushton et al., 1992) and the rivers may gain or lose water according to the season and position of the groundwater levels. The porosity of the limestones is in the range 15 – 20 % but the specific yield is not likely to exceed 5 %. The transmissivity is commonly in excess of 1500 m^2/d because of the interconnected fissure systems. However, the hydraulic conductivity of the matrix is very low and of the order of 10^{-4} to 10^{-3} m/d. Groundwater flow velocities vary with the size of the fissures and range up to several kilometres per day in the principal conduits. There is clear evidence for turbulent flow in fissure systems over distances up to 15km (Atkinson and Smart, 1981), although laminar fissure flow is also important.

In the Great Oolite, groundwater is able to move freely in any direction because of the high fissure density. Dye injected close to the boundary between two groundwater basins indicated that water moved in roughly equal amounts to spring groups in each basin (Smart, 1976). As the distance from the boundary increased, more dye flowed to one group; towards the centre of each basin, flow was to only one group. On this basis, recharge areas for particular spring groups were identified, although divides sometimes varied seasonally due to fluctuations in the water table.

The Corallian Group is between 100 and 150m thick, and its outcrop extends in an arc around the northern and western margins of the Vale of Pickering, forming prominent north- and west-facing scarps. Fissure flow predominates, for the matrix permeability is low, typically less than 10^{-3} m/d. Although the effective porosity ranges from 10 – 30%, the specific yield is only about 1%. The fissures were probably tectonic in origin and subsequently enlarged by weathering and by circulating groundwater. The groundwater chemistry in a narrow zone at and close to outcrop is of Ca-HCO_3 type away from outcrop. This probably implies that flow in the confined aquifer is slow. The aquifer is partly recharged by swallow holes and in North Yorkshire over 30 caves have been explored in limestones of the Corallian Group (Brook et al., 1988). Most are mass movement caves, known locally as windypits, but relict and active caves of dissolutional origin have been reported. The longest, Bogg Hall Cave, is entered at a rising on the bank of the River Dove and has been explored upstream for some 200m. The first 25m are largely water filled, but beyond is a streamway 3m wide and 1 – 2m high, ending at a sump pool that has been explored by divers to a depth of 15m.

The Lincolnshire Limestone Formation (locally part of either the Inferior Oolite Group or the Redbourne Group) is a major aquifer in eastern England extending southwards from the Humber to near Kettering, a distance of 130km. It attains a maximum thickness of 40m south of Grantham, thinning to the east and passing laterally into an argillaceous facies beneath the North Sea. Thus, it forms a large carbonate wedge dipping gently towards the east. North of Grantham the limestone forms a north-south escarpment up to 30 – 60m in elevation overlooking the Trent Valley. south of Grantham, as a result of a reduction in dip, it forms part of the East Midland Plateau with an elevation of about 120m, but the scarp feature is still evident. The Lincolnshire limestone is a prolific aquifer, yielding as much as 350 l/s from individual wells (Downing and Williams, 1969). The primary porosity is low, permeability depending upon secondary porosity, with water moving through fissures. However, isotope studies imply that significant storage is present in microfissures in the aquifer matrix. The permeability pattern in the south must be related to palaeo-weathering and dissolution associated with flow towards downgradient outlets, possibly buried glacial channels (Downing, 1994). The groundwater resources of the Lincolnshire Limestone are mainly replenished by infiltration over the outcrop, but there is also significant localised recharge through swallow holes and fissures that are common in south Lincolnshire at the junction with the overlying Rutland Formation (formerly the Upper Estuarine Series) or with the glacial till cover. Surface runoff, both in winter and summer, is input directly into the limestone through these dissolution features (Downing and Williams, 1969; Fox and Rushton, 1976). Closed depressions are common where the Rutland Formation and till have collapsed into swallow holes in the limestone (Hindley, 1965). There has been much debate about the age of groundwater in the Lincolnshire Limestone. Bishop and Lloyd(1991) consider that the potable water in the confined area may be up to 6000 years old. However, isotope and inert gas analyses imply that the saline groundwater zone contains an older component, at least of Pleistocene age and possibly much older (Andrews and Kay, 1982).

Middle Jurassic Limestones form the broad escarpment of the Cotswold Hills, the dip slope being crossed by numerous shallow dry valleys, mostly floored with Devensian periglacial deposits. The principal aquifers are the Great Oolite and the Inferior Oolite groups, which are separated by the relatively impermeable Fuller Earth Formation. Groundwaters in the Great and Inferior Oolite groups are of $CaHCO_3$ type where unconfined, but downgradient in the confined zone they are modified to a $NaHCO_3$ type by ion exchange.

The Isle Portland is jointed to the mainland by the shingle tombolo of Chesil Beach. Although now hydrogeologically isolated from the mainland, it is one of the most important sites in England for the significant dissolutional caves in Jurassic carbonates. Tectonic rift caves extend through the entire limestone sequence and locally intersect unrelated, pre-existing, dissolutional caves that confined to the various limestone beds within the Portland Freestone Member. The longest is Sandy Hole, with 400m of passage. Guidance by joint fissures is well marked in some caves (Graham and Ryder, 1983), but it also appears that inception horizons, such as a chert bed that forms much of the roof of Sandy Hole, may have guided early cave growth. Hence, early cave development may pre-date the current geological structure and surface topography, although the dissolutional caves have all been truncated by marine erosion or by quarrying, making details of their origins and palaeohydrology difficult to interpret.

Small areas of Jurassic limestone crop out in western Scotland and although they have no hydrogeological significance they contain some 15 caves. On the Applecross peninsular the 600m-long Uamh nam Breagaire(Cave of the Liar) is a steeply dipping, joint-guided system formed in a concretionary limestone within the Broadford 'Beds' (Ryder, 1982). There are several caves on the Isle of Skye, the most notable being Allt na Pairte, 200m long.

6.4 Evaporite Karsts

Rock salt, which is almost pure halite, forms thick units in the Triassic Mercia Mudstone Group, beneath the Cheshire Plain and in other smaller Triassic basins. In Cheshire, the Wilkesley and Northwich Halite formations, each over 100m thick, consist of salt interbedded with mudstone. Nowhere do they survive at outcrop, but they lie beneath thick covers of permeable drift deposits where groundwater dissolution has left residual breccias of collapsed mudstone over their buried outcrops (Earp and Taylor, 1986). The landforms of the salt karst are restricted to subsidence hollows, formed where circulation of the brine has allowed continued dissolution by influxes of unsaturated groundwater. The roughly circular meres are flooded dolines that evolved through much of the Holocene (Waltham et al., 1996); many linear subsidence hollows are formed over zones of groundwater flow close to the rockhead (brine streams), and have deepened considerably during the last hundred years in response to artificial brine pumping(Waltham, 1989).

Anhydrite occurs in the Permian succession of England, but in thinner units than the salt. At depths less than about 100m, it hydrates to form gypsum, which in turn is normally completely dissolved within the weathering zone. Only at a few sites near Ripon, in Yorkshire, does significant gypsum occur in temporary surface outcrops (James et al, 1981). Karst features on the gypsum include numerous dolines with active subsidence, notably around Ripon (Cooper, 1986; Patterson et al., 1995), and large breccia pipes in the overlying beds that are the product of interstratal karst but have little modern surface expression (Smith, 1972; Cooper, 1988). The largest gypsum caves in Great Britain are at Houtsay, in the Permian gypsum of the Vale of Eden; they have about 100m of tubular phreatic passages (Ryder and Cooper, 1993), and may indicate the potential extent of gypsum caves that are otherwise known only as fragments exposed in mines and quarries, elsewhere in the Permo-Triassic of England.

References

Andrews, J. N. and R. I. F. Kay, 1982. U－234/U－238 activity ratios of dissolved uranium in groundwaters from a Jurassic limestone aquifer in England. Earth and Planetary Science Letter, Vol 57, pp. 139－151.

Appleton, P., 1989. Limestones and caves of North Wales. In Limestones and Caves of Wales(ed. T D Ford), Cambridge University Press, Cambridge, pp. 217－254.

Atkinson, T. C., T. J. Lawson and N. J. Hebdon, 1995. Karst geomorphology. In The Quaternary of Assynt and Coigach: a guide. (Ed T J Lawson), Quaternary Research Association, pp. 61－86.

Atkinson, T. C. and P.L. Smart, 1981. Artificial tracers in hydrogeology. In A Survey of British Hydrogeology, The Royal Society, London, pp. 173 – 190.

Atkinson, T. C. and D.I. Smith, 1974. Rapid groundwater flow in fissures in the Chalk: an Example from south Hampshire. Quarterly Journal of Engineering Geology, Vol.7, pp.197 – 205.

Bishop, P. K. and J.W. Lloyd, 1991. Use of C – 14 modelling to determine vulnerability and pollution of a carbonate aquifer: the Lincolnshire Limestone, eastern England. Applied Geochemistry, Vol.6, pp.319 – 331.

Brook, A., D. Brook, G.M. Davies, J. Griffiths, M.H. Long and P.F. Ryder, 1988 – 94. Northern Caves. Dalesman, Clapham, Volumes 1 – 3, 853pp.

Campbell, J. B. and G.G. Sampson, 1971. A new analysis of Kent's Cavern, Devon, England. University of Oregon Anthropological Palaeontology, Vol.3, pp.1 – 40.

Campbell, S. and D.Q. Bowen, 1989. Quaternary of Wales. Nature Conservancy Council, 237pp.

Christopher, N. S. J., 1981. The karst hydrogeochemistry of the Carboniferous Limestone of North Derbyshire. unpubl. PhD thesis, Univ. of Leicester.

Cooper, A. H., 1986. Foundered strata and subsidence resulting from the dissolution of Permian gypsum in the Ripon and Bedale areas, North Yorkshire. In: The English Zechstein and related topics, (eds G M Harwood and D B Smith), Geological Society Special Publication, Vol.22, pp.127 – 139.

Cooper, A. H., 1988. Subsidence resulting from the dissolution of Permian gypsum in the Ripon area: its relevance to mining and water abstraction. Geological Society Enginnering Geology Special Publication, Vol.5, pp. 387 – 390.

Downing, R. A., 1994. Jurassic limestone environments. In An introduction to British limestone karst environments, (ed J Gunn), British Cave Research Association, Cave Studies Series, 5, pp. 25 – 29.

Downing, R. A., M. Price and G.P. Jones (eds), 1993. The Hydrology of the Chalk of northwest Europe, Clarendon Press, Oxford, 300pp.

Downing, R. A. and G.P.J. Williams, 1969. The groundwater hydrology of the Lincolnshire Limestone. Water Resource Board, Reading.

Earp, J. R. and B.J. Taylor, 1986. Geology of the country around chester and Winsford. Memoir of the British Geological Survey, sheet 109, 119pp.

Edmunds, W. M., 1971. Hydrochemistry of groundwaters in the Derbyshire Dome. Institute of Geological Sciences Report, 71/7.

Ford, D. C., 1968. Features of cavern development in central Mendip. Transactions of the Cave Research Group of Great Britain, Vol.10, pp.11 – 25.

Ford, T. D. (ed), 1977. Limestones and Caves of the Peak District. Geo – Books, Norwich, 469pp.

Ford, T. D., 1984. Palaeokarsts in Britain. Cave Science, VOl.11, pp.246 – 264.

Ford, T. D. (ed), 1989. Limestones and Caves of Wales. Cambridge University Press, Cambridge, 257pp.

Fox, I. A. and K.R. Rushton, 1976. Rapid recharge in a limestone aquifer. Ground Water, Vol.14, pp.21 – 27.

Graham, N. and P.F. Ryder, 1983. Sandy Hole, Isle of Portland. Transactions of the British Cave Research Association, Vol.10, pp.171 – 80.

Gunn, J., 1991. Water tracing experiments in the Peak District, 1950 – 1990. Cave Science, Vol.18, No.1, pp.43 – 46.

Gunn, J., 1992. Hydrogeological contrasts between British Carboniferous aquifers. In Hydrogeology of selected karst regions, International Association of Hydrogeologists, 13, pp.25 – 42.

Hancock, J. M., 1975. The petrology of the chalk. Proceedings of the Geologists' Association, Vol.86, pp.499 – 535.

Hancock, J. M., 1993. The formation and diagenesis of chalk. In: The hydrogeology of the chalk of northwest Europe (eds. R.A.Downing, M. Price and G. P. Jones), Clarendon Press, Oxford.

Higginbottom, I. E., 1966. The engineering geology of chalk. Proceedings of Symposium on Chalk in Earthworks and Foundations (1965), Institute of Civil Engineers, pp.1 – 13.

Hindley, R., 1965. Sinkholes on the Lincolnshire Limestone between Grantham and Stamford. East Midlands Geographer, 3, pp.454 – 460.

Irwin, D. J. and A.R. Jarratt, 1992. Mendip Underground, Mendip Publishing, Castle Cary.

Jenkinson, R. D. S., 1984. Creswell Crags: late Pleistocene sites in the East Midlands. British Archaeological Records, British Series, 122, 37pp.

Jenkinson, R., 1989. The archaeological caves of Creswell Crags. Transactions of the British Cave Research Association, Vol.16, pp.91 – 94.

Lowe, D. J., 1978. Farnham Cave, a rift cave in the Magnesian Limestone. Transactions of the British Cave Research Association, Vol.5, pp.23 – 28.

Lowe, D. J., 1992. The origin of limestone caverns: an inception horizon hypothesis. Unpublished PhD Thesis, Geography Department, Manchester Metropolitan University, 511pp.

Noel, M., 1987. The magnetostratigraphy of cave sediments in Masson Hill, Derbyshire. Proceedings of the Yorkshire Geological Society, Vol.46, pp.193 – 201.

Palmer, T. J., W.S. McKerrow and J.W. Cowie, 1980. Sedimentological evidence for a stratigraphical break in the Durness Group. Nature, Vol.287, pp.720 – 722.

Patterson, D. A., J.C. Davey, A.H. Cooper and J.K. Ferris, 1995. The inverstigation of dissolution subsidence incorporating microgravity geophysics at Ripon, Yorkshire. Quarterly Journal of Engineering Geology, Vol.28, pp.83 – 94.

Price, M., 1994. Cretaceous limestone (chalk) environments. In An introduction to British limestone karst environments (ed J Gunn), British Cave Research Association, Cave Studies Series, 5, pp.30 – 35.

Price, M., T.C. Atkinson, J.A. Barker, D. Wheeler and R.A. Monkhouse, 1992. A tracer study of the danger posed to a chalk aquifer by contaminated highway runoff. Proceedings of the Institute of Civil Engineers: Water, Maritime and Energy Journal, Vol.96, pp.9 – 18.

Proctor, C. J., 1988. Sea level related caves on Berry Head, South Devon. Transactions of the British Cave Research Association, Vol.15, pp.39 – 49.

Proctor, C. J. and P.L. Smart, 1989. A new survey of Kent's Cavern, Devon. Proceedings of the University of Bristol Spelaeological Society, Vol.18, pp.422 – 429.

Proctor, C. J. and P.L. Smart, 1991. A dated cave sediment record of Pleistocene transgressions on Berry Head, southwest England. Journal of Quaternary Science, 6, 233 – 244.

Ramsbottom, W. H. C., 1973. Transgressions and regressions in the Dinantian: a new synthesis of British Dianatian stratigraphy. Proceedings of the Yorkshire Geological Society, Vol.39, pp.567 – 607.

Reeve, T., 1981. Beachy Head Cave. Caves and Caving, Vol.12, pp.2 – 5.

Rowe, P. J., T.C. Atkinson and R.D.S. Jenkinson, 1989. Uranium – series dating of cave deposits at Creswell Crags Gorge, England. Transactions of The British Cave Research Association, Vol.16, pp.3 – 17.

Rushton, K. R., E.J. Smith and L.M. Tomlinson, 1982. An improved understanding of flow in a limestone aquifer using field evidence and mathematical models. Journal of the Institute of Water Engineers and Scientists, Vol.36, pp.369 – 387.

Ryder, P. F., 1982. MSG expedition to Skye and Applecross. Grampian Speleological Group Bulletin, Second Series, Vol. 3, No.5, pp.30 – 31.

Ryder, P. F. and A.H. Cooper, 1993. A cave system in Permian gypsum at Houtsay quarry, Newbiggin, Cumbria, England. Transactions of the British Cave Research Association, Vol.20, pp.23 – 28.

Smart, P. L., 1976. Catchment delimitation in karst areas by the use of quantitative tracer methods. Proceedings of the Third International symposium of Underground Water Tracing, Bled, Yugoslavia, pp.291 – 298.

Smith, D. B., 1972. Foundered strata, collapse breccias and subsidence features of the English Zechstein. In : Geology of saline deposits, (ed Richter – Bernburg G), UNESCO Earth Sciences, 7, pp.255 – 269.

Smith, D. I. (ed), 1975. Limestones and Caves of the Mendip Hills. David and Charles, Newton Abbott. 424pp.

Stanton, W. I. and P.L. Smart, 1981. Repeated dye traces of underground streams in the Mendip Hills, Somerset. Proceedings of the University of Bristol Spelaeological Society, Vol.16, pp.47 – 58.

Thomas, T. M., 1974. The South Wales interstratal karst. Transactions the British Cave Research Association, 1, pp.131 – 152.

Waltham, A. C., 1970. Cave development in the limestone of the Ingleborough district. Geographical Journal, Vol.136, pp.574 – 585.

Waltham, A. C. (ed), 1974. Limestones and Caves of North – West England. David and Charles, Newton Abbot, 477pp.

Waltham, A. C., 1989. Ground subsidence. Blackie, London, 196pp.

Waltham, A. C., D.B. Brook, O.W. Statham and T.G. Yeadon, 1981. Swinsto Hole, Kingsdale: a type example of cave development in the limestone of northern England. Geographical Journal, Vol.147, pp.350 – 353.

Waltham, A. C., M.J. Simms, A.R. Farrant and H.S. Goldie, 1996. Karst and Caves of Britain. Chapman and Hall, London, 500pp.

Ward, S. D. and D.F. Evans, 1976. Conservation assessment of British limestone pavements based on floristic criteria. Biological Conservation, Vol.9, pp.217 – 233.

Young, H. R., 1979. Evidence of former evaporites in the Cambro – Ordovician Durness Group, northwest Scotland. Sedimentary Geology, 22, 287 – 303.

Young, I., 1992. The highest cave in the British Isles. Descent, Vol.103, pp.32 – 33.

Global Karst Correlation
Edited by Yuan Daoxian and Liu Zaihua
Science Press and VSP BV, 1998

Chapter 7 Karst Regions of the Eastern United States with Special Emphasis on the Friars Hole Cave System, West Virginia

Percy H. Dougherty[1], Roy A. Jameson[2], Stephen R. H. Worthington[3], George N. Huppert, Betty J. Wheeler[4], John W. Hess[5]
[1]*Kutztown University of Pennsylvania*, *USA*; [2]*University of Minnesota*, *USA*; [3]*McMaster University*, *Canada*; [4]*University of Wisconsin*, *USA*; [5]*Water Resources Center*, *Desert Research Inst.*, *University of Nevada System*

When one thinks of karst in the eastern United States, Mammoth Cave and the adjacent Pennyroyal Plateau come to mind immediately. Much excellent scientific research has been published on the caves and karst of that area. It is not the intent of this chapter to summarize and report on that research. Most of the studies are available to the general cave and karst community worldwide and readers are referred to Palmer (1981), Brown (1966), Deike (1967), and Miotke and Palmer (1972) for more information on Mammoth Cave. Rather, it is the purpose of this chapter to introduce the reader to the other less well known but important karst regions of the eastern United States with an emphasis on Virginia, West Virginia and other areas of Kentucky.

The impetus for this study comes from an International Geographical Congress Karst Field Trip organized by Percy H. Dougherty, George Huppert, and Betty Wheeler in 1992. Also taking part in the trip were representatives from the several other hydrological and geological professional groups. Participants from nine countries drove from Washington, D. C. to Mammoth Cave, Kentucky with stops at caves and karst areas representative of several geomorphic regions.

Fig.7-1 is a map of the major karst regions of the United States, after Davies in Herak and Stringfield (1972), showing the karst landscapes encountered between Washington, D. C. and Mammoth Cave, Kentucky. For comparison, Fig.7-2 shows the Raisz physiographic diagram of the same region, thus enabling one to correlate the geomorphology with the carbonate terrains. From the east to the west one encounters several of the major karst regions of the United States. A short overview of each region, with the exception of the Central Kentucky karst around Mammoth Cave, is given before a more detailed account on Friars Hole, West Virginia. The regions from east to west include: the Great Valley of the Appalachians, the Appalachian Ridge and Valley, the Appalachian Plateau and Allegheny Front, the Pine Mountain Overthrust, the Cumberland Plateau, the Kentucky Blue Grass Basin, and the Central Kentucky Karst of the Mammoth Cave area.

7.1 Environmental Conditions

Climatically most of the karst regions in this paper are identified as Cfa, Humid Subtropical, on the Koppen climate classification map; although, they are the far northern portion of the climatic realm. Elevation has an important impact on the karst regions, resulting in colder winters than one would expect in this climate. The hot summers and cold winters are typical of a humid middle latitude climate and grades into a harsher climate toward the north where it becomes Dfa, Humid Con-

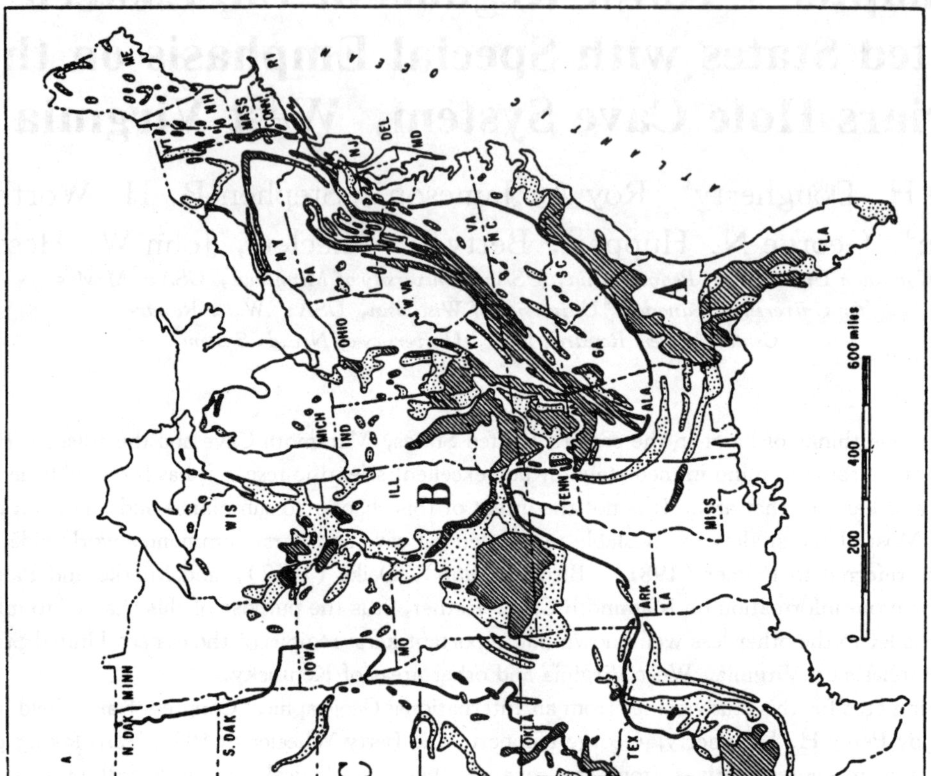

Fig. 7-1 Distribution of Karst Areas and Carbonate Rocks (Herak and Stringfield, 1972).
1 = karst areas; 2 = carbonates or sulphate rocks at or near the surface (by W. E. Davies)

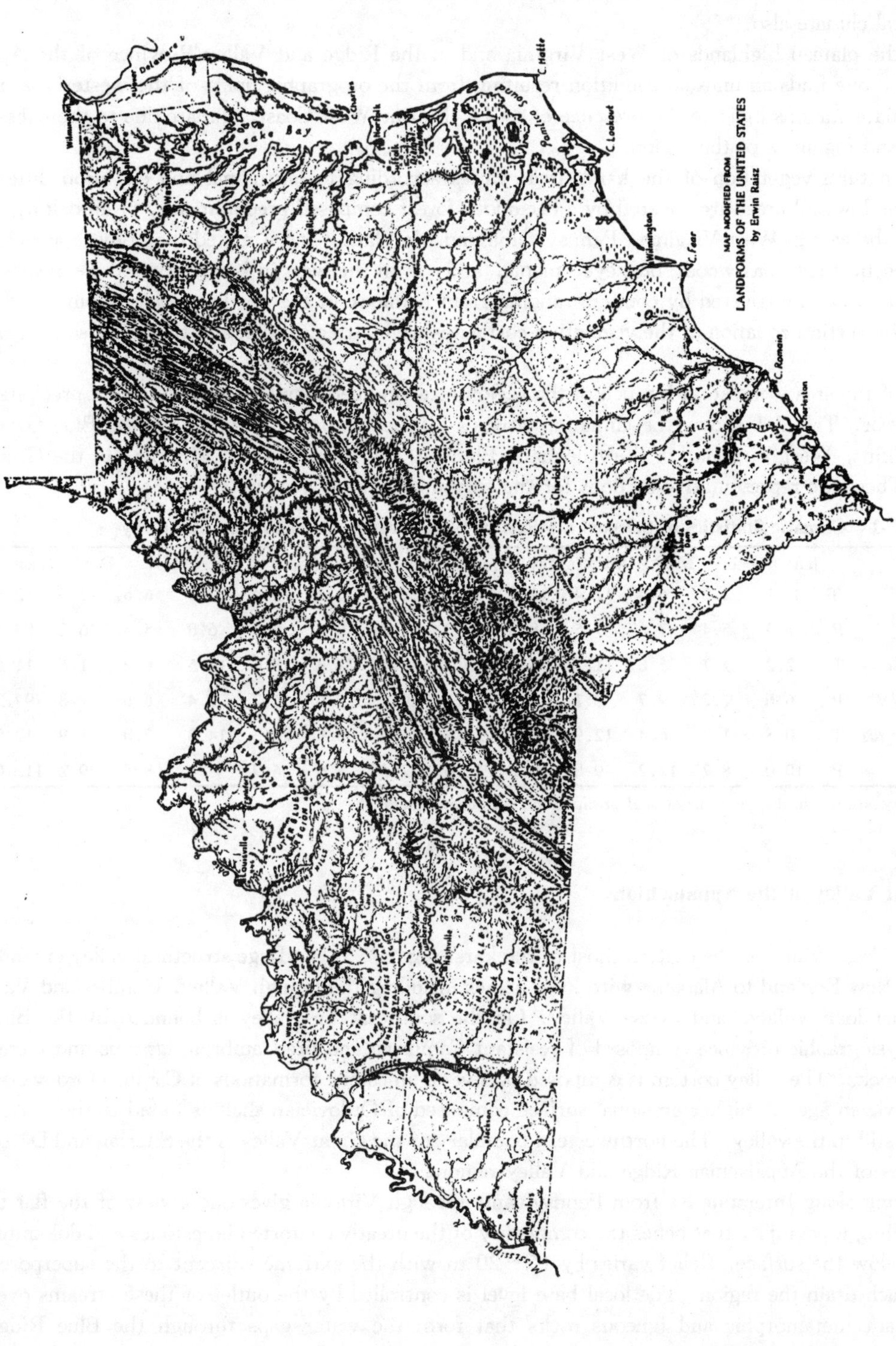

Fig. 7-2 Raisz Physiographic Diagram (Bennison, 1989)

tinental Long Summer, in Pennsylvania. High in the Appalachian Plateau, winter conditions get extremely cold and the climatic statistics of an individual station would indicate this to be a Humid Continental climate also.

In the plateau highlands of West Virginia and in the Ridge and Valley Province of the Appalachians, one finds an unusual condition resulting from the orographic uplift of the westerly wind belt. Climate stations indicate the presence of a Cbf, Marine West Coast, climate due to the excessive rain and fogginess of the region.

The natural vegetation of the karst areas varies according to latitudinal and elevation differences. The lowland areas are covered by a deciduous forest composed predominantly of an oak association in the east in West Virginia, Pennsylvania and Maryland, and a mixed mesophytic association of beech, tulip, basswood, buckeye, maple, and oak in the west in Kentucky and Tennessee. The upland areas are covered by conifers ranging from hemlock in the north to loblolly pine in the south. The vertical zonation of the vegetation correlates well with elevation and the decrease in temperature.

All of the area is moist with much of the region receiving between 800 – 1200 mm of precipitation per year. Tab. 7-1 shows the climatic statistics for Lexington, Kentucky, in the Blue Grass Basin; Elkins, West Virginia, in the Allegheny Plateau; and Front Royal, Virginia, in the Great Valley. These are representative stations for the surrounding karst regions.

Tab. 7-1 Climatic Statistics of Selected Stations in West Virginia, Virginia and Kentucky

		Jan	Feb	Mar	Apr	May	June	July	Aug	Sept	Oct	Nov	Dec	Year
Winchester, VA	T	1. 1	2.2	6.4	12.4	17.3	21.5	23.7	23.1	19.4	13.5	6.6	2.5	12.6
	P	5.3	5.4	7.6	7.5	8.3	9.3	9.7	9.0	8.0	6.0	5.5	6.2	88.3
White Sulfur	T	2.2	1.7	5.8	11.7	16.4	19.3	22.4	21.8	18.6	12.5	6.2	1.6	11.6
Springs, WV	P	6.6	7.7	9.7	8.1	8.9	8.6	10.1	9.0	7.7	6.4	6.6	7.8	97.2
Lexington, KY	T	0.5	1.8	6.4	12.9	18.2	22.8	24.6	23.9	20.3	14.3	7.0	1.9	12.9
	P	10.0	8.7	12.2	9.8	10.6	11.0	12.3	8.6	6.7	5.4	8.5	9.2	113.0

Note: Temperature is in degrees Celcium and precipitation is in centimeters

7.2 Great Valley of the Appalachians

The Great Valley is the eastern-most of the karst regions. It is a large structural valley extending from New England to Alabama with local names including the Lehigh Valley, Cumberland Valley, Shenandoah Valley, and Coosa Valley. On the southeast the valley is bounded by the Blue Ridge physiographic province composed of resistant Cambrian and pre-Cambrian igneous and metamorphic rocks. The valley bottom is composed of several limestone formations of Cambro-Ordovician and Ordovician age. A higher erosional surface composed of Ordovician shale is found to the northwest but still in the valley. The northwestern boundary of the Great Valley is the Silurian and Devonian ridges of the Appalachian Ridge and Valley region.

Driving along Interstate 81 from Pennsylvania through Virginia gives one a view of the flat to gently rolling topography that belies the complexity of the greatly contorted limestones and dolomites that lie below the surface. Relief varies by 15 – 20 m with the extreme adjacent to the superposed rivers which drain the region. The local base level is controlled by the outlet of these streams over the resistant metamorphic and igneous rocks that form the water gaps through the Blue Ridge Province. Sinkholes are a common feature of the valley bottom, but caves are usually small because of the lack of vertical development as well as the fact that many of the carbonates are dolomitic in nature.

Luray Caverns, a world famous commercial cave in this area that is a popular tourist attraction, was the object of an intensive study by Hack and Durloo (1977). Although not an extensive cave, it is well decorated (photo 24) and is located in a good market position near the Washington, D. C. Metropolitan market. Several other commercial caves dot the landscape of the Great Valley of Pennsylvania and Virginia.

The Great Valley of Virginia near Luray caverns differs from that in Maryland and Pennsylvania in that the valley bifurcates around Massanutten Mountain, a synclinal mountain where resistant Devonian sandstone forms the caprock overlying Silurian shale. The surrounding lowland of the Shenandoah Valley is composed of Ordovician limestones. Fig. 7-3 shows a cross-section of the area from a National Park Service brochure (undated).

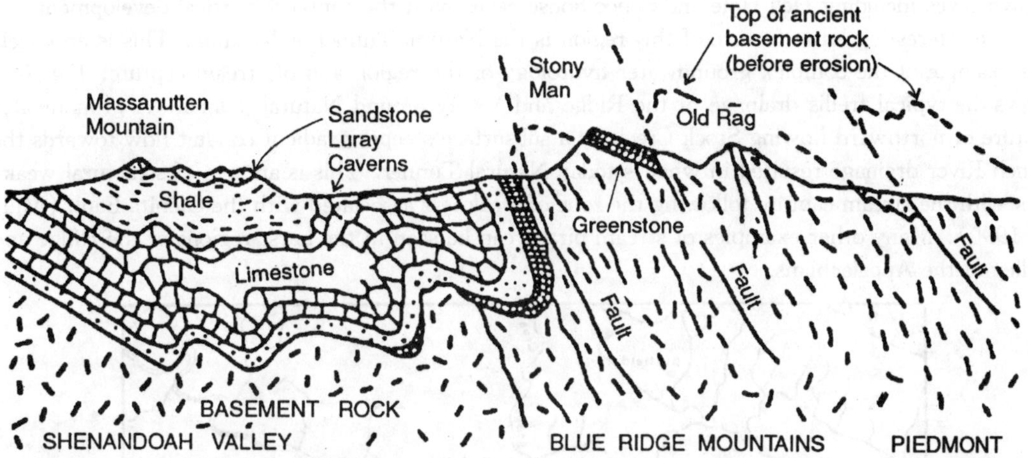

Fig. 7-3 Cross-Section of the Great Valley, Massanutten Mountain, Virginia (National Park Service, United States Department of Interior, undated)

The Great Valley is also noted for its fertile farmlands and its importance as a transportation artery since colonial times. Many westward-bound settlers moved through this valley on their way to the Cumberland Gap and many battles were fought here during the Civil War because of the military significance of the Valley.

Today it is the site of many industrial cities ranging from Allentown/Bethlehem/Easton and Harrisburg in Pennsylvania through a series of small industrial cities including Roanoke, Virginia. The Allentown area is especially noteworthy in karst because of the great number of karst collapses giving it the distinction of having the second worst annual damage after the Central Florida karst around Orlando, Florida (Dougherty, 1991). A recent sinkhole in 1994 caused the destruction of a $ 10 million, nine-story modern office building in downtown Allentown. The area is also of note as being the home of the Portland cement industry and a leading supplier of cement today.

7.3 Ridge and Valley of the Appalachians

To obtain an appreciation of this area, one must look at a satellite images or high altitude air photos in order to comprehend the long, narrow parallel ridges of Silurian and Devonian quartzitic sandstones and conglomerates and the narrow valley floors composed of limestones and shales. The ridges rise to elevations of 400 – 1400 m with local relief ranging up to 750 m. The drainage is concentrated in the limestone valleys and extensive cave systems are developed. Because of the folding, caves are often found in steeply dipping beds where the resulting pattern is often horizontal passages parallel to the valley walls; thus, the caves are strike-oriented. Most of the caves and karst features are found in two sequences of limestone. These include the upper Silurian Tonoloway limestone and the lower Devonian Helderberg Group, especially the Scotland limestone. Because of the clastic nature of the adjacent rock, the caves are often partially or wholly filled with debris and pose a difficult problem for cave exploration. A more detailed description of the physiography and geology of the region is given in the *Guidebook to Karst of the Central Appalachians* by Werner (1981).

The exception to the Devonian and Silurian age of karst features in the Ridge and Valley is Germany Valley where older Middle Ordovician limestones are exposed. Germany Valley is an anticlinal valley developed in the breached top of the Wills Mountain anticline. The areas is home of many well known caves including Hell Hole and Schoolhouse caves with their intense vertical development.

An interesting karst feature of this region is the Natural Tunnel of Virginia. This is an excellent example of the complex groundwater hydrology of the region and of stream capture. Fig. 7- 4 shows the typical trellis drainage of the Ridge and Valley around Natural Tunnel. A groundwater capture of northward flowing Stock Creek by a subsurface steeper gradient conduit flow towards the Clinch River drainage resulted in what is today Natural Tunnel. This is an area of structural weakness with the stream capture following the zone of weakness associated with the Glenita Fault (Milici, 1990). Many other examples of stream piracy can be seen in the karst regions of the Ridge and Valley of the Appalachians.

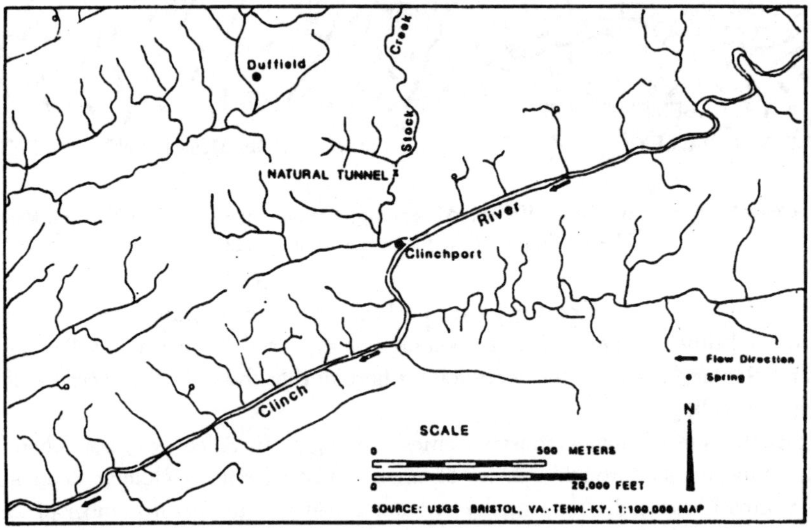

Fig. 7- 4 Stream Pattern at Natural Tunnel, Virginia (Milici, 1990)

7.4 Appalachian Plateau

The Appalachian Plateau, or the Allegheny Plateau as it is often called locally, is an upland surface to the west of the Ridge and Valley. Elevations on the plateau are higher than those in the Ridge and Valley. The upturned eastern edge of the plateau is known as the Allegheny Front and is characterized by steep relief and the outcrop of the Mississippian Greenbrier Limestone Group from under the mantle of Mississippian and Pennsylvanian clastic sediments, as can be seen on Fig. 7-5 (Hempel, 1976). Most of the large caves and karst features of the Appalachian Plateau are concen-

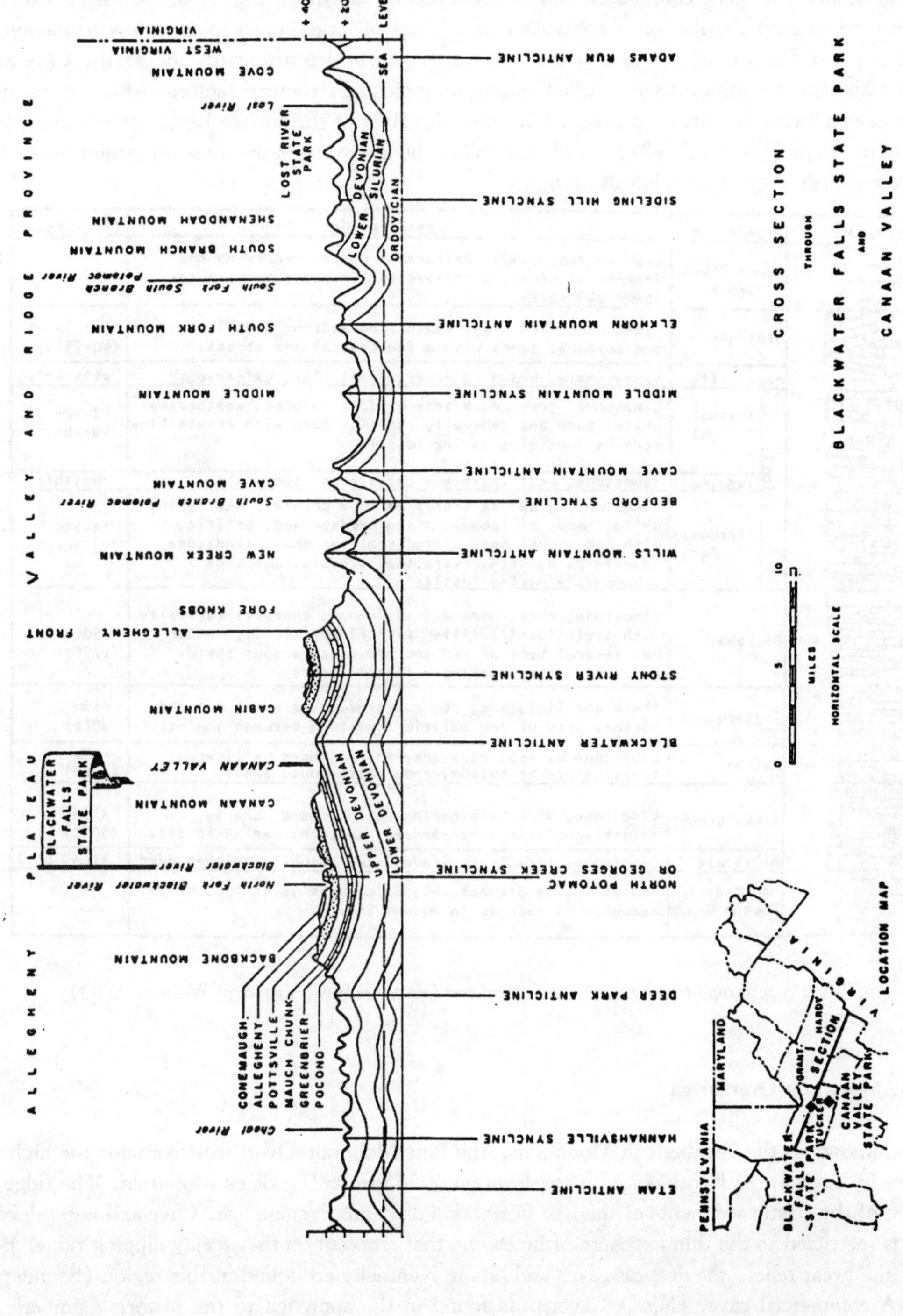

Fig. 7-5 Cross-Section of the Appalachian Plateau (Hempel et al., 1976)

trated along the eastern margin of the region. The Friars Hole Cave System, at over 72 km in length, and Organ Cave are two of the largest caves of the region.

The Greenbrier Group consists of a sequence of over twenty distinct units of limestone, sandstone, mudstone, and shale comprising eight formations as shown on Fig. 7- 6 (Werner, 1983). The limestone outcrop distribution is controlled by a series of large, open folds of low to moderate relief. The group has a thickness of 60 – 550 m, increasing in depth towards the south. Cave and karst development is significantly controlled by stratigraphic and structural factors. Much of the area does not have a limestone surface exposure with only 5 – 10% of the surface being carbonate rock in the northern basins (Werner, 1981). Hydrologically, the limestone is the most important factor influencing the hydrology of the plateau margin.

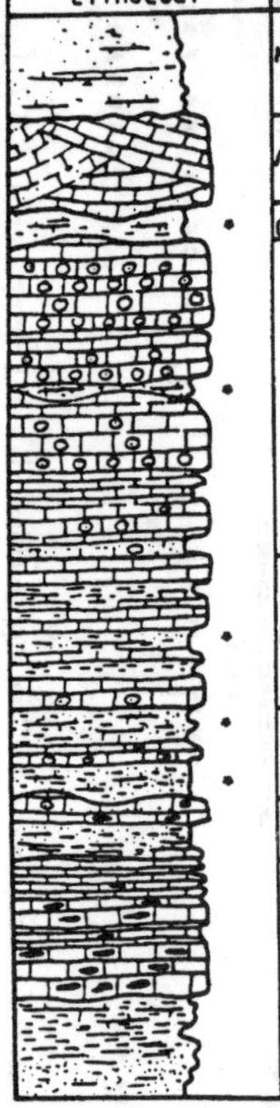

LITHOLOGY	FORMATION		DESCRIPTION	THICKNESS
	Mauch Chunk Group		Gray or red, sandy, calcareous shales overlying the Greenbrier Group, with several limestone beds in the lower 200 feet	
	Alderson		Limestone, dark gray, weathering yellow, usually hard and somewhat sandy with a few crystalline streaks	12-23m (40-75ft)
	Greenville		sandy shale, brown to green, lenticular, calcareous	<12m(40ft)
	Union	(Gasper Age)	Limestone, gray, dark-gray or dove colored, weathering white, pure and generally oolitic, hard with crystalline streaks; contains marine fossils	12-20m (40-60ft)
	Union	(=Bethel)	Sandstone, red, shaly and calcareous, lenticular	<6m(20ft)
	Union	(Fredonia Age)	Limestone, gray, dark-gray or dove colored, weathering white, hard, siliceous, often crossbedded, oolitic, with occasional beds of red shale or shaly sandstone, usually pure, with crystalline streaks; contains fragmentary marine fossils	15-25m (50-75ft)
	Pickaway		Limestone, dark, hard and siliceous, characteristically with stylolites(?) filled with fine siliceous matter, has several beds of red and brown calcareous shales and sandstones; sparingly fossiliferous	<50m (175ft)
	Taggard		Shale and limestone, red calcareous shales at top and bottom, gray or red oolitic limestone between shales	<10m (30ft)
	Patton		Limestone at top, dark-gray to red, hard, siliceous, shaly; shale at bottom, red, calcareous, sandy	<15m (50ft)
	Sinks Grove		Limestone, dark, weathering yellow, hard, cherty, slightly oolitic, thin-bedded; contains marine fossils	<15m (50ft)
	Hillsdale		Limestone, like Sinks Grove except usually thick-bedded	<10m(30ft)
	Maccrady or Pocono Group		Shales and sandstones, highly calcareous at top, deltaic sequence of redbeds in Pocono Group	

Fig. 7- 6 Stratigraphic Column of the Greenbrier Group in West Virginia (Werner, 1983)

7.5 Pine Mountain Overthrust

Also known as the Cumberland Mountains, the Pine Mountain Overthrust contains the highest elevations in the State of Kentucky with an elevation of 385 m on Big Black Mountain. The ridge is composed of the clastic sediments of the Lee Formation of Pennsylvanian age. Cave and karst development is restricted to the thin exposure of limestone that crop out on the steeply dipping ridge. Because of the great relief, the deepest caves and pits in Kentucky are found in this region (Saunders, 1985). A commercial cave, Cujo's Cavern, is found in the approach to the historic Cumberland Gap which was a favored transportation route for westward expansion in colonial times.

7.6 Cumberland Plateau and Pottsville Escarpment

The western edge of the Appalachian Plateau in Kentucky is known locally as the Cumberland Plateau. This upland surface lies to the east of the Blue Grass Basin and has an outcrop pattern running from the northeast to the southwest which can be seen on Fig. 7-7. The Cumberland Plateau has a surface comprised of Mississippian and Pennsylvanian clastics which are cut by deeply incised streams such as the Cumberland River, Rockcastle River, and Buck Creek. Large caves such as Sloans Valley Cave System, Cave Creek, Coral Cave, and many smaller systems are found in the underlying Mississippian limestone. For having such an extensive collection of large caves, this region is one of the world's least studied karst regions. The Sloans Valley Cave System, at nearly 40 km in length, has only one masters thesis and one monograph written about it (Ferry, 1984; Malott and McGrain, 1977).

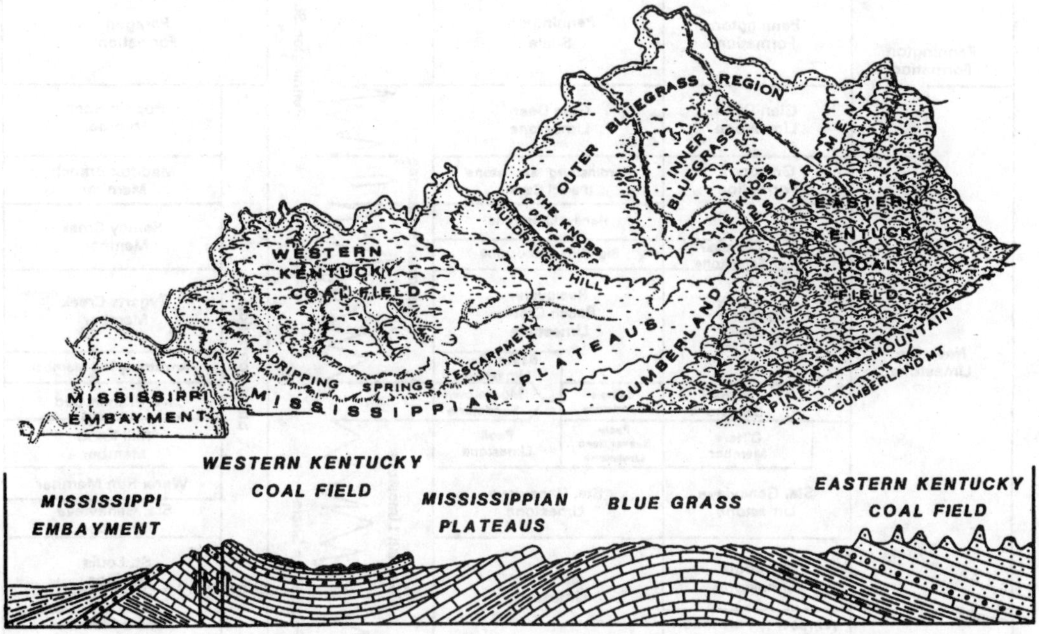

Fig. 7-7 Cross-Section of the Cincinnati Arch of Kentucky (McGrain, 1983)

Although the Cumberland Plateau karst is the mirror image of the Mammoth Cave region, which is found in the Dripping Springs Escarpment on the western flanks of the Cincinnati Arch, there is little similarity in the geologic nomenclature. Geomorphologically the areas are similar in their original depositional environments and in the structural similarity but the distance between the two is too great for there to be continuity in the characteristics of the geologic formations.

The major cave and karst formation of the Cumberland Escarpment is the Slade Formation, formerly called the Newman Limestone in which the St. Louis and Ste. Genevieve members are the major limestone units. The Slade Formation is primarily composed of carbonate rocks and consists of twelve members and one bed. It reaches a maximum thickness of 100 m in Pulaski County near the Sloans Valley Cave System. Fig. 7-8 shows a stratigraphic column of the Cumberland Escarpment area. Except the Maddox Branch and Ramey Creek Members and the Cave Branch Bed, which are shale, the rest of the Slade Formation is karstified carbonates. Maximum karst development occurs in the St. Louis and the Ste. Genevieve members, which occupy a smaller portion of the stratigraphic column than in the previous classification (Dever, 1980; Ettensohn et al., 1984).

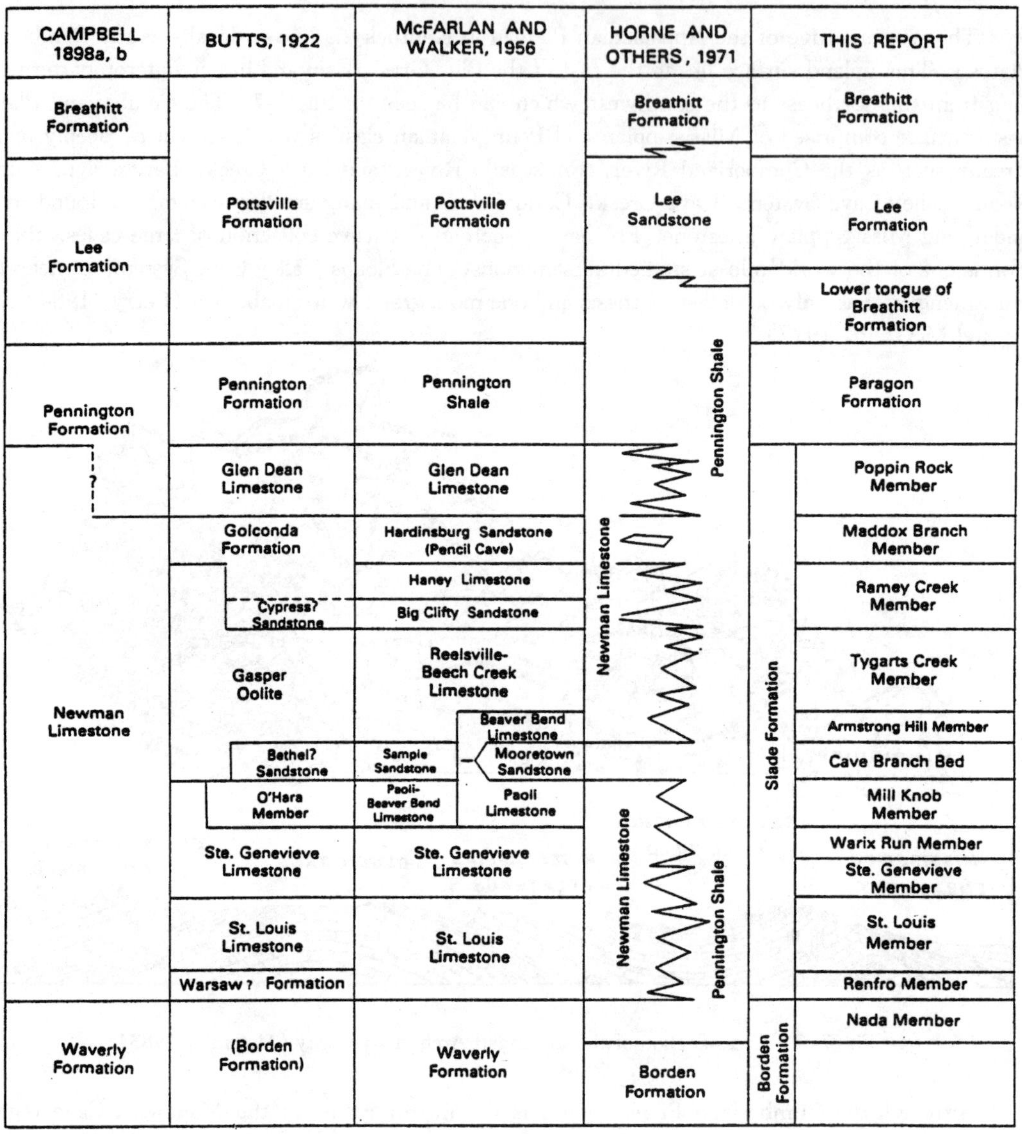

Fig. 7-8 Stratigraphic Column of the Slade and Paragon Formations of the Cumberland Escarpment (Ettensohn et al., 1984)

The Slade is overlain by the Paragon Formation, primarily shale and previously called the Pennington Formation, which is divided into four members (Ettensohn et al., 1984). In the valleys where the Paragon Formation has been eroded away to expose the Slade Formation such as in Sloans Valley, extensive cave systems have formed in the valley bottoms. Drainage sinks rapidly and is carried to the major streams of the region, which are incised 30 – 100 m below the plateau surface in gorges such as that of the Cumberland River.

The Sloans Valley Cave System consists of a multiple layer cave system. The area is currently the site of a hotly contested legal battle in which a landfill has been located on the Paragon Formation on the hilltops near the entrance to the cave system. Questions about the permeability of the Paragon Formation and the subsequent contamination of the cave system by landfill leachate have been raised by several local researchers.

7.7 Blue Grass Basin

Fig. 7- 7 shows a cross section of the Cincinnati Arch, a large anticlinal structure with its center at Lexington, Kentucky. Erosion of the Pennsylvanian and Mississippian clastics has uncovered a large area of thin-bedded Ordovician limestones. The area is characterized by an undulating upland surface, small karst features, generally less than 50 m of relief, and a number of short caves and karst springs which originally influenced the early settlement patterns of the area. The limestone bedding is too thin for the development of large caves.

The region has been subjected to urban sprawl associated with the Lexington Metropolitan Region and, as such, exhibits many karst related problems. Channelization of urban stormwater runoff into karst features and subsidence are examples of prevalent problems. Further information on this area can be found in a chapter by Thrailkill in *Caves and Karst of Kentucky* (Thrailkill, 1985).

This concludes the transect of the karst regions from Washington, D. C. to Mammoth Cave, Kentucky. The rest of the chapter will give an in-depth analysis of the research that is taking place at Friars Hole, West Virginia. Material on the speleogenesis and the dating of speleothems will highlight the research that is being done presently in the Appalachian Karst.

7.8 Friars Hole Cave System

The Friars Hole Cave System straddles the Pocahontas/Greenbrier county line in southeastern West Virginia. The cave is over 72 km long and has ten entrances. One of entrances and some of the passages associated with that entrance was named Snedegar's Cave, after its initial discovery. Other cave passages and associated entrances were also given names after those discoveries. Later, the caves were connected by further exploration, and eventually the entire system was named the Friars Hole Cave System. Greenville Saltpeter Cave is a separate cave and is located in Monroe County. Research by the second author of this chapter was conducted in Greenville Saltpeter Cave as well as in the Friars Hole Cave System.

According to Storrick (1992), the Friars Hole Cave System is largely developed in the Union and Pickaway Members of the Mississippian Greenbrier Group. The beds in this area strike approximately N 20° E and dip about 6°NW.

Storrick (1992) estimates the Union limestone to be about 40 to 50 m (130 to 160 feet) thick in the vicinity of Friars Hole. The rock is a hard, grey to dark grey oolitic limestone. It is largely massive with shaley beds at the top of the formation. Marine fossils are quite common.

The Pickaway limestone is about 26 m (85 feet) thick near the cave. It is a dark, brittle rock with many shaley layers and few fossils.

Storrick's (1992) description of Friars Hole Cave System is quite complete and details the morphology of the many rooms and passage segments of this large system. For more information beyond the scope of this paper, the interested reader should refer to his work.

7.9 Dating Surface and Cave Evolution at Friars Hole

Nearly fifty uranium-thorium dates from speleothems in Friars Hole Cave System have enabled the chronology of the cave and of the overlying surface to be established. Stalagmite and flowstone samples were collected from throughout Friars Hole Cave System. The aim was to investigate the antiquity of the cave, so only inactive speleothems were sampled. Thirty-seven of the 47 analyses yielded finite (< 350ka) uranium-thorium ages. The initial $^{234}U/^{238}U$ ratios for the 37 younger samples are 2.19 ±0.40. These ratios are sufficiently far from the equilibrium value of 1.00 that U/U ratios can be used to estimate the ages of the older speleothems (Gascoyne et al., 1983). Three of the older speleothems have U/U ages > 1 million years, and two of these, 82023 and 83067, are paleomagnetically reversed, which confirms their age to be > 750000 years. The third speleothem, 83061, has U/U in equilibrium but has normal polarity. This suggests that it was deposited during the Olduvai sub-chron or earlier, and has an age of > 1.72 million years.

7.9.1 *Age Distribution of Speleothems*

The distribution of speleothem ages is shown in Fig. 7-9, and may be described by:

$$A = 3.15\ e^{(0.13\ n)}$$

where A is the speleothem age in thousands of years before present and n is the cumulative number of speleothems of that age or younger. The paucity of old speleothems is expected for two reasons. First, speleothems are most common directly below surface outcrops of limestone; the area of the limestone inliers along Friars Hole has been increasing over time, and so the rate of speleothem deposition has increased. Second, speleothem "extinction" will be caused by erosion or by burial by clastic sediments, and so will also be a function of time.

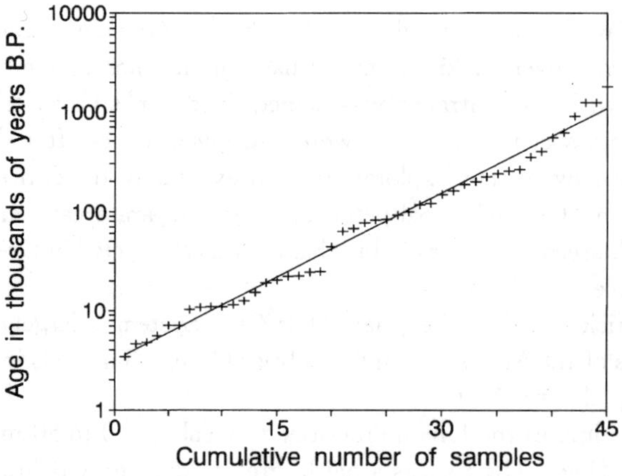

Fig. 7-9 Age Distribution of Speleothem Samples from Friars Hole Cave System

Friars Hole lay about 250 km south of the southernmost ice margin in the Pleistocene, so little speleothem deposition would be expected during cold periods. No speleothems were dated from the period 19 ka to 16 ka, which corresponds with the maximum extent of the late Wisconsin ice sheet. There are 11 samples dated from the Holocene, with the youngest speleothem date being 3400 years. The lack of younger dates is because actively growing speleothems were not sampled and because most speleothem dates were basal dates, from the oldest part of the speleothem.

7.9.2 *Evolution of the Cave*

Many of the larger passages in Friars Hole Cave System are subhorizontal and closely follow the strike of the strata. Worthington (1984) suggests that the major strike passages are associated with a falling water table, and proposes six stages in the evolution of the cave. In the central part of the cave these stages are associated with water table levels at or above 725 m, 717 m, 680 m, 665 m, 625 m, and 592 m above sea level. The two oldest speleothems are the most significant for estimating the age of the cave. Sample 83067 is >750000 years old, and grew 53 m above the present lowest point in the cave, at 676 m a. s. l. in a Stage 3 passage. This gives a maximum base level lowering rate of 123 mm/ka since the end of the Matuyama chron. However, since the U/U ratio is in equilibrium, the probable maximum lowering rate is 65 mm/ka since 1.24 million years before present (B. P.). Sample 83061 is >1.72 million years old (probability = 0.93), and grew at 640 m in a Stage 4 passage. This gives a maximum base level lowering rate of 31 mm/ka since the end of the Olduvai subchron.

This estimated maximum base level lowering rate at Friars Hole is similar to erosion rates estimated elsewhere on limestone strata in the Appalachian Mountains. At Mammoth Cave (Kentucky), paleomagnetic sampling of vertical sequences of sediments by Schmidt (1982) revealed both normal and reversed polarities. His preferred interpretation gives an age for the cave of 2 Ma, and a base level lowering rate of 34 mm/ka. In a West Virginia holokarst, Ogden (1982) estimates a lowering rate of 22 mm/ka.

If the lowering rate of not more than 31 mm/ka occurred throughout the history of Friars Hole Cave System, then the highest phreatic passage in the cave (the Skyway) was formed at least 4.2 Ma B. P.

7.9.3 *Evolution of the Surface above the Cave*

Parts of the Little Levels and Great Savanna, holokarst surfaces near to Friars Hole, have been attributed to the Harrisburg Peneplain (White and White, 1983). A base level lowering rate of not greater than 31 mm/ka would give an age of at least 6.3 Ma for this erosion surface, which correlates with the late Tertiary age suggested by several authors.

At Friars Hole, the evolution of the cave is closely linked to the drainage of Hills Creek. The original sinkpoint into the limestone was at 780 m a. s. l., at the highest outcrop point of the limestone along the Hills Creek valley. The flow from the catchment of 54 km^2 was captured underground into the Skyway, the highest phreatic trunk passage in the cave (Fig. 7-10, Stage 1). Over the last four million years, continued stream downcutting has exposed almost 3 km^2 of Union Limestone as inliers along Friars Hole. Hills Creek continues to provide the largest sinking stream, but there are several smaller sinking streams in addition (Fig. 7-10, Stage 6B).

7.10 Condensation, Condensation Corrosion, and Associated Features in Snedegar's and Greenville Saltpeter Caves

A number of interesting features are produced by condensation corrosion and associated processes in caves of the eastern United States. These features are rarely noted and receive almost no attention in the mainstream cave literature. The features include drop dents, condensation trails (or

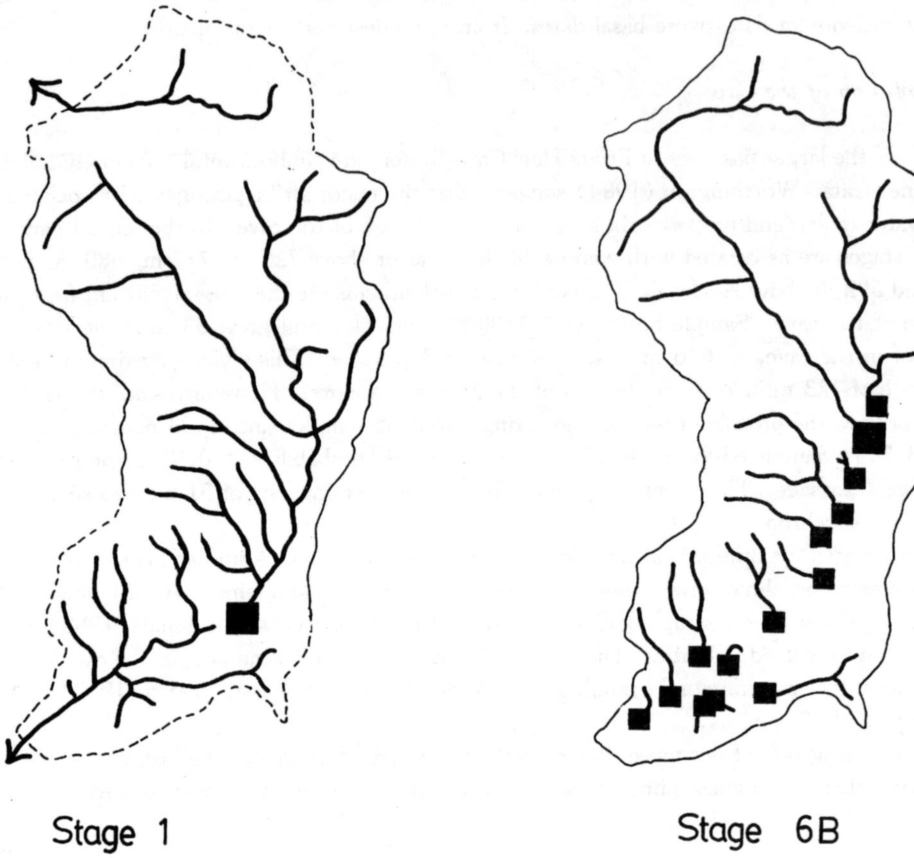

Fig. 7- 10 Surface Drainage Patterns along Friars Hole: Stage 1. Initial Breaching of the Limestone by Hills Creek. Stage 6B. Modern Surface Drainage

rills), associated evaporative crusts, edge patches, splash patches, drip holes, and drip hole rings (Jameson, 1985; Jameson, 1989; Jameson and Alexander, 1990; Jameson, in preparation). Such features are significantly different in form, distribution, and genesis from the features produced by condensation and evaporation processes in caves of the western U. S. Accounts of the latter features can be found in Hill (1987) and in Davis (1995).

7.10.1 *Air Circulation*

The bulk of the water involved in condensation corrosion and deposition is directly derived from surface atmospheric moisture via air circulation. To a large extent, air circulation patterns control the temporal and spatial distribution of condensation and thus also the distribution of the resulting features. However, some of the water can be derived from waters that first flowed into the cave and then evaporated from streams, waterfalls, or drip sites.

Snedegar's Cave (Pocahontas and Greenbrier counties, West Virginia) and Greenville Saltpeter Cave (Monroe County, West Virginia) are multi-entrance caves. Entrances lie at different elevations. Consequently, both caves have a well-developed air circulation. This is due in part to the chimney effect, whereby cooler air is relatively dense and tends to sink while warmer air is less dense and tends to rise (Wigley and Brown, 1976). When cave air is cooler than outside air, as in much of the summer, air flow is out of the lower entrances and into the upper entrances. When cave air is warmer than outside air, air flow is out of the upper entrances and into the lower entrances. Air also circulates as a result of the passage of frontal systems and in response to daily insolation and pressure cycles. The picture is further complicated by the effects of local winds, which can blow past an entrance, lower air pressure, and induce an outward air flow by the Bernoulli effect. Convective cells can operate, in which air flow is into the cave along the ceiling and out of the cave along the floor. Finally, sinking streams can frictionally entrain air, in effect pulling outside air into entrances just above stream level.

7.10.2 *Types of Condensation: Fogs, Films, Drops, and Absorbed Moisture*

In the summer, warm air that is relatively moist is available to enter the caves. That air is readily cooled to the dew point, resulting in condensation. Condensation occurs in the air as a fog or on bedrock as films and drops. Films and drops are highly visible as condensate because light reflects off the water. Most of the condensation is in the upper parts of passages, along ceilings and upper walls.

Condensation on clastic sediments on floors tends to be absorbed and is rarely reflective. Some condensation occurs on clays in cracks, clays on breakdown or walls, or on clay vermiculations. The moisture on vermiculations can be fully absorbed and give little evidence of absorption, or can be extensive enough to change the reflective and textural character of the clays. In many areas of Snedegar's Cave, the hue and textural appearance of vermiculations provides a subtle clue that condensation is active, though not at rates sufficient large or sufficiently lengthy as to produce an overall appearance of wetness. In some areas, the clays and other materials forming vermiculations appear to be relatively saturated and also support thousands of small drops ($<1-2$ mm) that hang delicately suspended from tiny threads of clay.

If condensation rates are sufficiently large, condensate drips from walls and ceilings. The floor rapidly becomes wet. It is difficult to tell how much of the floor moisture is from direct condensation and how much is from drippage. However, at many passage sites, air circulation patterns and measurements of dry and wet bulb temperatures at varying elevations clearly show that relatively warm air moves over cooler air. Most of the condensation occurs along ceilings and upper walls, a fact that is confirmed by noting the distribution of wet/dry lines on cave walls. Wet/dry lines can extend subhorizontally over hundreds to thousands of feet of passage. They can sharply demarcate areas of active condensation from areas lacking condensation. Alternatively — particularly early or late in the condensation season — they may be highly irregular. Irregular wet/dry lines mostly reflect differences in the distance films have moved down walls or are irregular where drips have fallen different distances before encountering morphologic irregularities on walls.

7.10.3 *Fogs and Fog Banks*

Snedegar's and Greenville Saltpeter Caves have extensive condensation fogs in near-entrance passages. The fogs develop by May or early June and may persist throughout the summer. The fogs can disappear rapidly — within a few days to a week — following the onset of cooler weather in the fall. Cool weather in the summer cuts off much of the energy differential that drives air circulation and condensation, so persistent cool weather tends to dissipate the fogs. The fogs can fill entire passages or be confined spatially within passages. The spatial distribution of fog is a function of the amount of time that favorable conditions have lasted. It is a function also of the type of fog-forming process. For example, some fogs form as a result of the introduction of warm surface water. The water vaporizes into relatively cool cave air in passages near swallet entrances. Such vaporization tends to fill the entire passage with fog, particularly in smaller passages or in circumstances in which warm summer thunderstorms produce rapid runoff that inundates the entire cave streambed.

In some passages, air circulation is inward along the ceiling and outward along the floor, but is sufficiently slow and nonturbulent that mixing is minimal. Then the fogs may be confined to the upper part of the passage. An erie effect is created, in which the lower passage is relatively clear, but the upper part is foggy and highly reflective of light. The effect is most surreal when the fog/no fog boundary lies at about waist level, and the caver is forced to remove lights from the helmet and hold them below waist level for safer visibility. The trunk passage just past the Saltpetre entrance to Snedegar's Cave is particularly susceptible to these fog/no fog boundaries. A useful term for these fogs is 'fog bank'. Fog banks are most likely to be observed early in the summer or late in the summer. They may appear anytime, however, if persistent cool weather interrupts the muggy summer days characteristic of the Central and Southern Appalachian Mountains.

7.10.4 *Features of Condensation Corrosion and Deposition*

The condensate absorbs carbon dioxide from the atmosphere, forming carbonic acid. It is thus capable of dissolving calcite. The condensate often has a sufficiently long period of contact with the limestone bedrock to dissolve distinctive features. Some of the typical features of condensation corrosion and deposition are shown schematically in Fig. 7-11, and in photos 59 – 61. These features include drop dents, condensation trails, edge patches, and splash patches. Such dissolutional features undoubtedly take many years to form.

Because cave passages undergo alternating condensation and evaporation cycles, redeposition of the dissolved calcite is common. Redeposition takes two primary forms. The most extensive is as calcite crusts on ceilings, walls, and breakdown. The drop dents and condensation trails (or rills) are usually accompanied by these calcite crusts. Drop dents and condensation trails may be thought of as being 'set into' the crusts, as shown in Photos 59 and 60. Photo 59 depicts relatively large drop dents set in a calcite crust on a horizontal undercut in the Saltpeter Maze of Snedegar's Cave. The larger drops are about 10 mm in diameter. The limestone is oolitic. Small holes can be seen within the drop dents; they mark the locations of ooids that have dissolved (or have been loosened by dissolution and fallen out).

Photo 60 depicts small drop dents, sinuous condensation trails, elliptical splash patches, and calcite crusts. The white crusts are not uniformly distributed on this wall of the North Canyon of Snedegar's Cave. Along the left side of the photo and at its base (to the left of the lens cap), the crusts appear superimposed on scallops. The crusts are confined largely to the lee eddies of the scallop flow patterns (flow is left to right). The scallops are actively being formed, through floods that occur for short periods each year, primarily in the spring. However, condensation corrosion and redeposition of calcite crusts also occur during the summer. Evidently there is a delicate balance between the rate of dissolution to form scallops and the rate of condensation corrosion and redeposition to form crusts on the scallops. The crusts are present on the scallops precisely in the scallop locations that are believed to have the lowest dissolutional rates during scallop formation.

The second form of redeposition of the calcite is as calcite crusts in or at the surface of clastic sediments (usually muds) on the floor. These crusts or 'drip hole rings' are primarily associated with drip holes, as depicted in the photo 61 and schematically explained in Fig. 7- 12.

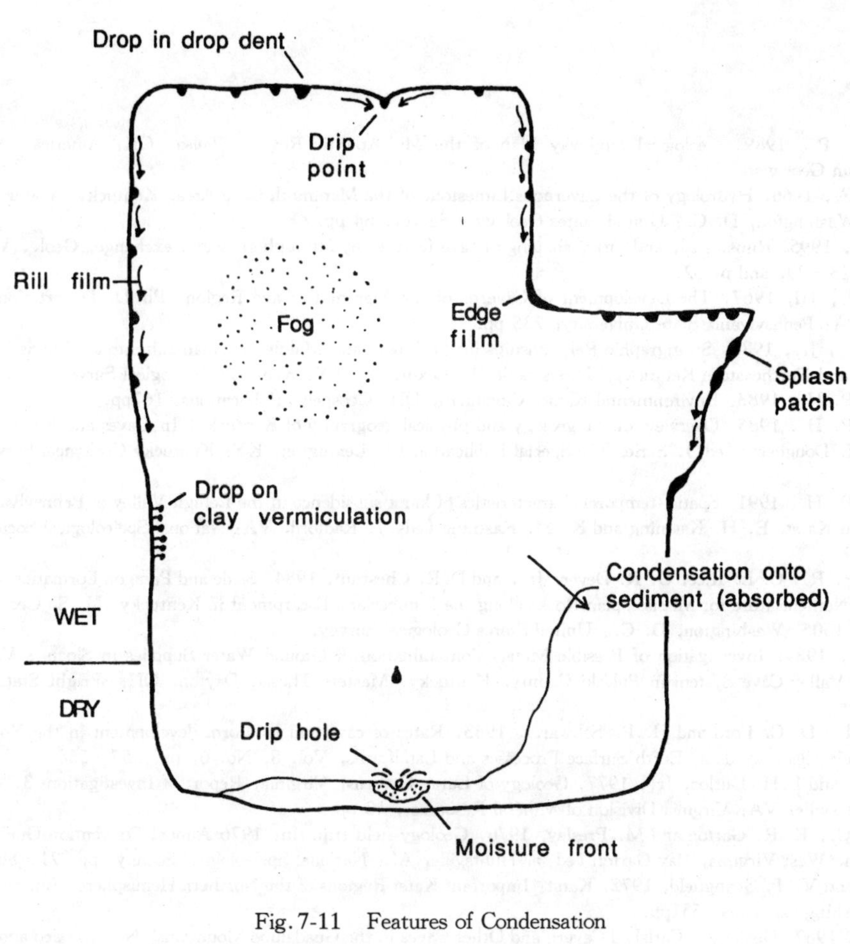

Fig. 7-11 Features of Condensation

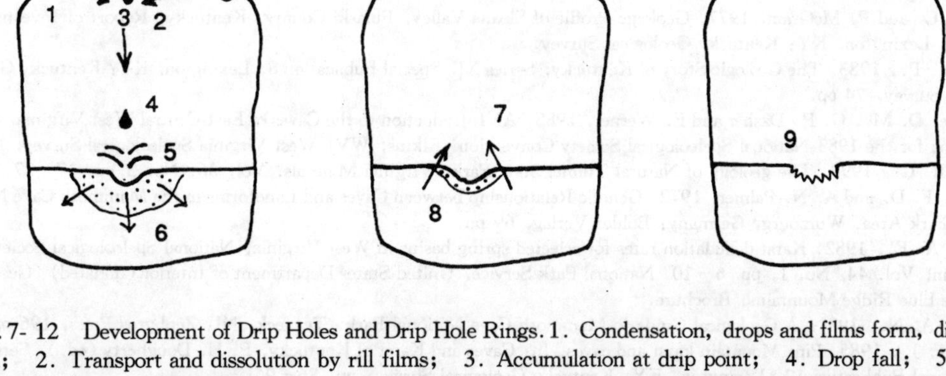

Fig. 7-12 Development of Drip Holes and Drip Hole Rings. 1. Condensation, drops and films form, dissolution; 2. Transport and dissolution by rill films; 3. Accumulation at drip point; 4. Drop fall; 5. Impact, splash erosion, drip holes form, exposing pebbles; 6. Absorption of water in sediment; 7. Evaporation at surface; 8. Decrease in water storage; 9. Precipitation of drip hole rings

References

Bennison, A. P., 1989. Geological Highway Map of the Mid-Atlantic Region. Tulsa, OK: American Association of Petroleum Geologists.

Brown, R. F., 1966. Hydrology of the Cavernous Limestone of the Mammoth Cave Area, Kentucky. Water Supply Paper 1837. Washington, D. C.: United States Geological Survey, 64 pp.

Davis, D. G, 1995. Rims, rills, and rafts: shaping of cave features by atmospheric water exchange, Geol., Vol. 22, No. 2, pp. 23 – 29, and p. 32.

Deike, G. H., III, 1967. The Development of Caverns of the Mammoth Cave Region. Ph. D. Dissertation. University Park, PA: Pennsylvania State University, 235 pp.

Dever, G. R., Jr., 1980. Stratigraphic Relationships in the Lower and Middle Newman Limestone (Mississippian), East-Central and Northeastern Kentucky. Thesis Series 1. Lexington, KY: Kentucky Geological Survey.

Dougherty, P. H., 1983. Environmental Karst. Cincinnati, OH: Geospeleo Publications, 167pp.

Dougherty, P. H., 1985. Overview of the geology and physical geography of Kentucky. In: Caves and Karst of Kentucky, Percy H. Dougherty (ed.). Series XI, Special Publication 12. Lexington, KY: Kentucky Geological Survey, pp. 5 – 17.

Dougherty, P. H., 1991. Spatial-temporal characteristics of karst subsidence in the Lehigh Valley of Pennsylvania, In: Appalachian Karst, E. H. Kastning and K. M. Kastning (eds.). Radford, VA: National Speleological Society, pp. 139 – 145.

Ettensohn, F. R., C. L. Rice, G. R. Dever, Jr., and D. R. Chestnut, 1984. Slade and Paragon Formations--New Stratigraphic Nomenclature for Mississippian Rocks along the Cumberland Escarpment in Kentucky. U. S. Geological Society Bulletin 1605. Washington, D. C.: United States Geological Survey.

Ferry, J. P., 1984. Investigation of Possible Metals Contamination of Ground Water Supplies in Sloan's Valley and the Sloan's Valley Cave System in Pulaski County, Kentucky. Masters Thesis. Dayton, OH: Wright State University, 75pp.

Gascoyne, M., D. C. Ford and H. P. Schwarcz, 1983. Rates of cave and landform development in the Yorkshire Dales from speleothem age data, Earth Surface Processes and Landforms, Vol. 8, No. 6, pp. 557 – 568.

Hack, J. T. and L. H. Durloo, Jr., 1977. Geology of Luray Caverns, Virginia. Report of Investigations 3. (revised ed.) Charlottesville, VA: Virginia Division of Mineral Resources, 43 pp.

Hempel, J. C., E. R. Garton and M. Presley, 1976. Geology field trip. In: 1976 Annual Convention Guidebook: Morgantown, West Virginia, Ray Garton (ed.). Huntsville, AL: National Speleological Society, pp. 71 – 80.

Herak, M. and V. T. Stringfield, 1972. Karst: Important Karst Regions of the Northern Hemisphere. Amsterdam: Elsevier Publishing Company, 551pp.

Hill, C. A., 1987. Geology of Carlsbad Cavern and Other Caves in the Guadalupe Mountains, New Mexico and Texas. Bulletin 117. Socorro, NM: New Mexico Bureau of Mines and Mineral Resources, 150pp.

Jameson, R. A., 1985. Structural Segments and the Analysis of Flow Paths in the North Canyon of Snedegar's Cave, Friars Hole Cave System, West Virginia. Masters Thesis. Morgantown, WV: West Virginia University, 421pp.

Jameson, R. A., 1989. Features of condensation corrosion in caves of the Greenbrier karst, West Virginia, Program, 1989 Convention of the National Speleological Society, Sewanee, TN, p. 56.

Jameson, R. A., and E. C. Alexander, Jr., 1990. Hydrology and chemistry of condensation waters in Snedegar's and Greenville Saltpetre Caves, West Virginia, Program, 1990 Convention of the National Speleological Society, Yreka, CA, pp. 34 – 35.

Malott, C. and P. McGrain, 1977. Geologic Profile of Sloans Valley, Pulaski County, Kentucky. Report of Investigations 20. Lexington, KY: Kentucky Geological Survey.

McGrain, P., 1983. The Geologic Story of Kentucky. Series XI, Special Publication 8. Lexington, KY: Kentucky Geological Survey, 74 pp.

Medville, D. M., G. R. Dasher and E. Werner, 1983. An Introduction to the Caves of East-Central West Virginia. Guidebook for the 1983 National Speleological Society Convention. Elkins, WV: West Virginia Speleological Survey, 146pp.

Milici, R. C., 1990. The geology of Natural Tunnel State Park, Virginia Minerals. Vol. 36, No. 3, pp. 17 – 27.

Miotke, F. D. and A. N. Palmer, 1972. Genetic Relationship between Caves and Landforms in the Mammoth Cave National Park Area. Wurzburg, Germany: Bohler Verlag, 69 pp.

Ogden, A. E., 1982. Karst denudation rates for selected spring basins in West Virginia, National Speleological Society Bulletin, Vol. 44, No. 1, pp. 6 – 10. National Park Service, United States Department of Interior (undated). Geology of the Blue Ridge Mountains. Brochure.

Palmer, A. N., 1981. A Geological Guide to Mammoth Cave National Park. Teaneck, NJ: Zephyrus Press, 196 pp.

Saunders, J., 1985. Pine Mountain karst and caves. In: Caves and Karst of Kentucky, P. H. Dougherty (ed.). Series XI, Special Publication 12. Lexington, KY: Kentucky Geological Survey, pp. 86 – 96.

Schmidt, V. A., 1982. Magnetostratigraphy of sediments in Mammoth Cave, Kentucky, Science, Vol. 217, pp. 827 – 829.

Storrick, G. D., 1992. The Caves and Karst Hydrology of Southern Pocahontas County and the Upper Spring Creek Valley. Bulletin 10. Barrackville, WV: West Virginia Speleological Survey, 215pp.

Thrailkill, J., 1985. "The Inner Bluegrass Karst Region," in: Caves and Karst of Kentucky, Percy H. Dougherty (ed.). Series XI, Special Publication 12. Lexington, KY: Kentucky Geological Survey, pp. 28 – 62.

Werner, E., 1981. Guidebook to the Karst of the Central Appalachians. Bowling Green, KY: Eighth International Congress of Speleology.

Werner, E., 1983. Self-guided geology field trip. In: An Introduction to the Caves of East-Central West Virginia, Douglas M. Medville, G. R. Dasher and E. Werner (eds.). Guidebook for the 1983 National Speleological Society Convention. Elkins, WV: West Virginia Speleological Survey, pp. 137 – 142.

White, W. B., and E. L. White, 1983. Patterns of cave development and speleogenesis in West Virginia. In: An Introduction to the Caves of East-Central West Virginia, Douglas M. Medville, G. R. Dasher, and E. Werner(eds.). Guidebook for the 1983 National Speleological Society Convention. Elkins, WV: West Virginia Speleological Survey, pp. 7 – 24.

Wigley, T. M. L. and M. C. Brown, 1976. The physics of caves. In: The Science of Speleology, T. D. Ford and C. H. D. Cullingford (eds.). London: Academic Press, pp. 329 – 358.

Worthington, S. R. H., 1984. The Paleodrainage of an Appalachian Fluviokarst: Friars Hole, West Virginia. Masters Thesis. Hamilton, Ontario: McMaster University, 218pp.

Global Karst Correlation
Edited by Yuan Daoxian and Liu Zaihua
Science Press and VSP BV, 1998

Chapter 8 Karst of Japan

Kazuko Urushibara-Yoshino[1], Naruhiko Kashima[2]
[1] *Dept. Natural Sciences, Komazawa University, Tokyo*
[2] *Dept. Geology, Ehime University, Matsuyama*

8.1 Distribution of Calcareous Rock in Japan

The karst in Japan is very limited. It totals about 1654 km^2, which is 0.44% of the whole territory of the country. The largest karst area is found in its southwest part. This contains about one-third of Japan's karst. Almost all of karst in the Southwest islands is on the Quaternary uplifted coral areas. However, some of the limestone are of Palaeozoic era. For example, in Honshu, there are many patchy areas: about 200 km^2 in Iwate Prefecture, 87 km^2 in Okayama Prefecture, 85 km^2 in Gifu Prefecture and 75 km^2 in Yamaguchi Prefecture. The longest cave is supposed to be the Akkado cave in Iwate Prefecture. The Akkado cave system is very complicated and it has not been investigated thoroughly as yet. The most famous show cave in Japan is Akiyoshi-do in Yamaguchi Perfecture. All of the karst areas in Japan are distributed as shown by dots in Fig. 8-1. Because the areas of calcareous rock are not wide enough in Japan, no complete karst system has developed. Therefore, no closed polje is seen on Akiyoshi Plateau, although semi and open poljes are observed. Japanese traditional terms for expressing karst phenomenon are few. In Okayama, people used the term "kanachiana" to express sinkhole and cave. The fields in the bottom of dolines are called "Kubobata", a sinkhole is called a pit "Jibasu" in Akiyoshi. In Okinawa and Kagoshima Prefecture, people have a special name for underground river, "Kurago", and "Gama" for cave.

The Akiyoshi Plateau, Kikai island and Minamidaito island will be discussed in the following sections as examples of Japanese karst.

8.2 Geology of Japanese Karst Areas

The Japanese Islands are divided geologically into two major regions, Northeast Japan and Southwest Japan. This division is caused by the Tanakura Tectonic Line which crosses the east central part of Honshu in N-S direction. Southwest Japan is divided into the Inner Zone (the Sea of Japan side) and the Outer Zone (the Pacific Ocean side), by the Median Tectonic Line which runs longitudinally through the Island Arc.

As shown in Tab. 8-1, calcareous rocks (limestone, dolomite and marble) occur in the Japanese Islands on numerous stratigraphic horizones. The main distribution and ages of these carbonate rocks are noted in stratigraphic order.

Pre-Cambrian marbles occur in the Hida metamorphic terrain, the north central part of Honshu (the main island of Japan) and are accompanied by the Hida quartzofeldspathic gneiss and the Unazuki crystalline schists in the Inner Zone of Southwest Japan.

Limestone occurs in the Silurian and the Ordovician Systems in three regions of Japan: the northern one being the Silurian Kawauchi Formation in the South Kitakami terrain, Northeast Ja-

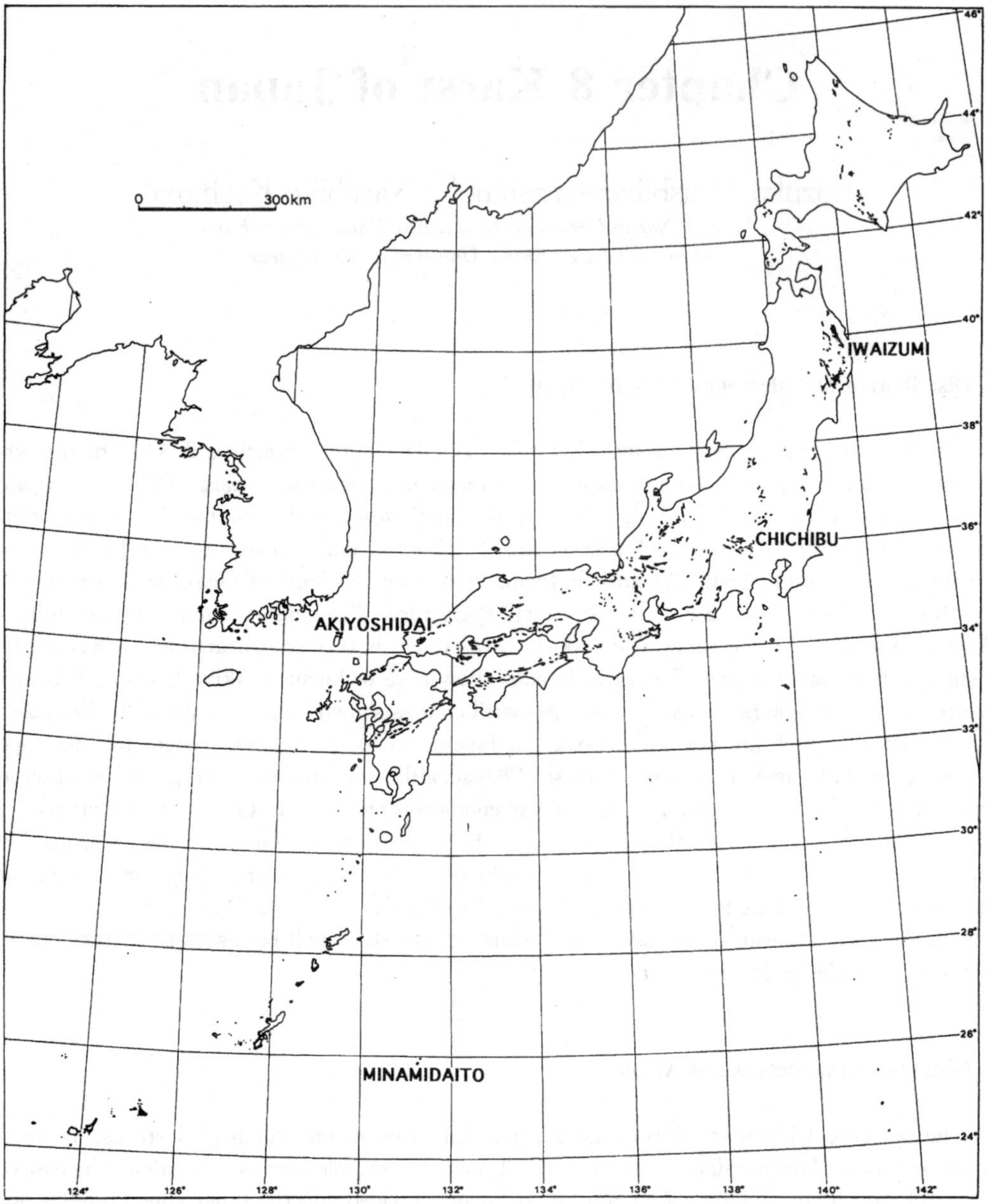

Fig. 8-1 Distribution of calcareous rock in Japan

pan; the middle one being the Devonian Fukuji Formation and it correlates with the Hida marginal tectonic belt (Hida-Gaien Belt) of the Inner Zone of Southwest Japan; the southwestern one being the Siluro-Devonian lenticular limestones of the Gionyama and Okanaro Groups and this correlates with the Kurosegawa Tectonic Zone of the Outer Zone of Southwest Japan.

Carboniferous limestones occur in the south Kitakami terrain of Northeast Japan, i. e. in the Yokota and Sumita groups, and the Outer zone of Southwest Japan, i. e. in the Ichinotani Forma-

Tab. 8-1 Geologic Ages and Distribution of Calcareous Rocks in Japan

Province / Geologic age		Southwest Japan: Inner Zone	Southwest Japan: Outer Zone	Northeast Japan: Southern Kitakami, Abukuma	Northeast Japan: North Kitakami	Hokkaido
Cenozoic	Quaternary		Ryukyu Ls.			
	Tertiary					Nakatonbetsu F.
Mesozoic	Cretaceous	Meso-Paleozoic E. of Hino T.	Sambagawa HR.			Hidaka G.
	Jurassic	Meso-Paleozoic E. of Tanba T.; Ryoke HR.	Meso-Paleozoic E. of Chichibu T.; Torinosu G.	Nakanosawa F.; Asio G.	Akka F. Shiriyamisaki Ls.	
	Triassic		Bukosan Ls. Sambosan G.			Kamiiso G.
Paleozoic	Permian	Omi Ls. Atetsu Ls. Taishaku Ls. Akiyoshi Ls. Yayamadake Ls.; Nabeyama F. Asio Ls. Ibukiyama Ls.	Nippara F. Oonogahara F.; Tsukumi Ls.	Yukizawa G.; Hitachi HR.		
	Carboniferous	Ichinotani F.	Itadorigawa G.	Sumita G. Yokota G.		
	Devonian	Kamianama G. Fukuji F.	Suberidani G. Okanaro G. Yokokura G. Gionyama G.	Ono F.		
	Silurian			Kawauchi F.		
	Ordovician					
	Cambrian					
Precambrian		Unazuki crystalline schists Hida metamorphic rocks(gneiss)				

Abbreviations, E:Erathem, G:Group, F:Formation, Ls:Limestone, HR:Metamorphic Rocks and T:Terrane.

tion and Itadorigawa Group.

Permo-Carboniferous fossiliferous limestone plateaus such as Omi, Atetsu, Taishaku, Akiyoshi, Yayamadake and its correlates are the most important karst regions in Japan. Limestone masses consist of reef complexes underlain by greenstone bodies.

Permian Limestone masses occur in as Nippara, Oonogahara, in the outer Zone and as Asio, Fujiwaradake, Ibukiyama in the Inner Zone of Southwest Japan.

Triaso-Permian Tsukumi limestone (contains some dolomite) occur in the Outer Zone of Southwest Japan. The Bukousan limestone and limestone beds in the Sambosan Group in the Outer Zone, and limestone in the Kamiiso Group in Hokkaido belongs to Triassic in age.

Jurassic limestones, so-called "Torinosu limestone" and its correlates have a distribution from the Outer Zone of Southwest Japan to Hokkaido.

The strata containing the pre-Cretaceous limestones belong to the Chichibu Belt of the Outer Zone in Southwest Japan. They are olistostromal and accretionary blocks and were constructed during the Late Jurassic or Early Cretaceous in age.

Marble beds are present in the Ryoke metamorphic terrain of Inner Zone, Southwest Japan and the age of the original sediments show that they are largely Upper Triassic to Middle Jurassic. Calcareous schist lenses have been recorded from the Sambagawa regional metamorphic terrain of the Outer Zone of Southwest Japan. The original rocks of the Sambagawa schists are accretionary complexes of Latest Jurassic and/or Early Cretaceous. Tertiary limestone occurs in Hokkaido. This belongs to the Nakatonbetsu Formation.

Finally, Quaternary Ryukyu limestone occurs in the Islands of Ryukyu archipelago where they occur mainly as uplifted reef limestone.

8.3 Akiyoshi Plateau

The Akiyoshi Plateau is composed by Carboniferous to Permian limestone. The geological map is shown in Fig. 8-2, which was published by Ota (1968, 1977). The northwestern part is covered by strongly faulted and reversed limestone, but the southeastern part of the Plateau is covered by gentlly faulted and normal Akiyoshi limestone. The surrounding area of the Plateau is covered by Palaeozoic sandstone, chert, granodiorite and porphyrite. The Akiyoshi limestone group has been studied by many geologists. According to Ota (1968), Akiyoshi limestone group was deposited as a geosynclinal organic reef complex, from the early Carboniferous to the late Permian age. The northwestern half of the geosynclinal organic reef complex was overturned by the Akiyoshi Orogenic Movement from the northwest to southeast during Permian or Early Triassic. On the other hand, Taira (1989) explained that the reef complex limestone of the Akiyoshi Plateau is an accretionary prism. This Plateau is divided into the east and west by Koto River. Akiyoshi-do (Akiyoshi cave) is located on the southwest of the eastern part of the Plateau. Fujii(1996) discussed the hydrogeology of this area. According to his results, the discharge area of Akiyoshi-do is estimated as 15.4 − 18.5 km^2. The circulation of underground water is rather fast. However, the high contents of Tritium has also been observed as temporary. Therefore, the slow circulation of underground mass is also suggested to have existed. The width of underground water system is estimated to be 500 − 800 m from a runoff area of about 7 km^2, and a watershed of 9 km^2. The hydrogeological map of Akiyoshi is shown in Fig. 8-3 (Fujii, 1996). The underground water levels of the limestone Plateau are also shown in this figure. On the Plateau, dolines and uvalas are distributed along the fault lines, joints and tectonic lines. As mentioned above closed poljes have never existed. Open and semi poljes are formed in the contact places (borders) of limestone and non calcareous rocks. The plains on the Plateau are divided into five levels by Kawano(1983), namely, Jigokudai 410 − 370 m, Managatake

350 – 320 m, Chojagamori 310 – 280m, Wakatakebara 260 – 240 m, and Kyozuka 210 – 218 m a. s.l. It is estimated that the formation of the Chojagamori Plain occurred at the early Pleistocene to middle Pleistocene. The Wakatakebara Plain is assumed to be the late Pleistocene. The cave levels are classified into three leveles. The high level cave group (higher than 250 m) is mainly a vertical pit. The caves higher than 320 m were formed probably before the formation of Chojagamori Plain. But most caves of 320 – 280 m are considered to have been formed during the Chojyagamori formation, early the Pleistocene to middle Pleistocene. The middle level cave group is situated at a height of 250 – 130 m (mostly 180 – 160 m). This cave group, with vertical difference of 80 – 50 m and horizontal caves (180 – 170 m) is mainly distributed on the Wakatakebara. This cave group is considered to have been formed at late Pleistocene after the formation of the Wakatakebara Plain. The low level cave group are formed on the foot of the Plateau. Vertical (130 – 120 m a.s.l.) and horizontal caves (120 – 100 m a.s.l.) make up this group.

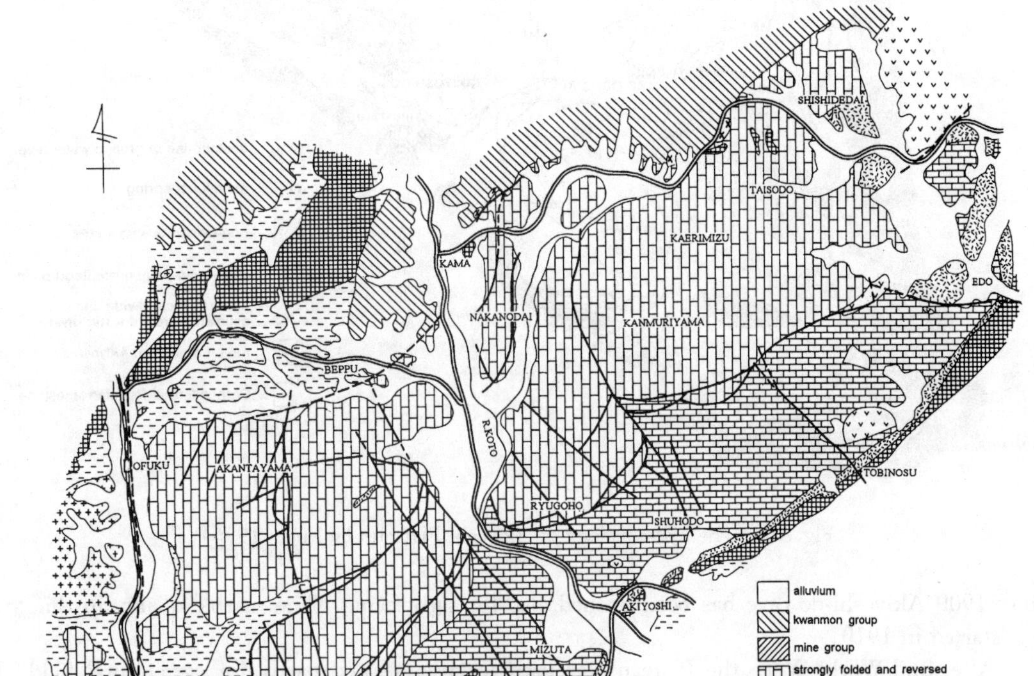

Fig. 8-2 The geology of Akiyoshi Plateau (Urushibara compiled the 2 figures by Ota 1968, and 1997)

On this Plateau, many pre-historic instruments have been found in uvalas and dolines. Since the middle ages, the bottoms of dolines have usually been cultivated. The limestone Plateaus were used as public grasslands, where people could harvest public grasses for cattle and house-roofing.

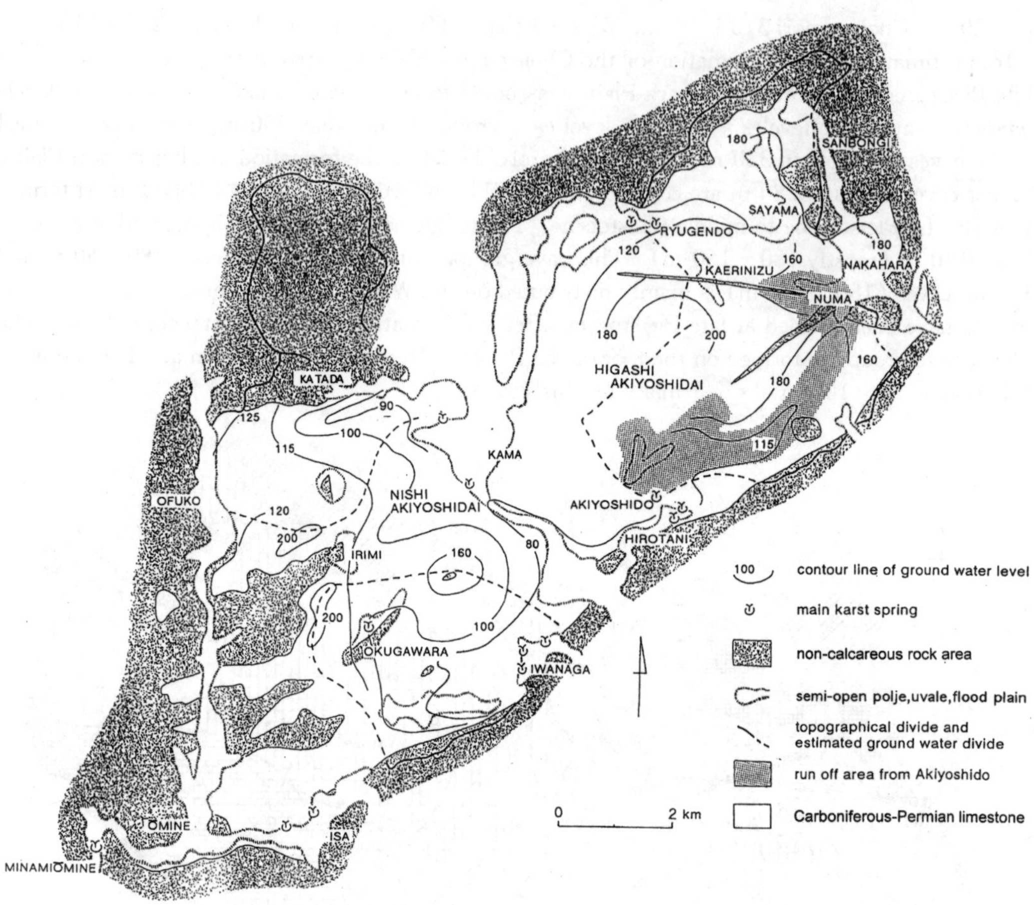

Fig. 8-3 The hydrogeology of Akiyoshi Plateau (by Fujii, 1996)

Since 1909 Akiyoshi-do cave has been opened also for sightseeing. The marble quarry in this area was started in 1910.

After 2nd World War, the Plateau was used for pasture and partly for agricultural field. In 1955, this plateau became a National Park. In early spring of every year, people in Shuhocho City burn off the vegetation to encourage the *Miscanthus cinensis* dominance.

8.4 Kikai Island

Kikai island is 55.7 km^2, located west of the Ryukyu trench. It is slightly tilted towards the west. This island is overlaid by the Pleistocene reef sediments on the Neogene sedimentary rocks (Somachi Formation) and forms a table like surface. The marine terraces are classified into five groups by Nakagawa (1967). Konishi et al. (1974) dated the corals by the Uranium series method as 125 ka, 100ka, 80 ka, 60 ka and 38 ka, which form the top layer of the terraces. These are being continuously uplifted. Koba et al. (1985) dated the corals on the highest elevation as 125 ka by ESR method. He concluded that the older limestone 500 − 400 ka was covered by younger limestone after 125 ka. Omura (1988) reported the result of detail dating of corals by the Uranium series method. The age is estimated as from 500 − 400 ka to 38 ka. The results are not parallel to the surface of the terraces. These terraces are mainly an accumulation of younger limestone and partly denudated surfaces of old corals. Ota and Omura(1992) discussed the limestone ages by the Uranium series method, and classified the Holocene terraces. They reported from Holocene terraces, (the highest one is about 13 m) from ca 6.8 ka to 1.5 ka B.P. Based on these results, Urushibara-Yoshino classified the terraces as shown on Fig. 8-4.

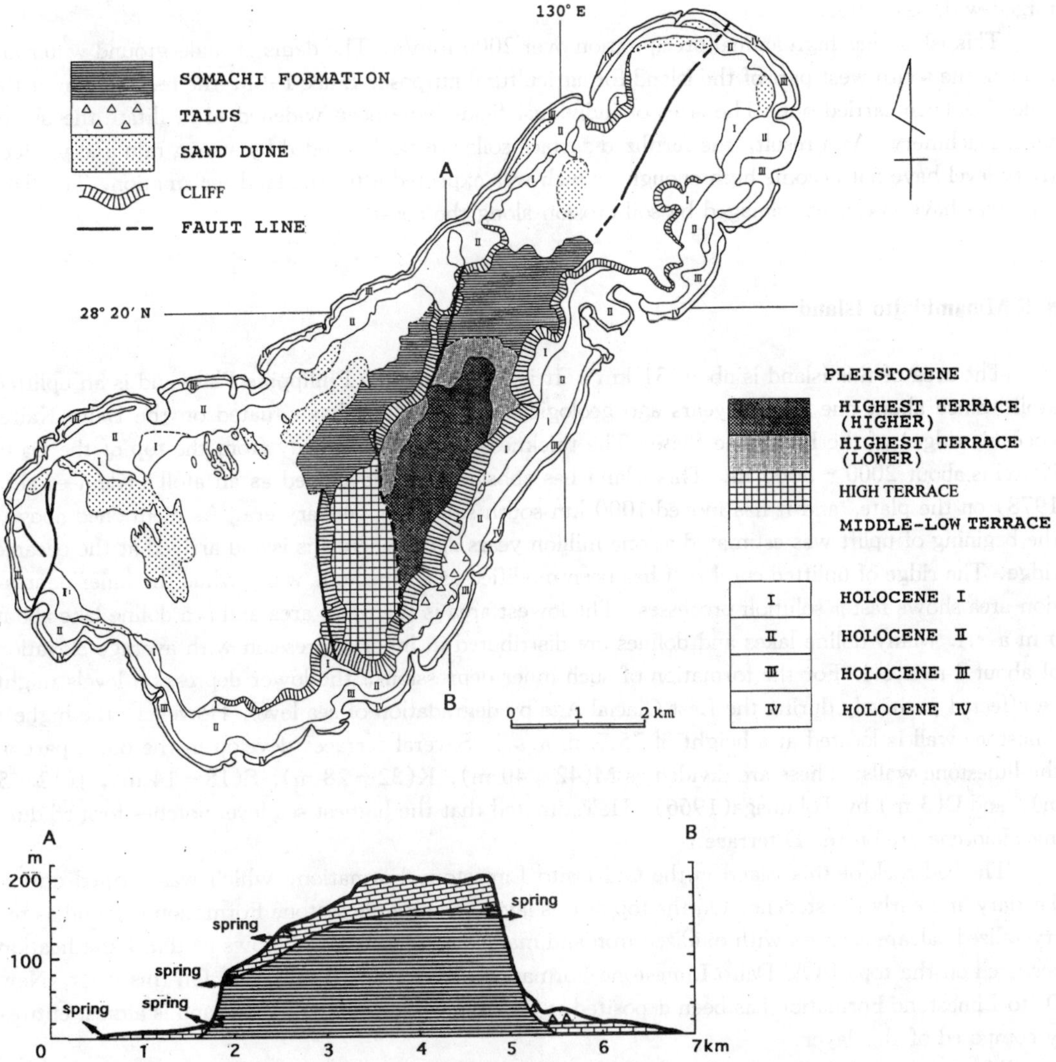

Fig. 8-4 The topographical map of Kikai Island

Karstification occurred on the highest terraces, dolines and isolated small coneshaped-hills and can be observed until today. Soil depth is changeable from place to place, but averages about 80 cm on the highest terraces. Mainly, these terraces are used as grass land, because agricultural productivity is poor. The middle terraces are used as agricultural land, mainly as sugar cane field. The old villages are located at places, where there are karst springs on the Pleistocene terraces. They use the water for domestic purposes and agriculture. Especially, Asado village has developed the springs for women and men separately. Many karst springs are distributed between the Pleistocene coral limestone and Tertiary siltstone. Even though such an underground water system has developed, the caves are generally quite short and narrow. Therefore the whole cave systems have been not discovered yet in this island.

On the Holocene terraces, the people use the underground water wells. The old villages have good fresh water, supplied from the karst rivers. However, new villages use underground water mixed with sea water.

This island has high annual precipitation over 2000 mm/a. The dams of underground water are built in the south west part of the island for agricultural purpose. Since 1965, the reclamation of the fields has been carried out. The sizes of individual fields have been widened to facilitate the use of farm machinery. As a result, the fertilized surface soils are easily eroded by strong rain and productivity level have not become high enough, which was expected after the land reclamation. The fishing areas have also been damaged by soil erosion along the coast.

8.5 Minamidaito Island

The area of this island is about 31 km^2. It is located on the Philippine Plate and is an uplifted atoll. Since about one million years ago geologically, this island has situated on the Daito Kairei (oceanic ridge) of the Philippine Plate. The thickness of the island body from the top of the Daito Kairei is about 2000 – 3000 m. This island has subsided and developed as an atoll (Klein et al., 1978) on the plate, and it has moved 1000 km south since the Tertiary era. As mentioned above, the begining of uplift was estimated as one million years ago, when this island arrived at the oceanic ridge. The ridge of uplifted coral reef has been modified as a limestone wall, while the inner depression area shows faster solution processes. The lowest area is the inner area and is a doline lake about 3 m a.s.l. Many doline lakes and dolines are distributed in inner depression with average elevation of about 8 m a.s.l. For the formation of such inner depressions, the lower depression levels might be affected positively during the Last Glacial Age by degradation of sea level. However, the highest limestone wall is located at a height of 75.2 m a.s.l. Several terraces develop in the outer part of the limestone walls. These are divided as M(42 – 40 m), K(32 – 28 m), S(18 – 14 m), J(12 – 5 m), and D(3 m) by Tokunaga(1966). He estimated that the highest sea level notches formed during Holocene are on the D terrace.

The bed rock of this island is the Old Daito Limestone Formation, which was formed during Tertiary and early Pleistocene. On the top of this layer, the Rainbowstone Formation is found as recrystalized calcareous rock with oxidized iron and manganese. This layer shows us that karstification occurred on the top of Old Daito Limestone Formation about 15 – 10 m a.s.l. On this layer, New Daito Limestone Formation has been deposited as an atoll. The surface of the island is almost entirely composed of this layer.

The outer part of this island is the lower uplifted coral about 11 m a.s.l. This has been dated as the Last Interglacial Age (Konishi, 1980) and is distributed along the coast. Koba et al. (1987) reported also the age of corals (about 12 – 7 m a.s.l.), which was from the Last Interglacial Age. Ota et al. (1991) reported that the corals were also formed at the Last Interglacial Age at a height of 12.7 m a.s.l. They estimated that the uplifted elevation was 5 m during 130 – 120 ka.

Many dolines and caves developed on the Haguuee between the limestone walls. One of these caves has been opened as the Hoshinodo cave for visitors. A lot of speleothem, helictite and long straws, longer than 1.5 m, have been formed. In the inner areas of limestone wall, dolines, deepened effectively during the Last Glacial Age, have frequently formed. Many doline lakes have fresh water on the surface layer. Since sea water below fresh water fluctuates in accordance with tidal change, the fresh water level changes twice a day. The deep soil coverage in the depression areas

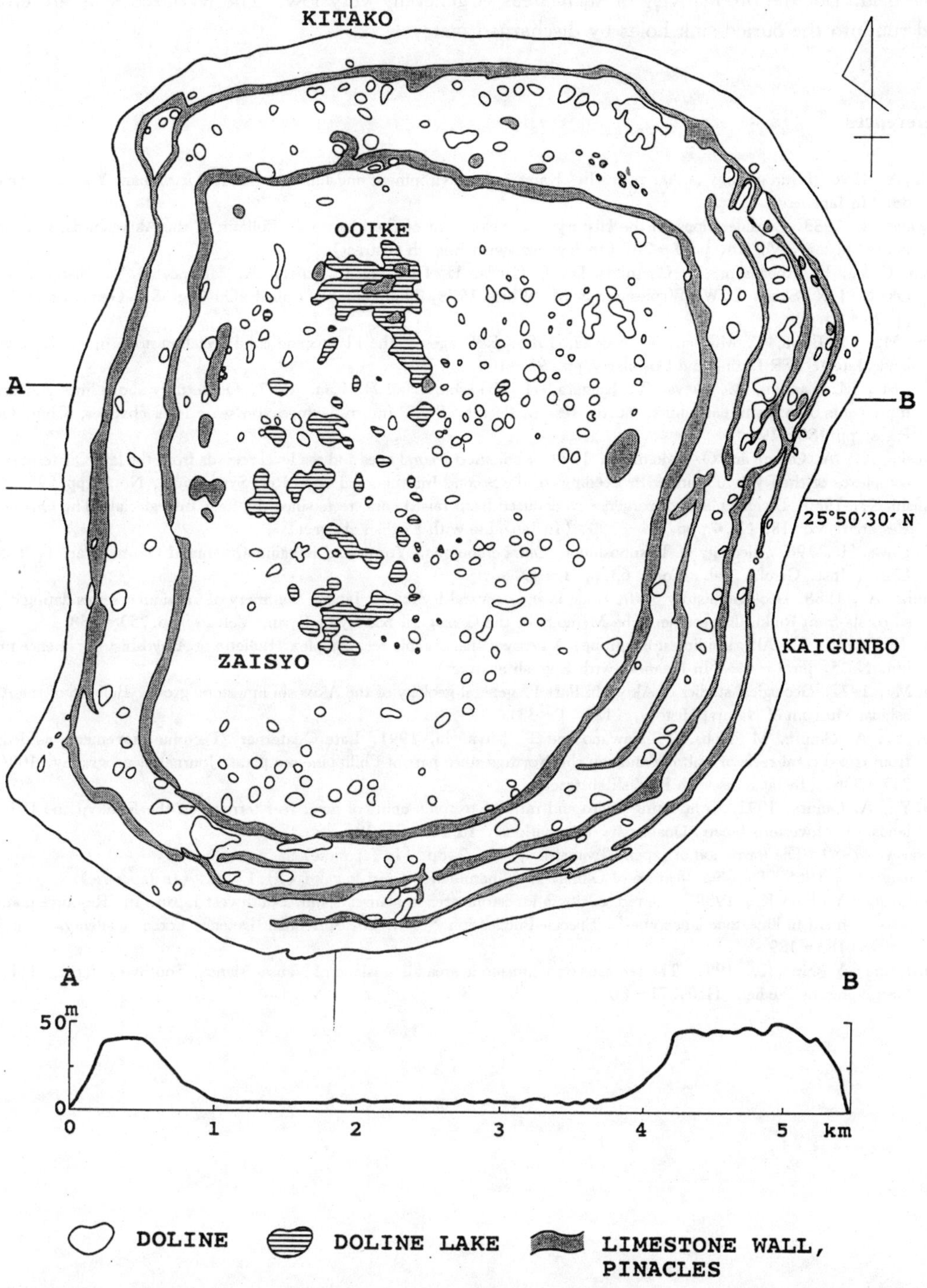

Fig. 8-5 The karst topography of Minamidaito Island

was reported by Urushibara-Yoshino(1988). Karst topography is shown in Fig. 8-5. In many small dolines, which have no water, soil accumulates in the bottom and farmers cultivate these as sugar cane field. But the productivity of such areas is generally very low. The fertilized soils are eroded and run into the buried sink holes by discharged water.

References

Fujii, A., 1996. Hydrogeology of Akiyoshi. In : Karst – the environment and human. ed. K. Urushibara-Yoshino, Taimeido. (In Japanese)

Kawano, M., 1983. Considerations on the History of Development of the limestone. Bulletin of the Akiyoshi-dai museum of natural history, Vol. 18, pp. 1 – 20. (In Japanese with English abstract)

Klein, G. V., K. Kobayashi, H. Chamley, D. M. Certis, H. Dick, D. J. Echols, A. Mizuno, G. V. Nisterenko, H. Okada, J. R. Sloan, D. W. Waples and S. M. White, 1978. Philippine Sea drilled (On Leg 58). Geotimes, Vol. 23, pp. 23 – 35.

Koba, M., M. Ikeya, T. Miki and T. Nakata, 1985. ESR ages of the Pleistocene coral reef limestone in the Ryukyu islands, Japan. ESR Dating and Dosimetry, pp. 93 – 104.

Koba, M., M. Tamura, M. Ikeya, T. Kaigara, H. Nakashima and H. Kan, 1987. Quaternary shore lines and crustal movements on Minami daito jima, north western Pacific. Proc. Intern. sympo. on sea – level changes, China Ocean Press, pp. 188 – 198.

Konishi, K., A. Omura and O. Nakamichi, 1974. Radiometric coral ages and sea level records from the late Quaternary reef complexes of the Ryukyu islands. Proceedings of the Second International Coral Reef Symposium, No. 2, pp. 595 – 613.

Konishi, K., 1980. Diverse plate convergence as deduced from raised coral reefs since the Last Interglacial. The Quaternary Research, Vol. 18, No. 4, pp. 241 – 250. (In Japanese with English abstract)

Nakagawa, H., 1967. Geology of Tokunoshima, Okinoerabujima, Yoron and Kikaijima, Amami Gunto, Part 1. Tohoku Univ., Inst. Gerol., Pal., Cont. 63, pp. 1 – 39.

Omura, A., 1988. Geologic history of the Kikai island, central Ryukyus, Japan: Summary of uranium – series dating of fossil corals from Riukiu Limestone. The Memoirs of the Geological Society of Japan, Vol. 29, pp. 253 – 268.

Ota, M., 1968. The Akiyoshi limestone group: A geosynclinal organic reef complex. Bulletin of Akiyoshi – dai science museum, No. 5, pp. 1 – 44. (In Japanese with English abstract)

Ota, M., 1977. Geological studies of Akiyoshi Part 1, general geology of the Akiyoshi limestone group. Bulletin of the Akiyoshidai Museum of Natural History, (12), 1 – 33.

Ota, Y., A. Omura, M. Koba, T. Kawano and T. Miyauchi, 1991. Late Quaternary Tectonic movements as deduced from raised coral reefs of Daito Islands on the Northwestern part of Philippine sea plate. Journal of geography, 100(3), 317 – 336. (In Japanese with English abstract)

Ota, Y., A. Omura, 1992. Contrasting styles and rates of tectonic uplift of coral reef terraces in the Ryukyu and Daito islands, Southwestern Japan. Quaternary International, 15/16. 17 – 29.

Taira, A., 1989. The formation of Japan. Iwanami syoten, 248p. (In Japanese)

Tokunaga, K., 1966. The shore feature of Okinawa, Minamidaito. Chiri kagaku, (5), 1 – 22. (In Japanese)

Urushibara – Yoshino, K., 1988. The red soils on a limestone area in Nansei island, Southwest Japan. In "Resource management in limestone landscapes". Special Publication No. 2, The Australian Defence Force Academy, Australia, 183 – 189.

Urushibara – Yoshino, K., 1992. The red soils on a limestone area kikai island of Nansei islands, Southwest Japan. Tubinger Geographische Studien, H109, 71 – 80.

Global Karst Correlation
Edited by Yuan Daoxian and Liu Zaihua
Science Press and VSP BV, 1998

Chapter 9 Karst of China

Yuan Daoxian, Li Bin, Liu Zaihua
The Institute of Karst Geology, CAGS, Guilin, China

9.1 Characteristics of Karst in China

The most important karsts in Mainland China are those developed on carbonate rocks. They total 3443 thousand km^2, including bare karst (907 thousand km^2), covered karst, and buried karst (Fig. 9-1).

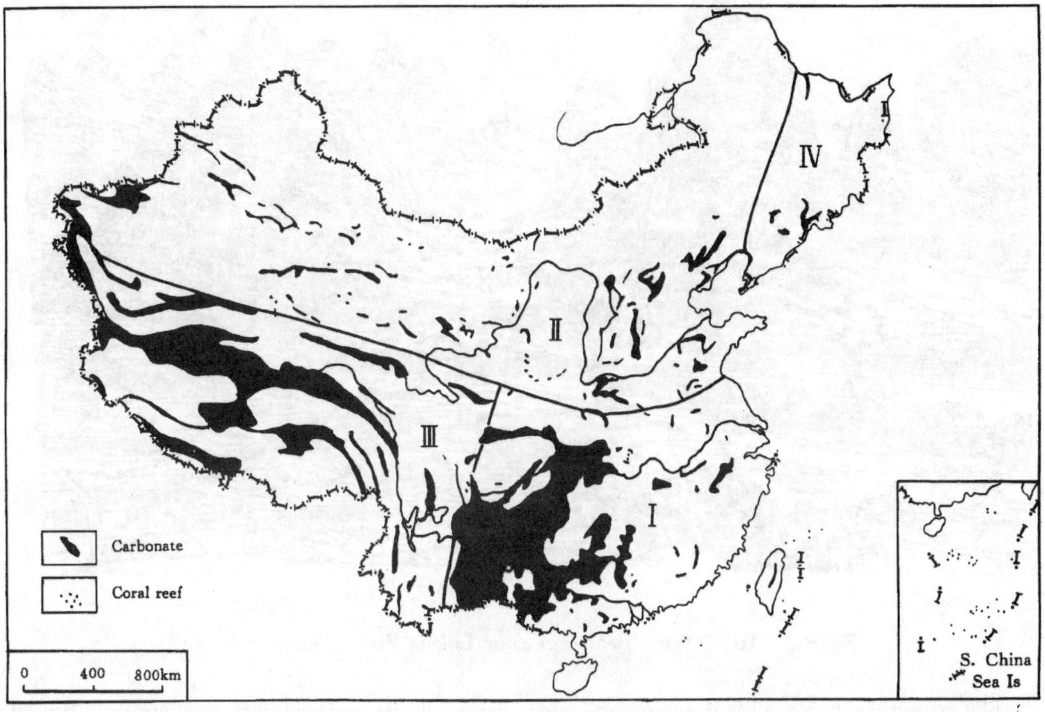

Fig. 9-1 The distribution of carbonate rocks, and major types of karst in mainland China. I —subtropical karst; II —arid, semi-arid karst; III—high mountain karst; IV—temperate semi-humid karst

Karst in mainland China is unique from a global view. This is the result from a series of favourable background for karst formation in China, e.g. old, hard, compact carbonate rocks in mainland China; strong uplift in Cenozoic Era; without continental ice sheet scouring during the last glaciation; and the matching between water and heat in the East Asia Monsoon region (Yuan, 1991a).

The major carbonate rocks in mainland China are pre-Triassic old phase, except Tibet, where there are more Jurassic and Cretaceous carbonate rocks (Li Datong, 1983). The porosities of carbonate rocks of different geological periods are generally less than 2% for limestone and 4% for dolomite respectively, with compressing strength above 1000 kg/cm^2, whereas the most widespread carbonate rocks in some other major karst regions of the world, such as southern Australia, the London Basin, the Paris Basin and Central America are those of Cenozoic or Mesozoic Era, with poor diagenesis and higher porosity (Downing, 1993). For example, the porosities of Tertiary limestone and dolomite in the Caribbean region are generally about 16% and 31 – 44% respectively. The physical mechanical properties of carbonate rocks in mainland China have strong influence on karst formation and karst features. On the surface, they bring about tower karst landform in south China rising abruptly from the plain (Fig. 9-2), whereas in the subsurface, they provide supporting skeletons for thousands of underground streams and great halls. However, in southeast Asia and Caribbean region, tower karst on Tertiary porous carbonate rocks are lower and rounded (Troester, 1992), even though they are developed under similar climate as south China. The hard lithological features have also provided favourable conditions to develop and preserve numerous microkarst features in China, such as deep sharp karren, kamenitza, notches and scallops.

Fig. 9-2 Tower Karst Landform along Lijiang River, Guilin, China

The strong Cenozoic uplift in mainland China, especially its western part, has not only brought about conspicuous karst landform, but also put the karst features formed in different geological epochs onto different altitude one after another. This tectonic background, along with the hard lithological features, has made China enjoying karst records with longest historic range and best continuity. But in other karst areas, such as South China Sea Archipelago, Yucatan Peninsula of Mexico (Back, 1992), the Quaternary uplift has been so weak and no more than the sea level fluctuation during glaciation and interglaciation. Accordingly, the historic records on karst development and paleoenvironmental change are mostly later than Late Pleistocene, with the earliest one being dated back to Early Pleistocene.

The basic tectonic features at the eastern part of mainland China, being configured by the alternate distribution of a series of northeast oriented uplift and subsidence belts of the Neocathaysian

System (Lee, 1939), are also important in featuring karst of China. They bring about the alternate appearance of bare karst, buried karst (karst underlying non-soluble bedrocks), and covered karst (karst covered by loose sediments), and are important to the formation of oil and gas field in carbonate rock reservoirs. In the bare karst of northern Guizhou plateau and southeast Sichuan Basin, because of northeast close foldings, and non-soluble rock intercalation in carbonate rocks, karst features including tower karst, dolinen, sinkholes, underground streams, and caves are all scatter or elongating in northeast direction, and form an unique karst region in China (Fig. 9-3).

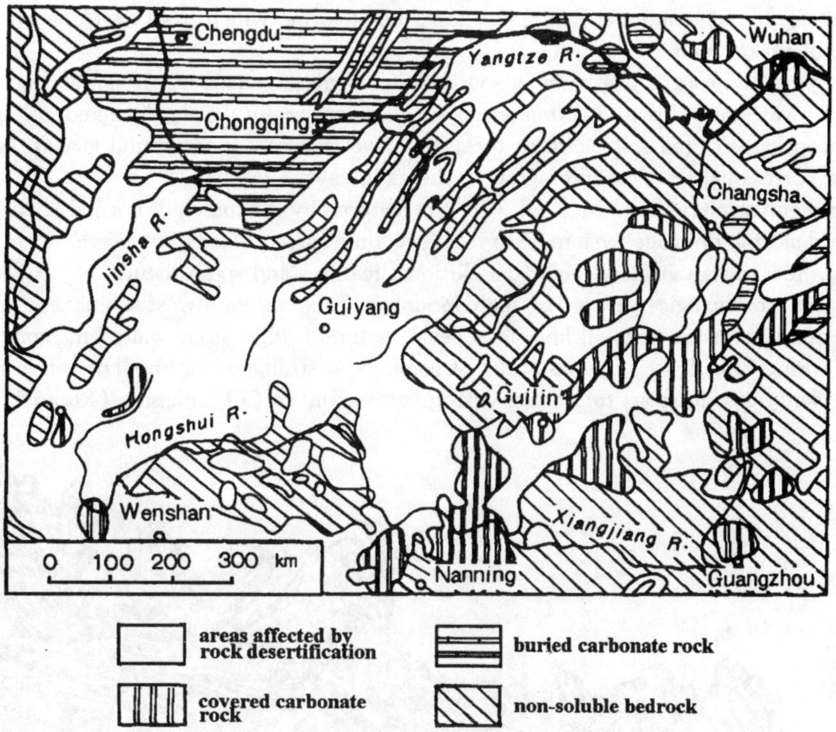

Fig. 9-3 Karst types in southwest China

Most of karst areas in Northern Europe and Northern America were scoured by continental ice sheet during the last glaciation. For instance, in Yorkshire of Northern England, Carboniferous limestone are widespread, but there are only minor karst features such as grikes, karren, kamenitza and shallow dish-shaped dolinen on the surface. They have developed after the last glaciation, and all the karst forms developed before the last glaciation have been scoured away in their entirety (Paterson and Sweeting, 1986). The Pleistocene ice sheet on Tibet plateau remains a question, but it is generally accepted that there were no ice sheets in eastern part of mainland China. With such Quaternary history, along with strong Cenozoic uplift and hard carbonate rocks, karst in China could be regarded as a paleoenvironmental karst archives with biggest information capacity.

The Mediterranean realm is another important karst of the world, but it has a climate where water and heat can not match each other, i.e. with a dry summer and wet winter. Although the snowmelting water in the summer is still favourable for big cave system to develop, the mechanical weathering has made the surface karst form seriously deteriorated (Yuan and Back, 1991b). On the contrary, the East Asia monsoon climate in mainland China enjoys good match between heat and water, i.e. with a wet summer and dry winter. The meteoric water in the summer associated with active biogenic processes, can bring about intensive chemical dissolution not only on the surface, but also underground. Thus in mainland China, especially its South, the marvellous subtropical karst shows a good match between tower karst on the surface, and underground stream systems.

The basic topographical and climatic settings of mainland China configured by the Qinghai-Tibet plateau and Qinling-Dabieshan Range bring about the tripod stand of three major karst types, namely, the humid subtropical karst in south China; the arid and semiarid karst in north China; and the high mountain karst in the southwest (Fig. 9-1). Each one has its particular karst feature complex. The latter is defined as a set of well-matched macro and micro karst forms; surface and subsurface karst forms; dissolutional and depositional karst forms which have developed under similar environmental background.

The tropical and subtropical karst in south China is characterized by the karst feature complex composed of tower karst(Photo 3), numerous dolinen, especially deeply dissected polygonal dolinen, sharp deep karren, red soil, surface tufa, big cave system, underground stream system, and many minor corrosional features and big speleothems in caves.

The arid and semiarid karst in North China is featured by the match of normal-shaped mountain (relief with dendritic drainage system), dry valley, tiny karren, limestone scree, loess cover, big karst spring, few caves with less minor dissolutional features and speleothem.

The basic morphologic features of high mountain karst in southwest China are various frost denudation products, such as small limestone peak, natural bridge, stone wall, limestone scree, and some karst springs(Fig. 9-4). On the outlet of some karst springs along modern active fault, there are usually plenty of calcareous tufa along with great amount of CO_2 emission (Photo 17).

Fig. 9-4 High mountain karst in Huanglong Ravine, Songpan County, Sichuan Province, characterized by frost denudation stone peaks and limestone scree

9.2 Mechanism of Karst Formation

To reveal the mechanism of karst formation, modern karstology takes and studies karst process as a part of global carbon cycle and its coupling water cycle and calcium (magnesium) cycle on the interfaces between lithosphere, hydrosphere, atmosphere and biosphere of the earth's system. The CO_2-H_2O-MCO_3 triphase disequilibrium open system is called as a karst dynamic system. The entering of more CO_2 into the system will form more carbonic acid, and thus intensify dissolution. In contrary, the escaping of more CO_2 from the system will deviate karst process to the direction of precipitation(Fig.1-3). Consequently, the system is quite sensitive to environmental change. For example, variation in the concentration of CO_2 in atmosphere, various biogenic processes including photosynthesis, the status of water flow including its depth, temperature, flow rate and turbulence will all change the intensity, manner, even direction of karst process. Accordingly, the only way to reveal the mechanism of karst formation is to know the characteristics of different types of karst dynamic system under different natural conditions in China through field monitoring.

Since 1981, limestone denudation rates have been observed in 13 karst areas under different natural conditions, which cover an area from Yichun, Heilongjiang province at north, to Guangzhou at south, and from Akiyoshidai, Japan (cooperation with Dr. Yoshimura Kazuhisa) at east, to Golmud, Qinghai at west. Moreover, since 1989, 7 typical karst sites have been selected to study the relationship between karst processes and the behaviour of carbon cycle, water cycle and calcium cycle in a karst dynamic system on the basis of associatedly monitoring the variation of pH, HCO_3^- and CO_2 in soil.

The results of monitoring have revealed the mechanism of karst formation in China from different angles (Yuan and Cai, 1988). For instance, the results of limestone denudation rate observation show that the intensity of dissolution has close relation with precipitation (Fig.9-5). Besides, because of the involvement of biogenic CO_2, the subsoil dissolution is generally much higher than subaerial ones. However, in some regions like Guangzhou, the subsoil denudation is weaker than subaerial as a result of the poor permeability of the stiff soil. In arid or semiarid regions like Beijing, because the annual mean evaporation is much higher than precipitation, the soil water is easy to be saturated with carbonate. The subsoil dissolution rate is not only less than subaerial ones, but the deposition of calcite could frequently happen there.

The monitoring on the behaviour of karst dynamic system has revealed more deeply the mechanism of karst formation in China. For example, in Yudong underground stream, Zhen'an county, Shaanxi province, the pH value lowers down during the summer, with the HCO_3^- rising up correspondently. It shows that following the intensification of biogenic process and carbon cycle in the summer, there will be more CO_2 entering into the karst dynamic system, and thus intensify dissolution process. The observation on the Sunjiawo calcareous tufa cascade has not only shown similar seasonal variation, but also the space variation downstream from the outlet of the karst spring. It discloses clearly the processes of water flow and disturbance, CO_2 outgassing from the system, the rapid rise of pH, and the deposition of great amount of calcareous tufa (Fig.9-6).

The observation in Huanglong Ravine, Sichuan province reveals that around some geothermal karst springs distributed along modern active fault, there are great amount of CO_2 emission into the atmosphere at a concentration as high as 23 – 78%. The $\delta^{13}C$ value of the gas bubble (−6.79‰) shows that it is originated from the depth of the earth. This finding has raised a new issue for the study on the source-sink budget of greenhouse gas in atmosphere. The rising up of pH value, and lowering down of HCO_3^- downstream on the tufa cascades in Huanglong Ravine can also tell the re-

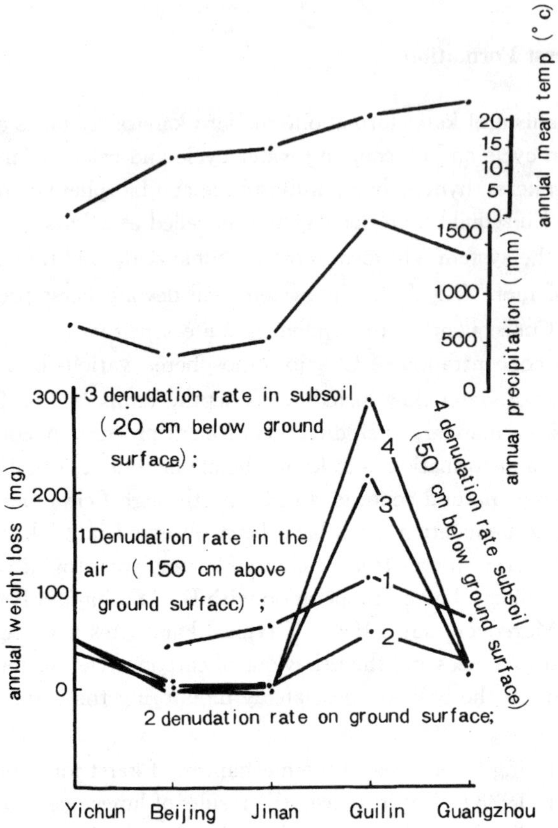

Fig. 9-5 The results of limestone denudation observation in north-south transect from Yichun to Guangzhou, east China

lationship between CO_2 degassing from the karst dynamic system and the precipitation of calcareous tufa (Liu et al., 1992).

9.3 Karst Records of Quaternary Climatic Change

A lot of works have been done in China to reconstruct Quaternary environmental change with karst sediments. Cave paleontology especially cave vertebrate paleontology and paleo-anthropology have been explored and studied for many years with success. The most important discoveries in north China are the Homo erectus Pekinensis Black (1929) from Yuanrendong cave, and the Homo sapiens sapiens from Shandindong cave (1933). Both caves are located on Dragon Bone Hill at Zhoukoudian, 48 km to the southwest of Beijing. In recent years, multidisciplinary researches with many new techniques for karst sediments in Zhoukoudian have been finished to reconstruct Quaternary environment. In South China, detailed works have been done for the Ailuropoda-stegodon fauna, and the Gigantopithecus fauna unearthed from many caves. It is noteworthy that the now extincted Gigantopithecus fossils are all found in high level caves located some 80 meters higher than the local plain, whereas the general Ailuropoda-stegodon fauna are found from low level caves. A correlated evolution sequence has been established (Ji, 1977, Tab. 9-1).

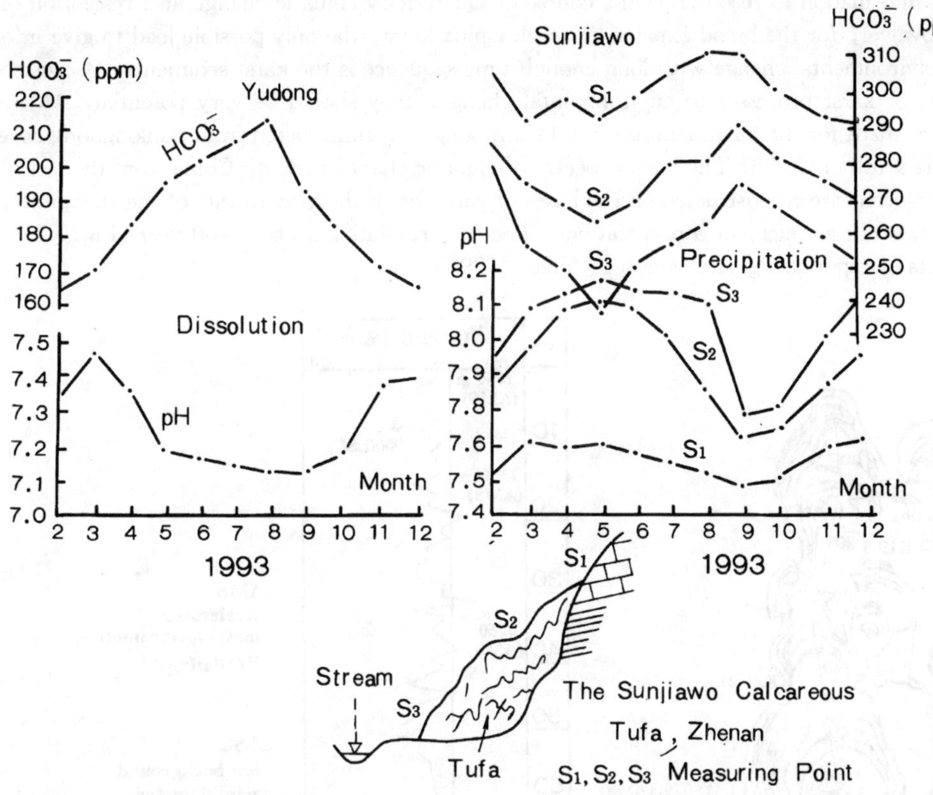

Fig. 9-6 The time and space variation of pH, HCO_3^- in a karst dynamic system, examples of dissolution (Yudong under-ground stream) and deposition (Sunjiawo calcareous Tufa cascade) in Zhen' an county, Shaanxi, China

Tab. 9-1 Evolution sequence of paleovertebrate and paleo-anthropological fossils unearthed from caves in south China(According to Ji Hongxiang, 1977)

Geological Epoch	Cave location		Representative fossils	
Late Pleistocene	cave of Liujiang Man, Guangxi		Homo Sapiens Sapiens	
	cave of Maba Man, Guangdong		Homo Sapiens neanderthalensis	
Middle Pleistocene	Juyuan Cave, Bama County, Guangxi		Bama Giganto-Pithecus fauna	Ailuropoda -Stegodon fauna
Early Pleistocene	Gaoping cave, Jianshi County, Hubei		Gigantopithecus fauna	
	Juyuan cave, Liucheng County, Guangxi		Gigantopithecus fauna	

In recent years, higher resolution records of paleoenvironmental change have been pursued in global change study. Detailed works have been carried out for loess in north China, ice cores and lacustrine deposits on plateau and high mountain of southwest China. Some of them have already provided information to reconstruct the course of Quaternary climatic change at a resolution of 100 year. However, for the broad expanse of south China karst, the only possible load to give information of environmental change with long enough time sequence is the karst sediments. Because of the sensitivity of karst processes to environmental change, they should be very potential. AMS C-14 dating was made for the micro laminae in a 1.22m long stalagmite taken from Panlongdong cave, 37 km to the south of Guilin. The whole spectra of climatic change in south China from the last glaciation to Holocene are reconstructed on the bases of variation in the growth rate of the stalagmite, isotopic data, and trace element concentrations. The time resolution is about 100 year (Fig. 9-7). Several events of rapid change are revealed (Yuan, 1994).

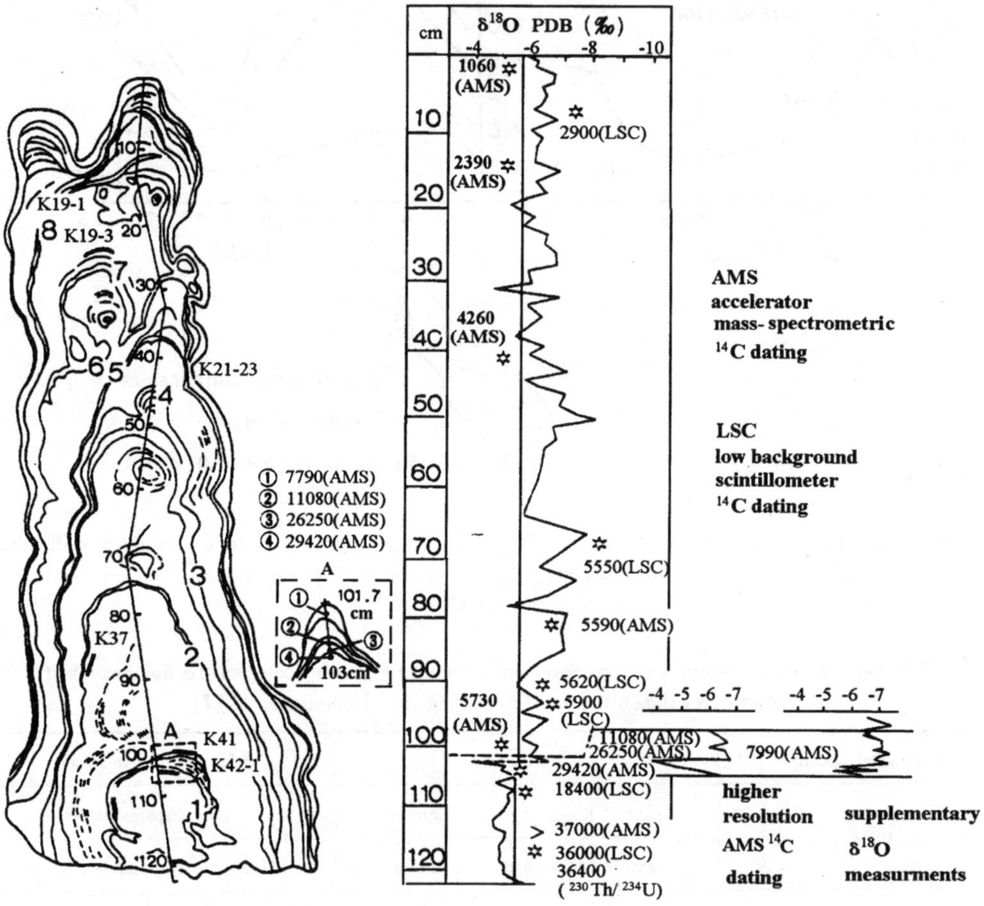

Fig. 9-7 A comprehensive profile showing the results of AMS C-14 dating and stable isotopic data

9.4 Resources and Environmental Problems in Karst Areas

Karst in China are rich in energy, mineral deposits, groundwater and tourism resources. The Shanxi plateau enjoys the key coal fields in China, but they overlie karst aquifer. In conjunction with the buried karst hill oil reservoir on its east flank, the Erdos paleokarst gas reservoir on its west flank, and the waterpower resources on middle reach of the Yellow River, it becomes the most important energy base of China. The karst plateau in south China is another important energy base because of its favourable condition for hydropower construction on Wujiang River and Hongshuihe River. The explored mineral deposit related to karst processes have more than 20 species including lead, zinc, antimony, mercury, iron, aluminum, tin, manganese, gold, uranium, copper, realgarite, kaolin, fireclay, phosphate, quartz, barite, fluorite, iceland spar, and talc. The karst groundwater resources in China total 2039.67×10^8 cm^3/a, making more than one-fourth of the total groundwater resources of the country. Especially the 2836 underground streams in south China, with a total length of 13919 km, and total flow of 1482 m^3/s, and the more than 50 big karst springs in north China, each having a discharge about 1 m^3/s, are usually the major source of local water supply.

The calcium-rich lithosphere in karst regions, with the unique surface and subsurface double-layer structure of its atmosphere, hydrosphere and biosphere, has brought about a series of particular environmental geological problems, such as leakage of water resources, drought and flood, poverty of soil, rock desertification, surface collapse, and water-gushing in mining tunnels, so that environment scientists regard karst area as a fragile environment just like desert margin. Pure carbonate rocks contain small percentage of non-soluble substances. Accordingly, its soil- forming capability is very low. The small amount of residual soil remained from intensive karstification is usually washed down and accumulated in the bottom part of karst depression, e.g, dolinen. However, this part is very unfavourable for vegetation growth, because it is inundated year after year by flood induced by the fluctuation of underground stream. Most of the trees are distributed on the upper part of doline slope with very thin soil, even bare rock. Consequently, they usually have a very long root system to get water and nutrition (Fig. 9-8). If once clearance takes place on this kind of karst forest, it is very difficult to recover, and will cause soil erosion and rock desertification. For example, in Guizhou province, the area of rock desertification had increased 3212 km^2 during the five years from 1974 to 1979. Moreover, the process has been accelerated in recent years and brought about spring exhaustion, and even shortage in drinking water for human being and animal husbandry.

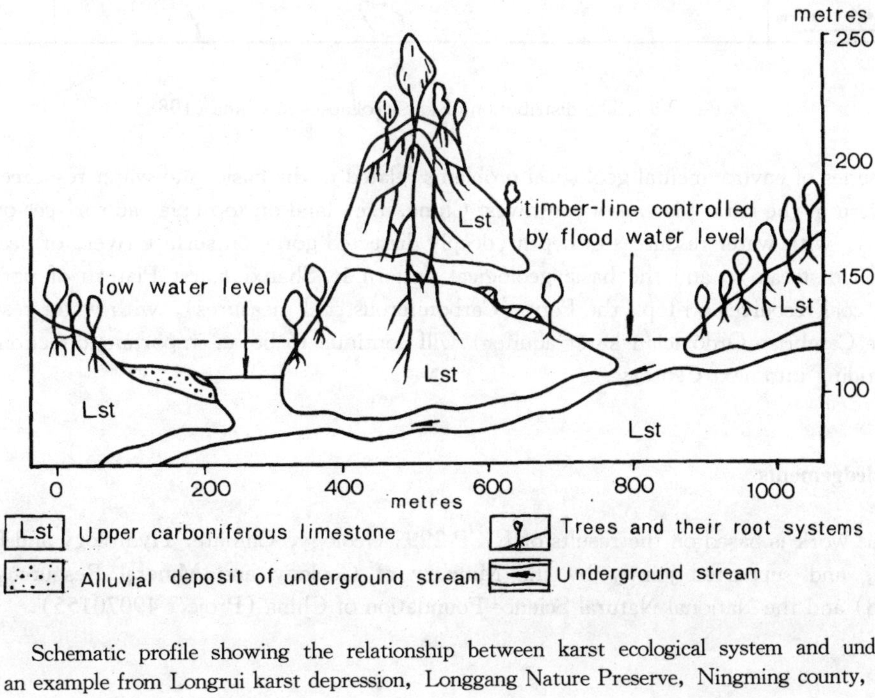

Fig. 9-8 Schematic profile showing the relationship between karst ecological system and underground stream, an example from Longrui karst depression, Longgang Nature Preserve, Ningming county, Guangxi

These areas are now the major poverty regions remained in the country.

The registered surface collapses in karst areas of China, number 738 sites, with more than 30 thousand collapse points. Karst collapse usually follows repeated and rapid fluctuation of water table induced by natural or artificial factors (Fig. 9-9). It is one of the major geological hazards in China, and can bring about serious disasters, such as building subsidence, overturning train, farmland collapse, inundating mine, and groundwater pollution.

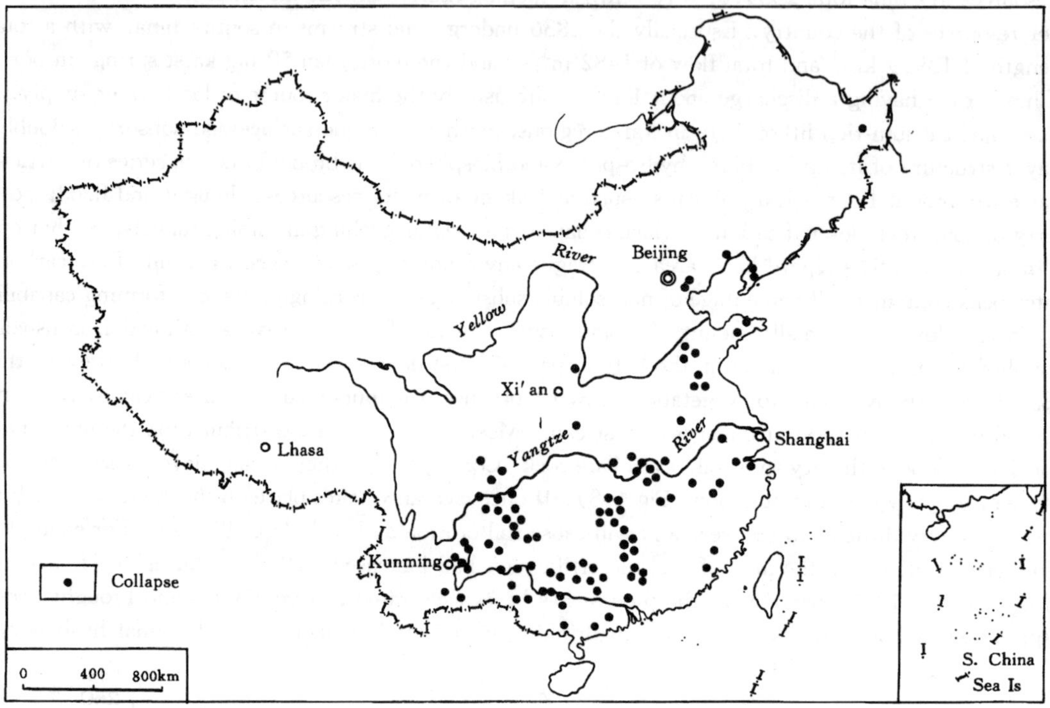

Fig. 9-9 The distribution of karst collapses in China (1988)

A series of environmental geological problems related to the basic land-water resources distribution pattern in the karst Plateau of southwest China, i.e. land on top (plateau surfaces on different elevation), with water resources at depth (deeply dissected gorge on surface river, or deeply buried underground stream), and the basic geological pattern in Shanxi Karst Plateau of north China, namely, coal resources on top (the Permo-Carboniferous coal measures), with water resources below (the Cambrian-Ordovician karst aquifer) will continue to be an important direction for karst study striding into next Century.

Acknowledgements

This work is based on the results of IGCP 299 "Geology, Climate, Hydrology and Karst Formation", and supported jointly by the Ministry of Geology and Mineral Resources (Project 8502218) and the National Natural Science Foundation of China (Project 49070155).

References

Back, W., 1992. Coastal karst formed by groundwater discharge, Yucatan, Mexico. In: Henri Paloc, William Back, Hydrogeology of selected karst regions. Verlag Heinz Heise, Hannover, Germany, pp. 461 – 466

Downing, R. A. et al., 1993. The hydrogeology of the chalk of north-west Europe, Oxford University Press, 310 pages.

Ji Hongxiang, 1977. The classification of Quaternary mammal fauna in south China, Vertebrate Palasiatica, Vol. 15, No. 4, pp. 271 – 277

Lee, J. S., 1939. The geology of China, The Woodbridge Press, LTD, Guildford, UK, pp. 211 – 246

Li Datong and Lo Yang, 1983. Measurement of carbonate rocks distribution area in China, Carsologica Sinica, Vol. 2, No. 2, pp. 147 – 150

Liu, Zaihua et al., 1992. Influence of Hydrodynamic Conditions and Water Chemistry on the Formation of Tufa in Huanglong, Sichuan. In Yuan Daoxian (Ed.), World Karst Correlation, Supplementary English Issue of Carsologica Sinica, pp. 79 – 93

Paterson, K. and M. M. Sweeting, 1986. New Direction in Karst, Geobooks, UK, 613pp.

Troester, J. W., 1992. The northern karst belt of Puerto Rico: A humid tropical karst, in Henri Paloc, William Back, Hydrogeology of Selected Karst Regions, Verlag Heinz Heise, Hannover, Germany, pp. 475 – 486

Yuan Daoxian and Cai Guihong, 1988. The Science of Karst Environment, Chongqing Publishing House, Chongqing, China, pp. 62 – 71

Yuan Daoxian, 1991a. Karst of China, Geological Publishing House, Beijing, China, 224pp.

Yuan Daoxian and W. Back, 1991b. IGCP 299: Geology, Climate, Hydrology and Karst Formation, Episodes, Vol. 14, No. 1, pp. 80 – 81

Yuan Daoxian, 1994. Sensitivity of karst process to environmental change and its records along - Ⅱ Transect, paper presented at PAGES/IGBP PEP- Ⅱ Working Group Meeting, April 9 – 12, 1994, Beijing, China

Global Karst Correlation
Edited by Yuan Daoxian and Liu Zaihua
Science Press and VSP BV, 1998

Chapter 10 Overview on Karst of Vietnam

Do Tuyet
Research Institute of Geology and Mineral Resources,
Thanhxuan, Hanoi, Vietnam

10.1 Introduction

The karst rocks in Vietnam cover about 60000 km^2, which is approximately 20% of the total area of Vietnam. Karst of Vietnam falls into the tropical karst belt of the Earth. The latter includes the karst in Laos, Thailand, especially karst in South China. In Vietnam, there are full conditions favourable for karstification, such as wide distribution of karst rocks being deposited between Pre-Cambrian and Holocene with some pure limestones strata of 2000 m thick, strong folding-faulting, high rainfall, high moisture, thick forest cover, action of microorganism, long duration of karstification and differentiation of neotectonic movements etc. In consequence of that, Vietnam is abundant in different karst landforms which are often seen in the world. Karst is interesting and should be considered to be a special resource which has been exploited and used for different economic and social purposes, particularly in renew and opening time of Vietnam.

10.2 The Major Type of Karst in Vietnam

From the map showing karstic distribution of the Earth, karst of Vietnam falls into the tropical karst belt which is the largest in comparison with karst in other climatic belts. Karst of Vietnam relates closely to karst of Laos, Thailand, South-East Asia countries and particularly of South China. These lands are similar in karst rocks, geological structure, climatic conditions with high rainfall and humid and active action of microorganism and long duration for karstification as well.

10.3 History of Karst Research in Vietnam

Although Vietnam karst covers about 20% total area of the territory, investigation for karst is just recently interested (Fig. 10-1). Before, knowledge of karst is from dispersional observations occurring in geological and geographical explorations only (Blondel, 1929; M. Colani, 1927; Le Xuan Phuong, 1957; Nguyen Duc Chinh, Vu Tu Lap, 1963; Hoang Thieu Son, 1965; Glazek J. 1966; Le Ba Thao, 1977; Dao Trong Nang, 1979; Hoang Thanh Thuy, 1972; Vu Do, 1979; Do Tuyet, 1993, 1995; Pham Khang, 1991, 1994; Nguyen Quang My, 1993, 1995; Nguyen Vi Dan, 1993; Dao Dinh Bac, 1993; Nguyen The Thon, 1993, 1994; M. Dusar, J. Masschelein, Phan Cu Tien, Do Tuyet, 1994; J. Masschelein, Ch. Delaere, Do Tuyet, 1996) There is no karst monographs in Vietnam up to 1995. Vietnam had a first project on karst but for tourism purpose only. Now a project on karst geology other than in the North-West Region of Vietnam has been carried out. It will be finished in 1998. Therefore, karst of Vietnam attracts international researchers from different countries such as England, France, Australia, Italy, Germany, New Zealand, Belgium. They often pay their attention to cave systems which may be considered as a new field of karst research.

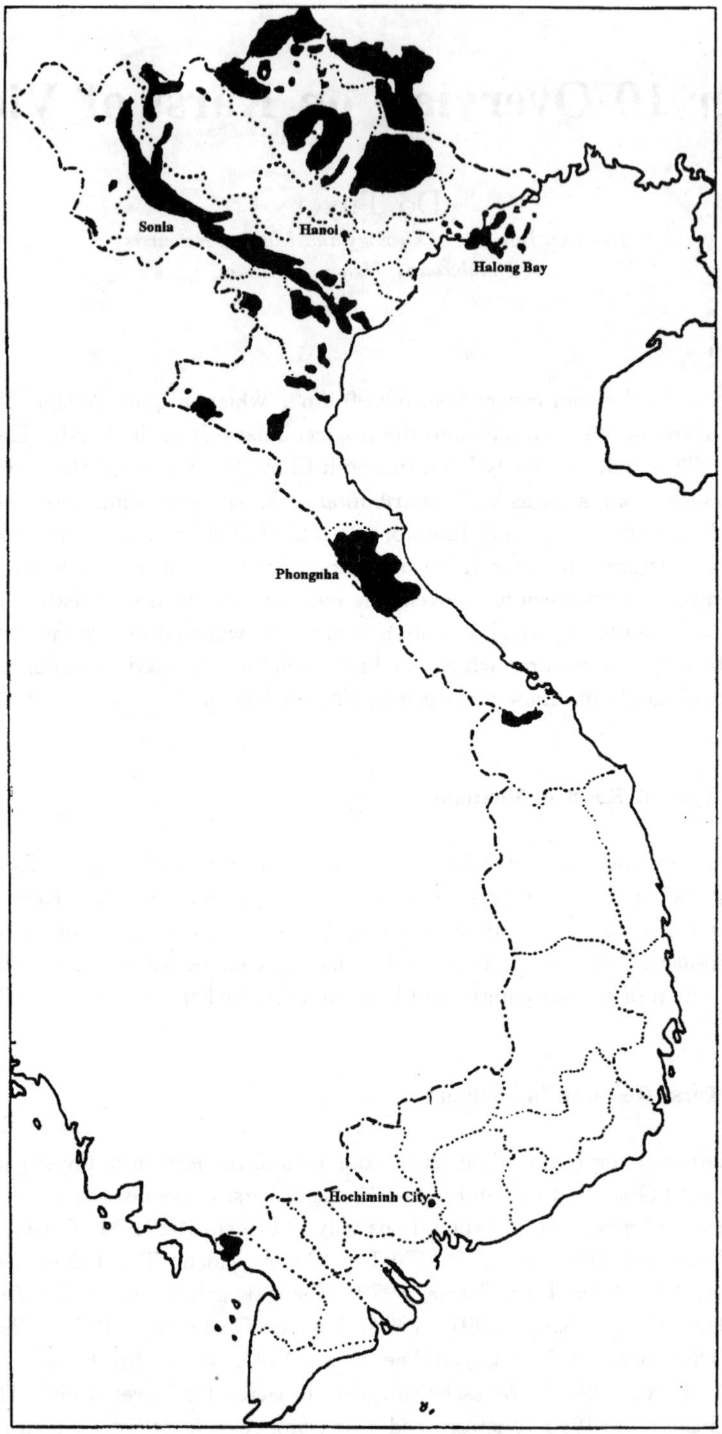

Fig. 10-1 Karst areas of Vietnam

10.4 Conditions for Karstification in Vietnam

10.4.1 *Limestone Occurring in Strata from Pre-Cambrian to Holocene*

In Vietnam, the karst rocks are principally limestones. In Pre-Cambrian limestones occur in some formations such as Sapa (PR_3sp), Deosen (PR_3ds), but they are often not very thick and are always crystallized in coarse to very coarse grained texture, which are often not very favourable for karstification. In Phanerozoic, limestones have been seen in Cambrian, Ordovician, Devonian, Carboniferous, Permian and Triassic with thickness of more than 5000m. Among them, the Middle Devonian (Banpap formation, D_2bp), Carboniferous-Early Permian (Bacson formation), Middle Triassic (Donggiao and Muong Trai formation) limestones are most favourable for karstification by high pure lime and high thickness and geological structure. Cenozoic limestones, particularly coral reefs have large distribution area and thickness of some thousand metres, but most of them are buried by young sediments or are below the sea water (Fig. 10-2).

10.4.2 *Abundance of Pure and Thick Carbonate Strata*

Most limestones in Vietnam are pure in composition, specially Middle Devonian, Carboniferous-Early Permian and Middle Triassic limestones. In their composition, CaO (plus MgO) are often more than 50% The disintegratable minerals under heating are more than 40%, and their mineral composition is mainly calcite, dolomite and secondary aragonite. These minerals are most favourable for karstification.

10.4.3 *Active Tectonic Region*

Falling into the region with long geological history of activities and changing, limestones of Vietnam are strongly folded and faulted. They belong to two main structural units named Bacbo Caledonite folding system and Indochina (Dongduong) Varicite folding system (Tran Van Tri et al., 1977). They make anticlines and synclines or take part directly in forming anticlinoria and synclinoria. In consequence of that, limestones everywhere often dip in $40-60°$ or vertical or very complicated crushing. Accompanying with active folding, strong faulting activities happened in different periods with some overlaying phases. Folding and faulting action leads to the state in which limestones are strongly cracked, so water can go deep to carry out karstification. It can be said that geological structure of Vietnam is favourable for karstification.

10.4.4 *Earthquake and Neotectonic Activities*

Neotectonic movements which are characterized by uplifting towards North-West Vietbac and subsiding towards Bacbo gulf together with strong earthquake along the earthquake-causing faults (Fig. 10-1) have controlled karstification and differentiation of karst which lead to form different karst regions in Vietnam. Those regions are different from each other not only in structure and complication of karst landscapes but also in underground karst cave systems and hydrology.

No	Formation	Symbols	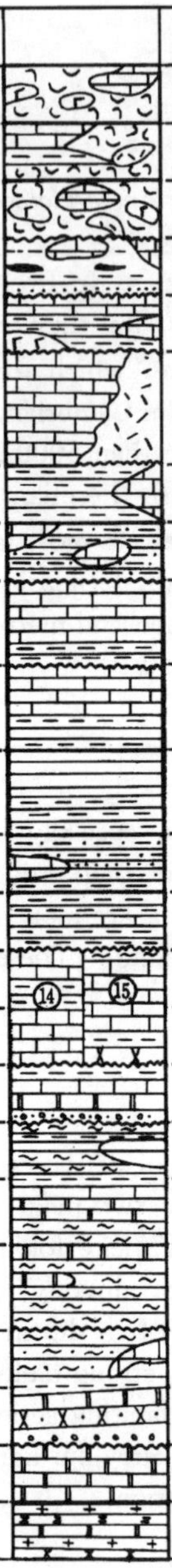	Thickness (m)	Distribution places	Characteristic
1	Suoibe	Ksb		150	Hieutrai, Baotin	Motted breccia limestone with block structure
2	Banhat	J-Kbh		100	Banhat, Ngoibo	Limestone lenses in shale,siltstone and tufaceous rock
3	Tule	J-Ktl		10-70	Ngoihut upstream	Breccia limestone in volcanic sedimentary rocks
4	Suoibang	T_3n-rsb		<50	East Yenchau	Limestone lense, thin layer in lower part
5	Muongtrai	T_2lmt		200-500	Muongtrai, Pytoong	Light and Grey limestone in layers or lenses
6	Donggiao Dongtrau	T_2adg T_2adt		600-2000	Axis of North-west Nghean	Lower part: Thin bedding;Upper Part: light thick bedding,fine grained texture; limestone in volcanic sedimentary rocks.
7	Tanlac	T_1tl		<100	Sonla,Yenchau Mochau,Tanlac,	Thin bedding, lense of limestone
8	Yenduyet Vienam	P_2yd P_2vn		100-150	Camthuy, Bavi, Nampan,	Light limestone lenses, thin bedding layers in volcanic sedimentary rocks
9	Bacson	C-P_1bs		700-1400	Vietbac, North Vietnam	Light limestone of massive structure, thick bedding.
10	Bancai	D_2g-D_3bc		700-1300	North-West, Vietbac	Limestone,chert-limestone
11	Banpap	D_2bp		700-900	North-West, Vietbac	Fine-grained limestone, somewhere dolomitized limestone
12	Bannguon	D_2ebn		320-600	North-West	Black,thin bedding limestone in shale
13	Suoitra	D_1st		400-600	North-West	Limestone lenses in shale
14	Bohieng	S_2-D_1bh		200-500	North-West, Vietbac	Lense and thin layer limestone in shale
15	Paham	O_3-D_1ph		100	North-West, Vietbac	Irregular bedding limestone in upper part of formation.
16	Sinhvinh	O_3-Ssv		100-500	North-West	Irregular bedding limestone
17	Langvac	Є$_3$lv		80	North-West	Fine-grained limestone in lense and thin layers
18	Dienlu Changpung	Є$_3$dl Є$_3$cp		600-750	North-West, Vietbac	Irregular bedding limestone with shale
19	Modong Sonma Hogiang	Є$_3$sm		100-200	North-West, Vietbac	Limestone,somewhere crystallized with irregular bedding layers in sedimentary rocks.
20	Camduong	Є$_3$cd			North-West	Lenses and thin layers in xericite schist containing apatite
21	Benkhe	Є$_2$obk		<50	North-West	Limestone and calcareous shale in lense and laminating beds.
22	Sapa,Deosen	PR_3sp, PR_3ds		200-300	North-West, North Central	Dolomite crystallized limestone in the form of lenses and thin layers in schist
23	Sinhquyen	PR_{1-2} sq		?	North-West	Lense & laminated marble in schist

Fig. 10-2 Carbonate strata of Vietnam

10.4.5 *Humid and Tropical Climate with High Rainfall*

Vietnam falls into tropical humid climatic region with large rainfall ranging from 1 100mm to more than 3000 mm/a and air average moisture of over 80% (Tab. 10-1).

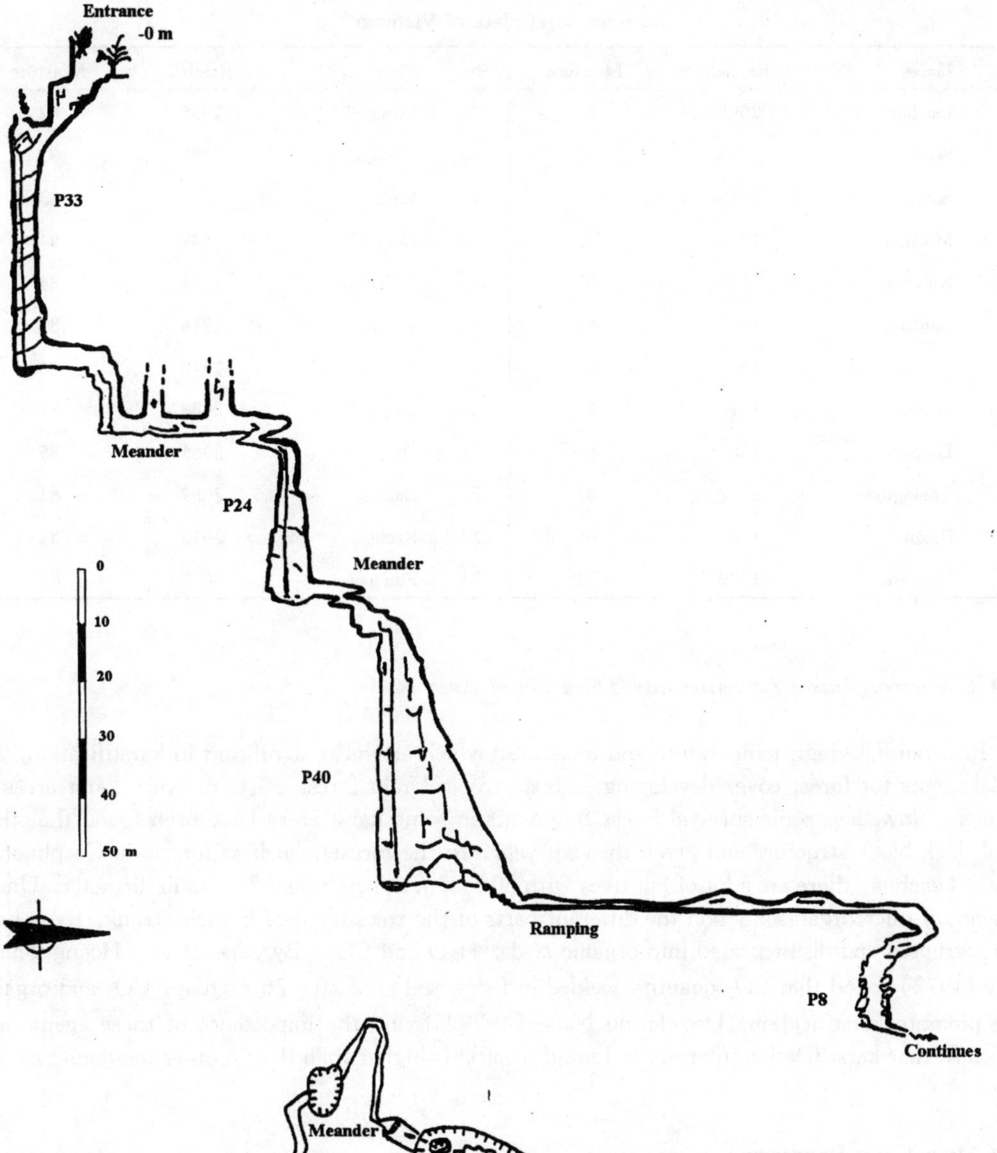

Fig. 10-3 Queen Cave

Tab.10-1 Annual average rainfall (mm/a) and average comparative moisture (%) in some karst place of Vietnam

No	Places	Rainfall	Moisture	No	Places	Rainfall	Moisture
1	Laichau	2090	82	13	Honggai	1995	82
2	Sapa	2759	87	14	Mongcai	2751	83
3	Sonla	1413	81	15	Hanoi	1661	83
4	Mochau	1445	86	16	Hoabinh	1848	84
5	Songma	1144	82	17	Nhoquan	1862	84
6	Haglang	2401	85	18	Thanhoa	1716	85
7	Tuyenquang	1600	84	19	Hoixuan	1648	86
8	Caobang	1410	81	20	Quangtri	2608	85
9	Langson	1383	81	21	Hue	2955	85
10	Thainguyen	2002	82	22	Danang	2089	82
11	Bacan	1586	84	23	Rachgia	2015	82
12	Bacglang	1539	82	24	Phuquoc	3038	83

10.4.6 *Microorganism Activities and Thick Forest Area*

Rich rainfall, high temperature and moisture, which are most significant in karstification, are special agents for forest cover developing. Thus, tropical rain forest exists in every karst areas in Vietnam. Nowadays some survival forest fragments in some karst areas have been found that they are of thick block structure and green through year. In the forests, such as forests in Cucphuong, Sinho, Tuachua, there are a lot of big trees with 60 – 80m in height and 2 – 4m in diameter. Under influence of microorganism action the different parts of the trees like leaf branch, trunk, roots have been corrupted and disintegrated into organic acids, H_2O and CO_2. By experiment, Hoang Thanh Thuy (1972) found that CO_2 quantity yielded in forest soil is of 20 – 26 mg/day. CO_2 and organic acids promote karstification. Dao Trong Nang (1979) found the importance of these agents and confirmed that karstification intensity in humid tropical is higher than that in other temperate zones.

10.5 Main Karst Landforms

In Vietnam there exists different karst hydrological systems which are autogenic, allogenic or their combination, so a series of different karst landforms have been formed.

1. Solution sculpture-microkarren and karren have been seen in every karst region of Vietnam. Micropits, pans, shafts, wells which belong to circular plan forms, and microfissures, splitkarrens, rillenkarrens, runnelskarrens fluted scallops are most common. Microkarrens are often less then 10mm, but karren can be 10 – 15m or more in dimension. Microkarrens have been observed not only in exposed karst, but also under terra rosa which are seen in Manduc, Caophong, Mochau, Phongtho, Trungkhanh and so on.

2. Karrenfields are of assemblages of individuals karrens with large area which have been seen at many places such as Tuachua, Mochau, Phongtho.

3. Coastal karrens have been formed under influence of solution of mixture of salt and fresh wa-

ter. Strong solution leads to formation of deep and large sinkholes and long notches in limestones blocks. Consequently, a special karst landscape with countless islands has been formed. A particular landform of "Halong bay" is formed in that way. Sea Level can be changed and coastal karst may become continental karst. To South-West Bacbo plain in Ninhbinh, Thanhoa, there is an ancient coastal karst landscapes which is called "*Dry Halong karst*". Over there, many notches of ancient sea level at different heights on scarps of residual limestone hills on flat sedimentary plain have been observed.

4. Dolines are most common in karst regions. They are of enclosed depressions with widely changed form and dimension. Most of them are usually circular or subcircular plan and vary from some metres to about kilometres in diameter and change from less 10m to hundreds m in height. Their sides ranges from gentle dipping to vertical. In Vietnam, there are both solution and collapse for origin of dolines. Form, dimension and density of dolines vary widely in different karst regions.

5. Through valleys are formed by allogenic input when underground cave systems are impossible to drainage the whole water coming from non-karst area. The Da river canyon of 20 km long to east Laichau town, the part of Namna river to North-East Phatan, the part of the Buoi river to North-West Cucphuong park are best examples.

6. Blind valleys are also formed by allogenic input but the underground cave systems are possible to drainage the whole water coming from the areas of non-karst rocks. The Namla through Sonla town, the Namluong at Chiengpac village are good examples.

7. Pocket valleys are formed at the underground water outlet. These forms have been seen at the border of Bacson, Kebang, Quyhop and North-West karst zones. Among them, the Namliep and Bansang valleys are most typical.

8. Poljes are widely developed in different karst zones in Vietnam. Some poljes, such as Sinho, Nasan, Maichau, Tanlac, Binhgia, are good examples. Most poljes in Vietnam are not larger than $100km^2$, often from $3-5km^2$ to $40-50$ km^2; they widely range in elevation from less 10m in coastal zone to over 1500m at Sinho. In the view of original classification, poljes of Vietnam belong to main types: border polje, structural polje and base level polje.

9. Corrosional plains have often been seen at the margin of different karst zones. Morphologically, most corrosional plains are of the plains with residual hills and terra rosa cover of considerable thickness on them.

On the scarps of residual hills, notches with different heights and lengths have often been observed, and some of them are about tens of metres long and 10 metres high, such as notches in Coma, Bacson, Hoabinh. The corrosional plains change from several km^2 to hundreds of km^2 in area and from less 10 to 1000m in elevation. The corrosional plains in Mochau, Quanba, Trungkhanh, Bacson, Phongtho, Myhoa are good examples.

10. Residual hills are common in the different karsts of Vietnam. They are distributed not only in the margin, but also in the center of the karst block, and most of them are seen in the poljes and corrosional plains. They vary widely in dimension and morphology. Their common forms are towers, cones, tables, trunks, and some cases of comparative mounts on the poljes or corrosional plains. Most towers are some tens to hundreds meters in diameter. Their height changes from less 10m to 100 – 200m or more. Their slopes are often vertical as scarps, but there are also gentle slopes covered by mixture of terra rosa with limestones breccia or expose of limestones. Towers in Vanlinh, Trungkbanh, Tamduong are excellent examples and in Halong, Ninhbinh, are of peculiar form.

11. Cave systems. In beginning of karst investigation of Vietnam, caves of hypogenous origin with CO_2 and H_2O of hydrothermal resource have not discovered yet. All caves are related to activities of meteoric water. The water for karstification is either rain to make autogenic input or the mixture of rain with allogenic input. Besides, in coastal zone karstification is carried out by mixture of

fresh and marine water. Because Vietnam underwent strong tectonic activity particularly in Mesozoic and Cenozoic, cave systems are characterized by complication in structure. They can be of single cycle or of multicycles, and are connected each other by siphons in some cases. One system lies directly on another such as Hangdoi 1 and Hangdoi 2 caves in Sonla, while God cave at Thay Pagoda looks like a maze system. Queen cave in Sonla is a good example for multicycle cave. In many cases, passages and chambers with different dimension are connected with each other to make a horizontal cave system such as Phongnha, Toi, Vom caves which have been recently discovered in Kebang, Quangbinh (Nguyen Quang My et al., 1993, 1995). From M. Dusan et al. (1994), J. Masschelein et al. (1996), caves in Vietnam should be divided into two main kinds, i. e., fossil caves and active caves. Up to the year 1996, hundreds of different caves in Vietnam have been discovered, explored and mapped (Tab. 10-2).

Tab. 10-2 Typical caves of Vietnam

No	Name	Karst zone	Length(m)	Depth(m)	Note
1	Thacbo	North west	339.7		
2	Bantham	Do	547.0		
3	Suolkhoang	Do	3368.1		
4	Queen cave	Do	367.5	171.0	multicycles
5	Lomcoco	Do	675.4	65.9	siphon
6	Chimen	Do	160.0	150.0	
7	Hangdoi 1	Do	1434.5	+47.0	continuous
8	Hangdoi 2	Do	318.4	−14.4	siphon
9	Namkhum	Do	1323.0		siphon
10	Snake cave	Do	1767.7	−86.7	continuous
11	Thidoi	Do	1561.3		
12	Thamtatoong	Do	361.0	−18.23	siphon
13	Canh	Bacson	1056.0		
14	Ca/Be	Do	3342.0		
15	Dumoc	Do	1600.0		
16	Pacnang	Do	1071.0		
17	Napung	Do	550.0		
18	Bonau	Halong	110.0		
19	Daugo	Do	330.0		
20	Hanh	Do	1300.0		
21	Vom	Kebang	15000.0		continuous
22	Toi	Do	5258.0		
23	Rucaroong	Do	2800.0		
24	Phongnha	Do	8500.0		
25	Rucmon	Do	863.0		
26	Chusong	Do	6667.0		

Some underground caves at 500m deep in South-West of Bacbo plain have been discovered by boreholes for underground water prospecting (Fig. 10-3, 10-4.)

12. Speleothems

(1) Travertine terraces are often observed at places of spring exposed. They are from less than $1km^2$ to $5-10$ km^2 in area and have been seen rich in North-West, North-East Vietbac and North Truongson mountain ranges.

(2) Cave sediments are often formed by allogenic rivers. They are often seen at the cave gates with length of less than $200-300$m and with less volume.

(3) Breakdown stones by collapse of cave ceiling and walls have been seen in most caves, particularly in the North-West Karst zone.

(4) Speleothems that are formed by precipitation of water from cave ceiling, walls or running water of the underground river. Most of them are of calcite and less aragonite, and they make stalactites, stalagmites, draperies, rimstones, flowstones, which are present in every cave of Vietnam, particularly in fossil caves. These speleothems are very abundant in form and dimension, and make cave to be more beautiful, wonderful and become living soul. Thus, caves always attract not only tourists, but also people for religion. Caves, such as Phongnha, Tuthuc, Huongsons are good examples, of which caves at Huongson area have been visited by hundreds of thousand persons from everywhere of Vietnam.

10.6 Main Karst Zones of Vietnam

Most Vietnam workers (Le Xuan Phuong, 1957; Nguyen Duc Chinh, Vu Tu Lap, 1993; Hoang Thieu Son, 1995; Dao Trong Nang, 1979; Vu Do, 1972; Nguyen Quang My, 1993, 1995) have a common idea on subdividing karst of Vietnam into 4 main zones. Dao Trong Nang named karst geomorphological regions which consist of different zones. Each contains common humid tropical karst characters and particularly in form, structure also.

10.6.1 *The Vietbac Karst Zone*

The zone should be considered as the largest karst zone of Vietnam. It is bordered by Hong river to south-west and China-Vietnam boundary to the north, where it comes gradually to the tropical karst of South China, belonging to Yunnan and Guangxi. The karst rocks are mainly Paleozoic, particularly Middle Cambrian, Middle-Upper Cambrian, Devonian and Carboniferous-Lower Permian. These limestones are folded and faulted to make synclines and anticlines embracing the Songchay Dome. Under influence of neotectonic uplifting on the zone, young karst forms such as enclosed and deep dolines, sinkholes in Hagiang, Bacquang, Bacson have been accompanied with corrosional plains, residual hills or towers etc. which reflect that the zone underwent some different karstification cycles since Early Paleozoic to Present. There are complicated cave systems consisting of vertical and horizontal ones and their combination. Some famous karst places such as Bacson, Cocxo, Kimhi, Dongvan, Hagiang, Bacha, west Caobang are examples. Inhabitants with high density population live at poljes, corrosional plains and dolines.

10.6.2 *The North-East Karst Zone*

This belongs to coastal karst zone extending from Quangninh to Haiphong, Haiduong. Active solution of mixture of seawater and fresh water leads to karstification intensity of the studied region to be stronger than other karst zones. The karst rocks are of mainly Carboniferous-Permian and a

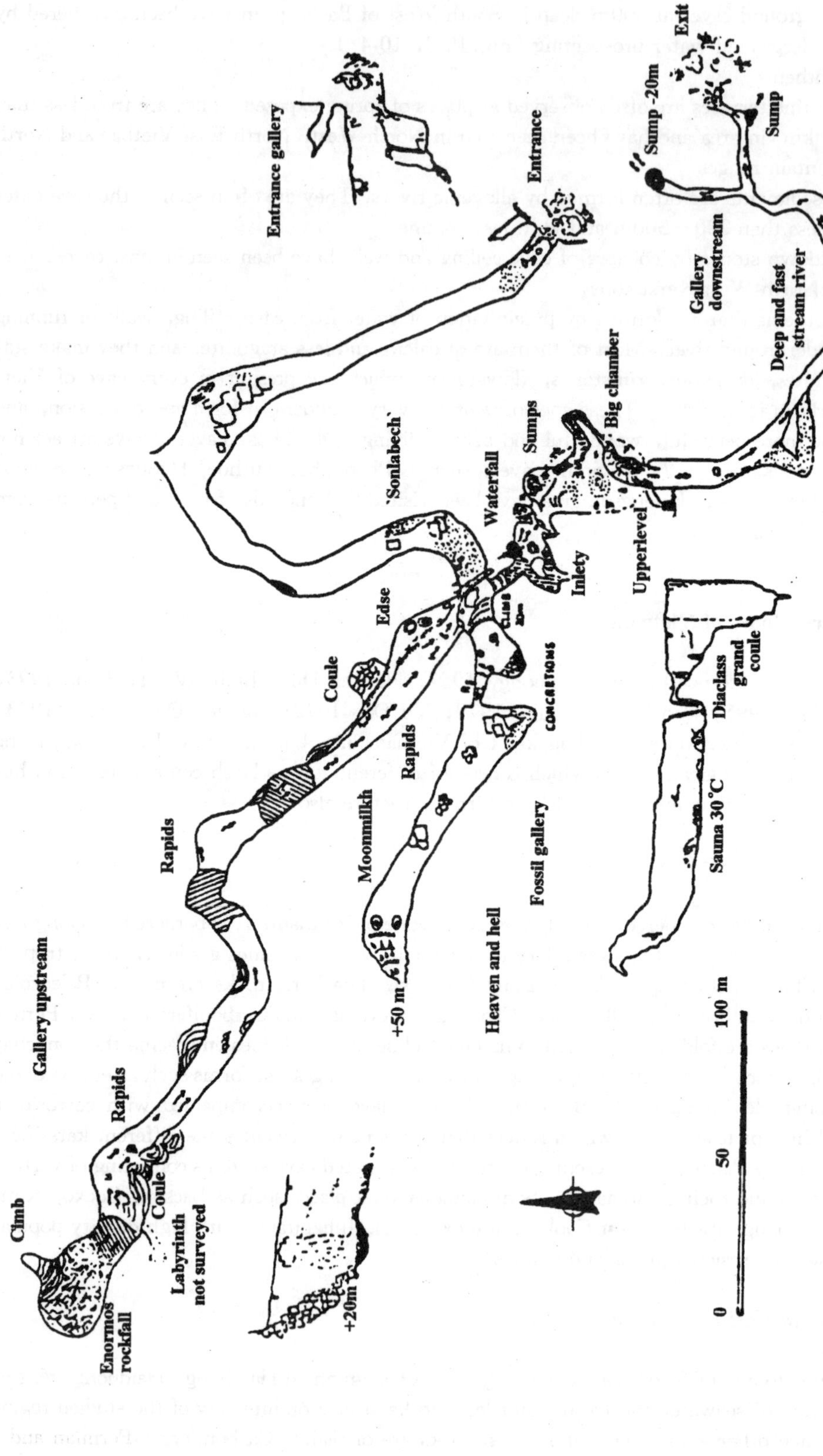

Fig. 10-4 Huangdoi Cave

certain part belongs to Middle Devonian. Under influence of neotectonic subsidence and high karstification, the karst landscape here is different from that in Vietbac. The wonderful scenery with innumerable karst islands on the marine surface have been formed. Every island is different from each other in form and dimension. Besides, on the karst islands in the studied region there are many horizontal cave systems with different galleries consisting of different chambers in which stalactites and stalagmites are beautiful and wonderful. Natural extraordinary, beautiful and most attractive landscape of karst in Halong bay makes it famous and has been confirmed as Natural Heritages of The World by UNESCO. On the zone there are some karst places being not much different from each other, such as Halong, Baitulong, Kinhmon, Catba.

10.6.3 *The North-West Karst Zone*

The zone is bordered by Hong river valley to the east, Laos-Vietnam boundary to the west, China-Vietnam boundary to the North-West, and its South-East part sinks gradually into Bacbo gulf. The karst rocks of the zone change in a wide range of strata since Proterozoic to Middle Triassic in which the strata of Middle Devonian Carboniferous-Early Permian and Middle Triassic are most favourable for karstification. Particularly, Middle Triassic limestones of 200 m thick, with pure composition and large distribution, makes a central axis zone of the North-West karst zone with 400 km in length and average 5 to 40 km in width. Different karst rocks of the studied region are suffered from folding, faulting, cracking and under influence of differential neotectonic movements, the zone is uplifted toward north-west and went down toward south-east. In consequence of that, there is complex landscape and structure of the karst zone. Its north-west part is characterized by mountainous karst with deep enclosed dolines, sinkholes, valleys, main vertical caves deep systems, while its south-east part by large poljes, dolines and main horizontal cave systems. On the zone, many large poljes and corrosional plains with residual hills, towers have also been observed. This zone consists of different karst places such as Sapa, Maluthang, Lannhithang, Tamduoug, Sinho, Tuachua, Sonla, Mocchau, Hoabinh, Huongson, Donggiao.

On the North-West karst zone, poljes, dolines, corrosional plains, valleys are often dense and prosperous, but the habitants suffer many hazards from flooding and waterlogging in rainy season, shortage of water in dry season, and serious pollution.

10.6.4 *The North-Central Vietnam Karst Zone*

On the zone, karst rocks are mainly concentrated in Quangbinh province to make famous Kebang karst block which extends to Central Laos.

Besides Kebang, some other karst areas have been seen in west Nghean, Thanhoa and Hoangmai. Kebang karst is formed by karst rocks of Carboniferous-Permian and characterized by mountainous karstic landscape with deep dolines, poljes and long horizontal caves systems consisting of different chambers. Of them Phongnha, Toa, Vom, Rucarong are of typical examples. At Hoangmai, karst rocks are Middle Triassic, while at the west Nghean karst, the karst rocks are mainly Pre-Cambrian(Deosen formation-PR_3ds) and residual karst landscape is most common.

10.6.5 *The South Vietnam Karst Zone*

This zone is composed of some small karst areas in lower north latitude of 17°. Karst rocks changed widely since Pre-Cambrian to Triassic, and at every places, karst is always small area and often makes residual landscape consisting hills, towers on young sedimentary plain. Karst in Nguhanhson and Kiengiang is considered as considerable size.

10.7 Some Problems of Applied Karst of Vietnam

10.7.1 *Water Supply*

In every karst region of Vietnam, where population is considerable, water supply for drinking, agricultural and industrial production is a big problem that is very hard to solve. Except for some small areas, including tens of pocket valleys, through valleys, poljes, which are favourable for presence of natural springs, the rest large areas have serious shortage in water supply not only for agriculture production but also for drinking, particularly in dry season the water resources are often polluted. Only few karst regions such as Mochau, Donggiao, Bimson are adequately supplied in water for agriculture and industrial production and drinking.

Problems of water supply in karst zone should be interesting and attractive, and they need to be studied and solved.

10.7.2 *Mineral Resource Related to Karst*

Some karst mineral resources have been discovered. In Langson industrial bauxite were formed by karstification of Bacson formation limestone and accumulated on the ancient karst field surface of Permian. Some casiterite placer mines on karst valleys in Caobang, west Nghean are also examples. Some gold placer in Napai, Caobang, Maichau, Phongtho are formed directly on dolines, caves and valleys. In most fossil caves of different karst zones, there is bird or bat excrement, which can be exploited to produce fertilizer or to make gunpowder.

10.7.3 *Karst Rock Materials for Many Industries*

Karst rocks, of which limestones should be said first, are used in many different industries, particularly in construction and communication. Limestones are used as materials for basement of railway, road, building and common construction. Besides, limestones, marbles are also used as decorative materials for architecture and art monuments, particularly for production of art statues and Buddha's statues in pagodas and temples. In Vietnam, limestones and marbles are used for most temples and pagodas, particularly the Phatdiem Church System had been made of limestone only.

For a long time, Vietnam people have produced quicklime from limestone to make mortar for construction. Vietnamese farmers used quicklime to dispose acidity for their cultivated land. Nowadays, limestone has been used with the higher and higher amount, for example, from 6 million of tons in 1996 to 10 million of tons at the end of this century in cement industry.

10.7.4 *Problems of Hazard by Karstification*

People populated in dolines, poljes, and karst valleys, but these places are often suffered from flooding seriously by chocking of most underground cave drainage systems and deforestation. The phenomena become more serious when it rains with rainfall of 400 − 500mm for some days in certain karst basins relating to storms or lower tropical atmospheric pressure. Flooding and waterlogging in Banhinh, Baphe, Chiengla are examples. Particularly catastrophic flooding on 27 July, 1991 killed many persons and damaged works and properties in Sonla town is a typical example. Other risks such as rockfall, subsidence are common phenomena in different karst places of Vietnam. Serious shortage of drinking water and problems of polluted water in many karst places should be reminded to be karst risk. These mentioned hazards and risks in karst zones of Vietnam have not studied and processed by remedial measures to improve the life of people.

10.7.5 *Problems of Construction on Karst*

We have not had many works built on karst yet, but some works met an unexpected problems, of which Bimson cement plan is an example. The plant was built on an underground cave, but it was not discovered in design by shortage of karst investigation. Overcoming this problem took higher financing and more time. Now Vietnam is carrying out industrialization, the more and more works will be built on karst, so engineering geological investigation of karst should be brought up.

10.7.6 *Problems of Karst Reservoirs*

Some small reservoirs on karst in Sonla are unsuccessful. Now, the government intends to build a large hydroelectric plant with power of 4000 MW on the Da river. The designed water level of reservoir is +265m. With this level a considerable karst area becomes bottom and karst windows of the reservoir, of which the Pytoong karst windows is most typical. There is a thick cracked layer of limestone of 400m over there. The limestone falls into a fault zone of NW-SE direction. Below 256m level, some bigger caves have been discovered. The problems have being studied and processed.

10.7.7 *Karst with Religion and Tourism*

—Many caves and karst places in different zones of Vietnam have been chosen to be worship places by people since long time ago, of which many places become temples, pagodas or religious places. Huongson is an excellent example.

—Nice-looking landscape in open air and seductive caves with wonderful stalactites and stalagmites always giving a strange sensation and leisure are objects for tourism purpose. They attract not only Vietnamese, but also people over the world. Famous karst sceneries are Halong, Langson, Huongson, Bichdong, Phongnha etc. Karst tourism of Vietnam indicates its particular attraction.

References

Blondel F., 1929. Les phen'omenes karstiques en Indochine Francaise Bull. Serv. Ge'ol. Indoch. Vol. XVIII, Fasc. 3, Hanoi.

Colani M., 1927. L'age de la piere dans la province de Hoabinh. Mem. Serv. Ge'ol. Indoch. Vol. XIV, fasc. 1, Hanoi.

Dao Dinh Bac, Nguyen Due Kha, 1993. Karst zoning of Bacson. In Selected works on tropical investigation, p. 32 – 37, Hanoi University, Hanoi.

Dao Trong Nang, 1979. Karst in Vietnam. Education Pub. House, Hanoi.

Do Tuyet, 1993. Characters of karst in North-West of Vietnam. In selected works on tropical karst study of Vietnam, p. 41 – 44, Hanoi University, Hanoi.

Do Tuyet, Thai Duy Ke, Dinh Xuan Quyet, Le Canh Tuan, Phan Trong Trinh, 1995. Report on "Study of effluence of karstification to s ome economic-social problems in North West". Research Institute of Geology and Mineral Resources of Vietnam, Hanoi

Dusar, M., J. Masschelein, Phan Cu Tien, Do Tuyet, 1994. Belgian-Vietnamese speleological expedition in Sonla 1993. Ministere des affaire economiques, service Geologique de Belgique. Brussel.

Glazek, J., 1966. On the karst phenomena in North Vietnam. Bull. Acad. Polonaise des Sciences, Vol. XIII No 1, p. 45 – 51, Varsovic.

Hoang Thanh Thuy, 1972. Characteristic development of tropical karst study in North Vietnam. National Scientific Library

of Vietnam, Hanoi.
Hoang Thieu Son, 1965. General geography. Vol. II- Karst. Education Pub. House, Hanoi (in Vietnamese).
Le Ba Thao, 1977. Nature views of Vietnam. Tech. and Scien. Pub. House, Hanoi.
Le Xuan Phuong, 1997. Outline of Geography of Vietnam. Education Pub. House, Hanoi.
Masschelein, J., Deblaere Ch., Do Tuyet, 1996. Observation on karst cave systems in Sonla-Tuachua regions made by geologists of joint Belgian-Vietnamese expedition since Dec. 15, 1995 to Jan. 13, 1996. In Geology and Mineral Resources, Vol. V, p. 121 – 127. Research Institute of Geology and Mineral Resources, Hanoi.
Nguyen Duc Chinh, Vu Tu Lap, 1963. Natural geography of Vietnam. Pub. House Eduction, Hanoi.
Nguyen Quang My, 1994. Karst in Vietnam. Proceeding, Symposium on applied tropical karst, Hanoi, p. 7 – 12, Hanoi University, Hanoi.
Nguyen Quang My, Nguyen Dich Dy, Nguyen Hoan, Nguyen Vi Dan, Nguyen Xuan Tung, Vu Van Phai, Nguyen Duc Kha, L. Howard, T. Allen, 1995. Karst landscape study for tourism. Hanoi National University, Hanoi.
Nguyen The Thon, 1993. Development of tropical karst in Mesozoic and caves in Quaternary in Bacson, Langson. In selected works on tropical karst study of Vietnam, p. 21 – 24, Hanoi University, Hanoi.
Nguyen The Thon, 1994. The karst cave in Kimbang and its tourism potential. Proc. Int. Symposium on "Applied tropical karst", Apr. 10 – 11, 1994, p. 82 – 83, Hanoi.
Nguyen Vi Dan, 1993. Outline of tropical karst of Vietnam. In Selected works on tropical karst of Vietnam. p. 24 – 28. Hanoi University, Hanoi.
Pham Khang, 1991. Some results on the quantitative study about intensity of karstification under humid-tropical climate of Vietnam. In Geology and Mineral Resources, p. 40 – 47, Tech. and Scien. Pub. House, Hanoi.
Pham Khang, Tran Van Thang, 1994. Initial observations on caves in different carbonaceous rocks in North-West of Vietnam. Proceeding. Symposium on applied tropical karst, Apr. 10 – 11, 1994, Hanoi, p. 13 – 19, Hanoi University, Hanoi.
Tran Van Tri et al., 1977. Geology of Vietnam, the North Part. Tech. Sci. PubHouse, Hanoi.
Vu Do, 1979. Some features on karst of North Vietnam. In Geology and Mineral Resources of Vietnam, book 1, p. 349 – 364, Geol. Mapping Division, Hanoi.

Global Karst Correlation
Edited by Yuan Daoxian and Liu Zaihua
Science Press and VSP BV, 1998

Chapter 11 Karst of Romania

George Ponta
Bucharest, Romania

11.1 General Data

Romania is situated in the Eastern part of Europe, with an area of 237500 km^2 (91 671 sq. miles), and historically is comprised by four regions: Walachia, Moldavia, Transylvania and Dobrogea (Dobruja).

One third of the territory is occupied by Carpathians Mountains, one third by lowlands hills and plateaus (Transylvanian and Moldavian Plateau) and one third by plains, Romanian (or Danube), Pannonian and Moldavian Plains.

The Eastern Carpathians (Pietros, 2 303 m) and the Southern Carpathians (known as Transylvanian Alps in geographical literature) with the highest point Moldoveanu of 2 544 m cross the country diagonally from north and south meeting in the east center. With the Western Carpathians (Bihor Massif-Curcubata Mare 1,848 m) in the west they enclose the cultivated Transylvanian plateau (300 m to 500 m elevation). The mountains are surrounded north-west, west, south, and east by Pannonian, Romanian and Moldavian plains. The Black Sea coast and Dobrogea are flat. The Danube river cutting through the Southern Carphatians at the Iron gate, forms most of the southern border (Fig. 11-1).

11.2 Climate and Geology

Romania's climate is characteristic to moderate temperate-continental zone, with average annual temperature from 4℃ to 10℃ and mean annual rainfall between 400 – 1200 mm. Average temperature in Bucharest: −2℃ (Jan.), +21℃ (July). Rainfall: 400 mm to 500 mm in Dobrogea, Moldavia and Walachia, 500 mm to 750 mm in the west and central basin, 750 mm to 1 500 mm in the mountains.

In the last 30 years the Romanian karst have been the subject of several classifications based on geomorphological (Bleahu, Sencu, Orghidan and Goran) or geological (Bleahu, Oraseanu) criteria.

Romania's karst can be classified into three categories, characterized by the hydrodynamic conditions of the karst aquifers, i.e., the confined, semi-confined, and unconfined or perched. The difference in the relationship between karst aquifer and landsurface (open karst hydrogeological system or confined) is another major factor to define the three categories.

1. Deep Karst type features occur in the sedimentary rocks underlying non-soluble bedrock and overlain by aquicludes or aquitard deposits (consolidated deposits). These confined aquifers are typical to the Walachian Platform (geological name used for Romanian Plain). The Carbonate Deposits of Malm-Barremian Ages are 1 500 m thick and were encountered by oil wells, thermal water wells and stratigraphic boreholes at a depth of 1 800 m to 2 000 m in the Romanian Plain. Towards south these deposits can be found in the Danube River's bluffs, which constitute the recharge area for the aquifer. The strata dip north with 30°to 40°, in Bucharest area being at 2000 m deep. Due to the

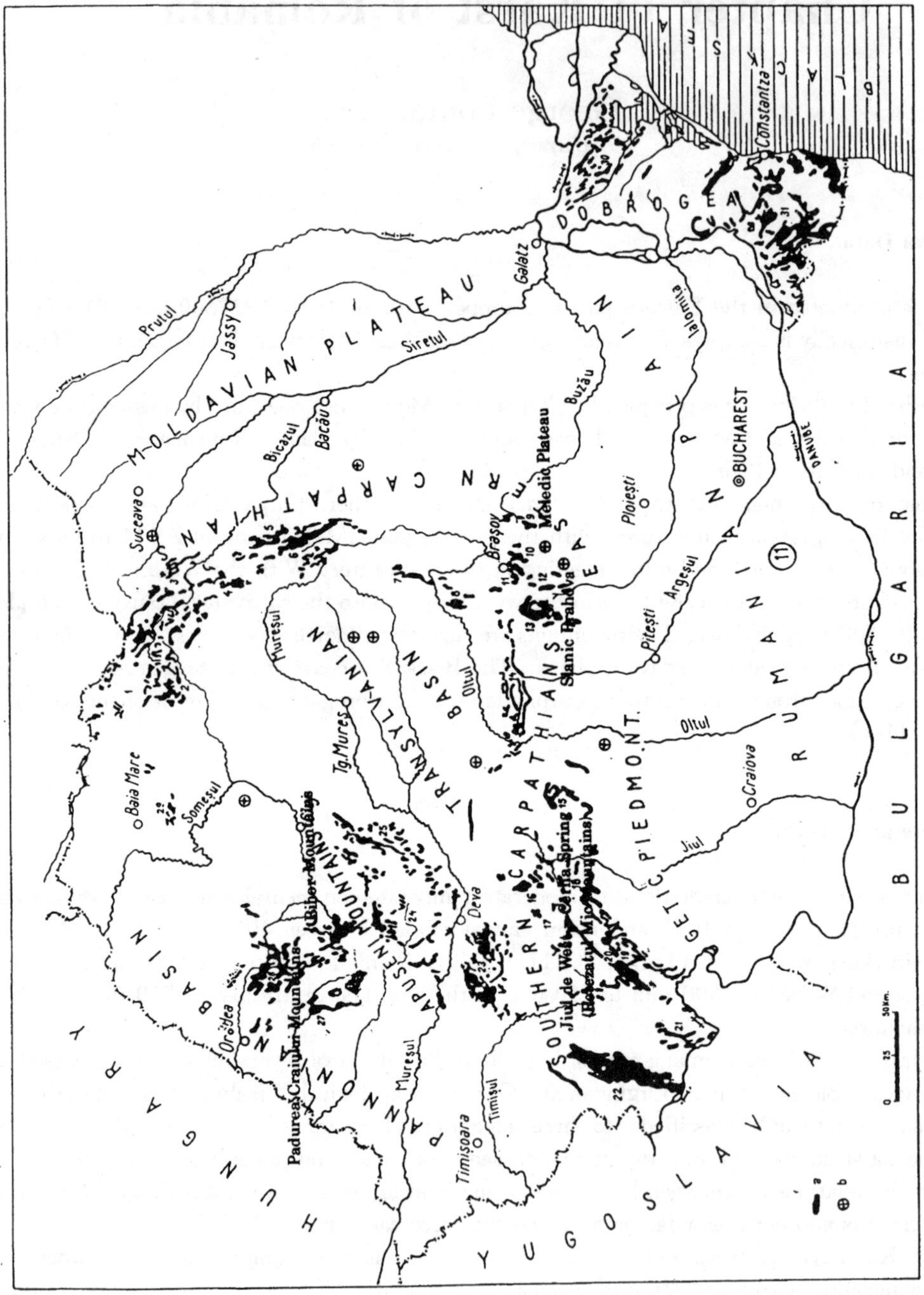

Fig. 11-1 Distribution of karst-forming rocks in Romania (after Bleahu, 1964). a = limestones and dolomites; b = karst developed on salt and gypsum

depth, the karst aquifer's waters are thermalized, their average temperature being +60°C.

In some areas, where the carbonate rocks are close to the oil bearing deposits, the TDS of karst waters are very high (approx. 35000 mg/l). The maximum extension of the deep aquifer is along the Romanian Plain and could cover approx. 25000 km^2. This is the largest karst aquifer in Romania, unfortunately too deep to be utilized at its maximum yield.

2. Shallow Karst type features are in sedimentary rocks overlain by unconsolidated sediments. The thickness of the overburden range between 10 m to 50 m. This type of karst is spread all over Romania, but the greatest extension is known in Dobrogea, where the overburden is formed mainly by loess. The shallow type karst aquifer is mostly semiconfined or unconfined. The average area covered by shallow karst type is approx. 2500 km^2.

3. Bare karst occupies about 4400 km^2 (Bleahu, 1965) or 5000 km^2 (Oraseanu, 1993) on the Romanian territory (approx. 1.4% of the total Romania's surface), and belong to Paleozoic, Mesozoic and Neogene deposits.

The bare karst type features are in the sedimentary rocks on which the karst proper is developed as limestones, dolomites, crystalline limestones, salt and gypsum.

The Paleozoic deposits are recrystallized and represent about 16% of the total bare karst.

The Mesozoic deposits belong to two sedimentary cycles (Triassic – 17.8% and Jurassic-Cretaceous 47.3%), and the Neogene deposits to a third cycle (Eocene, Tortonian and Sarmatian – 16.8%) (Bleahu, 1965).

The most karstified deposits belong to the Jurassic-Cretaceous sedimentary cycle, as a result of their lithological, structural, chemical and hydrogeological characteristics. As a result of this spread, the Southern Carpathians, for example, have the largest bared carbonates regions, but the most karstified are in the Bihor Mountains (Western Carpathians). The characteristic of this type of karst are unconfined, perched and sometime confined aquifers.

From geomorphological and structural (as they have been affected differently by the tectonic movements and have generated specific karstic forms) point of view were proposed three genetic types of karst relief specific to the Romania's territory: 1. Plateau type karst, 2. Ridge type karst, 3. Isolated massive type karst (Bleahu, 1965).

Plateau type karst. It is characterized by large dolomite or limestone plateau with surface karstic features like karren (lapies), dolinen, sinkholes, closed depressions, dry valley and streams with elevation range between 600 m to 2000 m, and covers areas between 20 km^2 and 120 km^2. The thickness of carbonate deposits ranges between 200 m and 600m and alternates with non-carbonate rocks. The most important plateaus are in the Bihor, Sebes or Banat Mountains.

Ridge type karst. The ridges derived from carbonate deposits with thickness approx. 200m dip over 45°. As in the previous case, most of the time, the carbonate rocks alternate with non-soluble rocks. Due to the differentiated erosion processes very prominent limestones-dolomite ridges appear. Their strikes are controlled by longitudinal faults with regional extension and are cut by transverse faults, on which the karst aquifer is opened and emerge to landsurface through springs.

Isolated massifs. This type is an intermediate one between the previous two, being a less extended plateau. In some places the massif is formed by coral reef or sometimes by elements of megabreccia, olistolites, etc.

11.3 Bihor Mountains Karst Area

Situated in the central part of the Western Carphatians, the Bihor Mountains present large karstifiable surfaces. The most representative is the Padis Karstic Plateau (Fig. 11-2).

In the area, the Bihor unit and posttectonic cover formations outcrop with Paleozoic, Mesozo-

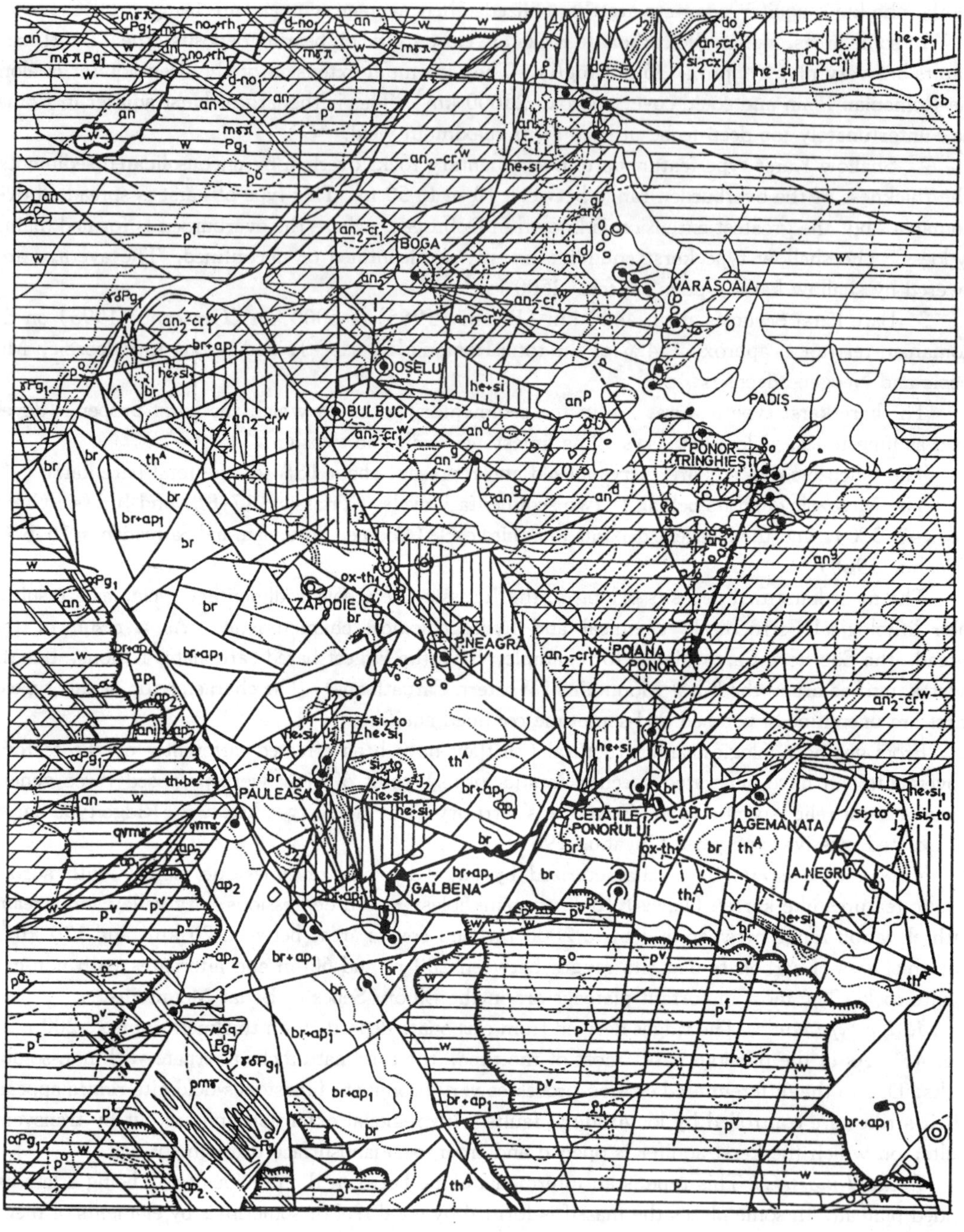

Fig. 11-2 Padis karstic

ic, Tertiary and Quaternary sedimentary formations that have metamorphic rocks in the basement (Mantea, 1985).

In the Mesozoic deposits several Triassic, Jurassic and Cretaceous formations have been separated.

The detrital rocks deposits, which continues with quartzites sandstones and a sequence of silty

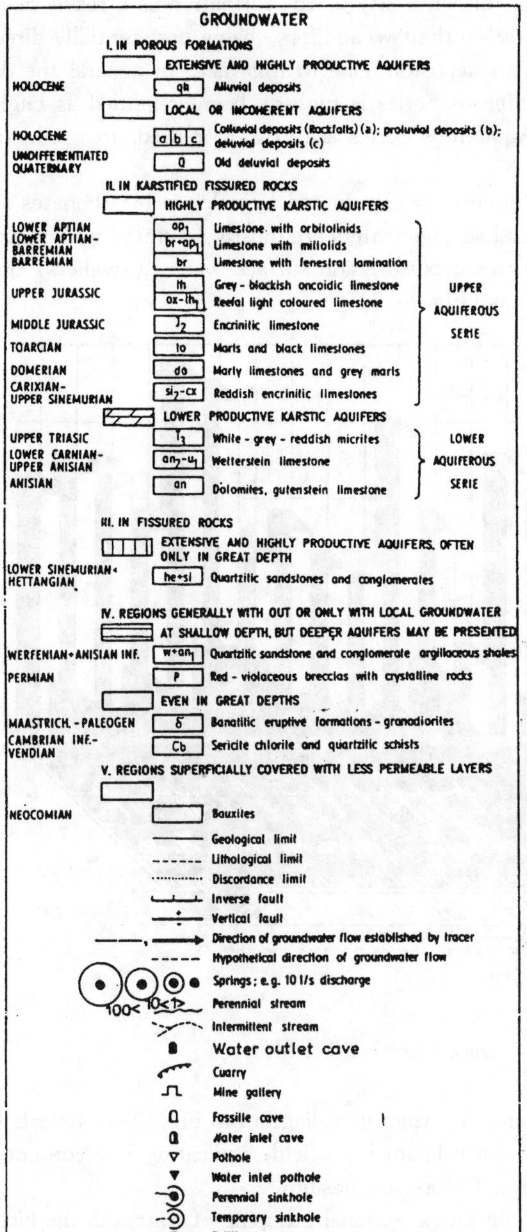

Plateau

shales, of Werfenian-Lower Anisian, or Werfenian age (about 70 m thick), associated with Permian deposits or Crystalline formations, form the main impervious rocks at the base of the limestones.

The Middle Triassic Deposits are represented by almost exclusively carbonates deposits, which appear as an alternation of Gutenstein Limestones (whose thickness does not exceed 150 m), dolomites of Anisian age (60 m thick) and Weterstein reef limestones (300 m in thickness). These carbonate deposits form the Lower Aquiferous Series (approx. 500 m thick).

Following the Old Chimeric movements on the whole territory of the Bihor Mts., due to the relief uplift, new sources of detrital sediments appear, dominantly continental.

Detrital Formation (Hettangian-Lower Sinemurian) attains 160 m in thickness and is built up of quartzoses conglomerates, sandstones and shales. These deposits form the impervious deposits between the Triassic and Jurassic limestones, separating the Lower Aquiferous Series from the Upper Aquiferous Series.

Calcareous formation up to 45 m thick, that is considered equivalent of Gresten Limestones (Upper Sinemurian-Carixian age) and the Middle Jurassic deposits occupy reduced areas and are not very thick, being formed by a succession of grey-blackish limestones, shaley (marly) limestones and encrinitic limestones.

The Upper Jurassic formations occupy remarkable areas and are represented exclusively by limestones. The thickness of the Upper Jurassic is generally variable, but not exceed 300 m.

After the Upper Jurassic sedimentation, the new Kimmerian phase, determinates the exposure of the territory and creates favorable conditions for the bauxites ore emplacement (Neocomian age), which are overlain by the Eo-Cretaceous age limestones. All these limestones of Jurassic and Cretaceous form the Upper Aquiferous Series (450 m thick).

The impervious bed between the two aquiferous series, formed by Hettangian-Lower Sinemurian age deposits is known as an aquifuge or some time aquiclude formation. In between two relatively impervious rocks, the Lower Aquiferous Series is like a confined aquifer. The impermeability of the impervious rocks is partially, especially due to the discontinuity of the formation as a result of the fractures which allows an intercommunication between the two aquifers, being preferentially directed from the Triassic to the Jurassic and Cretaceous deposits. Due to this fact, in general the discharge of the springs situated in the Upper Aquiferous Series is higher, being regarded as Highly Productive Karstic Aquifers, while the Lower Aquiferous Series are Lower or Medium Productive Karstic Aquifer.

The waters of the Bihor Mountains karst aquifers are dominated by calcium bicarbonates and the TDS varies with source. Cave streams and karst springs waters are mostly saturated with respect to calcite. Wells waters (installed in non-carbonates deposits) and surface waters (swallets) have higher concentration of sodium chloride and sulfates (Fig. 11-3).

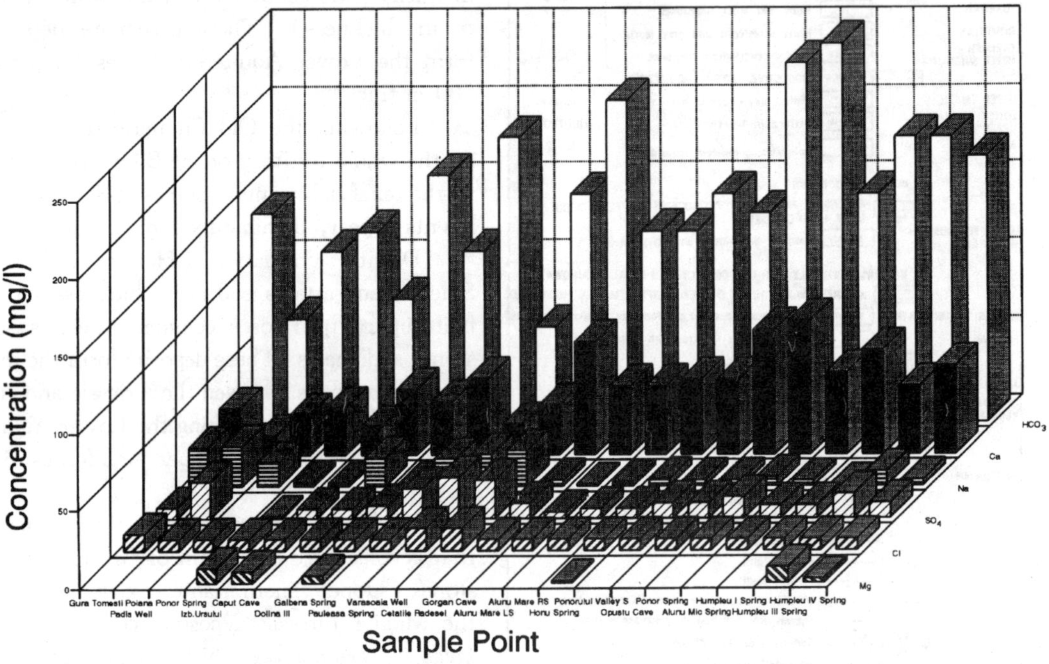

Fig. 11-3 Hydrochemical compositions at Bihor Mt.

Referring to the karst aquifers of Bihor Mountains, the Piper diagram in Fig. 11-4, reveals for the cations proportions a larger area overlapping the calcium type field, indicating low content of Mg, excepting a few major karstic springs which get more magnesium.

The diagram reveals for the anionic proportions an exceptional grouping of waters in the bicarbonate type field. Also a group can be observed in the diamond-shaped cation-anion graph, reflecting that the Bihor Mountains have calcium (magnesium) bicarbonates waters with low TDS.

The environmental isotopic analyses for Bihor Mountains waters showed in the Fig. 11-5 that the waters from the various resources presented above can be arranged in three distinct groups (Tab. 11-1):

Group A: Waters in which the relative Deuterium and ^{18}O content are between 11.12‰ and 1.95‰. This group includes surfaces waters, wells (wells installed in non-carbonate deposits) and springs waters with small recharge areas, over 50% of the discharged being supplied by sinking streams and precipitations.

Tab. 11-1 Environmental isotopes analyses at Bihor Mt., Romania

Sample Point Name	Sample Point Number	Oxygen $\delta^{18}O$	Deuterium δD	$d = \delta D - 8\ \delta^{18}O$
Alunul Mic Spring	1	-10.68	-74.32	11.12
Varasoaia Well	21	-10.80	-78.25	8.15
Padis Well	12	-10.74	-79.64	6.28
Honu Spring	10	-10.67	-79.64	5.72
Galbena Waterfall	15	-10.55	-78.84	5.56
Tringhiesti Swallet	11	-9.77	-74.20	3.96
Ponor Valley Swallet	4	-8.81	-67.52	2.96
Caput Cave(stream inl)	16	-5.92	-44.64	2.72
Cetatile Radesei(swallet)	19	-10.33	-79.44	2.70
Poiana Ponor Spring	134	-10.25	-80.05	1.95
Boga Well	28	-10.08	-79.44	1.20
Humpleu I Spring	9	-9.51	-75.55	0.53
Dolina III (karst window)	18	-8.66	-68.84	0.44
Galbena Spring	141	-9.38	-74.72	0.32
Humpleu IV Spring	8	-9.99	-81.02	-1.10
Ponor Valley Spring	3	-9.46	-77.02	-1.34
Coliboaia Spring	27	-7.98	-65.26	-1.42
Boga Spring	26	-8.26	-67.52	-1.44
Alunu Mare Right Spring	7	-10.03	-83.24	-3.00
Gorgan Cave Spring	5	-7.82	-65.84	-3.28
Alunu Mare Left Spring	6	-10.00	-85.12	-5.12
Pauleasa Spring	20	-8.39	-72.25	-5.13
Oselu Spring	22	-8.05	-70.72	-6.32
Bulbuci Spring	29	-7.71	-68.25	-6.57
Ursului Spring	17	-7.19	-64.26	-6.74

Group B: Waters in which the relative Deuterium and ^{18}O content range between 1.95‰ and -1.44‰. This group includes deep karst aquifers, where more than 20% of the yield comes from surfaces streams and less than 80% are percolation waters and endokarstic condensation waters.

Group C: Waters in which the relative Deuterium and ^{18}O content are between −1.44‰ and −6.74‰. This group includes deep karst aquifers, where less then 20% of the yield comes from surfaces streams and more than 80% are percolation waters and endokarstic condensation waters.

11.4 The Padis-Cetatile Ponorului Karstic Plateau

The Padis-Cetatile Ponorului karstic plateau, with a 54 km^2 of limestone outcrop, is formed by

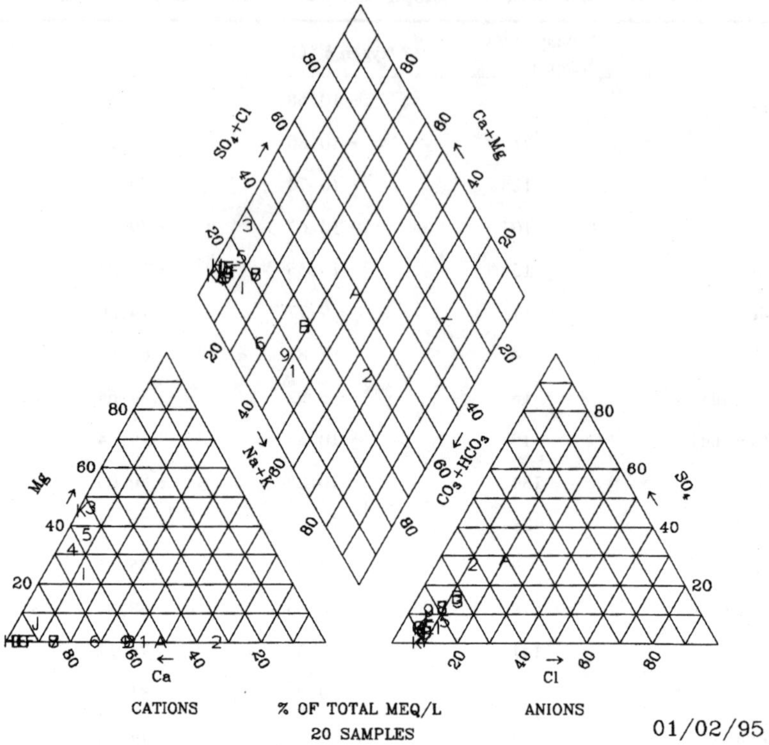

Fig. 11-4 Piper Diagram at Bihor Mt. 1. Gura Tomesti Swallet; 2. Padis Well; 3. Poiana Ponor Spring; 4. Izbucul Ursului-Spring; 5. Caput Cave-stream inlet; 6. Dolina Ⅲ-Karst Window; 7. Galbena Spring; 8. Galbena Waterfall; 9. Pauleasa Spring; A. Varasoaia Well; B. Cetatile Radesei-stream inlet; C. Gorgan Cave-spring; D. Alunu Mare(Left Spring); E. Alunu Mare (Right Spring); F. Ponorului Valley Swallet; G. Alunu Mic Spring; H. Humpleu Ⅰ Spring; I. Humpleu Ⅲ Spring; J. Humpleu IV Spring; K. Somesului Spring

23.5 km^2 Triassic limestones and 30.5 km^2 Jurassic and Cretaceous ones (Fig. 11-2).

In this area 26 stream-sinks and 18 karstic springs have been identified. The main sinking area is situated on Triassic limestones. The watershed in the central part of the plateau established by a sequence of tracing experiments (Oraseanu, 1985) shows the preferential discharge direction to West and South. According to the geological and tectonic map a dispersion of the discharges cannot be observed, the catchment areas being well individualized. The existence of the watershed in that place is determined by the outcrop of the Hettangian-Sinemurian deposits situated at the East side of the Oselu spring and continue under the Quaternary deposits.

The flow path reveals the strong dependence on the tectonic structures.

The Boga spring runs the waters from a 4.5 km^2 catchment area of Triassic limestones. The main stream sinks in Varasoaia, with a total discharge of 60 l/s, the waters being gathered on impervious formations, and will control the high level of Boga spring discharge, which is between 100 − 500 l/s. The same discharges of the streams-sinks can be observed in the Padis-Tringhiesti area (approx. 50 l/s), which were tested with a dye tracing experiment. The tracer appears in the Poiana Ponor spring. This stream after 1 km of subaerial course sinks once again, to be found in the cave of Cetatile Ponorului (karst window) like a subterranean stream, which end in a sump after two km of passages, the waters coming out finally through the Galbena spring. The Poiana Ponor stream-sink is formed along a fault which put in contact the Triassic and Jurassic limestones, being

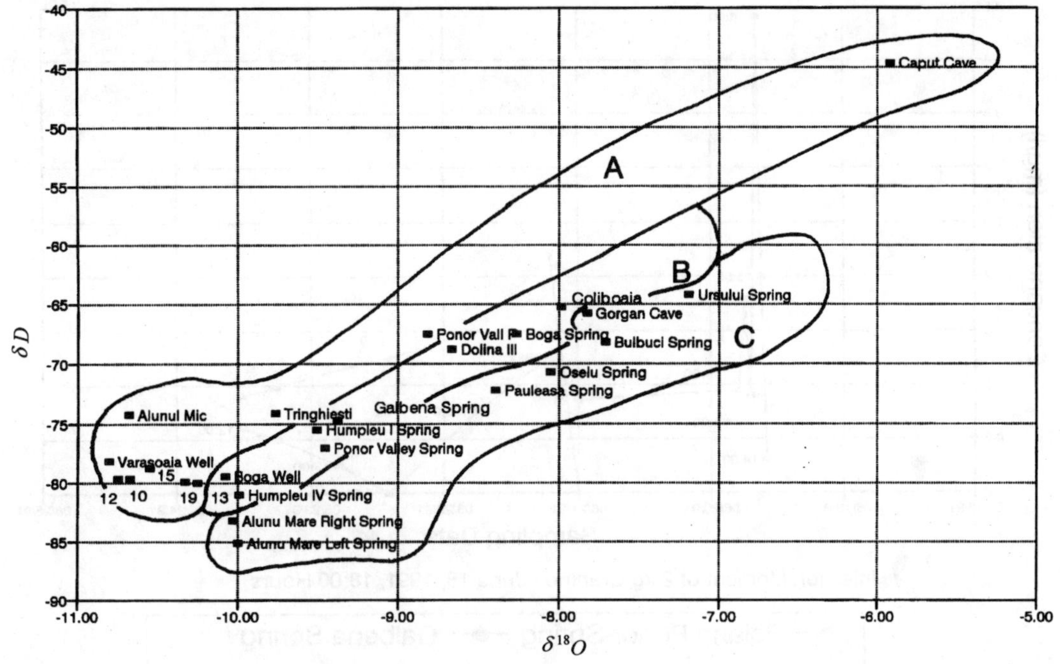

Fig. 11-5 Environmental isotopes ratio at Bihor Mt.

in the same time a connection between the Lower and Upper Aquiferous Series.

On June 18, 1991, 2 kg of Uranine was injected in the Tringhiesti stream-sink. The appearance of the tracer in the Poiana Ponor spring was after 14 hours (Tab. 11-2), the graph presenting 3 pulses of different amplitudes, the storage of the limestone massif being reduced (Fig. 11-6).

Tab. 11-2 Tracing test results

Stream Sink	Alt. (m)	Q (l/s)	Spring Name	Alt. (m)	Q (l/s)	Distance (m)	Difference level (m)	Mean Transit Time (h)	Flow Velocity (m/h)
Tringhiesti	1260	15	Poiana Ponor	1100	134	1980	160	96	20.62
			Galbena	800	228	5350	460	102	71.33

The appearance of the tracer in the Galbena Spring was after 40 hours, the graph being flatter, that shows that the storage condition are different, the vadose flow being shorter.

The flood hydrography of the Poiana Ponor and Galbena Spring, seems to be of a vadose cave stream and tend to be peaked and similar to a surface river (rapid response of large channels and enlargements). The storage is strongly influenced by the proportion of the rainfall input that runs off and the lag between the input event and the output response is very short.

The water quality data shows a relatively low mineralized water of the aquifer reservoir during normal and increasing flow-rates. Once the flood peak is passed, the newly infiltrated water reaches the spring through the karstic fissures and the mineralization increased. Once the main pulse passed, the decreasing of yield is followed by the dilution of mineralization (TDS).

The TDS of the springs waters ranges between 233 mg/l and 285 mg/l, which are very closed to the TDS (219 mg/l) of the stream sink, confirming once again the high speed flow of the underg-

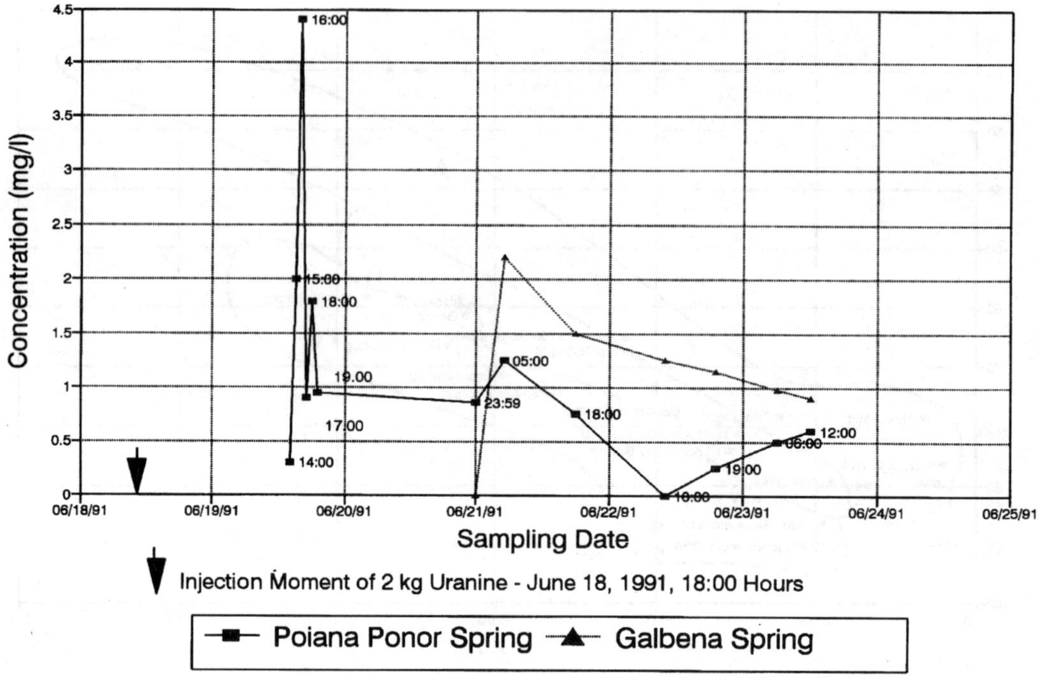

Fig. 11-6 Tringhiesti-Poiana Ponor-Galbena tracing experiment, Bihor Mts.

round stream through the limestones.

11.5 Jiul de West-Cernisoara Karst Area (Retezatul Mic Mountains), Southern Carphatians

Jiul de West and Cernisoara rivers form the natural boundary between the alpine massifs Retezat and Godeanu on one side and Vilcan Mountains on the other side and collect both surface waters and subterranean streams of karst area (Fig. 11-7).

Upstream the confluence of Buta Valley with Jiul de West River, the Jurassic limestones form an upstanding plateau in the Retezatul Mic Mountains (Piatra Iorgovanului-Piule-Plesa), into which an intensive dry valley network were developed.

The right side tributaries of Jiul de West valley collect waters from the Northern slopes of Vilcan Mountains, which are sinking through swallets along the main valley.

The karst area was affected by glaciers which penetrated deeply into the limestones and non-limestones. The glaciers had modeled the Soarbele, Gauroane and Scorota valleys. The first one formed a classic example of moraine behind a Jurassic limestone ridge and the second one present a glacier cirque.

The geological structure of the area includes two major tectonic units: Danubian Autochthonous and Getique Nape. The older basement deposits consisting of crystalline rocks and granites are overlain by Jurassic deposits formed by Liasic sandstones and Middle Jurassic-Aptian limestones and dolomites. These deposits are disposed in a synclinal structure with the southern slopes crossed by a main fault, which constitutes the boundary between the limestones and the crystalline rocks. Along a second fault, parallel with the first one the Jiul de West river flows and presents many active and dry sink-holes.

The limestones are stratified into 15-20 cm thick layers of pale gray to cream color. The bed-

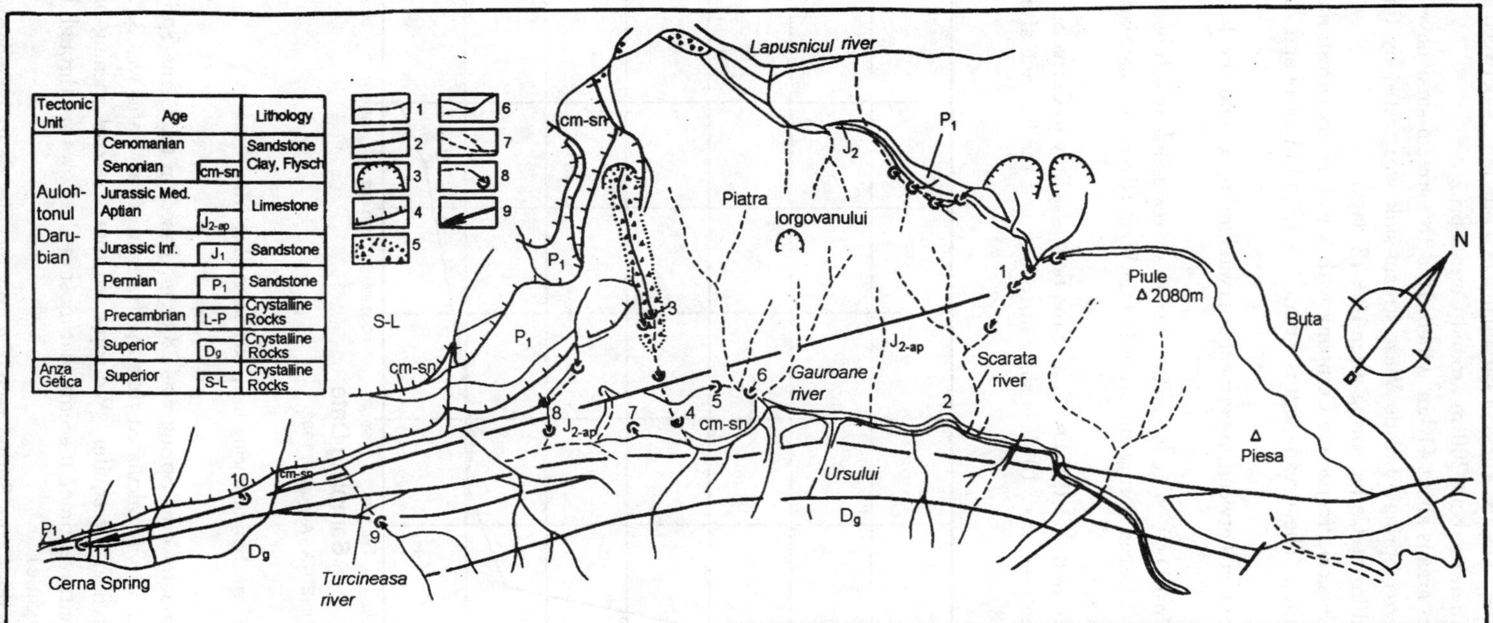

Number on the map	Point's name	Altitude (m)	Discharge (l/s)	Distance to Cerna Spring (m)
1	Scorota Swallet	1390	20	13350
2	Jiu	1100	15	12250
3	Soarbele Swallet	1530	17	8570
4	Soarbele II Swallet	1200	0.2	8480
5	Scocul Mic Swallet	1270	1.5	9250
6	Fundoane Swallet	1200	0.5	9750
7	Lacul Ratii Swallet	1330	0.1	7780
8	Sturu Swallet	1330	10	6800
9	Turcineasa Swallet	940	9	4160
10	Suspendat Swallet	850	2	2240
11	Cerna Spring	700	1300	

Fig. 11-7 Map of Jiul de West-Cernisoara Karst Area

ding plane dips south at 40 to 60 degree. The thickness of carbonates deposits ranges between 1500 m and 2000m in Retezatul Mic Mountain to about 200 m around Cerna Spring.

The Jiul de West-Cernisoara karst area is about 41 km^2 where 10 active stream-sinks have been identified, which flow towards to Cerna Spring. Jiul de West stream-sink was tested by Povara (1974) with uranine, which appeared in the Cerna Spring after 10 – 12 days.

In 1982 the Geological and Geophysical Prospecting Company with I. F. I. N. Bucuresti made a tracing experiment in the Scorota swallet. The stream-sink is situated at 13350 m away and 700 m higher from Cerna Spring.

Scorota inlet is situated at the contact between impermeable crystalline rocks and the Jurassic limestone.

On August 9, 1982, 100 g of In-EDTA were injected in Scorota stream-sink which had 25 l/s discharge. Samples were collected at Cerna Spring and from Jiul de West River, downstream the contact with the non-carbonate deposits.

Samples collected and analyzed showed that the direction of the flow was only to Cerna Spring. The first tracer appearance was encountered after 10 days since injection, and the last one after 38 days since tracer's injection (Fig. 11-8).

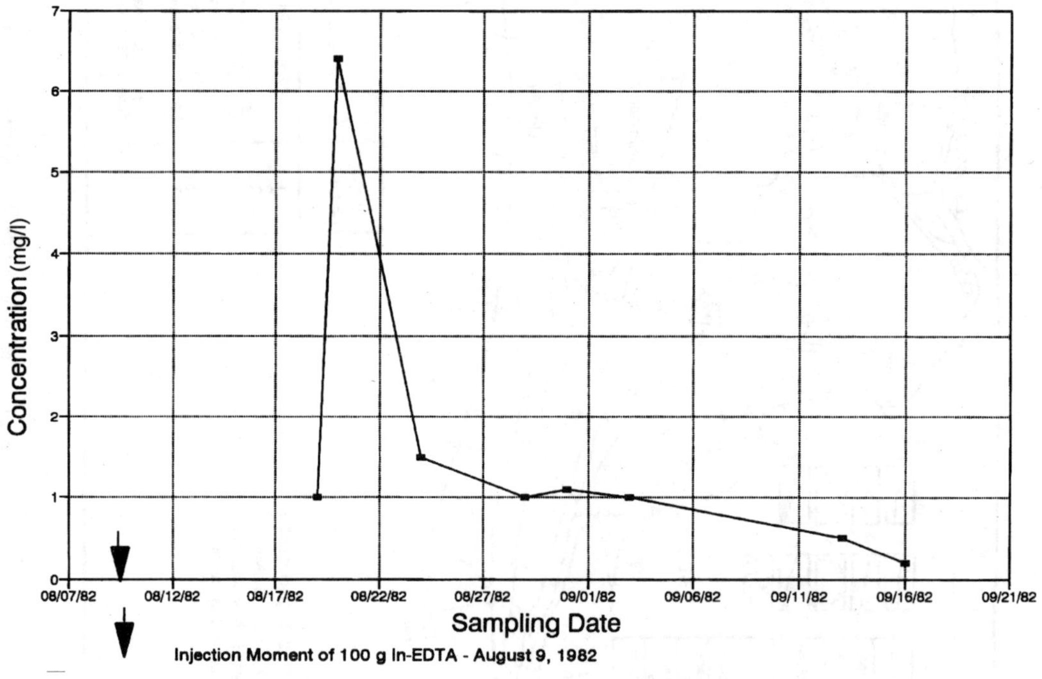

Fig. 11-8 Scorota-Cerna Spring tracing test, Retezatul Mic. Mts.

The travel time of the tracer through Cerna Spring was 28 days. Based on the Cerna Spring's yield measurements done by I. M. H., it was calculated that the tracer recovery ratio was 33.5% and a part of the tracer remained stored in the aquifer. We supposed that a second opening of the aquifer did not exist, and based on the travel time, it seems that most of the flows are through large channels and enlargements (vadose regime).

Based on this tracing experiment the Cerna Spring recharge area includes on its boundaries the Retezatul Mic Mountains.

The Jiul de West-Cernisoara karst area is an excellent example of subterranean stream piracy facilitated by main fault systems and the synclinal structure of limestones. It is a great possibility that a second recharge point of this aquifer to be situated on Buta valley.

Yield measurement of inlet-outlet relationship suggests that under average condition the sink provides about 20% of the outflow water. Study of the catchment characteristics, (especially done on karren areas), suggests that 80% of spring discharge is formed by percolation waters on bare rock and endokarstic condensation waters.

11.6 Evaporites Karst

The karst formed on evaporitic rocks represents 5% of the Romania's bare type karst and is developed on small areas.

Exocarst in gypsum formation is not so widely spread. Some sinkholes occur in the Southern Carphatians, near the Cumpana village area and also some small karren fields.

On the contrary the salt deposits are intensively karstified. The salt outcrops in the lowland hills of Eastern, Southern Carphatians and Transylvannian plateau. Salt karst occurs more frequently than gypsum under the form of the salt rocks in Miocene formations. These massifs sometime outcrop in the Eastern and Southern SubCarphatians Hills.

In most areas the salt deposits are overlain by unkarstifiable rocks, on which karstic forms appear due to the salt dissolving processes.

In the area of Slanic Prahova is a large salt massive, along the axis of Slanic syncline.

During the 18th century the exploitation of salts started. At Baia Baicului two salt mines were dug. Due to the work on vertical system, from lowers part to upper one, the results were two bell shape mine, which had only an ephemeral existence being inundated by waters. The salt dissolved produced the collapse of the ceiling in one of the mine. Now a salt lake is in that place, used as a spa. Due to the collapse a land slide was produced on the slopes of the second mine, the results being an isolated mountain. Beginning with that moment, the salt mountain slopes were exposed to dissolution and precipitation processes and typical forms as microkarren, karren and cave corals on the outside walls were formed and the collapse of the ceiling in the mine was produced, which now looks like the opening of a large pothole. The mine was inundated by waters and form a 20 m deep salt lake. The name of the mine is Grota Miresei (Bleahu et al., 1976).

Salt outcrops in several places in the Slanicul de Buzau basin (Eastern Carpathians). The largest zone is Sareni-Trestioara situated between Slanic Valley, Sarii Valley and Meledic Valley. It is known under the name of Meledic plateau.

The average altitude of the area is 600 m. It has a lowland parts with deep valleys and steep slopes affected by land-slides and streams.

The karstic pattern are represented by precipitation and dissolving forms which can be found on salt adjacent formation too.

Karren are often met on salt karst. They are 0.01 to 3 m long and are 2 – 8 cm deep, having short ridges between them. Their size depends on salt quality. It is obvious in the case of the salt mountain from Slanic Prahova that in the zones where the salt is dark colored karren completely disappears. In the area where the slopes present shelters, cave corrals and salt stalactites are formed.

Sinkholes are formed on salts outcrops or where are covered by thin unconsolidated deposits. The largest forms are situated in salt exclusively.

The sinkholes are 50 m in diameters and some of them attain 30 m in depth. Between the sinkholes are thin sinuous ridges, the areas having a chaotic aspect. At the bottom of the sinkholes impermeabilized with clay, small lakes are formed (max. 0.7 ha). Sometime two or three dolinen fuses, forming uvala.

When sinkholes are situated on a tectonic alignments, dolinen valleys are generated.

Due to the rapidity of the dissolution processes, these dolinen valleys becomes real valleys with a longitudinal profile. In the early stages the drainage is reduced to an underground flows, which passes later to a surface flow. Due to the limited extension of the salt and gypsum, 31 caves are situated in salt and 5 in gypsum, distributed as bellow:

Mountain	Salt	Gypsum
South Volcanic Mountains	1	–
Vrancea Mountains	–	1
Vrancea SubCarphatians	27	1
Buzau SubCarphatians	3	3
Teleajen SubCarphatians	–	–
Total	31	5

The five caves developed in gypsum are situated in Eastern Carpathians and have 10 to 12 m length and 1.2 – 10.5 m in vertical development. The size of the caves are extremely reduced and controlled by the discontinuity of gypsum formations which mostly alternate with non-soluble rocks.

Most of the salt caves are situated in the Meledic plateau (Sareni-Trestioara Zone) where 27 salt caves are known with a cumulated length of 2169 m and a total vertical development of 300 m.

The longest cave of the area is the cave known under the name "6S from Minzalesti", which is situated in the north part of the plateau. The cave's opening is situated at the bottom of a sink hole where another three caves openings were identified. A narrow passage with a few steps, a temporary water inlet, is towards to the main stream passage of the cave. The cave is 1221 m in length and – 32 m in depth and developed on three levels. The lower one is completely active and the other two are fossilized. The connections between the levels are made through chambers, pits and chimneys.

The passages are generally 1 to 4 m wide and 1.5 m to 5 m high. The maximum vertical extension of the cave (– 32 m) is developed along the underground stream passage. The end of the cave is situated just 80 m from the Meledic Creek, at the same elevation with the river. The horizontal extension of the system at this place is 244 m.

The most usual forms in salt caves are stalactites of tubular or conical shape, with or without central opened channel. Their length is 60 cm in maximum and 8 cm in diameter.

Anemolites often attain 50cm to 100 cm in length and about 2 cm in width and are grown in all directions. Their position in space doesn't seem to be related only to the presence of an air current flow with a constant direction, but also to some turbulent currents.

There are also anemolites, 40 cm in length composed by salt crystals, which are growing in rectangle angles. The longest one has 2 m in length and 20 cm in diameter (Giurgiu et al., 1980). All these types of stalactites appear in different colors, from immaculate white to pink, bright red, grey, yellowish-brown and brown.

Stalagmites are not so often met as stalactites. They have a few tens of centimeters in height and 10 cm in width. Generally, the exterior cover of the formations are composed by little crystals.

Also there are a few parietal flows and sometime occurred salt crusts, isolated excentrites and salt powder as well.

Where water drips intensively, a salt crust occurs on the floor as a crystal carpet.

The yield of the creeks which pass the salt deposits are low. On both benches of the creek salt crust are formed, till 10 m long and 1 to 3 m wide. At the bottom of large sink holes waters flow was noticed, generally with low yield, which is going underground through a swallet.

Eight of the Meledic plateau caves are water inlets, four of which having these function just during raining period. The other two caves have an underground stream.

References

Bleahu, M., 1964. Karst of Rumania; Important Karst Regions of the Northern Hemisphere. Elsevier Publishing Company, Amsterdam, Netherlands

Bleahu, M. and T. Rusu, 1965. Carstul din Romania. O scurta privire de ansamblu; Lucrarile Institutului de Speologie "Emil racovita" Tom. IV

Bleahu, M. et al., 1976. Pesteri din Romania. Bucuresti: Ed. Stiintifica si Enciclopedica

Bleahu, M. et al., 1985. Harta geologica Pietroasa, sc. 1:50.000, IGG Bucuresti Issar, A. and Gat J. 1981. Environmental Isotopes as a Tool in Hydrogeological Research in an Arid Basin. Groundwater Vol. 19, No. 5

Giurgiu I. et al., 1980. Observatii asupra carstului pe sare din zona Meledic (M. Buzau). Buletin CSER nr. 7.

Mantea, Gh., 1985. Geological Studies in the Upper Basin of the Somesul Cald Valley and the Valea Seaca Valley Region (Bihor-Vladeasa Mountains). Anuarul Institutului de Geologie si Geofizica Bucuresti, 66: 1 – 91.

Oraseanu, I. and N. Oraseanu, 1985. Studii hidrogeologice asupra zonei carstice din Munti Bihor, cu privire speciala la zona Baita Bihor. Raport Arh. I. G. G.

Oraseanu, I., 1993. Hydrogeological regional classification of the Romanian karst; Theoretical and Applied Karstology, 6, 175 – 181.

Ponta, G. et al., 1984. Subterranean Stream Piracy in the Jiul de Vest-

Ponta, G., 1986. The Evaporite karst of Rumania; Atti simposio internationale

Ponta, G. et al., 1992. The hydrogeology of Padis karstic plateau-Bihor

Ponta, G., 1992. Harta hidrogeologica Pietroasa, scara 1:50,000, Editat de.

Sencu, V. et al., 1973. Carstul. Atlasul Republicii Socialiste Romania

Valenas, L., 1984. Studiul Complex al Carstului din zona Izvorul Ursului / Piriul Sec (Muntii Bihor). Crisia Oradea p. 559 – 580

Global Karst Correlation
Edited by Yuan Daoxian and Liu Zaihua
Science Press and VSP BV, 1998

Chapter 12 Typical Karst Area – Skocjanske Jame, Slovenia

Andrej Kranjc, M. Knez, Andrej Mihevc, J. Kogovsek, T. Slabe, S. Sebela, N.Z. Hajna
Institut Za Raziskovanje Krasa, Slovenia

12.1 Introduction

12.1.1 *The History of Kras and Skocjanske Jame Investigations*

Karst presents distinctive type of earth surface with special(karstic) phenomena getting the name after the landscape Kras in the background of Trieste Bay. The name has pre-Indoeuropean origin (karra = stone) and in Antiquity it was used to be Carusardius. From 1177 the Slovene form "Grast" is known and from 1230 Croatian"Kras". In Italian and German form of the name the original base is preserved (Carso, Karst). In the international terminology the German version (Karst) remained, obviously after the regional name Kras. The first professional descriptions of this characteristic earth surface on limestones descend from our Kras (Gams, 1973). Decisive merits go to Viennese Geographic and Geological Schools. From proper name for landscape the word widened into general conception and today it means international professional designation of landscape on carbonate rocks with typical surficial and underground features and phenomena. After this name the relatively young term for the discipline is karstology (Karstologie, Karstkunde, krasoslovje, carsologia, karsztkutatas, karstovedennije) (Kranjc, 1989).

The landscape among Adriatic Sea and flysch Vipava valley, flysch Brkini hills and Friuli lowland covering about 700 km^2 is considered as Kras in narrow sense of meaning. The landscape designation changed during the centuries, but to the entire complex of "Slovene Typical" or "Classical Karst" belongs the whole Dinaric Karst between Ljubljana Marsh and Adriatic Sea.

12.1.2 *The History of Kras Investigations*

The Timavo springs are mentioned by numerous antique authors, Valvasor(1689) cited 13 of them even, from poets(Vergilius) to scientists. Poseidonius from Apamea (135 – 50 B.C.) studied one of its springs in particular. Skocjanske jame the ponor of Reka (taking its spring as Timavo on the coast) – were known in Antiquity already. Poseidonius wrote: "Timavus... flows into abyss (= Skocjanske jame)

In New Age F. Imperato(1599) explored the connection between Reka and Timavo by help of floats (Gruber, 1781). Reka, its ponor(Skocjanske jame) and Timavo springs usually appear on the maps of the time, as f.e. on Mercator map in Novus Atlas(Bleau, 1637) and they were mentioned by Cluverius too (1624).

The cave Vilenica near Lokve evidences that the voyagers and visitors were not only interested for Reka and Timavo in the second half of 17 century. It was a "show cave" already giving the income from "tourism " (Habe and Kranjc, 1988).

Valvasor(1689) may be considered as the first seriously interested in our karst. He started a new epoch of investigations and descriptions of karst. Among the men who ventured deeper in the underground are: Nagel (1748), Hacquet (1778 – 1789), Gruber(1981). Skocjanske jame were the main curiosity in Trieste vicinity which is evidenced by the work of French artist Cassas. According to the order of Joseph II he made some illustrations for a book about Trieste curiosities and its vicinity. It included the cave castle(Lueg), Reka canyon and Skocjanske jame(1782).

The virtual investigations on karst started in the 19th century, when the wells in Trieste were no longer sufficient and alternative sources for water supply were searched. The underground Reka which probably flows near Trieste and other water caves and underground flows seemed to suit to the request.

As we've mentioned there are on Slovene part of Kras 800 caves known till now. Nevertheless numerous cavers from the area, involved in several caving clubs on Kras (in Triete, Goriza, Udine, among them two slovenes, and in Koper, Divaca, Sezana and Ilirska Bistrica) are discovering new caves or new parts in already known caves. Kras is specially noted for features of contact karst-blind valleys and big ponor caves as are Skocjanske jame with several collapse dolines; for traces of fluvial surface transformation (dry valleys); and for big underground flows connecting the waters of Reka, Vipava and Soca with submarine springs, with springs on the coast and with Timavo springs themselves. Not only one of the oldest show caves in the world lies here but the entire spectrum of cave tourism development is preserved: from abandoned former show caves (Dimnice) to partly displayed caves, and caves accessible under special conditions (Vilenica, Divaska jame, Sveta jame), to virtual show caves important in international scale as are Skocjanske jame and Grotta Gigante.

12.1.3 *The History of Explorations of Skocjanske Jame*

Before the explorations for water supply, Skocjanske jame were prepared for tourism: on 1 January, 1819. Mahorcic introduced the entrance and memorial book "Liber Cavernae St. Canziani", unfortunately the fascists burnt it in 1924 (Moser, 1886; puc, 1986). In 1823"Tominceva jama" was discovered by the initiative of land councillor M. Tominc. In the same year the stairs were built into Velika dolina and to the cave. Svetina tried to penetrate deeper into the cave by Reka without success in spite of several attempts. His work was continued by A. Schmidl under the help of miners from Idrija and natives. They came about 500m far, discovered "Schmidlova dvorana" and the passage to "Rudolfova dvorana".

In 1884 the Littoral (Kustenland) Caving Section of DOAV was founded and it held on lease the caves and surroundings. The time of systematic exploration and cave management started: in 1884 the 6th cascade (Key problem) was surmounted; in 1885 Mullerjeva dvorana was discovered; in 1887 the 14th cascade was reached; in 1887 Ponvice (Giant Gours) were found; in 1890 the final siphon (Dead Lake) was reached (still today the last point of the cave). The 1904's climb to Tiha jama was the last great discovery in Skocjanske jame.

The caving techniques included: the exploration of river cave with boats; the then alpine, mountaineering technique was used; natural features in the walls were used to access to the holes on the walls and roof; the steps and stairs were cut, pitons hammered into rock, holders for iron ropes, simple wooden foot-bridges were placed. The first exploration paths were at the same time the tourist ways, but they were not convenient for all the visitors except those suitably equipped, as was then noted that the underground tourist must has "firm hand and firm leg without dizziness". Main touristic paths were widened, later they were moved to more favourable position, because the lower path was frequently flooded as it is still the case today in Mahorciceva jama.

In the first year of rent the local cave workers constructed the way into Schmidlova and Rudolfova dvorana, in 1885 they built the Tommasini Bridge and prepared the road above Velika dolina, in

1891 they built the "high way " to Mullerjeva dvorana and the path to Martelova dvorana, in 1902 the tourist path from Schmidlova dvorana to giant gours, in 1902 Swida Bridge was made, and in 1909 the "cat's wooden foot-bridge", and the path under the ceiling of Hanke channel.

Under the Italian administration the cave display started with more vigour: in 1931 Bertarelli Bridge in Mala dolina was built, in 1933 Ponte della Vittoria(Hanke's Bridge), the bridge in Mahorciceva jama and the tunnel from the doline Globocak to Tiha was get by digging.

The main changes after war were electrification in 1959 and elevator from Velika dolina in 1986.

Important works for the development of cave tourism included: "about 1902, 15000 pine trees were planted; in Italian period the paths under village Skocjan to Reka ponors were made; the most important novelty in last years was the construction of new reception and administrative center above Velika dolina. The plans about reconstruction of tourist paths, display and protection of the caves are not yet fulfilled as the intervention to cave entrance and to the caves themselves is planned. International importance of Skocjanske jame is evidenced by decree of Sezana commune to protect them as natural and cultural monument in 1980. In 1986 they were registered in a list of UNESCO natural and cultural world heritage.

Beside speleological explorations and underground discoveries, the natural history science went frequently parallel,with the explorations. The tracer experiments of Brother Imperato in 1599, and Gruber's notes (1781) about Reka were the first hydrological investigations. In addition to the Brother Imperato water tracing which is among the oldest in the world, the tracing test with fluorescein in 1891(Doria, 1893) is another important hydrological research in the region. Between the two wars the best known hydrological studies are presented in Oedl's (1924) doctor thesis and Timeus (1928) and Boegan (1938) studies of Reka and Timavo. The studies of water connections continued after the 2nd war (Mosetti, 1963), extended from water budget calculations (Bidovec, 1956) to tritium studies (Eriksson et al., 1963), vertical percolation, autopurification and pollution research (Kogovsek, 1984; Rojsek, 1983; 1984).

Geological, mineralogical, sedimentological and morphological studies were carried out by Morlot(1848), and Later Schmidl(1850), Martel(1894; 1897; 1904; 1909), Marinitsch (1897), Timeus(1912), Boegan (1924), Gams (1968; 1983), Gospodaric (1983; 1984; 1985), Chiaramonti et al. (1973), Kranjc (1983; 1986; 1989). Geophysical investigations were made by Soler (1934), climate research by Vercelli (1931)and Petkovsek (1968), radon measurements by Kobal et al. (1979). Obviously this is just a summary review as the whole bibliography of Skocjanske jame is much bigger.

Serious and extensive researches are results of organized activity, either professional or amateur: Schmidl was engaged by Southern Railway Corp. Between the two wars the influence of Italian Speleological institute was strongly felt. After the war amateur conventions were held (6th Yugoslav Speleological Congress in Lipica 1972; Symposium on Karst Protection at 160-anniversary of tourist development of Skocjanske jame 1982). The activities of the Institute of Karst Research (ZRC SAZU), were concentrated on Kras in the period 1981 – 1985 mostly.

12.2 Backgrounds

12.2.1 *Geological Background*

12.2.1.1 *Stratigraphy*

In the sense of geotectonic distribution of Slovenia (Buser, 1988) Skocjanske jame Karst belongs to Outer Dinarids making part of Dinaric carbonate platform(Fig. 12-1).

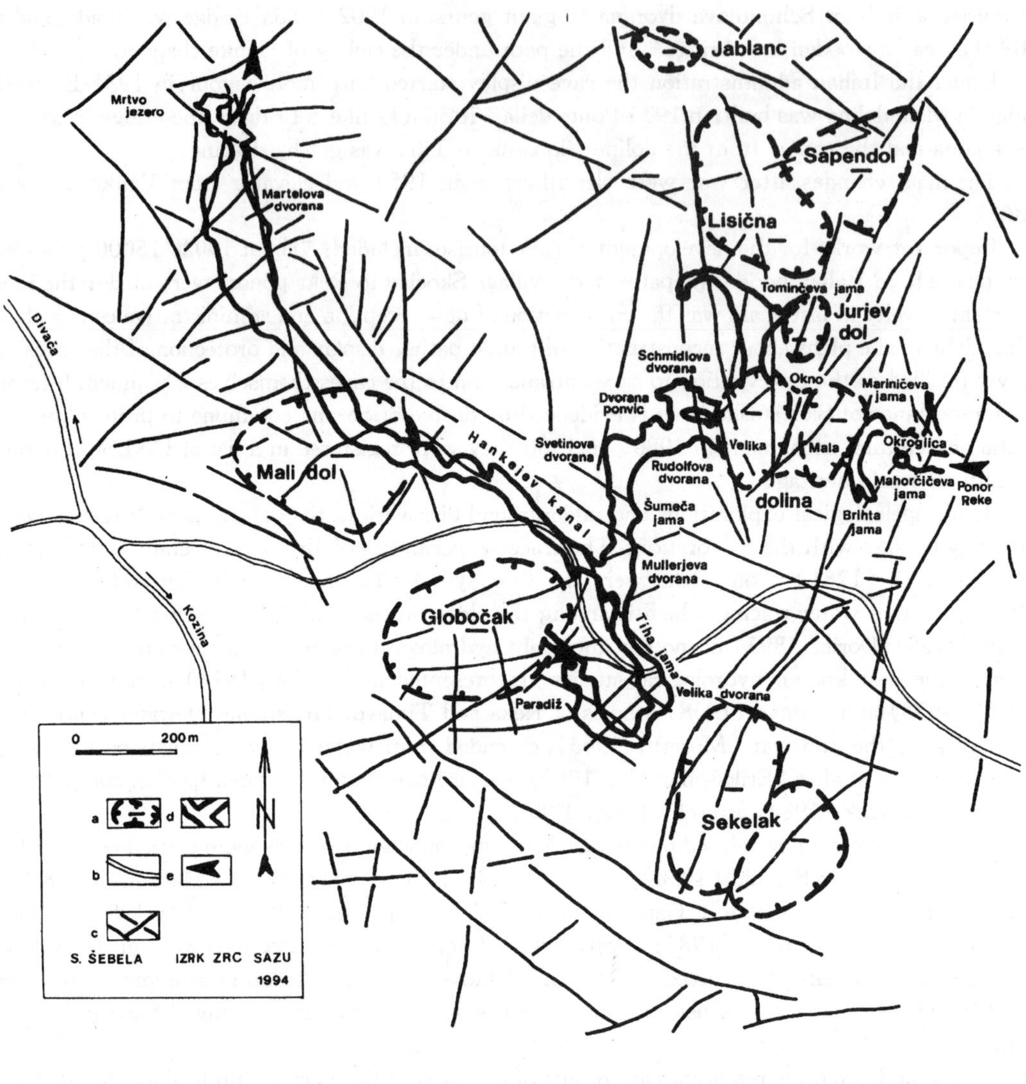

Fig. 12-1 Aerophoto interpretation of the surface above Skocjanske jame (Sebela, 1994)
a-collapse doline; b-road; c-tectonic lines; d-Skocjanske jame ground plan; e-Notranjska Reka flow direction

The oldest rocks are limestones of miogeosyncline facies of the Cretaceous age. They are followed by Paleocene limestones developed in miogeosyncline facies too. Younger flysch rocks occur in eugeosyncline facies of Eocene age(Fig. 12-2).

The rocks of lower Cretaceous developed as bituminous limestones and dolomites laterally passing to each other. Turonian age(K_2^2) is dark grey, dense, bedded limestone alternating with rudist limestone. In these rocks the majority of surface and underground features on Skocjanske jame Karst are developed. Senonian block (K_2^3) is composed by lower and upper part. In lower part there are rudist limestones, the upper part is built by lower Liburnian beds. They developed in form of dark grey micritic bedded limestone, lithologically differing from other Cretaceous rudist limestones. The karst phenomena are there less intensively developed (Buser 1972). The Youngest Cretaceous rocks (K_2^4) are grey-brown, partly fresh water and partly marine limestones.

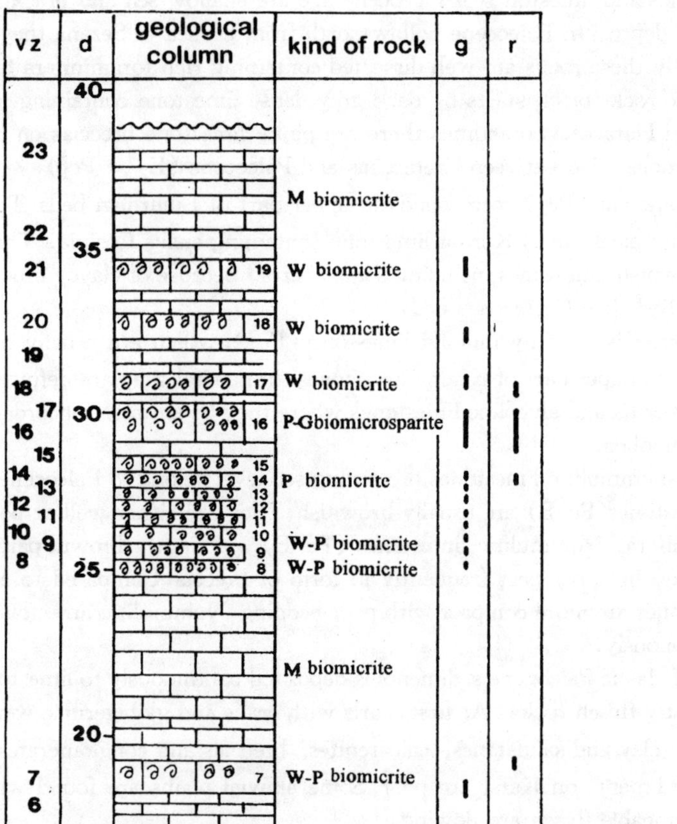

Fig. 12-2 Geological column of Vremski Britof profile (Knez, 1994a)

1-limestone, 2-very bituminous rock, 3-Gyropleura and Apricardia, 4-Rhapydionina, 5-no. of Gyropleura and Apricardia horizon, 6-Gyropleura and Apricardia, 7-Rhapydionina liburnica, 8-sample, 9-thickness(in m)

Marl limestones and limestones of Paleocene age are shallow-sea and brackish facies rocks, developed in unequal depth. In Paleocene hollow north from Divaca to Sezana they are strongly eroded. Stratigraphically these rocks are well dissected containing rich foraminifera fauna.

The Paleocene rocks block starts by dark grey dense limestone containing in upper part shells Gyropleura sp. and Haracea. Sometimes there are pinky limestone breccias on base. According to age these rocks are classified between Cretaceous and Paleocene ($K_2^4 + Pc_1$).

Lower Paleocene part(Pc_1) corresponds to upper part of Liburnian beds. The layers developed as dark grey micritic partly marl Kozina limestone containing snails Cosinia. There followed sheets of greyish and brownish limestones including some cherts. Because of clayey mixtures this limestone is much less karstified than Cretaceous beds.

Middle Paleocene is built by miliolid limestones(Pc_2), which are usually dark grey and their structure is similar to upper part of Kozina limestones. In general they are defined according to their position between Kozina and alveoline limestones where they lie entirely concordantly and because of great number of miliolids.

The alveoline-nummulitic limestones presenting sea level belong to Paleocene and partly Eocene age. Alveoline limestones(Pc, E) are usually brownish. They are either well or poor bedded containing typical foraminifera. Nummulitic limestones (Pc, E) are mostly brown, partly yellowish grey. These limestones are in upper part frequently in form of breccia. Compared to alveoline limestones nummulitic limestones are more compact with poor bedding. Nummulitic limestones are capped to alveoline ones continuously.

Lower part of clastic Paleogene sediments is deposited continuously to limestones with formanifera. These are mostly flysch rocks. At first marls with crabs and globigerinae were deposited (E_1), followed by marls, clay and sandstones, calcarenites, breccias and conglomerates($E_{1.2}$).

Quaternary sediments on Karst are poor. Some alluvial plains are found where the superficial waters from impermeable flysch are flowing.

12.2.1.2 *Tectonics*

Geological setting of Skocjanske jame karst has all the properties of autochthonous and parautochthonous tectonic zones of Dinarids between the Adriatic Sea and the unit of High karst (Sikosek, Medwenitsch 1969).

The area between Sezana and Vremska dolina belongs to two tectonic units mostly: Trieste-Komen anticline and Reka Paleogene synclinorium.

Trieste-Komen anticline is composed by several smaller anticlines and synclines with dinaric folds direction. Near Vojscica the fold axes and the main anticline axis turn westwards(Buser, 1972).

In a part of Trieste-Komen anticline two expressive dinaric faults along Rasa(Rasa fault)and between Divaca and Sezana(Divaca fault)are passing. Along Rasa fault the limestones are tectonically crushed in a wide zone. From main fault several lateral ones are divided, uniting and dividing again. Divaca fault is oriented along the rocks direction and dips steeply towards NE. On both sides it is accompanied by mylonite zone in limestones and dolomites(Buser, 1972). Such geologic setting obviously influenced to the direction of Reka river underground flow from Skocjanske jame to Timavo springs.

Reka Paleogene synclinorium starts near Lipica and passes further towards SW into Brkini area. The whole region is folded in several smaller or bigger synclines and anticlines(Buser 1972).

12.2.1.3 *Skocjanske Jame*

Geological investigations evidenced (Gospodaric, 1983, 1984) that accessible channels of Skocjanske jame developed in Turonian and Senonian, mostly thick-bedded limestones(K_2^2, K_2^3)

with exception of Tiha jame, built in thin layeredCretaceous and Paleocene limestones. This lithostratigraphic difference in limestones is reflected in the channel morphology. Along rare bedding planes and along fissures and faults of upper Cretaceous limestone the canyon-like water channels from Reka ponor to the beginning of Hanke channel developed. Huge entrance to Mahorciceva jama and Mariniceva jama in the continuation are directed towards NW and towards SW. In the left wall of Mahorciceva jama on elevation of 330m asl opens the passage to rocky bottom of young collapse doline Okroglica. On the same altitude in Mala dolina lies the bottom of filled up cave Brihta jama. Both present the remains of the former higher lying smaller and more meandering ponor channel than is the modern ones.

In the initial part of Czoernigova dvorana the 40m high elliptical shaped profile with erosional step approximately 5m under the roof is seen. In the continuation this rocky passage developed in thick layered Senonian limestone filled up by 15m thick deposit of loam, sand, gravel and breakdown rocks. The deposit is partly covered by flowstone and partly by flood loam to 345m a. s. l. The upper final passage part is fissured and covered by flowstone. The composition of the entire deposit between the rocky bottom 330m a. s. l. and ceiling 345m a. s. l. cannot be seen as it is covered by recent sediments and material falling from the roof and from upper part of the deposit.

The rocky bottom on Senonian limestone in Brihta jama is covered by 5m thick deposit, here and there covered by flowstone. Somewhere the flowstone as erosional remain is preserved on the walls 1.5m above the floor, evidencing that once the channel was filled up by sediments higher.

The collapsed doline Mala dolina is on the top elongated in N-S direction and at the bottom transversally to this direction narrowed and canyon-shaped. From here the river flows into 40m deep gravitational canyon under Okno into collapse doline Velika dolina where the vertical walls are 140m high. Mala and Velika dolina developed in thick layered Senonian limestone.

Okno (between Mala and Velika dolina) presents the remain of horizontal, 15m wide passage with rocky step 330m a. s. l. Some flowstone is preserved in it. Reka has lowered its river bed into continuous underground channel after the collapse of Mala and Velika dolina down to the actual rocky bottom 270m a. s. l. In upper, wider part of Okno collapse blocks are seen, with older flowstone and agglomerated gravel. The flowstone was deposited in time when this passage was connected to others of the same altitude.

The roof of Tominceva jama smoothly passes to walls and rocky bottom in Senonian limestone as the cave is filled up by 7m thick deposit. The rocky bottom of Schmidlova dvorana on 300m of altitude can be morphologically connected with the bottom of Tominceva jama into common development level. The bottom of Schmidlova dvorana is covered by 6m thick deposit composed by breakdown rocks and loam.

Above the flowstone in Dvorana Ponvic there is the flood loam preserved to 340m a. s. l. It was deposited in Holocene. Except recent sediments on the river bed and in erosional forms in canyon-like Sumeca jama there are no sediments preserved. Sumeca jama lies in unbedded Senonian limestone. It is formed in wide fissure zone noticed in Senonian limestones at the beginning of Tiha jama already.

Suhi rov of Tiha jama is composed by two elongated breakdown halls (Velika dvorana and Paradiz), and between them is narrow and low 100m long passage on the altitude of 340m to 350m, the rocky bottom is presumably on 310 or 315m. The longitudinal section of Tiha jama shows that three quarters of otherwise 40m high passage are filled by breakdowns and sediments. In particular the final part lying in thin-bedded and bedded Vreme(Maastricht) beds is collapsed and there lies the collapse doline Globocak (with artificial entrance into the cave).

From Suha jama the 1.5km long Hanke channel continues in fissure zone of non-bedded Senonian limestone. It ends at the cross fault where Martelova dvorana terminates with 100m high wall above the outflow siphon.

12.2.2 *Climatic Background*

The landscape Kras lies in a moderate belt (45° 39' N, 13° 59' E), in the immediate background of the Mediterranean coast, the northernmost part of Adriatic Sea, or the Trieste Bay respectively. As it lies in South of the Dinaric-Alpine barrier it is well protected against the continental and more opened towards the Mediterranean influences. Climatically it belongs to the Littoral Slovenia with sunny summers and cooler and rainy winters. In Skocjan the average annual temperature is 9℃ and the average annual rainfall 1392mm (Reya, 1946). The precipitation maximum occurs in November and the secondary one in June. Frequent bora wind accelerates the evaporation and thus diminishes the percolation water quantity (Kogovsek, 1984, 1986). Annual maximum potential evaporation is estimated to be 400mm.

Skocjanske jame are climatically divided into three main sectors:

A) Climatically static passages of Skocjanske jame. The air temperature is controlled by rock temperature. In Tiha jama the temperature is mostly between 11 and 12.5℃ (Kogovsek, 1983). A part of Tominceva jama belongs to this type.

B) The climate of water borne underground canyon. Through the hole above Reka the cooler air is coming periodically, the connection with Schmidlova jama in higher position rendering possible the escape of warmer air into Velika dolina and out. In Dvorana Ponvic the temperature lowers in cold winters under 0℃. During strong winters the lower parts of tourist path are frozen although they are about ten meters above the cave bottom and they have to be cleaned for safety. When the Reka water in the cave is warmer the mist occurs, which is frequent specially in the afternoon of the late summer and early autumn.

C) The climate of initial part of Skocjanske jame, including Mala and Velika dolina. In cooler half of the year the temperature inversion prevails. It is interrupted by bora (eastern wind) blowing through ponor, through Mala dolina and through Velika dolina. In summer this part is warmed by warmer west wind. According to several measurement done by Petkovsek (1963, 1965) the bottom is for about 3℃ cooler than the atmosphere, as the cave is of cold type with wide influx of night cold air. Inside this climatic type there are the subvariants, cooler air near the floor in lower part of shady slopes, and warmer rocky sunny slopes (Gams, 1987).

12.2.3 *Topographical Background*

Karst area of Skocjanske jame covers about 10 km^2 with the altitude of the surface between 317 – 474 ma.s.l., the terminal syphon in the cave being at 175m.

The ponor Skocjanske jame was formed by Reka which previously, supposingly in Pliocene, had flowed on the surface from flysch Brkini across the whole Kras and left the traces in the relief and sediments (Radinja, 1967). To the development of Classical Karst surface the tributaries from Vipava flysch and probably from Podgrad plain are relevant (d'Ambrosi, 1982). Local corrosional denudational processes were important too, contributing to corrosional applanation and pediplanation as well to the dissection of structurally generated ridges on both borders of carbonate plateau and on central ridge Taborski hrbet. After formation of two longitudinal fluviokarstic lowered surfaces, Nabrezina and Brestovica, still in the level of karst underground water there has been, as it is evidenced by morphological analyses, strong influence of young tectonic movements contributing to surface dissection beside vertical karst drainage in karstified rocks (Habic, 1983).

Thus the plain and plateau surface are uplifted from 10 – 50m near Doberdob to 450 – 650m near Divaca and Lipica, the average inclination being 10‰. After relief formation of carbonate and near flysch rocks we can conclude that the area between Vremscica (1027) and Artvize (817) was the most uplifted and in between lying valley of Vreme which has perhaps subsided a little even. Namely, it is longitudinally crossed by regionally important wrench-fault, so-called Divaca fault of Dinaric direction where the series of opened fissures accelerated the runoff.

By gradual karstification starting after erosional or tectonic lowering of impermeable flysch border of Kras the valley of Reka on the transition from flysch to limestone incised more and more. At the ponor into the surface under 450 m a.s.l. blind valley, 130 m deep, 5 km long and up to 2 km wide, was cut in four terraces levels, which are Skocjan (430 – 440 m), Naklo (400 – 410 m), Zavrh (389 m), Vreme (365 – 370 m) and the recent on 320 m.

Ponor channels distributed in levels correspond to the terraces in blind Vreme valley. But the network in Divaski Kras, distributed in the altitudes between 400 and 160 m has not yet been completely paralleled with the mentioned fluvial terraces. The reasons are numerous, e.g., the former ponors are on several places filled up by fluvial sediments, the ceilings above the caves collapsed which is well seen in numerous collapse dolines around Skocjanske jame.

According to shape and situation the collapse dolines were classified by Gams (1983) into four generations. The bottoms of the collapse dolines of the oldest phase are on average altitude 430 m, second and third phase on 355 m and the youngest fourth phase on 296 m. The rate between the width and depth of the particular collapse doline generation is characteristic, from 9, 4.2, 4.0 to 1. On the base of morphometric classification Gams defined the development phases and relevant positions of ponor channels in Skocjanske jame (Fig. 12 – 3) but they correspond with other speleological results partly only (Gospodaric, 1984).

Although the age of collapse dolines and ponor channels in Skocjanske jame and in Divaski Kras is not yet absolutely dated we infer it by the geomorphological data to be Quaternary development. Valley incision and underground hollowing were followed because of climatic changes, and perhaps tectonic movements have also influenced the changes in the underground.

Two kilometers in front of the ponor under Skocjan Reka flows through 60 to 80 m deep narrow canyon. It is sharply cut into plain of Naklo terrace on 400 m of altitude but the origin is not yet well explained. Some think that it originated by the roof fall above the cave and others that it was formed by Reka superficial flow by the same manner as it had cut its canyon riverbed into lower Vreme terrace. In canyon before Skocjanske jame about 20000000 m^3 of limestone is missed and in the whole Vremska dolina, if we don't take into account younger tectonic deepening, ten times as much (Jakopin, 1982).

The actual Reka ponor lies under 108 m high wall of Skocjan (425 m) on 317 m a.s.l. According to the shape and position it is relatively young as on the left, but on the right of it the older filled up steepheads are lying. The entrance passage is narrow and high developed along bigger fissure 50 to 80 m long. The axis of Skocjanske jame is presented by 2.5 km long underground canyon which has no lateral active water channels. The accessible part of water cave ends with siphon lake on 195 m a.s.l. The Reka inclination in Skocjanske jame amounts to 45°, while the inclination of superficial riverbed between Ilirska Bistrica and Skocjan is 2.8‰ only, the riverbed lowering on 28 km of distance for 80 m only.

There are several entrances to the underground. Under the village Skocjan between ponor and Mala dolina is twisted channel with Mahorciceva and Mariniceva dvorana(jama). In Mala dolina lies partly filled up passage of Brihta jama, under the natural bridge between Mala and Velika dolina is short passage called Okno. In Velika dolina there are two lateral dry passage. Tominceva jama on the right and Prunker on the left side of the river, under precipice west wall in Velika dolina lies on the right above the water channel Schmidlova dvorana, which is connected with Rudolfova dvorana lower near Reka and Svetinova and Muller jeva dvorana above it. Through the last one Reka flows into narrow Hankejev canal. High under the ceiling on the left Reka side is the entrance to Tiha jama which is connected with collapse doline Globocak by artificial tunnel. Now the tourist visit starts there and the visitors return from Velika dolina by elevator.

The contact karst near Skocjanske jame enjoys big permeability. The volume of the biggest collapse doline Sekelak is more than 8000000 m^3, and the biggest hall Martelova dvorana more than 1500000 m^3, is obviously the results of favourable geological setting and big erosion and corrosion power of sinking river Reka in the contact area.

12.2.4 *Hydrological Background*

Reka river gathers the water from more than 350 km^2 of the surface, from it 214 km^2 (60%) on impermeable flysch while the karst background on Sneznik (1797 m) and in the area of Slavenskokosanski kras are not yet precisely defined. Reka takes its spring in flysch SE from Ilirska Bistrica on 720 m a.s.l., only 15 km from Kvarner Bay, but it flows into Trieste Bay 73 km away. Near Ilirska Bistrica a strong lateral karst tributary joins it from right and near there the strongest superficial stream Molja comes from the left side. The confluence of waters in shallow Bistrica basin is connected to tectonic subsidence, the earthquakes with epicenter near Koseze are frequent and near Bukovica the Pleistocene loams are in relatively low position. The second tributary from right is Susica draining high waters from Kosanska dolina only, where the water table in karst near Gabranca effluent lowers for more than 120 m, therefore low waters from this area are flowing under Vremscica (1027 m) into Timavo, as it was proved by water tracing of Sajevski potok. The minimal Reka discharge is 0.16, the medium 8.95 and the highest above 387 m^3/s. The relation between low and high discharge is 1:2400 evidencing its torrential character. At the highest the water is dammed in the underground and floods occur in Skocjanske jame. In 1826 the flood reached the Hill 346 m, in 1851, 336 m, in 1965, 320 m. Thus the biggest differences in water level near Mrtvo jezero is 150 m, in Hankejev canal 86 m and the flood comes deep into Tiha jama interior. At drought Reka disappears in karstified riverbed 5 km before Skocjan already and at such occasion there are no traces of Reka water flow neither in Skocjanske jame nor in near Kacna jama. We infer, that under known caves the unknown water conduits exist. Reka swallow-holes in Vremska dolina were filled up by millers in past already in order to have water in the dry summer time. The last bigger sinkhole opened in riverbed near Gornje Vreme in summer 1982. Into 27 m deep and 5 m wide ponor all the waters of Reka disappear when the discharge lowers under 0.8 m^3/s which is happening regularly during summer droughts.

Underground continuation of Reka between Skocjanske jame and Kacna jama is unknown on the distance of 1.5 km, but probably water flow avoids the collapse doline Risnik near Divaca. Unknown is also the flow between Kacna jama and the 30 km away Timavo springs. Generations of cavers tried for more than 150 years to reach the underground flow from somewhere on the surface. They succeeded in 329 m deep Labodnica near Trebce only and in no other among almost 1000 explored caves.

Till now Reka underground flow was traced and proved by help of suspended load mineral substance, by salts, by organic dyes, by marked eels, by yeast bacteria and by isotopes (Timeus, 1910; Boegan, 1938; Bidovec, 1967). These researches have given important knowledge on hydrological properties of Kras through which Reka and other waters flow feeding the Timavo springs by a velocity of 0.5 to 10 cm/s. In average the main flow from Skocjanske jame to Timavo springs needs 9 days, but for its underground tributaries from Pivka border need 2 months even at low waters.

12.2.5 *Pedological and Vegetational Background*

According to phytogeographical division of Slovenia, Kras belongs to submediterranean region. On the limestone substrate there are the soils of rendzina type, in the genetical sequence from shallow protorendzina to rendzina. On the Eocene flysch the soil is deeper and more humid (Zupancic, 1976).

For the area the thermphyl-xerophyl submediterranean Illyric forest association Seslerio autumnalis-Ostryetum carpinifoliae HT. et H-ic 1950 is characteristic. The original association form is rather changed. Various degradation states appeared from bushes to more or less interrupted forest, over rocky karst pastures to bare rocks. Just above Skocjanske jame the landscape is partly overgrown by artificially planted Pinus nigra. Reforestation intensively started at the end of the last century and in the beginning of the 20th century and lasted to the first years after the 2nd World War. Other surface is covered by pastures and meadows. There the rocks are cleaned and constructed into dry stony walls. There are some fields in the bottom of the dolines, where the soil is thicker but this is mostly due to human activity (cleaning of stone, widening and leveling of the bottoms, adding of soil).

Floristic properties of Skocjanske jame themselves are interesting too. In Velika and Mala dolina the symbiosis of plant species with different categories from meadows to glacial relicts are stated. There are 250 species of phanerogamme and 25 species of cryptogamme flora known. The symbiosis is composed by representatives of autochthonous Illyrian flora (Ostrya carpinifolia Scop.), Mediterranean flora (Ciclamiy purpurescens Mill.), Pannonian flora (Euphrasis tatarica Fisch.), Baltic flora (Viola mirabilis) and very characteristic glacial relicts (Primula auricula L. ssp. bauhinii, Beck, Saxifraga incrustata Vest., Viola biflora L., Silene saxifraga L. and Aconitum paniculatum L.). There are more then 100 species of mosses known (Grom, 1959).

12.3 Hydrochemical Features (Carbon Cycle)

12.3.1 *The Precipitation, Percolation through the Roof*

In the area of Skocjanske jame (meteorological station Matavun near Divaca) about 1000 to 1700 mm of precipitation falls annually. In 1982 it was 1523 mm, but in dry year such as 1983, it was 1052 mm only.

Two years of regular observations (1981, 1982) in Skocjanske jame were carried out, including the percolated waters in Tiha jama where the ceiling is 55 to 90 m thick, and in Dvorana Ponvic where the ceiling thickness is 100 m. Sampling points are indicated in Fig. 12-3. Discharge, temperature, specific electrical conductivity were measured each week and besides definition of carbonate, total and calcium hardness, the chlorides, nitrates and o-phosphates contents were measured (Kogovsek, 1984).

Two types of percolation could be distinguished in Skocjanske jame, i.e., the permanent tiny drippings and the big periodical trickles.

In the case of tiny permanent drippings, the discharge and hardness oscillate seasonally. The points 1 and 4 belong to this type (Fig. 12-3). The droppings are connected to less permeable conduits impeding quick water discharge through the cave roof.

Watering of background is permanent and brings about water homogenisation, which is reflected in small oscillations in hardness throughout the year.

The big trickles, even drying up in longer dry periods present a specific case. We suppose that water flows through more pervious conduits. Thus partial homogenisation in the background of these trickles occurs in wet periods only when the watering of trickles background is the greatest. In the period of modest or irregular precipitation the background watering changes quickly and periodically diminishes therefore the trickles dry up. These important changes in trickle background probably influence the jumping discharge and hardness changes. Increased trickle discharge is followed by in-

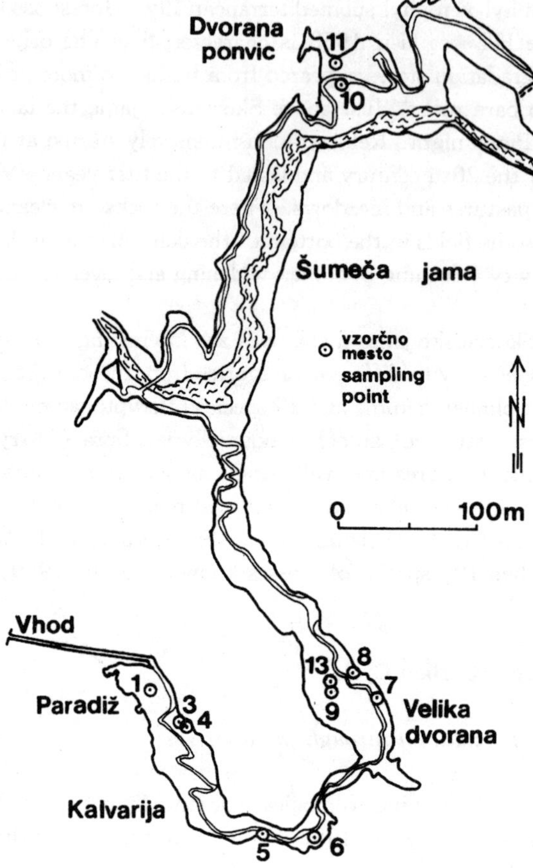

Fig. 12-3 The location of observation points in Skocjanske jame (Kogovsek, 1984)

creased water hardness. The representative of this group is trickle 8 (Fig. 12-3, 4). But in Planinska jama the opposite relation of discharge and carbonate hardness was stated at big permanent trickles.

Trickles carbonate hardness in Skocjanske jame reaches the values from 80 to 300 mg $CaCO_3$ l^{-1}, similar to total hardness. The calcium content is high, and there is only a few milligrams per liter of magnesium only. The percolated waters contains low content of chloride (some mg Cl l^{-1}), 1 mg NO_3 and under 0.05 mg PO_4^{3-} l^{-1}. The exceptions are the water from chimney (point 3) and the nearby drippings (point 4) with increased nitrates content (up to 30 mg $NO_3 l^{-1}$). Higher nitrates values can be explained by manuring the field in doline on the surface above the observed points 3 and 4.

Comparison between the properties of Reka river water (in the cave) and percolation waters in the cave is as follows:

Parameter	Reka river	percolation water
T℃	1 - 21	5 - 17
pH	7.8 - 8.3	7.2 - 8.3
Na^+ (mg/l)		to 1.5
K^+ (mg/l)		to 0.2
Ca^{2+} (mg/l)	42 - 80	30 - 115
Mg^{2+} (mg/l)	1 - 19	1 - 7
HCO_3^- (mg/l)	138 - 310	100 - 370
SO_4^{2-} (mg/l)		to 4
Cl^- (mg/l)	to 12	1 - 9

12.3.2 *Flowstone Deposition*

In most cases the percolated water in Skocjanske jame is oversaturated. In Tiha jama the flowstone is deposited all over. In general two groups could be distinguished. When droppings are tiny and permanent the flowstone deposition is quite regular, similar as in Pisani rov of Postojnska jama. Around big trickles in Velika dvorana the flowstone is deposited in bigger quantity.

In the case of small trickle 1 (discharge from 0.1 to 360 ml min^{-1}) in Paradiz during the whole year regular flowstone deposition was recorded, from 15 to 60 mg $CaCO_3$ from 1 liter of percolated water. For the annual calculation of percolated water flowed through this trickle and carbonates quantity deposited in one year out of it, we have used the measurements of two weeks. In one year through this trickle 16 m^3 of water have flowed and 600 g of flowstone were deposited. Similar deposition rate was established in Pisani rov of Postojnska jama (Kogovsek, 1983). The annual quantities of deposited flowstone depending on annual quantity of percolated water are presented on Fig. 12-4.

As an example of flowstone deposition from big trickle we have chosen the trickle 8 in Velika dvorana having extreme oscillation of discharge and hardness and drying up periodically even. The percolated water trickles down on a 10 m high speleothem Orjak. From 1 liter of this water 37 to 170 mg $CaCO_3$ were deposited, giving 23 to 65% of carbonates of percolated water. Parallel to discharge and hardness oscillations the flowstone deposition oscillated too. As higher hardnesses of percolated water occur during bigger discharges and the quantity of deposited flowstone is the product of both factors, the maximal rates of flowstone deposition occur during bigger discharges. Although during the summer drought the flowstone deposition stops for four months, on the base of weekly measurements, we estimate that the annual quantity of deposited flowstone in Velika dvorana of Skocjanske jame overpasses the deposition in Planinska jama and in Pisani rov of Postojnska jama. The flowstone deposition on point 8 in Velika dvorana is presented in Photo 62.

12.3.3 *Limestone Denudation Rate*

This rate, based upon hydrochemical data, gives for the upper part of carbonate rocks mass the values between 2.8 and 10.2 mm/ka. The rate of denudation in the underground river bed of Reka and in its immediate surroundings, based on surface measurements (by the means of microerosionmeter), is between 13 – 28 mm/ka (Miheve...).

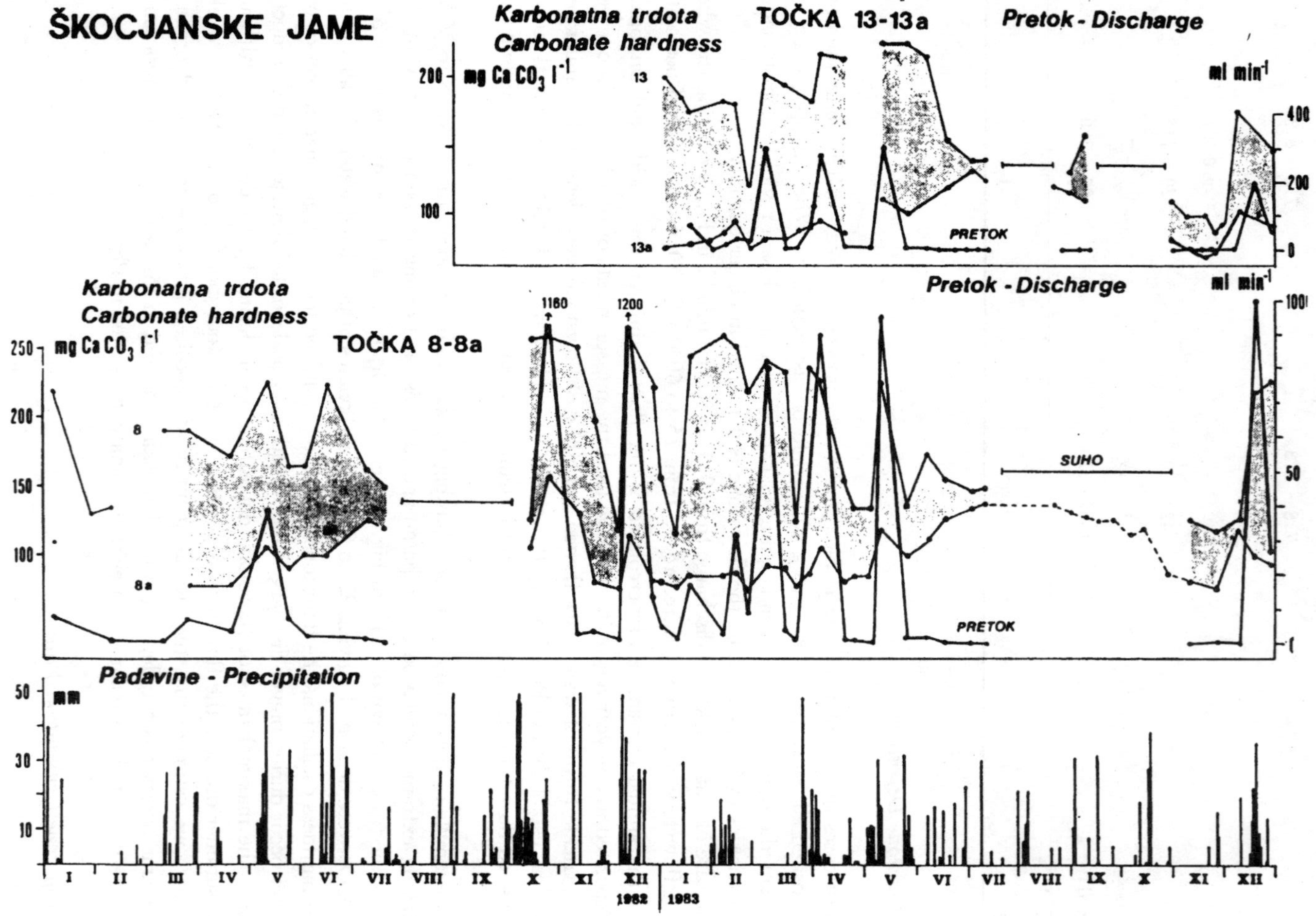

Fig. 12-4 The flowstone deposition in Velika dvorana of Skocjanske jame. On the points 8 and 13 the hardnesses of the percolated water were measured above the stalagmite, while on points 8a and 13a at the stalagmite; the difference in hardness presents the deposited carbonates (Kogovsek, 1984).

12.4 Karst Feature Complex

Skocjanske jame present the biggest natural curiosity of the whole Classical Karst between Trieste Bay and Vipava valley. Together with blind valley of Vreme and Divaski Kras along the narrow ponor border of Notranjska Reka they make a part of typical morphogenetical unit of contact karst, unique in Europe regarding its phenomena and dimensions (Gams, 1983).

Distribution of old water channels on Kras among Skocjan, Kacna jama and Timavo springs is defined according to the distribution of collapse dolines and bigger caves where fluvial sediments are preserved. The actual flow is indicated by rare blow holes near Povirje and Sezana where periodically the smell of polluted underground river is felt.

12.4.1 *Speleomorphology and Speleogenesis*

Reka is one of the bigger sinking streams in the world (Gospodaric, 1983) and it excavated huge underground caverns. Skocjanske jame are about 6000 m long all together, the total altitude difference is 255 m. The caves are composed by several separated upper dry passages and by uniform low water level, both interrupted and at the same time connected by two big collapse dolines.

Lower water level lies near the ponor on the altitude 317 m, the bottom of Velika dolina is at 260 m, and the final siphon Mrtvo jezero is on 195 to 200 m a.s.l. It is canyon-type with steep walls along the river bed. Canyon-like Hankejev canal is expressive in particular, at the beginning the riverbed is 5 m wide, 77 m high, and under the roof the channel is widened to 15 m. Before the final Mrtvo jezero the channel widens to 70 to 100 m being more than 100 m high. The inclination of Reka riverbed between ponor to Mahorciceva jama and Martelovo jezero before the siphon is 45‰. After heavy rains the water stagnates in this channel and water level starts to increase. In the entrance part up to Sumeca jama the riverbed is cut in solid rock, the parts with cascades and falls alternating with lakes. In several places solution cups are cut into solid rock. In Sumeca jama and in Hankejev canal Reka flows among the breakdown rocks. In them and in the rocky riverbed bottom characteristic small facets and rock mills are incised resulting from quick and strong water flow. On the bottom of big Martelova dvorana there is a lot of gravel, breakdown rocks and loam. In Mrtvo jezero flood wood and other floating materials are found which were not able to be sunk down to the siphon by the water.

On several places the levels are connected by breakdowns as the ceiling above the big channels collapsed and the strong water flow transported the breakdown rocks away simultaneously. This is the genesis of collapse doline Okroglica. Mala and Velika dolina, the results of breakdowns are also huge caverns as 70 m high Sumeca jama.

Upper level lies on 310 – 330 m a.s.l. It is composed by Czoernigova jama, Brihta jama, Okno, Dvorana Ponvic and Tiha jama. The passages of this level are smaller, more meandering having smaller inclination than those on modern water level. R. Gospodaric (1984) considered Tominceva jama as independent level too which was excavated by sinking stream under the village Gradisce and flowing into the channels near Sapen dol and Lisicna, while from Tominceva jama it has flowed under the then Velika dolina into Schmidlova dvorana.

We suppose that the remains of higher and the oldest levels are presented by Luknja v Lazu and Roska spilja 370 – 390 m a.s.l. and farther the inclined caverns with horizontal passages as are Jama 1 and 2 "Na Prevali", which are above the actual Skocjanske jame. The flysch gravel in collapsed cave near Matavun belong to it too. It was found while digging the sanitary dump for new touristic center. Still higher, on 420 m a.s.l. there are remains of Prelusova luknja, Jama na Skrljici, Jama v Sapendolu passages and channels filled up by sediments in the wall of Sekelak collapse doline.

12.4.2 *Speleogenesis*

The origin and development of upper level on 370 – 390 m a.s.l. belongs according to Gospodaric(1984) to Middle and Old Pleistocene period. From this period or even from before Pleistocene phase remained the traces of erosional passage in Prelusova luknja on 420 m, Jama na Skrljici and Jama v Sapendolu. The sediments in these caves reveal different climatic, hydrographic and morphological conditions of the time. The filled up fossil caves belong to this oldest period, as are the caves near Fernetici or on Koblak near Dane.

According to sediments R. Gospodaric (1984) concluded that maybe in the last interglacial, but in any case before last glacial, in Middle Pleistocene phase respectively (2) water level on 310 – 330 m was active. It means from Czoernigova to Tiha jama. From the same period are roof solution cups in Mariniceva jama, big current markings in south-eastern wall of Mala dolina and ceiling solution cups in Dvorana Ponvic and maybe also the solution cups in the roof of entrance part of Hankejev canal, showing that the water, flooding the cave had more conduits to flow through at the period. The then water channels were less steep, more width than height and more meandering. The sinking flow was less torrential, probably sinking on several places upwards in the Reka canyon (Gospodaric 1983). We can infer that later the collapse of Globocak doline closed the way to water through Tiha jama. At first I. Gams (1967/68) supposed that Tiha jama was formed by Brkinski potok, a tributary of Reka, but later he contributed it to meandering of Reka itself (1983). Progressively the upper part of Hankejev canal became the main conduit and when the new direction was again penetrable for all waters for short time the filled up channels of second level were regenerated, as verified by the small current markings in Czoernigova jama and Brihta jama. Water quickly flowed on the old sediments in vadose zone this time. To this Young Pleistocene period belong Tominceva jama and Schmidlova dvorana (Gospodaric, 1984) which are connected with ponor near Sapendol and Lisicna and later they remained hang above the actual water channels. Quick incision followed and the role of the main conduit in the initial part of the cave was taken over by Mahorciceva and Mariniceva jama. At the same time the breakdown scree in Mala and Velika dolina is supposed to be transported away. The cave's central part and Hankejev canal were quickly incised too. Water channels tended to be more direct and canyon-like lowered. For the period of quick erosional incision R. Gospodaric (1988) correlates it to the upper and middle Wurm glacioeustatical changes in Adriatic Sea and the thus induced changeable hydrological and climatic conditions. In cold extreme of Wurm (W3) the ceiling of Mala and Velika dolina is supposed to be collapsed and then the cave was connected to the surface (Gospodaric, 1983).

Anastomoses above the sediments in Tominceva jama, in upper part of Hankejev canal and in Tiha jama, are seen in cave's parts which at present are not genetically related to this secondary forms. Probably they developed above the Holocene fine grained sediment which is found in other cave's passages to the 350 m a.s.l. (Gospodaric, 1984) and once filled up the cave entirely. The floods are seen in the flowstone in Tiha jama which is out of erosion activity for 13000 years at least (Gospodaric, 1983). In this period the riverbed in the cave was incised, older higher passages weathered and collapse dolines above them were formed. But the speleogenesis of Skocjanske jame is not yet entirely explained, the temporal and space relation between hollowing and filling has to be enlightened more in detail and the influence of climatic oscillations and tectonic movements in the whole Skocjanske jame and Kras have to be studied.

12.4.3 *Cave Sediments in Skocjanske Jame*

In Skocjanske jame fluvial sediments as gravel, sand, loam and some rubbles and flowstone are preserved.

The gravel in Reka river bed is recent. In entrance to Mahorciceva jama there are several flysch pebbles, and near the siphon in Hankejev canal the limestone pebbles prevail (Kranjc, 1983). Fossil gravel is found in Czoernigova jama deposit only. In lower part cherts and in upper part flysch and limestone pebbles prevail. This fossil gravel is four times more rounded than the recent one. Similar gravel was not found anywhere else in Skocjanske jame but on the terraces before the Reka canyon.

In other channels of Skocjanske jame loam sands and loam together with rubble and flowstone compose the stratigraphic series. In some erosion forms these sediments are recent; in Tominceva jama and in Schmidlova dvorana above the rocky bottom at the altitude 308 to 300 m they are Holocene, similar are found among the flowstone and above it to 350 m of altitude in Dvorana Ponvic and in Tiha jama; sediments supposed to be Wurm age were found among the flowstone layers and breakdown rocks in Velika dvorana and in Paradiz in Tiha jama. The loams of any age are composed by 10% of carbonates without organic material. According to colour they do not essentially differ, they are all in shades of dark yellowish-brown. These properties show that the loam's origin were from weathered flysch but transported to the underground. Thin layers and regular granulation tell their deposition from turbid water overflowing the underground channels.

The stratigraphic position of loams, in between and above rubble and flowstone show that the floods were more permanent before the Wurm 3 and in the beginning of Wurm and that in Holocene the high flood waters periodically deposited flysch loam in Tiha jama even as the loam is found between the flowstone layers from this age. Breakdown rocks and rubbles are preserved in Velika dvorana and Paradiz of Tiha jama. In other channels, nearer to the underground canyon they are mostly preserved on the roof, elsewhere they are eroded. Recent stalactites, stalagmites and various covers on the roof, walls and on the bottom are white. The stalagmites on the top of deposits in Dvorana ponvic and in Tiha jama are Holocene or Late Glacial. They were radiometrically dated to 1500, 8900 and 10300 – 12300a B. P. These datings chronologically helped to define the flood loams and the recent phases of the underground development. The oldest flowstone in Tiha jama belongs to Wurm or is even older. It is layered and cone-shaped, among the flowstone beds the sediment layers are deposited.

According to deposit and flowstone investigations and their radiometric dating, R. Gospodaric (1988) elaborated temporal and climatic scale of Skocjanske jame development.

12.4.4 *Recent Fluvial Sediments*

In accessible underground of Reka there are all categories of recent fluvial sediments, from big boulders to cave loam and clay.

According to Austrian data the maximal turbidity of Reka is 1930g of suspension load per m^3 of water in the Timavo springs and approximately 2000 g/m^3 in front of the ponor to Skocjanske jame. The average suspension quantity for the years 1909 – 1911 was 22.8 g/m^3 (Boegan, 1938). Mean value calculated for the recent period is 17.3g. Regarding the mean discharge we can calculate that Reka annually transports into the underground about 6000 tons of suspension load, which is 12% of loose slope material in the Reka river basin, 25% of the material coming annually into the river bed respectively (ZVSS, 1978). So annually about 30 t/km^2 of fine grained material is loosened from the flysch part of the Reka river basin.

During the low water level the ratio of organic material in the suspension load was 70%. Organic particles are in great extent the consequence of anthropogeneous pollution.

The finest sediment deposited by modern Reka waters belongs to silt, mud, muddy sand, and sand (classification after Shepard, 1954). The ratio of sand and silt oscillates very much (between 10 – 80 %) while the clay ratio is pretty equal (8 – 22 %).

The gravel's petrographic composition changes strongly and essentially along the Reka. In the superficial riverbed flysch sandstone and chert are prevailing. After the transition of Reka to limestone relief the percentage of limestone pebbles increases quickly and correspondently the percentage of flysch sandstone pebbles diminishes. Under Skoflje the limestone pebbles reach 20 %, in Mahorciceva jama (Skocjanske jame) 30 %, and in Kacna jama they surpass 60 %. If the same trend remains downwards Kacna jama then in the underground Reka riverbed 5 – 10 km downstream, there must be limestone pebbles only.

According to data of ZVSS (1978) in the Reka river basin 395 $m^3/km^2 \cdot a$ of rock debris is loosened on impermeable relief. In addition men have to reckon with another 20 % of traction load (gravel) from carbonate rocks. Relief deficit of carbonate rocks is relatively small compared to this one in flysch.

The underground course along Reka river is an example where the changes in granulometry and morphology of recent cave fluvial sediments are well seen. At the same time, the feedback of the sediments and their transport to the formation of underground channels is seen well too. Results, obtained by study of recent sediments show that the development was similar in the past, as confirmed by the testimony of suitable older, fossil sediments (Gams, 1968, 1983).

References

Bidovec, F., 1956. Vpliv odvzenia vode Notranjske Reke na izvire Dolnjega Timava. Hidrometeoroloski zavod, 1-22, Ljubljana.

Boegan, E., 1924. Le grotte di San Canziano. Soc. Alp. d. Giulie, 1-46, Trieste.

Boegan, E., 1938. II Timavo, Studio sullidrografia carsica subaerea e sotterranea. Memorie dell'Istituto Italiano di Speleogia, II, 1-251, Trieste.

Chiaramonti, C. P. and M. Bussani, 1973. Studio mineralogico delle argille di S. Canziano, dell'Abisso di Trebiciano e delle foci del Timavo (Timavo inferiore), Mondo sotterraneo, Numero unico, 37 – 48, Udine.

Doria, C., 1983. Cenni intorno alle ricerche sulla continuita delle acque del Carso, eseguite coll'impiego della fluoresceina nel giugno 1891, Atti e memorie della Comm. Grotte "E. Boegan", 22, 27 – 32, Trieste.

Eriksson, E., F. Mosetti, K. Hodoscek and L. Ostanek, 1963. Some new results on the karstic hydrology with the employ of tritiated water as tracer, Bolletino di Geofisica teorica ed applicata, 5, 17, 18 – 32, Udine.

Gams, I., 1968. Tiha jama v sistemu Skocjanskin jam, Proteus, 30, 6, 146 – 150, Ljubljana.

Gams, I., 1983, Skocjanski kras kot vzorec kontaktnega krasa, Mednarodni simpozij "Zascita Krasa ob 160 – letnici turisticnega razvoja Skocjanskih jam, SOZD Timav, 22 – 26, Sezana.

Gospodaric, R., 1983. O Geologiji in speleogenezi Skocjanskih jam, Geoloski zbornik, 4, 163 – 172, Ljubljana.

Gospodaric, R., 1983. O starosti sige v Skocjanskih jamah, Mednarodni simpozij Zascita Krasa ob 160 – letnici turisticnega razvoja Skocjanskih jam, SOZD Timav, 20 – 21, Sezana.

Gospodaric, R., 1984. Jamski sedimenti in speleogeneza Skocjanskih jam, Acta Carsologica, 12, 27 – 48, Ljubljana.

Gospodaric, R., 1985. Age and Development of Collapse Dolines above the Cave Systems. The examples from Classical Karst of Slovenia (NW Yugoslavia), Annales de la Societe Geologique de Belgique, 108, 113 – 116, Liege.

Habic, P., M. Knez, J. Kogovsek, A. Kranjc, A. Mihevc, T. Slabe, S. Sebela and N. Zupan, 1989. Skocjanske jame Speleological Revue, Int. J. Speleol. 18, 1 – 2, pp. 1 – 42

Knez, M., 1991. Sedimentological and stratigraphical properties of limestones from Skocjanske jame area (Outer Dinarids). The Second International Symposium on the Adriatic Carbonate Platform, Abstracts, 105, Zagreb.

Kobal, I., M. Skofljanec and D. Zavratnik, 1979. Pojav radona v slovenskih kraskih jamah, Nase jame, 20(1978), 41 – 47, Ljubljana.

Kogovsek, J., 1993. Karst waters and how they are endangered, Nase jame, 35, 1, 67 – 76, Ljubljana.

Kogovsek, J. and M. Luzar, 1983. Vertikalno prenikanje na obmocju Skocjanskih jam, Mednarodni simpozij "Zascita Krasa ob 160 – letnici turisticnega razvja Skocjanskih jam, SOZD Timav, 60 – 64, Sezana.

Kogovsek, J., 1984. Vertikalno prenikanje vode v Skocjanskih jamah in Dimnicah, Acta Carsologica 12, 49 – 65, Ljubljana.

Kogovsek, J., 1992. Flowstone deposition in the slovenian caves, Acta carsologica, 21, 167 – 173, Ljubljana.

Kranjc, A., 1992. Older theories on karst and underground water, Zivljenje in tehnika, 43, 6, 45 – 47, Ljubljana.

Kranjc, A., 1992. Zadnji "veliki problem" Skocjanskih jam po sto letih resen, Nase jame, 34, 149 – 151, Ljubljana.

Kranjc, A., 1992. 45 let raziskovanja degradacije in varstva slovenskega krasa v Institutu za raziskovanje krasa, (45 Years of Karst Degradation and ProtectionResearch in Karst Research Institute), Acta carsologica, 21, 195 – 207, Ljubljana.

Kranjc, A., J. Kogovsek and S. Sebela, 1992. Les concretionnements de la grotte de Skocjanske (Slovenie) et les changements climatiques, Karst et evolutions climatiques, Bordeaux.

Kranjc, A. and M, Kranjc, 1992. Older Theories on Underground Accumulations in Karst, Karszt es Barlang, Special Issue 1992, 63 – 66, Budapest.

Kranjc, A. and A. Mihevc, 1991. December Floods along Notranjska Reka River, Ujma, 5, 142 – 144, Ljubljana.

Kranjc, A., 1993. The Skocjanske jame Caves, Nase jame, 35, 1, 57 – 65, Ljubljana.

Kranjc, A., 1983. Recentni fluvialni sedimenti v Skocjanskih jamah, Mednarodni simpozij "Zascita Krasa ob 160 – letnici turisticnega razvoja Skocjanskih jam, SOZD Timav, 27 – 31, Sezana.

Kranjc, A., 1986. Transport recnih sedimentov skozi krasko podzemlje na primeru Skocjanskih jam, Acta carsologica, 14 – 15, 109 – 116, Ljubljana.

Kranjc, A., 1989. Recent fluvial cave sediments, their origin and role in speleogenesis, Opera 4. razreda, SAZU. ZRC. Institut za raziskovanje krasa, 27, 1, 1 – 167, Ljubljana.

Marinitsch, J., 1897. Les absorptions de la Recca a Saint-Canzian (Istrie), Spelunca, 3, 9 – 10, 37 – 43, Paris.

Mihevc, A., 1992. Cave tourism and the problems of the cave protection in Slovenia, Educating for Sustainable Tourism, Proceedings of the International Conference held in Slovenia, September 17 – 24, 1992, 113 – 116, Ljubljana.

Mosetti, F., 1963. Sui nuovi criteri per gli studi idrologici con acque marcate, risultati di un esperimento sul Carso Triestino, Atti del Istituto Veneto di Scienze, lettere ed arti, 121, 138 – 150, Venezia.

Oedl, R., 1924. Der unterirdische Lauf der Reka, Eine karsthydrographische Studie uber das Hohlen-und Dolinengebiet von St. Kanzian und Divaca auf der Triester Karsthochflache, Doktorska teza, 1 – 334, Munchen.

Petkovsek, Z., 1968. Climatic conditions in the swallow-holes at cave entrances, Actes du 4e Congres International de Speleologie, 3, 181 – 188, Ljubljana.

Reya, O., 1946. Padavinska karta Slovenije, Ljubljana.

Rojsek, D., 1983. Hidrogeografske znacilnolsti in degradacija porecja Notranjske Reke ter Skocjanske jame, Mednarodni simpozij "Zascita Krasa ob 160-letnici turisticnega razvoja Skocjanskih jam, SOZD Timav, 52 – 56, Sezana.

Rojsek, D., 1984. Vodne razmere v porecju Reke in Skocjanskih jamah leta 1983, Nase jame, 26, 69 – 71, Ljubljana.

Schmidl, A., 1850. Die Hohlen des Karst, Laibacher Zeitung, 193, 195, 201, 204, 207, 210, 216, 222, 226, 229, 243, 247, 864, 873, 897, 910, 923, 936, 962, 988, 1005, 1018, 1078, 1094, Laibach.

Slabe, T., 1992. Jamski skalni relicf kot odsev speleogenetskih dogajanj v izbranih predelih slovenskega krasa, Doktorsko delo, 1 – 243, Ljubljana.

Slabe, T., 1992. Naravni in poskusni obnaplavinski jamski skalni relief, (Natural and Experimental Cave Rocky Relief on the Contact of Water and Sediments) Acta Carsologica, 21, 9 – 34, Ljubljana.

Soler, E., 1934. Campagna geofisica eseguita dall' Istituto di geodesia della R. Universita di Padova nel 1932 nella zona S. Canziano-Trebiciano, Boll. della Societa Adriatica di Scienze Naturali, 33, 67 – 90, Trieste.

Timeus, G., 1928. Nei misteri del mondo sotterraneo, Risultati delle ricerche idrologiche sul Timavo 1895 – 1914, 1918 – 1927, Alpi Giulie, 29, 1, 1 – 39, Trieste.

Vercelli, F., 1983. Il Regime termico nelle Grotte di San Canziano, Atti e menorie della Comm. Grotte "E. Boegan", 22, 171 – 178, Trieste.

Zupan, N., 1991. Flowstone datations in Slovenija, Acta carsologica, 20, 189 – 204, Ljubljana.

Zupan-Hajna, N., 1992. Mineralna sestava mehanskih sedimentov iz nekaterih delov slovenskega krasa, (Mineral Composition of Mechanical Sediments from Some Parts on Slovenian Karst) Acta Carsologica, 21, 117 – 130, Ljubljana.

Global Karst Correlation
Edited by Yuan Daoxian and Liu Zaihua
Science Press and VSP BV, 1998

Chapter 13 Karst and Caves in Australia and New Guinea

David Gillieson[1], Andy Spate[2]
[1] *Department of Geography & Oceanography, University College, University of New South Wales, Canberra ACT 2601, Australia.*
[2] *New South Wales National Parks & Wildlife Service, Southern Region, Queanbeyan, NSW 2620, Australia.*

13.1 Introduction

Australia is not regarded as a continent with an overabundance of karst resources. Indeed, as the late Joe Jennings (1975) very graphically pointed out, there is a paucity of cave and karst features in the most arid of continents outside Antarctica. However, soluble rocks are present and karst features are well represented, if subdued. Caves are relatively small and are not present in large numbers. For example, the Nullarbor Plain over 220 000 square kilometres in extent has about three hundred recorded caves in over 1400 dolines. Many of the tiny impounded karsts of the eastern states have similar numbers of caves. The longest cave is the Jenolan Tourist Caves complex at 45km, while the deepest is Niggly Cave in Tasmania at 375m (Eberhard, 1994). The caves and karsts are, however, of great scientific interest as the tectonic stability and wide climatic variation of the Australian continent has resulted in a wide array of karst landforms and the preservation of truly ancient caves and karst.

In contrast, the island of New Guinea is well endowed with karst and caves, with extensive high plateaux completely punctuated by closed depressions and some of the most rugged karst landscapes on earth. Caves over 900 metres deep and over 50 kilometres long such as Muruk and Mamo Kananda, with large underground rivers, have been discovered and mapped since the 1970s by Australasian and French expeditions.

This contrast in karst abundance and styles over a latitudinal transect from 2°S to 43°S makes the region almost ideal for global comparisons. In this chapter we briefly review the major karsts of each island and concentrate on those in which we have extensive personal experience. A fuller account of sites visited by IGCP 299 in southern Australia is provided in Gillieson (1992).

13.2 Karsts of Australia

Australia is well known as a dry continent; this reputation can be best demonstrated by the fact that two thirds of the continent has no runoff at all. One third has less than 250 mm of rainfall and the 750 mm isohyet is rarely more than 250 kilometres inland. Much of the remainder is only seasonally or episodically moist and therefore karst processes can only operate for relatively short periods. The fact that many of the larger bodies of soluble rocks are found in the drier areas further reduces the opportunity for karst development. Even the well watered fringe is subject to extreme variability and the precipitation/evaporation ratio generally does not favour the ready availability of water. The distribution of Australian karsts is shown in Fig. 13-1; this is about 4% of the continent

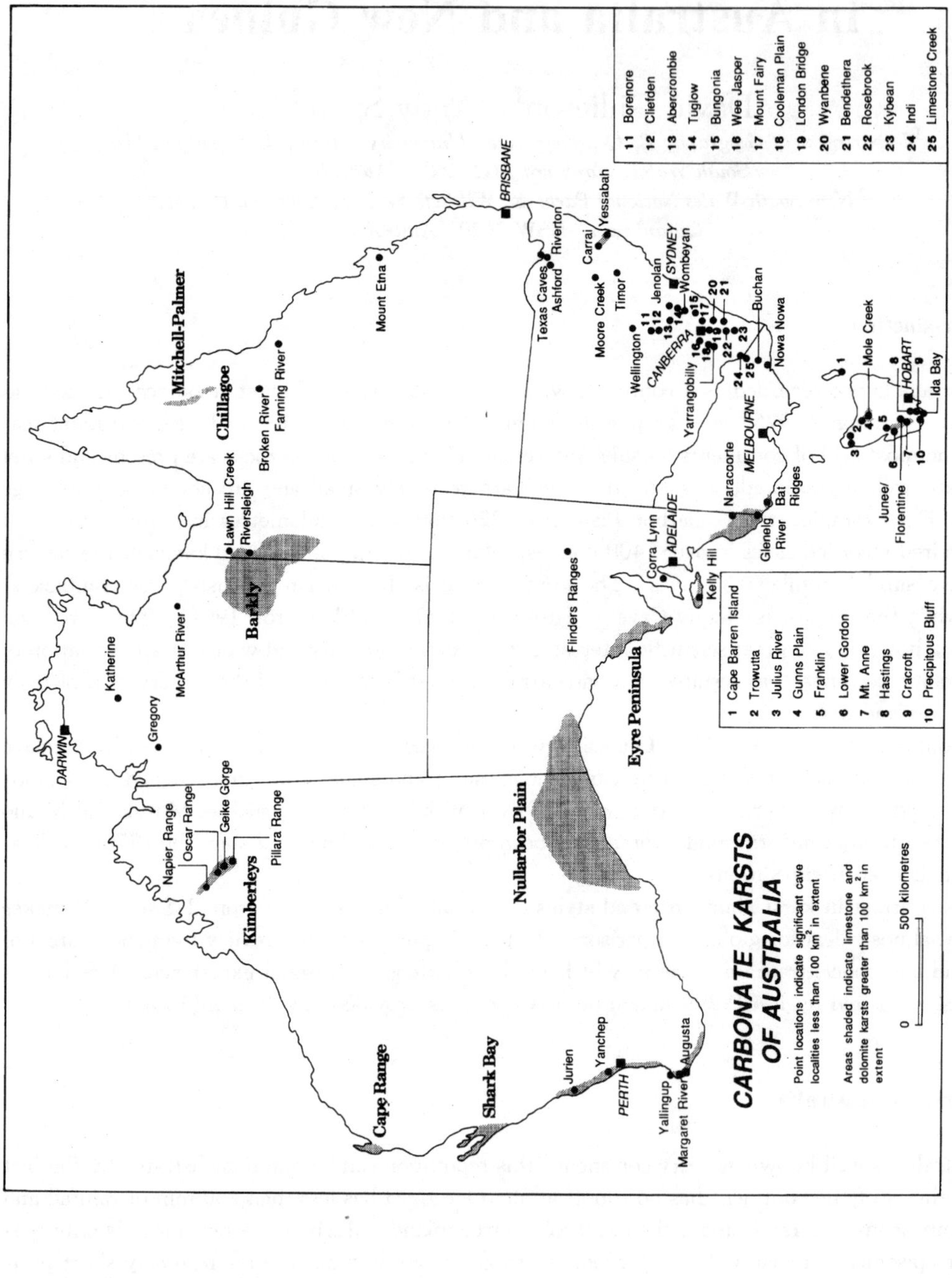

Fig. 13-1 Distribution of carbonate karsts of Australia

and is an underestimate due to incomplete geological mapping. It should be noted that a much larger area (around 15%) is underlain by limestone groundwater basins with a thick overburden of Quaternary deposits.

Climatic control of karst development can be seen dramatically in the difference between the dry Nullarbor Plain and the moist southeast of South Australia. Although the lithologies of the horizontally bedded, Tertiary limestones are very similar, the latter has extensive karstification in stark contrast to the Nullarbor. This may in part be due to watertable change through tectonics as well as sea level fluctuations. Sea level changes have had an influence on the development of the Nullarbor caves but it may well be that the karst features of the Nullarbor are relics of former, more effective, precipitation regimes. There is, however, little evidence for this over the fifteen million years that the limestones have been above sea level.

In common with the other Gondwanaland continents Australia is poor in carbonate rocks. This is because much of the continent developed before carbonate rocks became an important proportion of the geological makeup of the earth. However, if the Precambrian shield area is ignored limestones and dolomite are present in relative abundance, but there is an extreme paucity of evaporite bedrocks in which karst features occur elsewhere in the globe. Australia is the only continent lacking Tertiary orogenic belts (excepting the Cape Range of W.A.); these usually contain extensive limestones and Australia misses out on this count as well.

The age of the karst forming limestones ranges from Precambrian to Pleistocene (Tab.13-1).

Tab.13-1 Geologic age of some Australian cavernous rocks

Pleistocene	Basaltic lava of western Victoria; Einasleigh-Mt Surprise, Queensland. Dune limestone in SW of Western Aust; Eyre Peninsula and Kangaroo Island, South Australia; western Victoria.
Pliocene	
Miocene	Nullarbor Plain, Murray Valley, South Australia; Cape Range, Western Australia.
Oligocene	Southeast Province, South Australia; Glenelg River, Victoria.
Cretaceous	
Jurassic	
Triassic	
Permian	Kempsey, New South Wales.
Carboniferous	Texas, Queensland.
Devonian	Buchan, Victoria; Wee Jasper, Timor, Wellington, New South Wales; Mt Etna, Broken River, Queensland; Limestone Ranges, Western Australia.
Silurian	Yarrangobilly, Wyanbene, Colong, Cooleman Plain, Bendithera, Bungonia, Wombeyan, Jenolan, New South Wales; Chillagoe, Queensland.
Ordovician	Mole Creek, Gunns Plains, Florentine Valley, Ida Bay, Tasmania; Walli, Abercrombie, New South Wales.
Cambrian	Katherine, Northern Territory, Cammooweal, Riversleigh, Queensland; Curramulka, South Australia.
Precambrian	Coorow, Western Australia; Flinders Ranges, South Australia; Hastings, Tasmania.

Internationally, perhaps the most significant of Australia's karst features are the very young dune limestones. These calcareous aeolianites were formed at times of lower sea level and range in age from 25000 to 700000 years BP and sometimes present spectacular unconformities, as in Western Australia where they directly overly Precambrian gneisses. Southern Australia, from several hundred kilometres north of Perth to Western Victoria, is blessed with an extensive array of the so-called syngenetic karsts developed in these Pleistocene rocks in which caves and their surrounding bedrock compete for youthfulness-and unrivalled speleothem displays.

The syngenetic karsts are characterised by caprock development, usually over the original dune surface, symmetrical solution tubes reaching down to extensive watertable caves and preservation of the internal dune structures and palaeosols. The unconsolidated nature of the limestones results in plentiful collapse structures. The syngenetic karsts have been discussed in detail by Jennings (1968) and more recently by White (1984, 1989).

Karst landforms have been reported in relatively insoluble rocks such as sandstone and granite. In the case of the very large Whalemouth Cave in the North Kimberleys it seems certain that silica solution, enhanced by high temperatures, is the primary agent for cave development. Thus this area and other sandstone landscape in northern Australia, such as the "Ruined Cities" of Arnhem Land and Cape Crawford, are examples of genuine karst. The extensive sandstones of the Sydney Basin also contain a number of karst-type caves in addition to thousands of rock overhangs locally termed caves.

There is also a suite of pseudokarst caves in other lithologies including the very extensive and complex lava caves of western Victoria (Ollier and Brown, 1965) and northern Queensland. Grimes (1975) provides a useful discussion and introduction to Australian pseudokarst. Examples include the Big Hole (Jennings, 1968) of southern New South Wales which is 110 metres deep and thirty in diameter and Sanchos Hole, near Jenolan, which is approximately fifty metres deep. Big Hole is thought to have formed as a result of collapse of Devonian sandstones, shales and conglomerates into a large cavity beneath the watertable in Silurian limestones. Sanchos Hole, in volcanoclastic rocks, has a more enigmatic origin. The extensive Undara lava tubes of North Queensland have been described by Atkinson (1990).

Australian karst areas are distributed in a broad, but discontinuous, fringe around the continental margin corresponding to limestones and dolomites overlying the Australian Craton and to the impounded karsts of the Tasman Mobile Zone in the Eastern Uplands. The following is a selective review of the major mainland Australian karst areas proceeding clockwise from the northwest coast.

13.2.1 *The Cape Range, Western Australia*

This anticlinal ridge of Tertiary limestone forms the backbone of the North West Cape peninsula (Fig. 13-1), with coastal plains to the west and east. It lies within the arid zone, with rainfall of 200 – 300mm annually augmented by falls from tropical cyclones. Evaporation is 1780 – 3050mm annually; in no month is there a water surplus (May et al., 1983). The range is rugged with steep sided canyons dissecting the broad anticlinal ridge to depths of 120m. Surficial deposits cover much of the peninsula-aeolian, colluvial and raised marine deposits are widespread. Four emerged (post Miocene) marine terraces have been defined by van de Graaf et al. (1975) and dated by uranium series methods (Veeh et al., 1979): a broad terrace at 2.3 to 5.5m a.s.l. is the last interglacial high sea level (128 000 years BP). Higher terraces are undated and are mantled by cemented aeolian deposits. In these terraces dolines and small caves have formed, though conventional karstic surface forms are reduced to small solution pipes and pans. Many of these caves are vertical shafts leading to minor phreatic development. Permanent pools in the caves are important water sources for both cave fauna and pastoral activity. More than two hundred caves have been recorded, and speleothems in these may provide a valuable palaeoclimatic record. There are coastal caves and plateau caves, each morphologically distinct and each with a distinctive cave adapted fauna. Several are significant for their endemic troglobites which includes the eleotrid fish *Milyeringa veritas* and the synbrachid eel *Ophisternon candidum* (Allen, 1982). This fauna has strong taxonomic links with that of other fragments of Gondwanaland, is ancient and is clearly of world significance (Humphreys, 1993).

13.2.2 *The Kimberley*

The Limestone Ranges of the Kimberley region are among the most spectacular of Australian karst landscapes with an exhumed Devonian barrier reef being exposed for over 250 kilometres. The reef rises sharply from the surrounding plains and is up to 80 metres high (Photo 63). Although the flanks of the ranges present an appearance of tower karst, the plan morphology is more akin to labyrinth karst or a "giant grikeland" (Jennings and Sweeting, 1963). Pediments, some with low calcreted ridges parallel to the ranges, extend for kilometres on either side of the limestone walls. Large rivers such as the Lennard, the Barker and the Fitzroy have cut gorges of superimposition through the ranges, and these have associated caves and flood deposits (Gillieson et al., 1991). Many other caves are known and surface karst forms such as rillenkarren and large solution runnels are very well developed in spite of the shortness of the "wet" season. This region is tropical semi-arid with a monsoonal climate. 85% of the rainfall occurs from October to March, with most falls being of high intensity and associated with cyclonic depressions. Evaporation is high, around 3000 – 3500mm annually. Karst water chemistry (Ellaway et al., 1990) shows surprisingly low concentrations of solutes in springs, but discharges are seasonally high. Solutional erosion estimates from water chemistry suggest relatively low rates of 6.4 to 10.4 mm/ka, but these are based on limited data. Extensive tufa deposits flank the ranges and are associated with springs, cave entrances or cliff drapes (Viles and Goudie, 1990).

The area presents a number of interesting problems as to the origins of the landforms under the present seasonally arid climatic regime. The Devonian reefal limestones of the Napier, King Leopold and Oscar Ranges in northwestern Australia have been covered, exhumed, dissected and karstified over a long time, with the present relief dating from at least the Miocene. The karst has been subject to alluvial influence but the lack of recent uplift has reduced the relief in comparison to other tower karsts such as those near Guilin, China (colour photo 3). The remoteness of the area has precluded more than a few short expeditions to the area and much work needs to be done to build on the pioneering work of Jennings and Sweeting (1963). A recent joint British-Australian expedition has extended their work (Pain, 1988; Goudie et al., 1990). The area is also experiencing a dramatic increase in tourism, due to improvements in road networks associated with the pastoral industry. Large areas of land have recently been declared national park or given back to the traditional Aboriginal owners.

13.2.3 *The Barkly Tableland of Northern Territory and Western Queensland*

Carbonate rocks of Cambrian age occur discontinuously across the north of Australia. Again the area has been little studied in spite of the relatively large area of limestone and dolomite. Caves are known at Katherine, Camooweal and elsewhere and doubtless there are many more to be discovered as the area becomes better known. The caves at Katherine are largely watertable caves exhibiting strong joint control and remarkable development of spongework. Surface karst features are well developed in this strongly seasonally arid karst. Twidale (1984) suggests that the plain and low towers in which the caves are found dated to the Cretaceous; if this is the case the karst of the Katherine area is of very considerable interest. Recently Lauritzen et al. (1994) have studied the palaeokarstic fills in these towers using uranium series dating and have concluded that much of the stripping and lowering has taken place in the Quaternary, with the Cretaceous surface lying above the level of the highest karst towers and preserved as residuals. The Gregory karst of the western Northern Territory is an extensive crevice karst with several kilometres of mapped caves and extensive tufa barrages.

The cave microclimates are quite oppressive with high temperatures, relative humidities and carbon dioxide levels. There are hydrothermal sources in the caves and in the region there are extensive hot springs. The invertebrate and bat faunas are extensive and specialised. A highly significant Miocene vertebrate fossil locality has been discovered at Riversleigh, south of the Gulf of Carpentaria in Queensland (Archer et al., 1991) – this area is now a World Heritage site. To the north of this, there are extensive plateau karsts near Lawn Hill Gorge with extensive tufa barrages and some tower karst (Williams, 1978; Drysdale, 1994). New nickel mining ventures in the area will almost certainly exploit karst groundwater, and there may be impacts due to the excavation of a 400m deep mine pit near the karst. In particular the rich troglobitic fauna of Forbes Inferno Cave may be affected (P. Horne pers. comm.)

West of Mount Isa, close on the Northern Territory border, a gently undulating plateau of Cambrian dolomite is punctuated by steep sided dolines. This is the Barkly karst (Mathews, 1985) centred on the small town of Camooweal. Surface outcrop is sparse and relief is low, less than 2m. The few outcrops are pitted by rainfall, but rills are absent. Annual rainfall is 387mm at Camooweal and evaporation estimated at 3500mm. The regional drainage is predominantly subterranean, with springs along the Georgina River. The caves descend gradually to the water table, which in the dry season lies 70 – 80m below the plateau. In the wet season the water table may rise suddenly by 20m following thunderstorms, and is fed by long, low gradient ephemeral channels carrying trains of chert pebbles and cobbles. These gravels act a powerful abrasive tools when entrained, and thus the cave passages are clean and undecorated. The only land use in the area is pastoralism for beef production, at low stock densities of 1 beast for $1km^2$. Population density is correspondingly low, with densities of one person to $200km^2$.

13.2.4 *Chillagoe and Mitchell-Palmer Karsts, North Queensland*

A belt of Silurian limestones extends from Chillagoe to the Palmer River, a distance of some 150 kilometres. The area is characterised by a large number of towers in a strike belt arising from a pedimented plain. Between the Mitchell and Palmer Rivers, a distance of 60km, there are over 150 karst towers up to 100m high. Surface solution features such as runnels are again extremely well developed in spite of the seasonal aridity and there are a number of caves, chiefly at plain level but with shafts reaching up into the towers. Most of the towers have well developed pediments which appear to have thin veneer of rubble and spalled blocks. Close to the major rivers the karsts are alluviated at their margins and swamp slots are present, but this influence falls off rapidly. In recent years the area has been visited by a number of biospeleological expeditions and many new cavernicolous species have been found including that of a true troglobitic higher plant (Hoch and Howarth, 1989; Hamilton-Smith pers. comm.). In spite of the remoteness of the area and the small size of the local population there is an active caving club which has well documented the area and its caves. Tourist caves are well established, receiving increased visitors each year, and have developed specialised ecotourism programs.

13.2.5 *Mount Etna, Central Queensland*

Mount Etna and the adjoining Limestone Ridge is a small area of Devonian limestone containing a number of caves and again displaying fine surface karst features including extensive grike fields with well developed rillenkarren. The area was the scene of an long conservation battle between a cement company and conservationists (Vavryn, 1987). A number of caves have been destroyed since 1967 in an apparently wanton fashion by the mining company. Part of the area is now reserved as national park: interpretation and development of visitor facilities are proceeding at the same time as rehabilitation. The caves are the home of major colonies of the insectivorous Little Bentwinged Bat and the carnivorous Ghost or False Vampire Bat and a variety of invertebrates. Over half a million bats issue nightly from Bat Cleft on Mount Etna. The caves are notable for their phreatic spongework forms, deep phosphatic sediments and the control of andesitic dykes on their morphology. Sprent (1970) provides a useful summary of the area.

13.2.6 *Eastern Uplands*

Although both the Chillagoe and Mount Etna areas properly belong to the Eastern Uplands, both areas stand up out of the surrounding landscapes as residual forms. The remainder of the one hundred-odd karst areas of southern Queensland, New South Wales and eastern Victoria are karst barees-small impounded karsts mostly recessive in the landscape. The limestones are Palaeozoic, chiefly Silurian or Devonian, and are the remnants of limestone deposits emplaced during a number of orogenies in the Tasman Mobile Zone. However, it appears that carbonate deposition was limited in extent and the cycle of uplift, deformation and dissection has both removed and revealed small patches of limestone.

The cave and karst systems developed in these impounded karst are amongst Australia's best known and studied areas and include well-known areas such as Jenolan (Welch, 1976; Kiernan, 1988), Wombeyan (Sydney Speleological Society, 1972), Yarrangobilly (Photo 64) and Cooleman Plains (Jennings, 1983), all in New South Wales, and Buchan in eastern Victoria (Finlayson et al., 1992). This depth of study is largely the result of the peculiar population distribution in which the vast majority of Australians live southeast of a line between Newcastle and Adelaide. Most of the individual karsts also lie in that area.

The cave systems commonly reflect alternating uplift and consequent erosion and exhibit repetitive phases of vadose and epiphreatic development as a consequence. Coupled to this diversity of history is the long period available for karstification. Osborne and Branagan (1988) point to examples of karst landscapes of Permian and older age; areas such as Wombeyan appear to have been exposed to erosion since the Devonian. The karsts are much influenced by aggressive waters and high sediment loads generated on the surrounding impervious rocks.

The Tasmanian karsts, largely in Ordovician rocks, also belong in the Eastern Uplands (Kiernan, 1992). Tasmanian caves are particularly well developed due to the larger range of local relief, more effective and greater amounts of rainfall and the fact that dolerite sills have protected the limestone high on the valley sides. Many of the caves bear witness to the effects of multiple glaciations (Kiernan, 1984). The caves are the deepest in Australia and contain unusually diverse invertebrate faunas and increasingly provide evidence of long term use by Aboriginal people over the Last Glacial cycle. Recent closure of a limestone quarry overlying the 25km long Exit Cave in southern Tasmania has led to a major rehabilitation project to reduce impacts and maintain the World Heritage values of the cave (Kiernan, 1993; Gillieson and Houshold, in press).

As was pointed out above the Tasman Mobile Zone karsts are perhaps our best known caves and include sites of significance such as Wellington with its megafaunal fossils which excited European scholars last century; the large, complex and beautiful tourist cave systems such as Jenolan and Yarrangobilly. Cooleman Plain is of special interest to karst geomorphologists as it is a sub-alpine karst extensively studied by the late Joe Jennings.

13.2.7 *Southeast South Australia*

The southeast of South Australia and a small portion of western Victoria are underlain by horizontally bedded Oligocene limestones. These limestones are highly permeable and possess a wide array of karst features including some highly spectacular cenotes (Grimes, 1994). Although the land use is radically different, the area is broadly similar to the karst of the Yucatan peninsula. Much of the cave development appears to have taken place at times of lower sea levels and scuba divers are now discovering faunal remains and well decorated caves dating to the last glaciation. The coastal parts of this limestone are overlain by much younger calcareous aeolianites with well developed spitzkarren and some dolines. The Victoria Fossil Cave at Naracoorte contains Tertiary mammal fossils of international significance and is now a World Heritage site.

The lower southeast is perhaps the one area in Australia where karst, and particularly karst hydrology, impinge on the daily lives of the community in that pollution and overexploitation of the aquifer are readily apparent to the local population (Emmett and Telfer, 1994). Effluent from intensive dairy farms, piggeries and cheese factories enters the karst and has caused concern over nitrate pollution of water supplies. The area also produces some of Australia's premier red wines from grapes grown on the terra rossa soils at Coonawarra and Padthaway.

13.2.8 *Central South Australia*

The Mount Lofty-Flinders Ranges and the Yorke Peninsula contain some areas of Precambrian and Cambrian limestones and dolomites. Caves are present (Matthews, 1985) but are usually small as a result of the prolonged aridity of this part of the continent. The carbonate bedrocks themselves contain very early invertebrate fossils-jellyfish-of considerable significance.

13.2.9 *The Nullarbor Plain*

This is Australia's largest karst ($200000km^2$) and perhaps the most intensively studied. The region has an arid to semi-arid climate with annual rainfall between 150 and 250mm, with a winter maximum. Annual evaporation is 1250 – 2500mm (McKenzie et al., 1987). Relief is low, less than 5m, with slope angles of 1° – 3°. The Nullarbor Plain has no surface drainage, but relict stream channels are found on the northern and western flanks of the plain. These have meandering traces and are infilled with alluvium and aeolian deposits. Elsewhere there are aligned depressions with claypans; these are of structural origin (Lowry and Jennings, 1974). These claypans, locally termed "dongas" act to channel the slight runoff and direct it into dolines and blowholes. Dolines are sparse, steep sided and show evidence of collapse into underlying cavities (Photo 65). Blowholes are very numerous, fed by deep solution pipes of complex origin. The caves are extensive, much modified by salt wedging and collapse processes, and commonly descend gently to near-static pools and lakes of brackish to saline water. A low gradient watertable underlies the plain and its depth ranges from 30m in the north to 120m in the south. The flooded tunnels of Cocklebiddy Cave are in excess of four kilometres long-most of it only explorable by scuba diving. Withdrawal of hydrostatic support at times of lower sea level has led to collapse into these watertable caves, allowing entry into large caverns such as Koonalda, Abrakurrie, and Weebubbie Caves (Fig. 13-2).

A particular feature of the Nullarbor caves is the abundance of halite which produces both speleothems and many weathering forms through wedging during recrystallisation. Gypsum speleothems are also abundant with calcite speleothems less obvious largely because of destruction through salt wedging. Speleothem history has much to contribute to the study of past climates and

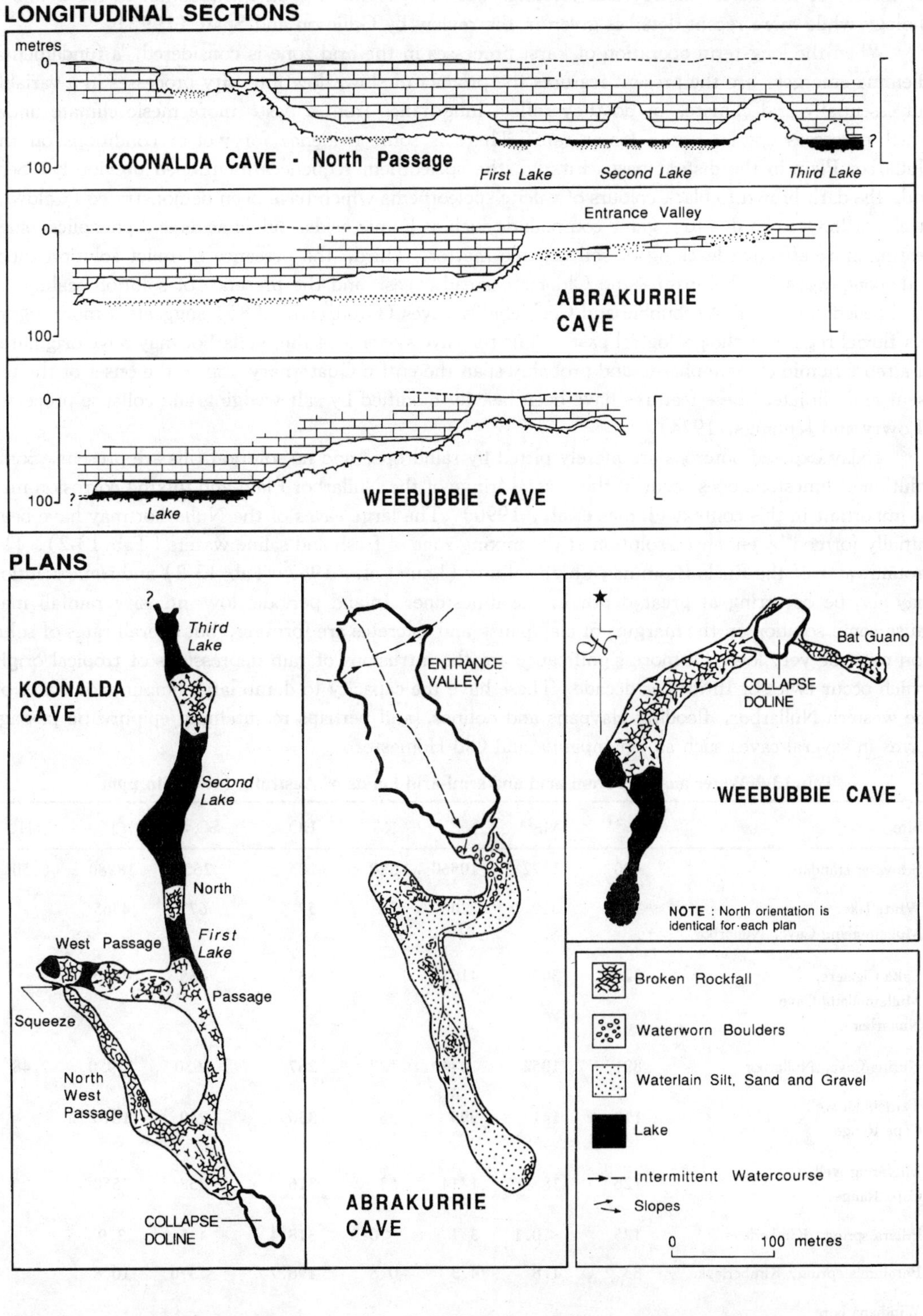

Fig. 13-2 Deep caves of the Nullarbor. From Gillieson and Spate (1992)

the history of the caves. Lowry and Jennings (1974) provide a good introduction to the geomorphology while more recent detail is given in the review by Gillieson and Spate (1992).

When the long-term operation of karst processes in the arid zone is considered, a fundamental dilemma emerges: are the present features the product of slow, low intensity processes in a variable but essentially arid climate, or do they reflect inheritance from a past, more mesic climate under which processes operated at a faster rate? There is some evidence for wetter conditions on the Nullarbor Plain in the distant past. Firstly, the speleothem sequences mentioned previously. Second, the dark brown to black colours of calcite speleothems which have been demonstrated (Caldwell et al., 1983) to be due to organic compounds such as humic acids, fulvic acids and phenolics, suggesting more effective leaching of soil organic matter. Third, the presence of relict solution tubes and spongework in Thampanna and Old Homestead caves, and the presence of solution scallops in the flooded tunnels of Weebubbie and Cocklebiddy caves (Grodzicki, 1985) suggests a more vigorous fluvial regime in the geological past. Thus the cave systems of the Nullarbor may have originated in a more humid climate phase, and probably span the entire Quaternary. Since the onset of the present arid climate, these features have been heavily modified by salt wedging and collapse processes (Lowry and Jennings, 1974).

Today exposed outcrops are merely pitted by raindrops, and no solution rills are present. Some solution of limestone does occur in the coastal fringe of the Nullarbor Plain and mixing corrosion may be important in this context (James et al., 1990). The large caves of the Nullarbor may have been initially formed by enhanced solution at the mixing zone of fresh and saline waters (Tab. 13-2). The groundwater of the Eucla Basin has a high salinity (Lau et al., 1987; Tab. 13-3) and some solution may also be occurring at great depth in the limestone. Inland periodic low-intensity rainfall may cause some solution on the margins of clay pans, and calcretes are forming, but overall rates of solution must be very low. Of more significance are the intrusions of rain depressions of tropical origin which occur twice or thrice per decade. These have the capacity to dump large amounts of water on the western Nullarbor, flooding claypans and dolines, and perhaps maintaining epiphreatic passage forms in several caves such as Thampanna and Old Homestead.

Tab. 13-2 Water analyses from arid and semi-arid karsts of Australia (values in ppm)

Site	Ca^{2+}	Mg^{2+}	Na^{+}	K^{+}	HCO_3^{-}	SO_4^{2-}	Cl^{-}	pH
Seawater standard	400	1272	10560	380	285	2650	18980	8.50
White lake, Mullamullang Cave, Nullarbor.	317	319	2200	26	57	677	4365	–
Lake Cigalere, Mullamullang Cave Nullarbor.	326	300	4165	–	33	855	4580	–
Nurina Cave, Nullarbor	891	1052	10440	127	267	3630	17950	7.48
Tantabiddi well Cape Range	113	141	999	36	336	240	1810	
Milyering well Cape Range.	126	188	1414	53	316	358	2550	
Pillara spring, Kimberleys.	125	<0.1	3.1	<0.5	318.4	4.5	3.9	
Baralumla spring, Kimberleys.	83.2	1.8	4.3	0.8	198.7	<3.0	10.8	
Windjana bore Kimberleys.	113	0.5	10.9	<0.5	272.6	6.3	11.4	

Tab. 13-3 Quality of karst groundwater in the Eucla basin (from Lau et al., 1987)

Type	Salinity($mg\ L^{-1}$ TDS)	% of potential yield
Fresh	<500	9
Marginal	500 – 1500	56
Brackish	1500 – 15000	31
Saline	>15000	4

During the last interglacial-glacial cycle the sea level dropped at least twice, steepening hydraulic gradients. This prompted a shift in the isohyets, as reflected in pollen stratigraphy (Martin, 1973). Thus during the last glacial maximum the arid chenopod shrubland of the interior plain extended across terrain which today lies closer to the coast and supports eucalypt woodland. Conversely, during the last interglacial eucalypt woodland would have extended further inland than it does today, and this may have enhanced solutional processes. These changes in the vegetation cover may have acted to destabilise the continental dunefields to the north of the Nullarbor, and allowed reddened quartz sands to accumulate downwind in caves and dolines on the eastern portion of the plain (Spate et al., 1984). Cave and doline infills on the eastern margin of the Nullarbor are dominantly red aeolian quartz sand with well developed wustenquarz. At least three different pedogenic cycles are involved, with some loessic additions (Spate et al., 1984). These sands have their origin in the Great Victoria Desert, and suggest a wind regime different to the predominantly southerly to southwesterly airflow today. The distribution of these sands, in a narrow belt around the Diprose Caves, suggests that they may have moved as sand streaks across the gravelly plain. The most recent disturbance of these sands, dated by thermoluminescence at <360 years B.P., may reflect the increased fire frequency consequent on pastoralism and the spread of rabbits across the Nullarbor Plain. Recent environmental impacts on the Nullarbor and other arid karsts are reviewed by Gillieson (1993).

13.2.10 *Southwest Western Australia*

The narrow coastal strip of Pleistocene dune limestone, and its associated syngenetic karst features, is the most important of the calcareous aeolianites which extend discontinuously from northwest Tasmania to Shark Bay, W.A. As well as the Western Australian occurrences, the dune limestones are important on the Eyre Peninsula and in the lower southeast of South Australia as well as in western Victoria.

The term syngenetic karst (Jennings, 1968) refers to karst processes operating parallel to diagenetic processes. These karsts are characterised by the development of solution tubes, collapse dolines and water table caves. The limestone surface is indurated to form a hard caprock commonly over weakly consolidated calcareous dunes. Although the situation sounds less than ideal for cave development many caves are present and may be surprisingly large with Easter Cave being in excess of 7.5 kilometres. They are often extremely well decorated with straw stalactites being particularly abundant and long (up to 9.8 m in Strongs Cave).

13.3 Karsts of Papua New Guinea

The large island of New Guinea has karst areas occupying around 15% of the land area and extending from sea level to nearly 4000m in the Star Mountains on the Irian Jaya-Papua New Guinea border. There is a great diversity of karst types in this tectonically active landscape where present uplift rates are 2 – 3mm annually. The major rivers of the central cordillera of New Guinea cut through the major karsts and there are extensive alluviated karst plateaux, one of which has an area of $15000km^2$ in the Kikori-Kutubu area of the Southern Highlands. On the large islands of New Britain and New Ireland there are extensive polygonal and doline karsts – the Lelet plateau of New Ireland has an area of $500km^2$ at 1300 – 1400m altitude (Gillieson, 1977). This holokarst drains to large springs, some of which are submarine, on the northeast coast. Loffler (1974, 1977) provides a useful map and overview of the major karst areas (Fig. 13-3). Karst areas are of importance for water supply and for their soil resources (Gillieson, 1989). More recently considerable gas and some oil reserves have been found in the Southern Highlands karst belt.

The combination of rugged relief, karst terrain and high rainfall makes the Victor Emanuel and Muller ranges some the least populated or visited areas of western Papua New Guinea. These lie on the southern flank of the central ranges of P. N. G., and experience a continuously heavy rainfall regime, with each week receiving more than 50 mm of rain (Brookfield & Hart, 1971). The maximum recorded annual rainfall is 11000mm at Mt. Fubilan (Ok Tedi). With available relief around 700 – 800 m, a sequence of pure limestones up to 1500 m thick, and rainfall in excess of 5000 mm over much of the area, high rates of karst denudation and cave development might be expected. The absence of human activity on the high karst plateaux and ranges provides the opportunity to study karst processes free of anthropogenic effects expectable in densely populated areas.

13.3.1 *Tectonic History and Geological Structure*

The principal geotectonic force for the development of the Papua New Guinea landmass has been the northwards drift of the Australian continental plate (Dow, 1977). Following deposition of the Mesozoic sediments on a slowly subsiding shelf, early Pliocene orogenic deformation occurred. This deformation involved large scale uplift along two east-southeast plunging anticlinal arches (Jenkins, 1974), the magnitude of uplift being of the order of 4000 m in the Victor Emanuel-Muller Range area. According to Jenkins (1974), this uplift was partially accommodated by high angle faulting, and gave rise to detachment tectonics in which decollements developed along the weaker mudstones and siltstones in the post-Palaeozoic cover. Detachment sheets composed mainly of the more competent Darai Limestones moved along the palaeoslope to the southwest, away from the zone of maximum uplift which lay to the north of the Victor Emanuel and Muller Ranges. Rupturing and overriding of the sheets formed detachment packages of multiple overthrusts (Jenkins, 1974), which were subsequently uplifted a further 2000 m. Although this uplift was largely completed by the early Pleistocene, gentle folding of Quaternary volcanics on the flank of the Mananda anticline in the Southern Highlands indicates that some movement has persisted until recently. It therefore seems likely that the overthrust structure were formed in the Pliocene and that the present relief has existed for at least the last two million years.

13.3.2 *Geomorphology of the Hindenburg Plateau*

According to Loffler (1977:16), the area of the Hindenburg Ranges covered by Fig. 13-4 is dominated by homoclinal ridges of Mesozoic sediments and Tertiary limestones. On the small-scale geomorphological map of Papua New Guinea (Loffler, 1974), the area is subdivided into the following landform classes:

Loffler (1977:36) defines ridge and ravine landforms as ridges with steep slopes and narrow to knife-edged crests separated by V-shaped valleys with steep gradients. Although this broad classification is useful, there is considerable variation within several of the units mapped by Loffler, and in

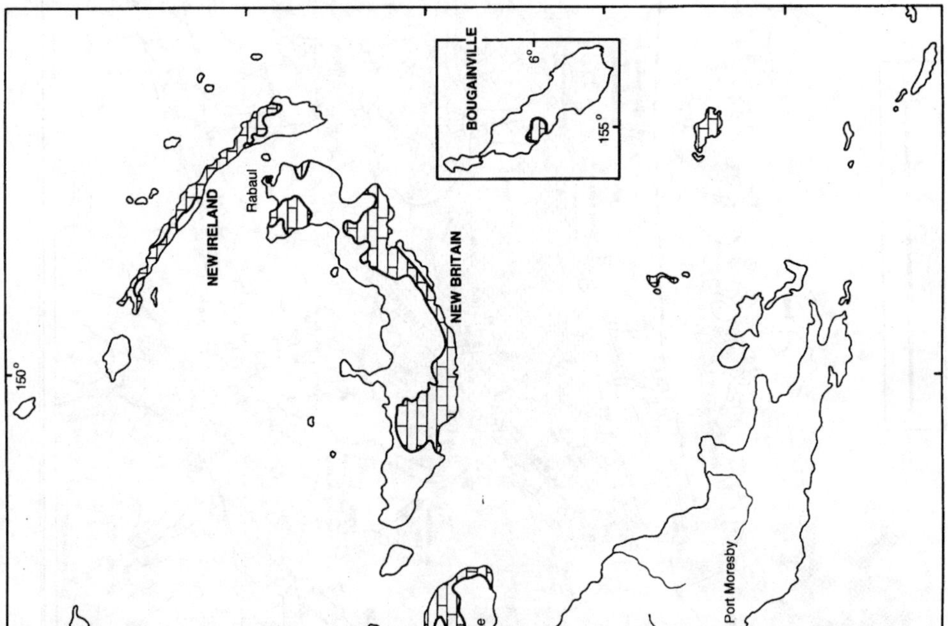

Fig. 13-3 Distribution of karsts in Papua New Guinea. From Loffler (1977)

FINIM
THRUST
ALICE THRUST
ALICE
ANTICLINE
5 Km

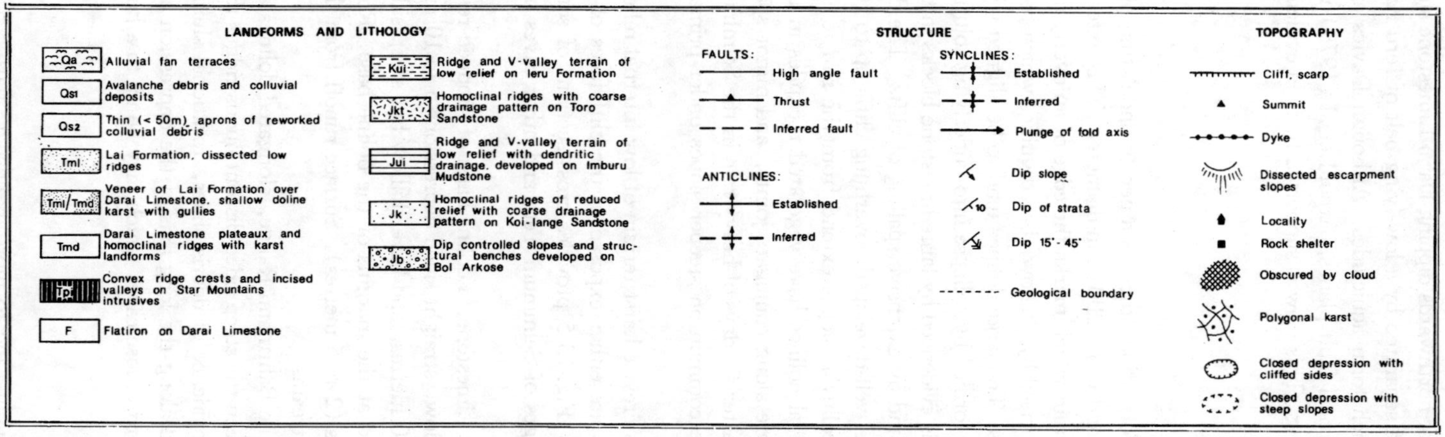

Fig. 13-4 Geology and geomorphology of the Hindenburg Plateau, Papua New Guinea

1. Polygonal karst on limestone. 2. Homoclinal ridge and ravine landforms on fine grained, non-calcareous sedimentary rocks. 3. Ridge and ravine landforms on mixed or undifferentiated calcareous sediments or limestone. 4. Ridge and ravine landforms on acid to intermediate igneous rocks (granites and granodiorites). 5. Alluvial fans

particular several tropical karst styles are represented.

The Hindenburg and Bahrmann Ranges are a series of northwards dipping Darai Limestone sheets outcropping as homoclinal ridges. The two ranges are separated by a low-lying belt of Ieru Formation and Lai Formation siltstones and mudstones which form aquicludes. Although Davies and Norvick (1974) attribute the scarps to movement on vertical fault planes, Arnold et al (1979) interpret these as being the result of low angle thrust faulting. This view is supported by field evidence from the Hindenburg Plateau and the upper Ok Tedi.

The following landform types are present:

13.3.2.1 *Doline Karst*

Where the Darai Limestone is not overlain by Lai Formation, there is a gently undulating plateau with deep, steep sided dolines up to 150 m in depth and 100 – 200 m in diameter. This extends from the Hindenburg Wall to a band of steep, gullied terrain which marks the edge of an overlying, eroded veneer of Lai Formation. The plateau surface is incised by shallow, broad gullies which have small dolines along their length and drain to larger dolines. The large dolines tend to be aligned with major joint sets and high angle faults, and have probably formed by collapse into underlying solution cavities as the Lai Formation receded to the north. This is evidenced by large limestone blocks in the base of dolines, clearly not dissected limestone *in situ*, and by extensive spalling of cliffs. The doline walls tend to be steeper on the up-dip side, and have well-developed, overhung cliffs up to 100 m high. On the less steep sides, low bluffs and steep colluvial slopes extend from the rim to the base, where colluvial fans coalesce and are gullied. Several dolines have vegetated rockpiles in the doline base, with skeletal soil development. Wedge failure along conjugate joints, and minor spalling, aid maintenance of the cliff angle, and were noted after six days of heavy rain in the Selminum Tem doline. Debris avalanches (Loffler, 1977: 141) are common on steeper slopes under primary forest.

Dissected collapse blocks in the doline base provide a crevice karst terrain of low internal relief, and facilitate soil loss down open joints. Cave entrances are either exposed in the cliff faces or at their base; they rarely appear to be active stream sinks. Fig. 13-5 provides cross-sections of some dolines on the Hindenburg Plateau. The extensive passages of Selminum Tem and other caves underlie the doline karst (Gillieson, 1985; Fig. 13-6).

Where a thin veneer of Lai Formation overlies Darai Limestone, a doline karst of subdued relief exists. A gently undulating surface is punctuated by shallow, straight sided depressions 5 to 10 metres in depth. The dolines vary in diameter from 30 to 50 metres, and have shallow but steep sided gullies draining to sediment choked sinks, usually located at the margins of the doline base. Rock outcrop is very restricted, and usually occurs as low cliffs (2 to 5 metres). Surface runoff from this zone may enter underlying cave passages as percolation streams.

On the steeply dipping (>25°) hogback ridges of the Bahrmann Range, elongated dolines are located either punctuating dip controlled surfaces or between the steep sided discontinuous ridges that disrupt the surface. These dolines are steep sided with evidence of debris slides, rotational slumps and debris avalanches. A series of sink points are located along the long axis of the depression and are separated by broad crested saddles. These sinks lead to vadose caves which may be up to a hundred metres deep.

13.3.2.2 *Polygonal Karst*

This is restricted to the summit plateau of Mt. Fugilil, and to more extensive, flatter ridge crests on the Bahrmann Range. The surfaces of these plateaux are completely punctuated by shallow depressions whose drainage divides, narrow crested ridges, form a cellular or polygonal network which entirely covers the available surface. The depressions vary between 30 and 70 metres in

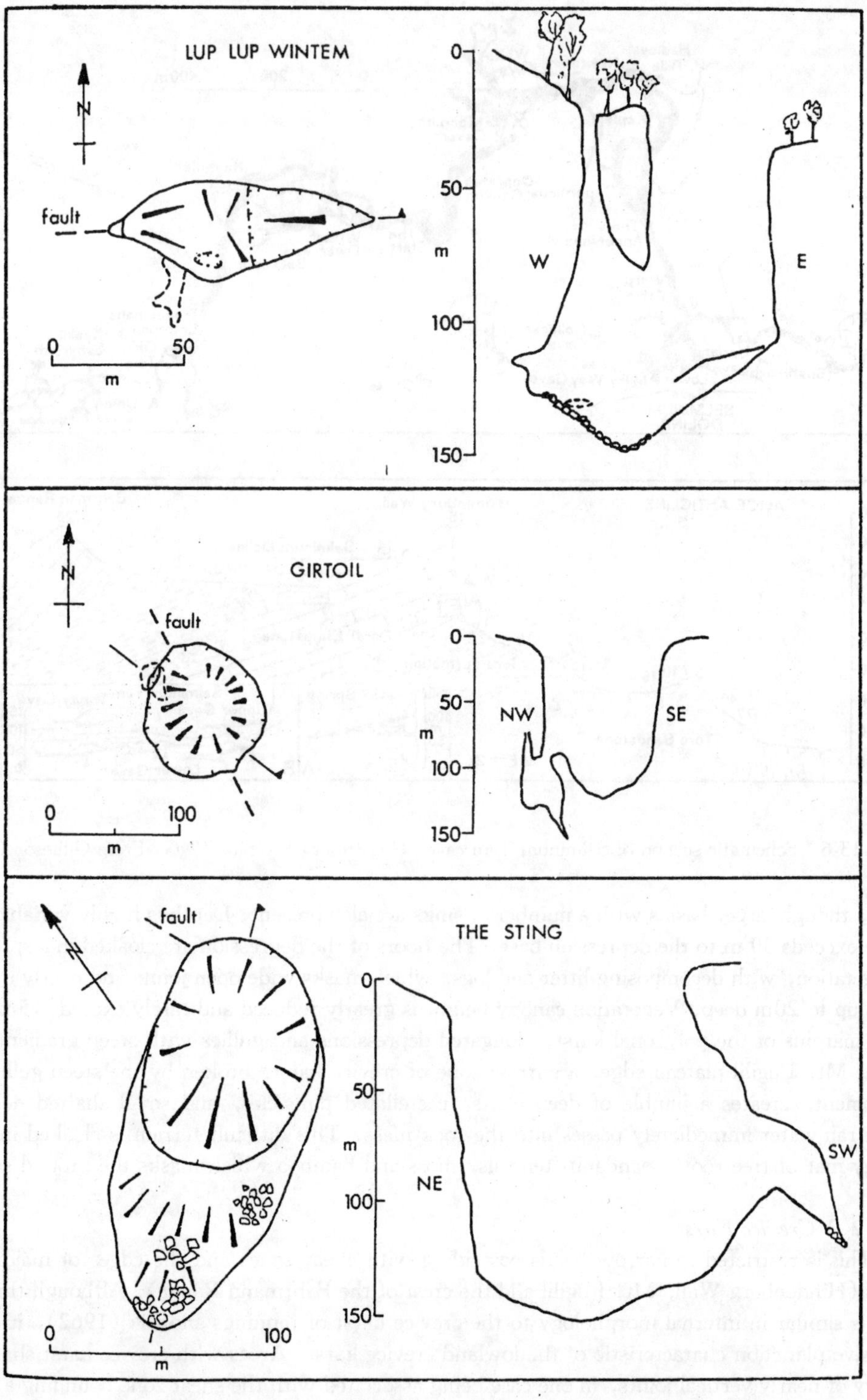

Fig. 13-5 Cross-sections of dolines on the Hindenburg Plateau

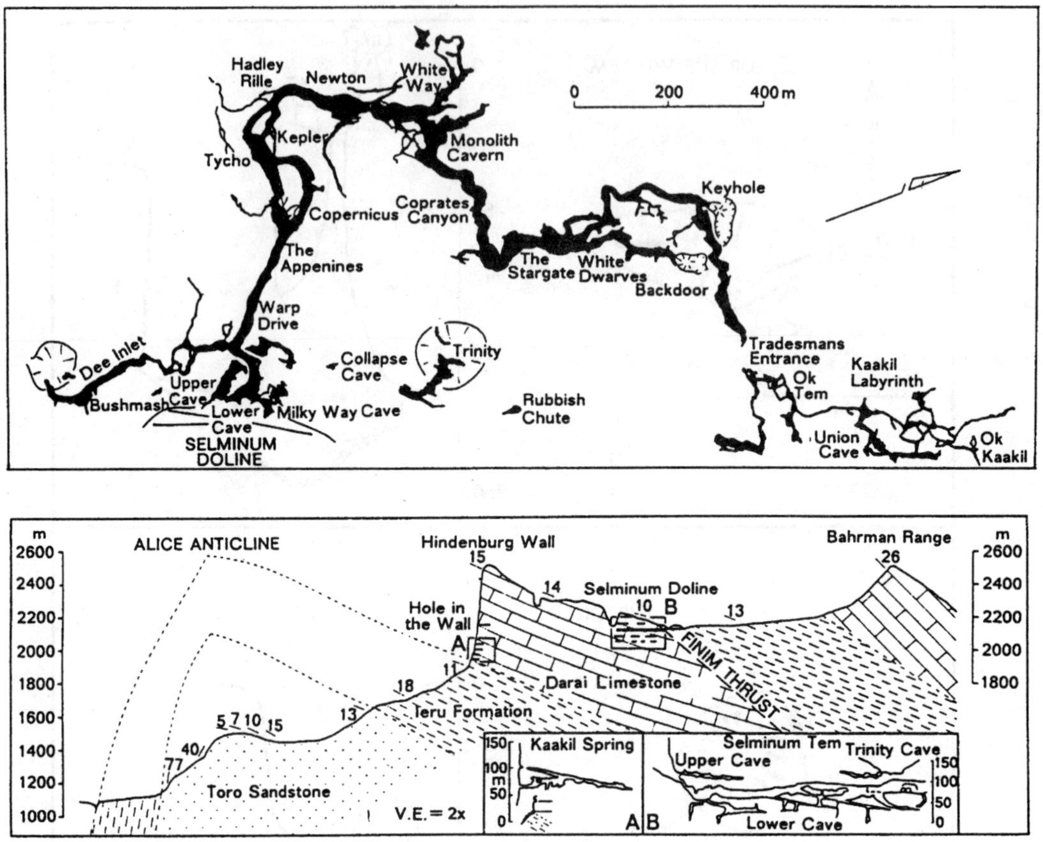

Fig. 13-6 Schematic section of Selminum Tem cave, Hindenburg Plateau, PNG. From Gillieson (1985)

width, though larger basins with a number of sinks are also present. Depth is highly variable but nowhere exceeds 30 m to the depression base. The floors of the depression are cloaked in a springy mat of vegetation, with decomposing litter and logs, which masks wide open joints and nearly cylindrical shafts up to 20m deep. Vegetation canopy height is greatly reduced and rarely exceeds 15m. At the lower margins of the polygonal karst, elongated depressions and gullies with steep gradients occur. On the Mt. Fugilil plateau edge, a narrow zone of crevice karst, broken by the steep gullies of the escarpment, creates a jumble of deep clefts, castellated pinnacles, and small shafted depressions where rainwater immediately passes into the rock mass. This difficult terrain is cloaked in a deep, springy mat of tree roots, pandanus tendrils, moss and bamboo which masks the ground surface.

13.3.2.3 *Crevice Karst*

This is restricted to narrow bands coinciding with shear zones and the edges of major escarpments (Hindenburg Wall, Mt. Fugilil and the crest of the Bahrmann Range). Although this crevice karst is similar in internal morphology to the crevice karst of Jennings and Bik (1962), it lacks the extensive planation characteristic of the lowland crevice karst. Areas with crevice karst share a high density of nearly vertical joints, in one case being associated with the shear zone bounding a high angle fault, and in the others associated with a dense network of conjugate joints widened by solution in a constantly moist environment where infiltration is rapid, and possibly by tensional release following rockfall on the escarpment.

This karst type is expressed as a series of broad, shallow dolines with joint aligned, castellated outcrops of limestone on the doline rims and across its floor. The castellated outcrops vary between 2 and 6 metres in height, and may be 10 to 25 metres long. The enlarged joints hade at 5 to 15 degrees and are solutionally widened to between 1 and 1.5 metres. A compact soil floor, of variable level, is usually present though short (less than 5 m) shafts also occur. Collapse blocks are frequently present and may partially obstruct the joint. The overhanging wall is usually broadly fluted with horizontal solution ripples. The opposing wall has well developed solution runnels, often choked with vines and creepers. Small kamenitzas (solution pans) are sometimes present. On the Hindenburg Plateau, Brook (1977) called this karst type 'tower karst' but this is a misnomer.

Under the influence of the continuously distributed, daily rainfall, solutional processes must proceed rapidly under the free drainage provided by the frequent open joints. Basal sapping and spalling of the overhung joint walls promotes collapse, further aiding reduction of the limestone blocks. Development of crevice karst is therefore the result of continuously wet conditions, and a high density of open joints promoting rapid removal of solutes and soil. It is altitudinally controlled (c.f. Loffler, 1977) in that these conditions tend to obtain at higher elevations adjacent to major escarpments and in the presence of major fault systems.

13.3.2.4 *Limestone Escarpments*

Both the Bahrmann Range and Hindenburg Plateau are bounded on their southern sides by escarpments from 300 to 750 metres high (Photo 66). The escarpments are steep (70° – 80°) and are entrenched by steep gullies separated by sharp crested ridges. Steep angled, chaotic deposits of rock fall and debris avalanche deposits at the base vary in texture from freshly fractured angular boulders and pebbles, often in a gritty clay matrix, to a weathered slurry of rock fragments, soft and chalky. Extensive aprons of such colluvial deposits are common beneath limestone escarpments. The colluvial aprons have slope angles between 5 and 25 degrees, and are entrenched by shallow gullies. In plan they tend to be broadest at the base of the scarp and narrow downslope. The limestone boulders, gravels and clays of which they are composed frequently become cemented to form breccias. These breccias tend to form small resistant steps on the slopes.

These colluvial deposits are rapidly revegetated but provide evidence of continuing, large scale mass wasting of the escarpments. They result from rockfalls and debris avalanches, which may have considerable volumes. The cliffs of the escarpment have fresh white fracture scars resulting from small scale spalling and massive wedge failure along conjugate joint planes. These processes may be aided by basal sapping, the consequence of differential erosion and spring-head enlargement at the contact between the Ieru Formation and the overlying Darai Limestone.

Examination of regrowth patterns on aerial photography (1964, 1974, 1975), and conversations with local informants, suggest that major debris avalanches occur every ten years in the Wok Kaakil basin below the Hindenburg Wall. One such event, in 1977, was well documented by Byrne et al. (1978). A large rock fall, 260 m wide by 600 m high, failed suddenly, the resulting debris travelling down valley as a fluidised mass at a speed of approximately 12 ms^{-1}. The debris forms an extensive colluvial apron below the Wall and for a short period the debris obstructed flow in the Wok Kam and Ok Tedi. Volume of the rockfall was estimated by Byrne et al. (1978) as 5 million cubic metres. Over the entire length of the Hindenburg Wall within the Wok Kam basin (15.25 km), this is equivalent to a rate of scarp retreat of 5.1m/ka. Although this is probably an overestimate, it is of the right order and indicates the rapidity of scarp retreat.

13.3.2.5 *Ridge and V-valley Terrain*

Within the zone of overthrust Darai Limestone sheets, areas of underlying Ieru Formation and overlying Lai Formation occur. The Ieru Formation has a subdued ridge and v-valley terrain with a dense trellised drainage network. The streams fed by this network sink at or near the limestone contact. Internal relief does not exceed 50 m and the whole forms a low-lying belt of land between the Bahrmann Range and the doline karst abutting the Hindenburg Wall. Areas of glauconitic sandstone on the northern and western side of Mt. Fugilil tend to form low, homoclinal ridges. Stream channels are deeply incised with unstable banks prone to debris slides and flows.

Terrain developed on rocks of the Lai Formation shows a transition from shallow doline karst, where a thin sheet of Lai Formation overlies Darai Limestone, to ridge and v-valley landforms on the thickest sequence adjacent to the Finim Thrust. Relief is subdued (less than 20 m) and small debris slides and soil flows are common, creating a complex pattern of vegetation regrowth, including climbing bamboo (*Nastus* spp.) along gullies.

13.3.3 *Geomorphology of the Muller Range*

The Muller Range (Fig. 13-7) consists of plateau, ridge and ravine terrain on limestone with dolines (Loffler, 1974). To the northeast, the range is bounded by the elongate Tumbudu valley, while to the southwest the Muller Range ends in a scarp about 600 m high with numerous embayments and resurgences. To the west lies the huge Strickland River valley, incised into the Mesozoic rocks which underlie the Tertiary Darai Limestone. Most of the Muller Range lies between 1700 – 2500 m above sea level, with the highest peaks reaching 3000 m. The extensive caves of the Muller Range have been explored by Australasian expeditions since 1973 (James and Dyson, 1980). The deepest cave, Mamo Kananda, is 525m deep and over 50km long.

Drainage from the Muller Range runs either northeast to the Tumbudu valley, or southwest to the alluvial plains of the Fly Platform. The major stream on the Muller Plateau is the Yu Atea, which rises to the southwest of Anu Pass and flows to the west across the large polje of Geloro. The Yu Atea sinks near the Atea Doline and resurges at the base of the Nalirege escarpment, some 700m lower, as the Yu Nali.

13.3.3.1 *Closed Depressions*

(1) *Dolines and Uvulas*

The Muller Plateau and adjacent areas are pitted by numerous dolines. These dolines vary from 50 to 300 m in diameter, and are up to 150 m deep (Photo 67). Maintenance of steep, cliffed sides is aided by basal sapping of the more competent Darai Limestone along interbeds, producing extensive rock avalanches. Several dolines on the Muller Plateau have been shown to be associated with underground passages and collapse chambers. The dolines are therefore likely to be of collapse origin, with solutional processes and mass movements important for doline side-slope retreat. Large elongate dolines on Mamo have walls developed in Lai Formation, and may have formed as subjacent collapse dolines along faults and shear zones.

Uvulas are larger complex closed depressions with two or more dolines nested within them. Features of this type are well developed at Rorogepo near the crest of the Muller Range. The uvulas of Rorogepo were examined on the 1978 expedition. The largest is almost 1 km long and is asymmetrical. On the eastern side are cliffs up to 25 m high that are composed of interbedded limestones and clastic sediments of the Darai Limestone. On the western side are prominent sub-horizontal slope facets separated by steeper risers. The uppermost one of these facets is a bench developed on limestone bedrock but the lower two are mantled by fine grained alluvium and may be depositional terraces. If this is the case then there has been infilling of the uvula and partial removal of this fill caused either by Quaternary climatic fluctuations or more likely by constriction of the underground water conduits through collapse and subsequent enlargement of new flow routes. In one uvala there is a

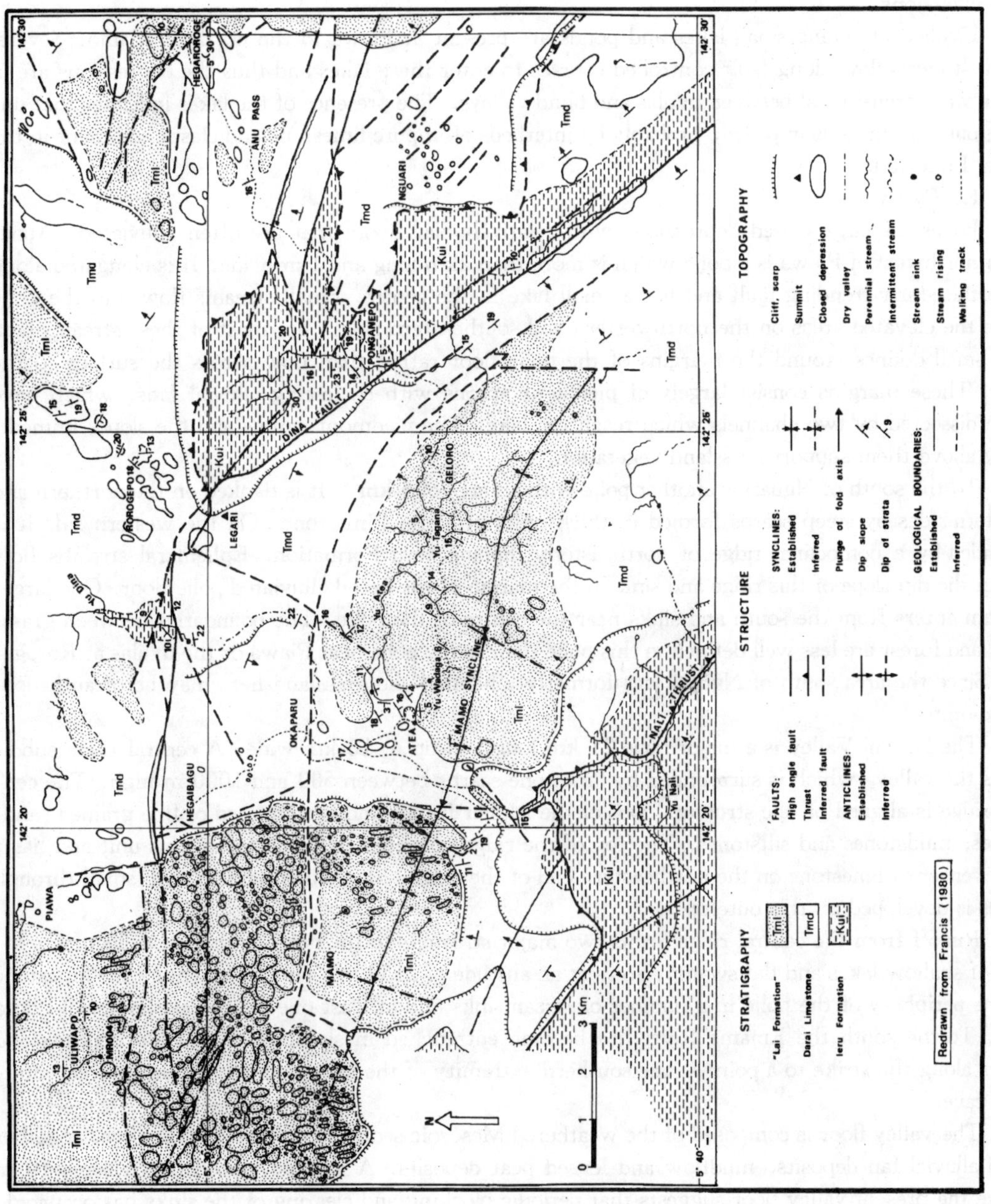

Fig. 13-7 Geomorphology of the Muller Range, PNG. From Francis et al., (1980)

depositional terrace composed of crudely stratified orange-brown mud up to 5 m thick with a greyish weathering profile developed on it. The floors of uvulas at Rorogepo support grasslands which have abrupt boundaries with the forests on the surrounding slopes. Since this area has never been cultivated it is probable that the distribution of the grassland is controlled by cold air drainage and temperature inversions.

Uvulas containing small lakes and ponds are present at Piawa to the north of Mamo. Several small streams flow along fault controlled courses to enter these lakes and thus the depressions are in some ways transitional between uvulas and blind valleys. The presence of the lakes indicates that underground drainage is impeded, probably by interbeds of impure limestone and clastic sediment in the Darai Limestone.

(2) *Poljes*

Poljes are large closed depressions with relatively flat floors that are often alluviated. About 3km northwest of Piawa is a polje which is more than 2km long and 1km wide. It is elongated along a northeasterly trending fault and has a small lake in the centre. Small streams flow into the polje from the elevated areas on the northwestern and southeastern sides, but most of these streams sink into small dolines around the margins of the polje floor rather than flow across the surface to the lake. These margins consist largely of piedmont aprons with coalescing alluvial fans, which have been dissected by two channels which reach the lake. The piedmont aprons and the slopes immediately above them support grassland vegetation.

To the south of Nguari is another polje with an area of 5 km^2. It is flanked on the northern and western sides by steep scarps formed in thick units of Darai Limestone. On the western side it is bounded by a homoclinal ridge of northeasterly dipping Ieru Formation. Ephemeral streams flow down the dip slope of this ridge and sink on the margin of the broad alluviated polje floor. One larger stream enters from the south and sinks near the centre of the polje. The boundaries between grassland and forest are less well defined in this polje than in the polje near Piawa or the uvulas at Rorogepo. Since the area south of Nguari was formerly inhabited the grassland here may be of anthropogenic origin.

The Lavani Valley is a major polje 21 km long and up to 12 km wide. A central ridge subdivides the valley, which is surrounded by limestone scarps between 500 and 1000 m high. The central ridge is aligned on the structural axis of the Muller Range and is composed of fine grained sandstones, mudstones and siltstones. The top of the ridge coincides with the top of this unit and has a thin veneer of limestone on the northeastern end of the ridge. Fluviokarst terrain with small through caves is developed on this outcrop.

Runoff from the central ridge forms two major streams: to the north, drainage collects in a series of shallow lakes and flat swampy areas at an altitude of 2150 m. This water enters the limestone at the periphery of the polje in a number of streamsinks and at least one major cave system (Photo 68). To the south the Emama River has become entrenched in slumped alluvial fan deposits and flows along the strike to a point at the southern extremity of the valley where it sinks into an enterable cave.

The valley floor is composed of the weathered Mesozoic sediments of the central ridge, together with alluvial fan deposits, mudflow and lensed peat deposits. A well developed bench some 10 m above the present valley floor suggests that periodic blocking and clearing of the sinks has occurred. Local informants reported that the lower valley floor becomes inundated following heavy rainfall. The marginal limestone walls show numerous fresh scars from spalling and cliff foot caves are poorly developed. This polje and others in the Muller Range would be classified as the peripheral type of Gams (1978).

At Oksapmin there are two large poljes developed in a structurally complex zone of overthrust and folded Darai Limestone sheets (Photo 69). In the area the limestone is superimposed four times, each limestone sheet being overlain by mudstones of the Lai Formation. Erosion in the Tekin Polje, west of Oksapmin, has left a double boatshaped klippe of limestone inside the synclinally folded limestone sheet which forms the rim of the valley (Jenkins, 1974). The Tekin dome is an anticlinal structure associated with the synclines, and forms a plateau inside the polje.

The area exhibits a range of karst landforms due to this structural complexity. The Tekin dome and broader ridge crests are covered in polygonal karst depressions elongated down-dip to give directed karst. The steeply dipping slopes of the overthrust sheets have small dolines and flatirons, while the escarpments bounding the sheets have extensive aprons of avalanche debris, some cemented to form resistant and inverted relief. The two poljes are each bounded by steep cliffed limestone slopes with gullies which end in streamsinks. The poljes are floored by Lai Formation mudstones, and a number of marginal springs unite to form fast flowing rivers which meander across the flat floor to sink into large cave passages.

In the Tekin polje, the Ariga and Tekin rivers flow in deeply entrenched channels to unite 1km from a major streamsink at the polje margin. Measured flow on one occasion was $15m^3 s^{-1}$. The watersinks in a broad, cliffed depression 200 m in diameter and choked with decaying stems of pit-pit cane (*Miscanthus* sp.). This mat of pit-pit is saucer shaped and at least 10 m thick. Beneath it can be heard the turbulent flow into the streamsink. A fine patina of mud coating the branches and leaves to a uniform level 10m above the sink point suggests considerable back up after rainfall. The sediment entering the streamsink is a very well sorted fine muddy sand, partly glauconitic. Beyond this streamsink a flood overflow channel cut in limestone leads for 500 m to a second, similar basin choked with pit-pit. A short flood channel extends beyond this for 200 m and has a series of open shafts in its bed. Flood debris wedged against boulders suggests this channel is intermittently active.

Between the two streamsinks, a number of dolines breach the underground conduit. A vadose canyon 10 m wide and 30 m deep is visible, with deep accumulations of fine sandy mud causing standing pools of water, and the rock surfaces coated in fine mud. On radar imagery a prominent joint trend runs from this streamsink to a large spring at 1600m near the source of the Teranmin River. The underground conduit therefore drops 190 m from its streamsink at 1790 m, and emerges at the spring which is perched on a mudstone sheet. The underground conduit is most likely to be phreatic given the low gradient (190 m in 5 km; 1:26) and high flow rate.

Within the Oksapmin polje, a number of springs have formed at the northwestern margin of the polje. The water emerges as discrete and seepage springs which have entrenched colluvial fans. The streams unite to form the Oksapmin River which meanders across a floodplain to sink amongst large boulders below the southeastern escarpment. Soil stratigraphy in the polje shows a number of decayed pit-pit mats separated by gleyed fine sandy muds derived from Lai Formation. These pit-pit mats are really extensive and suggest that periodic blocking of the streamsink results in inundation of the whole polje floor. At present a 100 ha swamp of pit-pit surrounds the streamsink, and local informants confirmed that periodic flooding occurs. The caves examined in the Oksapmin and Tekin poljes are vadose canyons leading to phreatic mazes which appear to be controlled by base levels due to impermeable aquicludes of Lai Formation mudstone. Initial phreatic flow regimes, with later vadose incision, are indicated.

13.3.3.2 *Polygonal Karst*

On the Muller Range there are a number of karst areas that are characterised by the polygonal shape of the catchment of their depressions and that fall into the category of polygonal karst according to the classification of Williams (1972).

(1) *Pyramid and Doline Karst*

This karst type consists of bowl-shaped depressions and concave pyramidal hills. This assemblage together with cockpit karst was thought by Loffler (1977) to be the dominant form on the

Muller Plateau. However, much of the area he considered consists of random dolines sometimes aligned along major structural features. These dolines occur where the Lai Formation covers the Darai Limestone so much of this area would better be described as doline karst. Where the Lai Formation has been stripped, pyramid and doline karst has formed in a few places. A number of these areas lies around the Mamo Plateau and two of them have been examined in detail, one between Hegaibagu and Okaparu and the other on the southeastern fringe of Mamo. In this second area the dolines are shallow, in the order of only 20 m deep and the pyramids only rise 20 m above the saddles and ridges. The pyramids are occasionally capped by a few metres of Lai Formation but mostly they are developed entirely in Darai Limestone. The pyramid profiles are frequently stepped because the upper layers of the Darai Limestone contain a variety of impure limestones and clastic sediments (Francis et al., 1980).

(2) *Arete and Pinnacle Karst*

This variety of polygonal karst occupies an area of about 4 km^2 on the summit surface of Nguari, 2900 – 3000m asl. It is bounded by scarps up to 500m high on the northern, western and southern sides. It has formed in thick beds of pure biomicrite with a few interbeds of calcareous siltstone and impure limestone. These strata dip very gently to the northeast in the southern part of Nguari but the dip increases to about 15° on the northeastern margin of this elevated area. The arete and pinnacle karst consists of narrow sawtoothed strike ridges which rise locally into steep sided pinnacles (Photo 70). The ridges are separated by vertical walled depressions up to 80 m deep which are aligned along northwesterly trending strike faults and joints. The depressions are separated from each other by extremely narrow, sharp crested cols which lie 20 – 30 m below the general level of the strike ridges. In some cases the cols have been breached by erosion, forming complex closed depressions which are kidney-shaped in plan and possess aretes which terminate in gendarmes. Because the vegetation on Nguari is sparse and stunted, outcrop is much more prominent here than on other upland surfaces in the Muller Range. The walls of the depressions are furrowed by huge wall solution runnels (Wandkarren) which disappear into shafts up to 50m deep near the depression floors.

Karst of this type was first described by Jennings and Bik (1962) from Mt. Kaijende, 70 km east of the Muller Range. At Kaijende the karst has developed in the gently dipping Lower Miocene Tibinini Limestone which consists of thickly bedded algal-foraminiferal biomicrite with some interbeds of calcareous mudstone and chert (Dow et al., 1973) and is thought to be the same unit as the Darai Limestone (Davies and Norvick, 1974). The limestone forms a massif which is bounded by scarps up to 1000m high on the northern, western and eastern sides and is strongly jointed; one joint set which trends slightly east of north controls the orientation of the main aretes.

Jennings and Bik (1962) and Williams (1973) believed that arete and pinnacle karst was confined to elevations between 3700 m and 2600 m and that its development was controlled partly by climate. Although the arete and pinnacle karst at Nguari falls within this altitudinal range, it is present at an elevation of about 2300 m near the Pori River, 40 km southeast of the Muller Range, and at an elevation of less than 2000 m to the west of Poroma. Moreover, this karst type has been recorded at elevations of 400 to 600 m in the Poya region of New Caledonia (Harris, 1976). In this locality arete and pinnacle karst with internal relief of 80 m occurs on resistant outcrops of strongly jointed, pure Jurassic limestones. Thus arete and pinnacle karst is not confined to high elevations and it seems likely that its development is related to the geological setting and local relief, rather than elevation above sea level.

13.3.3.3 *Crevice Karst*

This is terrain which is dissected by systems of solutionally enlarged fractures which are up to 15 m wide and 30 m deep. These enlarged fractures often form intersecting networks which are approximately rectangular in plan. Crevice karst is well developed in the Muller Range at elevations of

2000 – 3000 m. in crevice karst the surfaces of residual clint-like blocks between large fractures usually define a roughly horizontal plane and in many cases lie on flat valley floors which were formerly alluviated (Jennings and Bik, 1962). However, in the Muller Range crevice karst has often formed on dip surfaces with inclinations of 10° – 20°. The solutionally enlarged fractures often pass downwards into cave shafts, or laterally into phreatic fissure passages that display features such as joint wall and ceiling cavities. This suggests that the initial enlargement of these fractures takes place through solution by groundwater moving laterally or downdip. The presence of an acidic, humic soil under conditions of free soil drainage may enhance a "positive feedback" erosional system. Subsequently the groundwater levels are lowered by incision of adjacent valleys or closed depressions, draining the fracture system. The fissures are then sculptured by surface flow moving down the walls, giving rise to features such as solution ripples and wall solution runnels. Erosion by surface and throughflow sometimes loosens blocks of limestone along the rims of the grikes and corridors, dropping chockstones into these fissures. In addition logs and branches fall into the fissures, entrapping soil and leaf litter to form false floors which are treacherous underfoot.

The walls of the fissures evolve by parallel retreat which eventually widens the corridors and sometimes breaches the narrower intervening blocks, giving rise to rows of isolated pinnacles. The crevice karst appears to develop in areas with very close joint spacings; this high fissure frequency is also evident in the phreatic mazes of Atea Kananda cave, which underlie areas with well developed crevice karst. The precise form that crevice karst takes thus depends on the orientation and spacing of fractures, the dip of the bedding and the stage of evolution.

The trees growing on the rocky elevated clints are usually stunted, whereas the trees growing in soil floored fissures are somewhat taller. Consequently the rugged small scale relief in crevice karst terrain is almost entirely concealed by the forest canopy, and the crevice karst is difficult to identify by air photo interpretation. Workers such as Jennings and Bik (1962), Williams (1973) and Loffler (1977) have all considered that crevice karst was confined to lowland areas in New Guinea. Nevertheless this karst variety is common in the Muller Range. Since Williams (1973) and Loffler (1977) in particular relied heavily on air photos, it seems likely that the occurrence of crevice karsts in highland areas has been overlooked because of the limitations of air photos as data sources.

13.3.3.4 *Soils*

The distribution of soil types is closely related to parent material. Although the soils may all be placed within the one group of humic brown clay soils, the individual units display significant differences. In general, the soils are deep, severely leached acidic soils on steep to moderate slopes. Shallow soils are only found on Steep, freely draining limestones and on unstable siltstones and mudstones. Soils developed on Darai Limestone are far from uniform due to the presence of interbeds and to variations in soil drainage. Mull rendzinas are characterised by their shallow depth (0 – 40 cm), well developed crumb structure and dark colour (5YR 2/1). These soils are found as shallow pockets or thin layers on exposed limestone outcrops in positions of free soil drainage. A dense fibrous root mat overlies a humic granular clay with white specks of limestone, resting on chalky, shattered bedrock.

Strongly weathered, uniform textured clay soils are by far the most widespread in the area, and are developed on Darai Limestone. These yellow brown (7.5YR 5/4) soils are relatively impermeable and thus runoff is rapid. These soils grade into a strongly differentiated group in areas of impeded soil drainage. The latter soils are yellow brown (7.5YR 5/6) clays with a marked increase in clay content with depth. The impeded drainage gives rise to grey or reddish mottling in the saturated subsoil.

Similar soils have developed on the calcareous sediments of the Lai Formation and Ieru Formation. On these lithologies a greater proportion of sandy material results in a gritty clay texture, and where splash erosion is important (for example in the Geloro and Ponganepo clearings) this results in a very thin surface crust of fine white sand. Areas of montane shrubland underlain by slumped colluvial fan deposits have gleyed clay soils. In these soils, a shallow humic A horizon overlies a plastic clay subsoil which grades into the weathered cobbles and gritty clay of the parent material. Small depressions in these areas have peaty soils. The presence of acid conditions at the soil-rock interface, the high humic content, and the low permeability of most soils are the factors of most relevance to geomorphic processes in the area.

The vegetation of the Muller Ranges has not received any detailed study Paijmans (1975) maps the area as lower montane forest. This is a small crowned evergreen forest with canopy between 20 and 30 m. On the limestone, the forest tends to be dominated by *Nothofagus* sp., with other canopy trees belonging to the Families Lauraceae, Cunoniaceae, Elaeocarpaceae and Myrtaceae. The shrub layer is dense and contains climbing bamboos, immature trees, tree ferns, and *Pandanus* sp. The ground flora is dense and consists of mosses, ferns, herbs and epiphytes. A dense mat of fibrous roots and leaf litter masks the soil surface. Extensive areas of *Miscanthus* and *Imperata* grasslands are present at Geloro and in the Lavani Valley. These grasslands may well be anthropogenic, as soil exposures contain old tree roots and carbonized plant remains.

13.4 Concluding Remarks

The karst areas of Australia are relatively well documented though long-term studies of karst hydrology and solution chemistry are restricted to a few areas in the eastern uplands and in Tasmania. There is a diversity of karst styles reflecting the great geological and climatic diversity of the continent. Australia has extensive arid limestone areas such as the Nullarbor Plain, studies of which have made a substantial contribution to understanding of the geomorphology of desert karst. The karst of the lower southeast of South Australia is a province which is similar to the extensive Yucatan karst and which deserves more intensive study, especially given the economic importance of limestone groundwater there. The small impounded karsts of the eastern uplands, modest on a global scale, have yielded valuable information on the geomorphology and palaeoecology of the region where most Australians live. Their main importance lies in the demonstration of their persistence as landforms from the Permian onwards. Palaeokarstic features are widespread and it is likely that Australia has the oldest caves as well as being the oldest of lands (Jennings, 1975). The caves of Australia have the potential to reveal very long records of natural processes on a stable tectonic plate over latitudinal range from 10° to 44°S.

In contrast the karst and caves of New Guinea are young and are actively forming under a humid tropical climate with continuing uplift on an active plate margin. The diversity of karst landforms in New Guinea reflects the great complexity of geological structure there. Extensive overthrust limestone plates with high angle faulting provide an array of possibilities for tropical limestone morphology. Alluviation of the karsts is modest, in contrast to the classical tower karst of Guilin, and large horizontal caves are restricted to coastal and lacustrine settings. Earlier interpretations of altitudinal zonation and climatic control on karst landforms may not be totally applicable. There have been no long-term studies of karst processes in New Guinea. This must remain a challenge for karst geomorphologists of the twenty-first century who will find ready application of their research given the importance of limestone groundwater and petroleum resources in a rapidly developing nation.

References

Allen, G.R., 1982. The Inland Fishes of Western Australia, Western Australian Museum, Perth.

Arnold, G.O., T.J. Griffin and C.C. Hodge, 1979. Geology of the Ok Tedi and Southern Atbalmin 1:100000 sheet, Geol. Surv. PNG Rep. 79/3.

Atkinson, A., 1990. The Undara lava tube and its caves, Helictite 28:3 – 14.

Brook, D., 1977. Caves and karst of the Hindenburg Ranges, Geogr. J. 143:27 – 41.

Brookfield, H. and D. Hart, 1966. Rainfall in the Tropical Southwest Pacific, Canberra, Dept. Geography ANU Publ. G/3.

Byrne, G.M., M.M. Ghiyandiwe and P.M. James, 1978. Ok Tedi landslide study, Geol. Surv. PNG Report 78/6.

Caldwell, J.R., A.G. Davey, J.N. Jennings and A.P. Spate, 1983. Colour in some Nullarbor Plain speleothems. Helictite 20:3 – 10.

Davies, H.L. and M. Norvick, 1974. Explanatory notes on the Blucher Range geological sheet, Aust. Bur. Miner Res. Report.

Drysdale, R.N., 1995. Tufa formation and late Quaternary environments at Lawn Hill Gorge, northwest Queensland. Unpubl. PhD thesis, University College, UNSW.

Dow, D.B., 1977. A geological synthesis of Papua New Guinea, Bull. Bur. Mineral Res. Aust. 201.

Eberhard, R., 1994. Inventory and Management of the Junee River Karst System, Tasmania, Hobart, Forestry Tasmania 125pp.

Ellaway, M., D.L. Smith, D.S. Gillieson and M. A. Greenaway, 1990. Karst Water Chemistry-Limestone Ranges, Western Australia, Helictite 28(2):25 – 36.

Emmett, A.J. and A.L. Telfer, 1994. Influence of karst hydrology on water quality management in southeast South Australia, Environmental Geology 23:149 – 155.

Finlayson, B., J. Webb and M. Ellaway, 1992. The Buchan Karst, in Gillieson, D.S. (ed.) Geology, climate, hydrology and karst formation: field symposium in Australia: guidebook, Special Publication No. 4, Department of Geography and Oceanography, University College, Australian Defence Force Academy, Canberra, pp. 3 – 24.

Francis, G., D.S. Gillieson and J.M. James, 1980. Surface Geomorphology of Some Muller Range Karst Areas, pp. 91 – 100 in James, J.M. and Dyson, H.J. (eds.), Caves and Karst of the Muller Range.

Gillieson, D.S., 1977. Lelet: report of the 1976 New Ireland speleological expedition, Nuigini Caver 5:62 – 101.

Gillieson, D.S., 1985. Geomorphic Development of Limestone Caves in the Highlands of Papua New Guinea, Zeitschrift fur Geomorphologie, 29:51 – 70.

Gillieson, D.S., 1986. Cave Sedimentation in the New Guinea Highlands, Earth Surface Processes and Landforms 11:533 – 543.

Gillieson, D., 1989. Limestone soils in the New Guinea Highlands: a review, in Gillieson, D. and Ingle Smith, D. Resource Management in Limestone Landscapes: International Perspectives, Special Publication 2, Dept. Geogr. Oceanogr., University College, Aust. Def. Force. Acad., pp. 191 – 200.

Gillieson, D.S. (ed.), 1992. Geology, climate, hydrology and karst formation: field symposium in Australia: guidebook, Special Publication No. 4, Department of Geography and Oceanography, University College, Australian Defence Force Academy, Canberra, 117pp.

Gillieson, D., 1993. Environmental Change and Human Impact on Arid and Semi-arid Karsts of Australia, in Williams, P. (ed.) Karst Terrains: Environmental Changes and Human Impact, Catena Supplement 25: 127 – 146.

Gillieson, D., D. Ingle Smith, M. Greenaway and M. Ellaway, 1991. Flood history of the limestone ranges, Kimberleys, Western Australia, Quaternary Australasia9(1):21 – 25.

Gillieson, D.S. and A.P. Spate, 1992. The Nullarbor Karst, in Gillieson, D.S. (ed.) Geology, climate, hydrology and karst formation: field symposium in Australia: guidebook, Special Publication No. 4, Department of Geography and Oceanography, University College, Australian Defence Force Academy, Canberra, pp. 65 – 99.

Gillieson, D. and I. Houshold, (in press) Rehabilitation of the Lune River quarry, Tasmanian Wilderness World Heritage Area, Australia, in Karst Hydrogeology and Human Activities: Impacts, Consequences and Implications, International Association for Hydrogeology.

Goede, A., R.S. Harmon, T.C. Atkinson and P.J. Rowe, 1990. Pleistocene climatic change in Southern Australia and its effect on speleothem deposition in some Nullarbor caves. Journal of Quaternary Science 5:29 – 38.

Goudie, A., H. Viles, R. Allison, M. Day, I. Livinsgstone and P. Bull, 1990. The geomorphology of the Napier Range, Western Australia, Trans. Inst. Brit. Geogr. 15:308 – 322.

Grimes, K.G., 1975. Pseudokarst: Definition and Types, Proc. 10th Aust. Speleol. Fedn. Conf. pp6 – 10.

Grimes, K.G., 1982. Karst denudation experiment, Report for the first three years 1979 – 82. Typescript, 12pp.

Grimes, K.G., 1994. The South-East Karst Province of South Australia, Environmental Geology 23:134 – 148.

Grodzicki, J., 1985. Genesis of the Nullarbor Plain caves in Southern Australia, Zeitschrift fur Geomorphologie 29, 37 – 49.

Harris, S. (ed.), 1976. Caves of New Caledonia, Hobart, Southern Caving Society. Hoch, H. and Howarth, F. G. (1989). Six new cavernicolous cixiid planthoppers in the genus Solonaima from Australia (Homoptera: Fulgoroidea), Systematic Entomology 14:377 – 402.

Humphreys, W.F., 1993. The significance of the subterranean fauna in biogeographic reconstruction: examples from Cape Range peninsula, Western Australia, in Humphreys, W.F. (ed.) The Biogeography of the Cape Range, Western Australia, Records of the Western Australian Museum 45:165 – 192.

James, J.M. and H.J. Dyson (eds.), 1980. Caves and Karst of the Muller Range, Sydney, Speleological Research Council.

James, J.M., P. Rogers and A.P. Spate, 1990. The role of mixing corrosion in the genesis of the caves of the Nullarbor Plain, Australia. Proceedings 10th International Congress of Speleology, Budapest, 263 – 265.

Jenkins, D.A.L., 1974. Detachment tectonics in western Papua New Guinea, Bull. Geol. Soc. Amer. 85:533－548.
Jennings, J.N., 1968. Syngenetic karst in Australia, in Contributions to the Study of Karst. Pubn. G/5, Dept. of Geog. Aust. Nat. Univ., pp41－108.
Jennings, J.N., 1965. The Big Hole near Braidwood, New South Wales, J. Proc. Roy. Soc. NSW 98:215－219.
Jennings, J.N., 1975. How well off is Australia for caves and karst? A brief geomorphic estimate, Proc. 10th. Aust. Speleol. Fedn. Conf. pp82－90.
Jennings, J.N., 1983. A map of karst cave areas in Australia, Aust. Geog. Studs., 21(2): 183－196.
Jennings, J. N., 1983. Further studies at the Blue Waterholes, Cooleman Plain, N.S.W., 1969－77: Part 1 Climate and Hydrology. Helictite, 21: 3－20.
Jennings, J.N. and M. Bik, 1962. Karst morphology in New Guinea, Nature 194:1036－1038.
Jennings, J.N. and M.M. Sweeting, 1963. The Limestone Ranges of the Fitzroy Basin, Western Australia, Bonner Geographische Abhandlungen 32, pp60.
Kiernan, K., 1984. Glaciation and karst in Tasmania: review and speculations, Helictite 20:11－16.
Kiernan, K., 1988. The Management of Soluble Rock Landscapes: An Australian Perspective, Speleol. Res. Council, Sydney.
Kiernan, K., 1992. The Exit Cave Quarry, Ida Bay Karst System, Tasmanian World Heritage Area: A Hydrogeological Perspective, report to Dept. Parks, Wildlife and Heritage, Tasmania, 81pp.
Kiernan, K., 1993. The Exit Cave Quarry: tracing waterflows and resource policy evaluation, Helictite 31:3－12.
Lau, J.E., D.P. Commander and G. Jacobson, 1987. Hydrogeology of Australia. Bureau of Mineral Resources, Geology and Geophysics Bulletin 227, 21pp.
Lauritzen, S.E., D. Karp and D. Megirian, 1994. Quaternary denudation on the Tindall karst plain, N.T. Australia, Abstract of paper presented at Changing Karst Environments Symposium, Universities of Oxford and Huddersfield, September 1994, Cave and Karst Science 21:17.
Loffler, E., 1974. Explanatory notes to the geomorphological map of Papua New Guinea, Canberra, CSIRO Land Res. Series No. 33.
Loffler, E., 1977. Geomorphology of Papua New Guinea, Canberra, CSIRO/ANU Press.
Lowry, D.C. and J.N. Jennings, 1974. The Nullarbor karst, Australia, Z. Geomorph., 18:35－81.
Martin, H.A., 1973. Palynology and historical ecology of some cave excavations in the Australian Nullarbor. Australian Journal of Botany 21:283－316.
McKenzie, N.L. and A.C. Robinson, 1987. A biological survey of the Nullarbor region, South and Western Australia in 1984. Department of Environment and Planning, Adelaide, South Australia, 413 pp.
Matthews, P., 1985. Australian Karst Index. Australian Speleological Federation, Melbourne.
May, R.F., R.C.J. Lenanton and P.F. Berry, 1983. Ningaloo Marine Park. Report and recommendations by the Marine Park working group. National Parks Authority, Western Australia Report 1, 67pp.
Ollier, C.D. and M.C. Brown, 1965. Lava caves of Victoria, Bull. Vulcanol., 28: 215－229.
Osborne, R.A.L. and D.F. Branagan, 1988. Karst Landscapes of New South Wales, Australia, Earth Science Reviews 25: 467－480.
Pain, S., 1988. Flood warnings in the sand. New Scientist. 1628, pp. 56－61.
Spate, A.P., D.S. Gillieson and J.N. Jennings, 1984. Anomalous Red Sands in Certain Nullarbor Plain Caves and Dolines, Proc. 2nd Aust. N.Z. Geomorphology Conference, Broken Hill, July 1984, pp.93－97.
Sprent, J.K., 1970. Mount Etna Caves, Univ. Qld. Speleol. Soc., Brisbane, pp116.
Sydney Speleological Society, 1972. Wombeyan Caves, Sydney, Speleological Research Council, 224pp.
Twidale, C.R., 1984. The enigma of Tindal Plain, Northern Territory, Trans. R. Soc. S. Aust., 108(2): 95－103.
Van de Graaf, W.J.E., P.D. Denham and R.M. Hocking, 1975. Emerged Pleistocene marine terraces on Cape Range, Western Australia. Annual Report Geological Survey of Western Australia.
Veeh, H., D. Schwebel, W.J.E. Van de Graaf and P.D. Denman, 1979. Uranium series ages of coralline terrace deposits in Western Australia. Journal Geological Society of Australia 26:285－292.
Viles, H. and A. Goudie, 1990. Reconnaissance studies of the tufa deposits of the Napier Range, N.W. Australia, Earth Surface Processes and Landforms 15:425－443.
Welch, B, R. (ed.), 1976. The Caves of Jenolan 2. The Northern Limestone. Sydney, Sydney University Speleological Society 131pp.
White, S., 1984. Karst landforms and their relationship to Pleistocene dune ridges, Bats Ridge, Portland, Victoria, unpub MSc thesis, University of Melbourne.
White, S., 1989. Karst features in Pleistocene dunes, Bats Ridge, Western Victoria, Helictite 27:53－71.
Williams, P.W., 1972. Morphometric analysis of polygonal karst in New Guinea, Bul. Geol. Soc. Am. 83:761－796.
Williams, P.W., 1973. Variation in karst landforms with altitude in New Guinea, Geogr. Z. Suppl. 32:25－33.
Williams, P.W., 1978. Interpretations of Australasian karsts, In Davies, J.L. and Williams, M. A.J. (eds) Landform Evolution in Australasia, Canberra, ANU Press.

Global Karst Correlation
Edited by Yuan Daoxian and Liu Zaihua
Science Press and VSP BV, 1998

Chapter 14 The Subtropical Karst of Bonito, Western Brazil

Heinz Charles Kohler[1], Augusto Auler[2], Maria Bernadeth Cattanio[3]
[1] *Museu de Historia Natural-UFMG., Belo Horizonte/MG-Brasil*
[2] *Geography and Geology Department, Western Kentucky University, USA*
[3] *Departamento de Geografia. UFMS, Tres Lagoas. Mato Grosso do Sul, Brasil*

14.1 Introduction

The Bonito Karst region is located at Mato Grosso do Sul state, midwestern Brazil, 200km away from Campo Grande, the state capital. The karst occurs in a stripe more than 100km long running north-south. The area lies in the eastern limit of Brazilian Pantanal(Fig. 14-1).

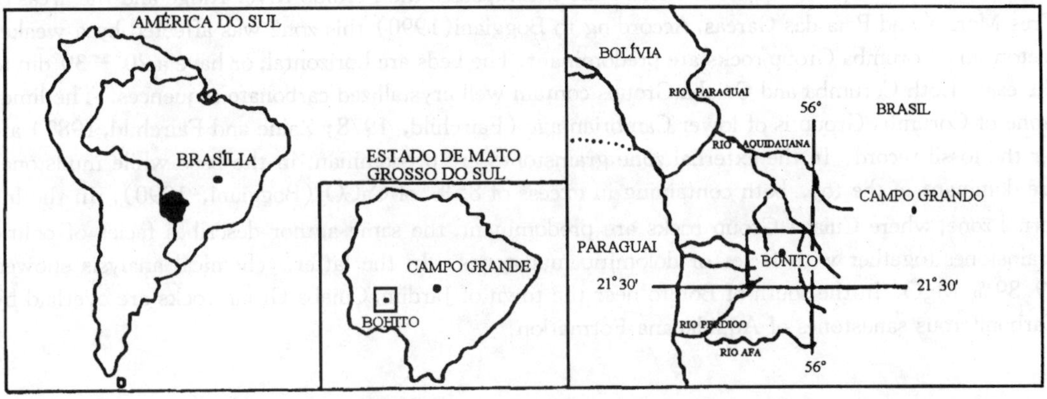

Fig. 14-1 Location of the studied area

The area lives on cattle farming and agriculture, mainly wheat and soybeans. Limestone is mined for agricultural purposes. The only cement industry is at Bodoquena city, 70km to the north. The tourism industry is developing rapidly due to the natural beauty of the area.

The mean annual temperature in western Mato Grosso do Sul is around 23℃, the mean rainfall is around 1400mm/a. In Aquidauana(149m asl) the maximum mean annual temperature is 33℃ and the minimum is 20℃ (Santanna Neto, 1989). Tarifa (1984) argues that the high mean temperature and thermal amplitude are due to the tropical and continental character of the climate associated to the low altitudes.

The karst area of Bonito has the basic climatic pattern of the region, such as:

– Dry winter and wet summer.

– Affected by Atlantic Tropical and Atlantic Polar air masses during the winter and Continental Equatorial air mass during summer.

– Rainfall around 1400mm/a.

– Winter lowest temperature below 10℃ and summer highest temperatures around 40℃.

– Thermal stress due to high amplitude.

– High relative humidity, around 75%.

There is no study dealing with the local climate of Bonito area. However there is a temperature difference between the highlands(700m asl) and the lower plain (400m). The difference in water temperature will play a role in the geochemical behavior of the karst groundwater between the recharge and discharge zones.

The Bodoquena Ridge is the head of the local hydrographical network. The Bonito area is the origin of Perdido and Salobra-Miranda rivers basins. Both have their source at Tres Morros area at an elevation of 650m asl, less than 1 km away from each other. Perdido River flows to the southeast, towards Apa River and eventually Paraguay River, in the border Paraguay/Brazil. Miranda River flows to the northwest, discharging at Paraguay River more than 350km upstream from the Apa Confluence (Fig. 14-2).

The fluvial pattern is a consequence of the tectonic framework of Bodoquena Ridge. The ridge is located in the Paraguay orogenetic belt (Alvarenga, 1988) of Brasiliana age (550 million years). Boggiani(1990) divides the Paraguay belt at Bodoquena Ridge into two zones, the external (W) and the internal (E)(Fig. 14-3). The internal zone is characterized by a more intense tectonism. The strata present inverse faulting and isoclinal folding. In this zone, in the surroundings of the town of Bonito, occur a series of thrust faults trending eastward that place the lithologies of Cuiaba Group, over Corumba Group rocks. The external zone encompasses the Perdido River Ridge and the areas of Tres Morros and Baia das Garcas. According to Boggiani(1990) this zone was affected by a weaker tectonism. Corumba Group rocks are predominant. The beds are horizontal, or have a 20° – 30° dip to the east. Both Corumba and Cuiaba Groups contain well crystallized carbonate sequences. The limestone of Corumba Group is of lower Cambrian age (Fairchild, 1978; Zaine and Fairchild, 1987) after the fossil record. In the external zone grainstones are predominant in the base while mudstones are dominant in the top, both containing in excess of 85% of $CaCO_3$ (Boggiani, 1990). In the internal zone, where Cuiaba Group rocks are predominant, the same author describes facies of oolitic grainstones together with facies of dolomitic mudstones. In the latter, chemical analysis showed 19.89% MgO. In the south of Bonito near the town of Jardim, Cuiaba Group rocks are overlaid by Carboniferous sandstones of Aquidauana Formation.

14.2 Surface Karst

Four physiographical domains can be distinguished in the Bonito area: 1. Fluviokarst of Perdido River; 2. Residual hills; 3. Karst plain; 4. Fluviokarst of Miranda River tributaries.

14.2.1. *Fluviokarst of Perdido River (Upper Surface)*

Perdido River flows over the top of Bodoquena Ridge, around the altitude of 500m. This domain develops over carbonate rocks of Corumba Group. The rock layers are horizontal in most of the area. In some places they have a gentle dip to the east. The upper portion of Bodoquena Ridge lies at an altitude of 750 – 650m. This section is the water divide between the Salobro and Perdido River basins. There is a well developed surface at elevations between 650 – 600m, characterized by a flat relief covered by lateritic soil. This surface can be associated to the South American Surface of King (1956) of Cretaceous age. The origin of this surface can be attributed to sub-surface horizontal erosion of clayey sediments. These sediments could have been preserved through the formation of an endured crust. Although these crusts cannot be found in the upper surface at present time, fragments of endured material were observed at the lower elevations(350 – 300m).

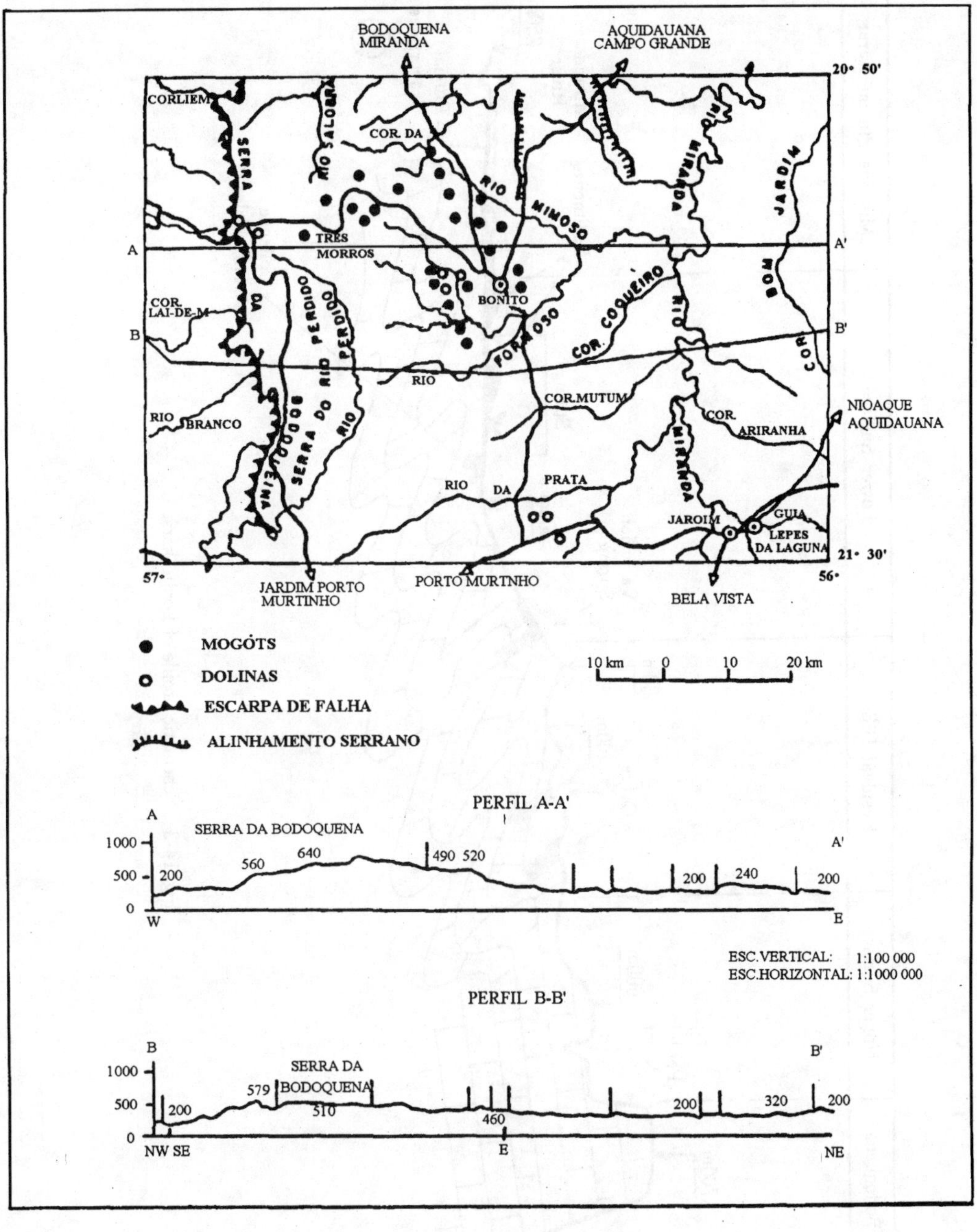

Fig. 14-2 Distribution of hydrographic nets

The best developed karst terrain in the upper surface occurs at Baia das Garcas Farm and at the headwater of Perdido River. In the latter there is a small uvala with active drainage, the presumed source of Aquidaba River. Few other karst landforms were observed, such as the sequence of swallets and springs of Seputa River, the first tributary of Perdido River. Some caves were recently found in this upper surface(Luis Enrique Sanchez, personal communication).

The Perdido River valley has not been explored due to logistic problems. The observations

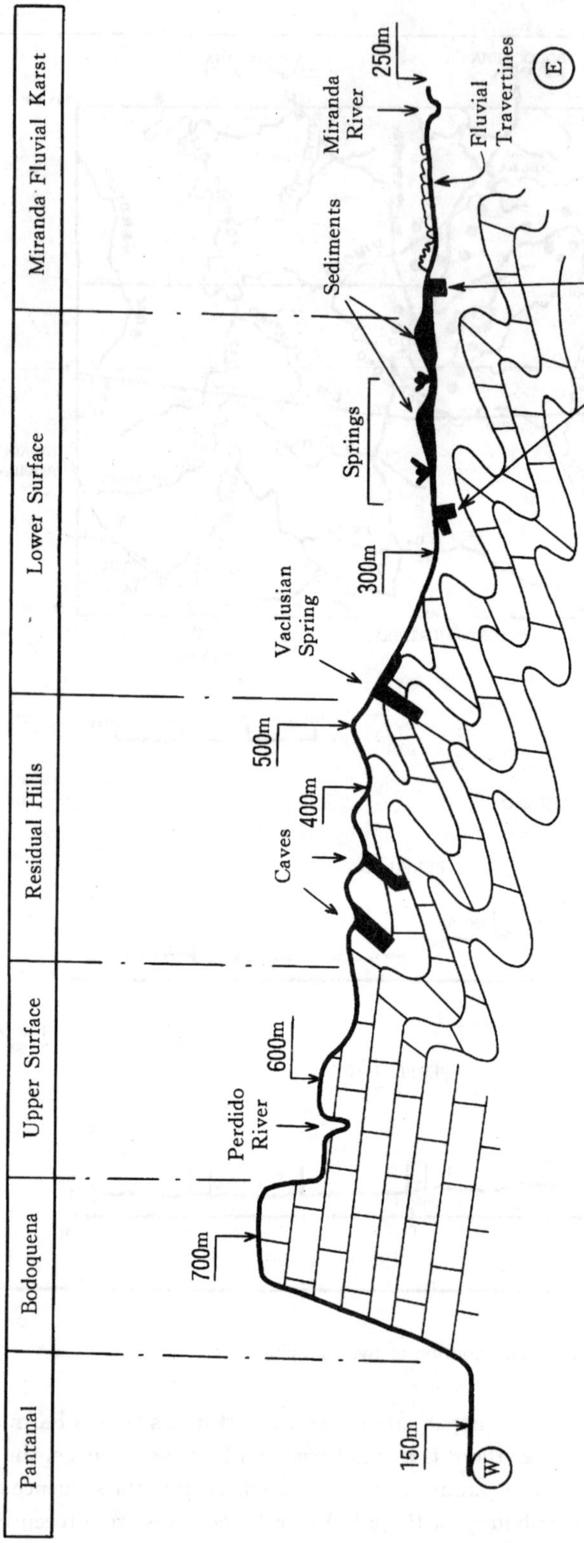

Fig. 14-3 Schematic profile of Bonito karst

made so far were based solely in aerial photographs. Even so, in many places the canyon of Perdido River is hidden by the dense vegetation. Travertine deposits were observed in the river bed at the place where the road crosses the river. Of note is the distinct pattern of Perdido and Salobro Rivers. The latter flows to the north with a profile typical of mountainous rivers. The former drains to the south with a profile of low gradient river under structural control. Furthermore, the Perdido river has very few tributaries. The water at Perdido River may sink partially somewhere in the stream channel, originating springs in the lower surface.

14.2.2 *Residual Hills*

This domain is situated mainly in the upper basin of Mimoso and Formoso Rivers, above the elevation of 400m. It can be described as residual rounded hills up to 100m high separated by a plain. It resembles "mogotes", described in the Caribbean tropical karst. Some hills are aligned in the North-south direction. Wandkarren is present in the surface. Breakdown is common in the base of the hills.

These landforms were formed due to erosion of the Upper surface by the tributaries of Miranda River. Caves occur at the side of the hills. The size and quantity of the residual hills tend to decrease to the west, away from Bodoquena Ridge. The morphology of the hills is related to the dip of the carbonate. Lateral erosion by the rivers that flow to the west may have played an important role in the genesis of the hills. The domain of residual hills can be considered a transition between the Upper Surface (Fluviokarst of Perdido River) and the Lower Surface (Karst plain).

14.2.3 *Karst Plain (Lower Surface)*

This domain develops between 350 – 300m asl. consisting of a plain limited in the east by Rio Perdido Ridge and in the north by a series of residual hills. The predominant karst landforms in this domain are collapse sinkholes. In some selected collapse sites, the soil cover is at least 10m thick. Many of these collapses have happened during the last 50 years, probably due to natural causes considering the limited human impact in the karst aquifer. The collapse is probably due to the infiltration of soil in the inclined fissures of the carbonate. A few collapses are related to caves, such as Cure cave, near the town of Jardim (Lino et al., 1984)

In the southern portion, the carbonates are overlaid by sandstone of Aquidauana Formation. Sinkholes due to subjacent karst exist in this area, such as Misteriosa Lagoon (80m deep below water level), Araras Pit and others.

The karst plain contains a number of springs that drain highly saturated water. This water precipitates slightly clayey carbonate with more than 98% $CaCO_3$. Similar material has been described at Sao Geraldo Farm by Cattanio et al. (1991) as:

"At the top there is dark brown organic soil with silt and clay, becoming gray at 2m depth. Between 1.5 and 3.5m a perched aquifer was crossed. The soil becomes red to gray with predominance of clay. Shells were observed during all the soil profile, becoming more frequent towards the base. At 4.6m deep there is a duricrust, with quartz and oolites of $CaCO_3$".

Similar material sampled at Salobro River basin yielded ages of 5200 years for gastropods and 2150 years for organic clay (Turcq et al., 1987).

14.2.4 *Fluviokarst of Miranda River Tributaries*

This physiographic domain is a plain situated over the highly tectonized rocks of Cuiaba Group, in the southeastern portion of the area. All the right margin tributaries of Miranda River precipitate travertine. The origin of these deposits is linked to the over saturation of the karst water. The CO_2 is released due to both the agitation of water in rapids, and the difference between the groundwater temperature and surface temperature. Algae are believed to contribute in the $CaCO_3$ precipitation. Tab. 14-1 shows a chemical analysis of a travertine deposit.

Tab. 14-1 Chemical analysis of travertine (Lino et al., 1984)

CaO	MgO	Al_2O_3	SiO_2	NO_n solubles	CO_2
51.95%	2.71%	0.057%	0.89%	0.96%	43.79%

14.3 Underground Karst

There are many caves in the area. Lino et al(1984) studied 17 caves. Cave diving expeditions in 1991 and 1992 surveyed underwater passages in four known caves, besides finding one new cave (Auler, 1991; 1992). Tab. 14-2. attempts to summarize the morphometry of the known caves.

The known caves show a well marked bedding control added to important collapse features. Caves 1 to 4 and 11 develop according to the inclined bedding planes. Morro do Mateus Cave(9) is an exception, since its passage is perpendicular to the bedding plane (Lino et al., 1984). Breakdown is frequent in most of the caves. Cave collapse is favored by the jointing system of the carbonate.

Tab. 14-2 Speleometry of the Bonito karst

Cave	Length (m)	Depth (m)	Depth (m below water)	position	Ref.
1. Lago Azul	290	107	57	1	2, 3
2. N. Sra Aparecida	200	?	–	1	2
3. Anhumas	120	133	62	1	2, 3
4. Sao Miguel	100	15	–	1	1
5. Jaragua	100	?	–	1	2
6. Morro do Mateus	96	25	–	1	2
7. Poco do Urubu	15	10	–	1	2
8. Mimoso	230	40	35	1	3
9. Ametista	40	8	–	1	2
10. Joao Arruda	100	?	–	1	2
11. Nascente Rio Formoso	245	51	51	3	3
12. Cure	80	25	–	2	2
13. Misteriosa Lagoon	–	56	66	2	3
14. Misteriosa Lagoon II	–	72	82	2	3, 4
15. Abismo do Poco	–	20	?	2	2
16. Araras Pit	125	60	?	2	2

Key to position: 1-side of residual hills; 2-collapse at the karst plain; 3-base of Bodoquena Hills.
Key to references: 1-Lino et al., 1984; 2-SBE, 1990; 3-Auler, 1992; 4-J. Hallak, personal communication.

14.4 Karst Hydrology

The local hydrology is characterized by a series of springs that drain to the east. Most of the springs are located at the base of Bodoquena and Rio Perdido Ridges. Fazenda Jatoba spring is the only observed spring located at the top of Bodoquena Ridge. Tab. 14-3 give a preliminary characterization of the springs in the area.

Tab. 14-3 Characterization of karst springs.

Spring	Type	Magnitude
Formoso River	conduit	medium
Sucuri River	diffuse	medium
Anhumas River	diffuse	small
Baia Bonita	diffuse	medium
Fazenda Jatoba	diffuse	small

Note: magnitude levels: small $<0.5m^3/s$;
medium $0.5-10m^3/s$;
high $>10m^3/s$

Most of the springs are diffuse flow ones. These are always crystal clear, without sediment load even during the wet season. They have a slow response to rainfall. They probably represent the outlet of slow moving water through joints. These springs have usually multiple discharge points under arenaceous sediments, creating a "sand boil" effect. Sucuri River Spring and Baia Bonita Spring belong to this class.

Conduit flow was observed at Rio Formoso Spring. This underwater cave was explored to a length of 250m to a total depth of 51m with going passage (Auler, 1992). It has turbulent flow. The water level at this spring rises rapidly after heavy rain. The sediment load also increases during the wet season. This spring supposedly drains water from a partial swallet of Perdido River. The difference in elevation between the river and the spring can account for its "vauclusian" pattern. A tracing experiment may yield definite results.

A free karst aquifer exists through most of the area. Considering the local geomorphology and the base level, a general flow to the east towards Miranda River can be implied. Some caves reach the water table. The underground lakes are basically static, suggesting laminar flow.

Lago Azul Cave and Anhumas Pit are located 2km apart. They hold an enormous amount of water, estimated in $450000m^3$ for Lago Azul and $380000m^3$ for Anhumas. Although close to each other they appear to have a distinct water chemistry. The underground lake at Anhumas has very large deposits of subaqueous speleothems, such as cave cones and coralloids. These speleothems are formed by saturated water. Lago Azul shows no subaqueous speleothems at all. The large underwater calcite coatings at Anhumas may have sealed the cave, creating an isolated underground reservoir. Furthermore, Lago Azul has a very peculiar aquatic cave fauna that has not been observed in the other caves. The elevation of the underground lake surface at Lago Azul Cave lies 15m below the level of Anhumas River, located only 2km away. The karst aquifer at Lago Azul probably is not immediately connected to nearby streams.

Mimoso Cave and Misteriosa Lagoon are located away from Lago Azul and Anhumas caves.

Mimoso Cave shows large deposits of subaqueous speleothems. Misteriosa Lagoon lacks speleothems. It drains towards Prata River to the north.

14.5 Karst Evolution

Karst evolution occurs in two different ways. The drainages that issue at the base of Bodoquena Ridge are dissecting the relief. Lateral and vertical undermining is taking place in the residual hills, leading to the progressive lowering of the relief and the expansion of the karst plain. This process may have been attenuated in present time due to the relative rise in the water table. In addition to that, Bodoquena and Rio Perdido Ridges are experiencing regressive erosion.

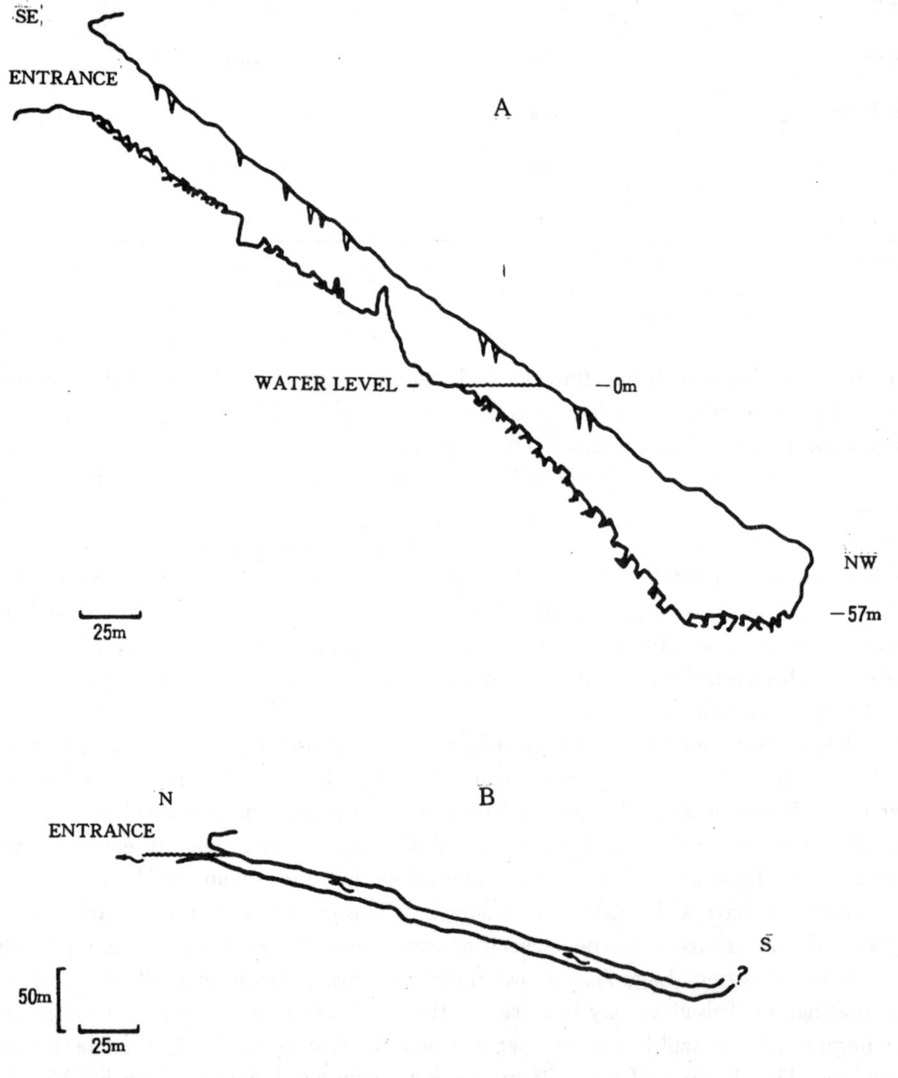

Fig. 14-4 Profile of Gruta Do Lago Azul(A), A presumed relict spring and nascente do rio Formoso (B), an active conduit spring (after surveys by Auler, Rubbioli, Rosello, Dusz, Laboutique, Boggiani and Karmann)

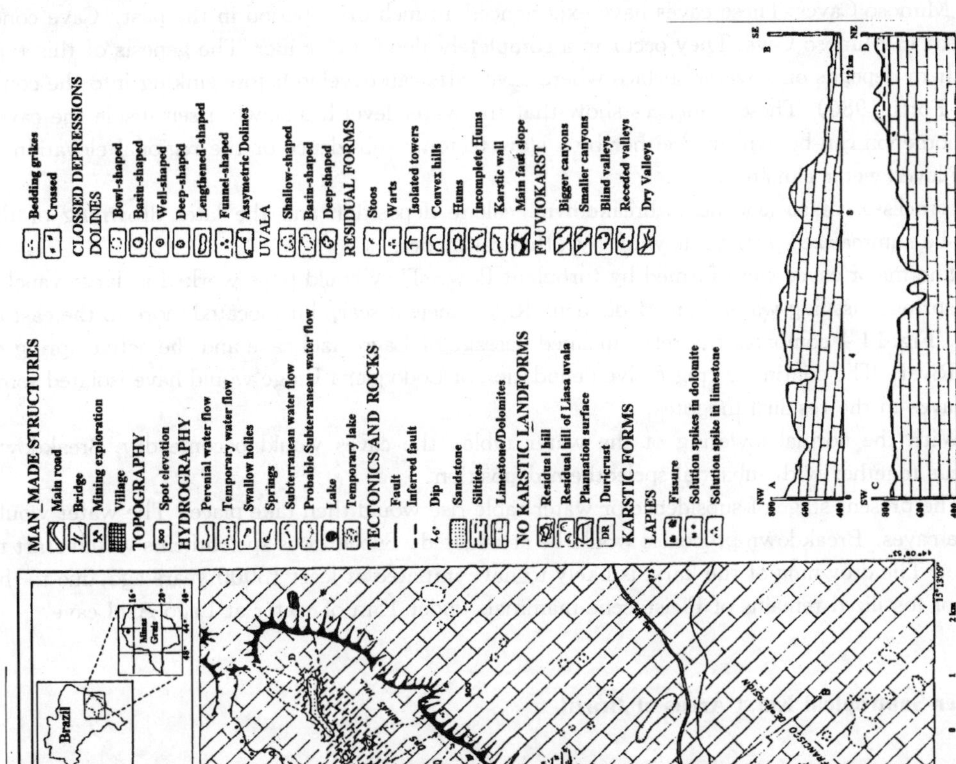

Fig. 14-5 Karst Geomorphological Map of Peruacu River Valley Region, North of Minas Gerais State, Brazil

Observation made inside the caves point toward a sequence of evolutive events. Stalactites and other subaerial speleothems can be found in depths in excess of 15m below the water level at Lago Azul and Mimoso Caves. These caves have experienced a much drier period in the past. Cave cones are frequent in Mimoso Cave. They occur in a completely flooded chamber. The genesis of this type of speleothem depends on a water surface where cave rafts can develop before sinking into the cones (Hill and Forti, 1986). These evidences show that the water level has slowly risen inside the cave. This phenomenon can be explained either by a slow tectonic subsidence or the regional elevation of the water level(weter climate).

The processes of speleogenesis, breakdown, calcite deposition and the later drowning of the caves can be summarized in the following hypothetical model:

A) The major caves were formed by turbulent flow. They could have worked as large vauclusian type springs, issuing water from Bodoquena Ridge ancient scarp line, located more to the east at that time. Fig. 14-4 compares the relict inclined passage of Lago Azul cave and the active spring of Formoso River. The continuous regressive denudation of Bodoquena Ridge would have isolated some of these caves in the residual mogotes.

B) With the normal lowering of the water table, the caves would become dry. Breakdown would occur together with subaerial speleothem deposition.

C) The present stage of subsidence or water table rise would then take place. The water would invade the caves. Breakdown processes would be attenuated. Subaqueous speleothems would start to precipitate. The drowning of the karst is likely to have initiated at least 13000 years ago, due to the existence of fossilized remains of Pleistocene mammals under 15m of water at Lago Azul cave.

14.6 Other Subtropical Karst Areas of Brazil

In the eastern part of Brazil, there are some typical subtropical karst landforms at Minas Gerais state, such as the Peruacu River Valley region at its north, and the Lagoa Santa region at its central south. Tower karst, doline and microform are all well developed (Fig. 14-5).

References

Alvarenya, C. J. S., 1988. Turbiditos e a glaciacao do final do Proterozoico Superior no Cinturao Paraguai, Mato Grosso. Rev. Bras. Geoc. 18(3):323–327.

Auler, A., 1991. Mergulhando nas aguas cristalinas do Mato Grosso do Sul. O Carste 3(8):47–49.

Auler. A., 1992. Expedicao franco-brasileira Bonito 92. O Carste 4(12): 81–87.

Boggiani, P. C., 1990. Ambientes de sedimentacao do Grupo Corumba na regiao central da Serra da Bodoquena, Mato Grosso do Sul, Msc Thesis, Instituto de Geociencias, Universidade de Sao Paulo. p. 91.

Cattanio, M. B., H. C. Kohler, A. O. Alcantara, J. G. N. Rubelo and W. D. Lima, 1991. Os sedimentos do polje do Sucuri na regiao carstica de Bonite / Mato Grosso do Sul. Proceedings Third Congress of ABEQUA, Abstracts. p. 72–73.

Fairchild, T. R., 1978. Evidencias paleontologicas de uma possivel idade "ediacariana" ou cambriana inferior, para parte do Grupo Crumba(Mato Grosso do Sul). Proceeding of Congress, 30(1); p. 181.

Hill, C. A. and P. Forti, 1986. Cave minerals of the world. National Speleological Society, USA.

King, L. C., 1956. A geomorfologia do Brasil Oriental. Rev, Bras, Geod. 18(2): 147–265.

Lino, C. F., I. Karmann, J. Cortesao, N. M. Godoy and P. C. Boggiani, 1984. Projeto Grutas de Bonito. Unpublished report. p. 212.

Santanna Neto, J. L., 1989. Algumas consideracoes sobre a dinamica Pantanal Matogrossense. Bol. Paulista de Geog. 67, 75–88. da porcao sudeste.

Sbe, 1990. Cadastro nacional das cavidades naturais, Brazilian Speleological Society. p. 222.

Tarifa, J. R., 1986. O sistema climatic do Pantanal, da compreensao do sistema a definicao prioridades de pesquisa climatologica, Proceedings 1 Simposio sobre Recursos Naturais e Socio -Economicos do Pantanal. p. 9–27.

Turcq, B. et al., 1987. Alguns terracos fluviais do Sudeste e do Centro-Oeste brasileiro datados pelo radiocarbono: possiveis significados paleoclimaticos. Proceedings 1 Congress of Abequa. p. 379–392.

Zaine, M.F. and T.R. Fairchild, 1987, Novas consideracoes sobre os fosseis da Formacao Tamego, Grupo Corumba, SW do Brasil. Proceedings of Brazilian Paleontological Congress. 10:797–807.

Global Karst Correlation
Edited by Yuan Daoxian and Liu Zaihua
Science Press and VSP BV, 1998

Chapter 15 High Resolution Records of Climatic Variations and Solar Forcing from the Luminescence of Speleothem in Duhlata Cave, Bosnek, Bulgaria, Cold Water Cave, Iowa, USA and Rats Nest Cave, Calgary, Canada

Y.Y.Shopov[1], D.C.Ford[2], C.Yonge[3], W.MacDonald[3], L.Georgiev[1] M.Sanambria[1], V.Dermendjiev[4], Al.Benderev[6], G.Buyukliev[4], S.Georgiev[5], M. Delchev[5], M.Sirakova[5]

[1] *Faculty of physics, Sofia University, Sofia* 1126, *Bulgaria*
[2] *Geography Dept., McMaster Univ., Hamilton, Ont., L8S 1K4, Canada*
[3] *Dept. of Physics, University of Calgary, Calgary, T2N 1N4, Canada*
[4] *Institute of Astronomy & NAO, Bulg. Academy of Sci., Sofia, Bulgaria*
[5] *Institute of Soil Science, Bulg. Agric. Academy, Sofia, Bulgaria*
[6] *Institute of Geology, Bulg. Academy of Sci., Sofia* 1000, *Bulgaria*

15.1 Introduction

Many calcite cave speleothems (stalactites, stalagmites and flowstones) display luminescence when irradiated with UV light. In 1954 it was suggested that much of this luminescence is produced by organic substances (Gilson et al., 1954). The presence and incorporation of the organic substances in the calcite have since been demonstrated experimentally (Lauritzen et al, 1986). With Laser Luminescence Micro Zonal Analysis technique (LLMZA)-(Shopov, 1987; Shopov et al., 1988; Shopov et al., 1991) samples from Bulgaria have been shown to exhibit cyclic variations in luminescence (Shopov et al., 1988; Shopov et al., 1991) which in many cases are annual. Examples of 11-, 22-year and longer solar cycles were suggested. Here we report results for a set of North American samples, collected along a mid-latitude transect across the continent. Their stable isotope profiles (O and C) were also established for paleo-environmental information (Schwarcz, 1986).

The organic luminescing substances in speleothems (White & Brennan, 1989) are calcium salts of humic and fulvic acids, plus small proportion of low-molecular weight organic esters (Y.Shopov, M.Williams-in preparation). Other inorganic sources of luminescence in speleothems are known to include Mn, P, Pb, U and REE, etc. (Shopov, 1987), and these activators are rare in conventional vadose zone cave deposits such as those discussed below, but become predominant in hydrothermal calcites, etc. (Shopov, 1987). The organics derive from soils above the cave (Shopov & Dermendjiev, 1991), where they are released (i) by roots of living plants, and (ii) by decomposition of dead matter. Root release is modulated by visible solar irradiation (SI) via photosynthesis, while rates of decomposition depend exponentially upon soil temperatures (Kononova, 1966) that are produced mainly by infrared solar irradiation (Veklich, 1987; Malinin and Burenin, 1987; Alisov and Poltaraus, 1962; Chromov, 1964), for grassland or bare soil. So it is possible that variations in solar radiation may play a significant role in determining the variations of the intensity of luminescence in vadose speleothems. Soil moisture supply is also important, but chiefly in determining the growth rate of the calcite. The effect of dilution by the water is eliminated by the linear dependence of the production of this organics on the soil humidity (Kononova, 1966). The amplitude of the luminescence varies in a banded pattern parallel to growth layer and is proportional to organics production in the past. There is only 25% difference between the solar irradiation of the earth surface in the observed range of the spectra at the same solar declination from the cloudiest to the clearest day (Veklich, 1987). So at resolution better than a month the luminescence signal contains mainly information about the climatic modulation (cloud and rain frequency), but at resolution less than one year the time averaging makes this influence close to the experimental error of ± 0.5 to 1% and the solar irradiation component predominates.

The experimental set-up used is presented in (Shopov, 1987). The method LLMZA and some of its applications are given in (Shopov, 1987; Shopov et al., 1988; Shopov et al., 1991; Shopov and Dermendjiev, 1991; Shopov et al., 1992; Shopov et al., 1994). The mass spectrometry U/Th dating of speleothems is given in Li et al (1989).

Here we report luminescence records(with resolution from 4 years to 6 hours) from Holocene stalagmites from US, Canada and Bulgaria. The obtained resolution(Shopov et al., 1988; Shopov et al., 1994) is 1000 to 10000 times higher than that of the paleoenvironmental records obtained with other methods from continental samples and is the highest resolution of any paleoenvironmental record so far. Luminescence records with resolution of several years can be correlated with the sunspot numbers and the atmospheric production of ^{14}C, suggesting solar modulating, while records with resolution 100 yrs and less can be correlated with global climatic signals (Shopov et al., 1994). Using annual cycles we have measured annual growth rates of the speleothem and attribute them to annual precipitation. ^{18}O and ^{13}C stable isotope ratios are being determined also, for paleotemperature and other environmental information.

15.2 Experimental Results

In the laboratory luminescence of speleothems is excited by UV light and recorded on film. The optical density of the negative (logarithm of the intensity of luminescence-lgI) is a measure of the concentration of contained organics and other foreign molecules, because calcite itself has no luminescence and is transparent to the luminescence emission (Shopov and Dermendjiev, 1991). The equipment (Shopov, 1987) comprises an UV excitation source, sample scanning mechanism, filters, an optical magnification system and a registration system. Speleothem samples are prepared as polished sections, cut normal to growth layers of the calcite, and photographed with magnification. The luminescent spectra of all samples discussed below have been analyzed to confirm that their luminescence is of organic origin(Shopov and Dermendjiev, 1991).

It is established that sections of some speleothems display annual growth bands that can be distinguished by light microscopy (Broecker and Orr, 1960; Lungershauzen, 1963) due to the optical anisotropy produced by growth hiatuses during the dry season. However, such time series tend to be very brief and discontinuing.

Attempts to measure the luminescence annual banding using long UV excitation (Baker et al., 1992) was not successful in 88% of the samples, because long UV is not able to excite the luminescence of that part of the organics, which produce the annual banding in the luminescent images(otherwise not visible). The luminescent annual banding is visible only at excitation with short UV (Shopov et al., 1988; Shopov et al., 1994). I the rest of the samples the annual bands are due to growth hiatuses in a part of year as visible from the shape of their pseudo luminescent photos (Baker et al., 1992) and are not useful to estimate the past rainfall, because of the unknown duration of the break in speleothem growth. Annual layering is apparent and continuous only in LLMZA photos of the speleothems (Shopov et al., 1988; Shopov et al., 1991). We are studying annual structure detected in samples of Holocene age from McFail's Cave, near Albany, New York and from Cold Water Cave in northeastern Iowa. Autocalibration dating determines the average annual growth using power spectral analysis of sample sections with pronounced annual bands(Shopov et al., 1991). Such dating is the most accurate means of determining the passage of time within short, well-banded sections of speleothems from temperate climate sites such as those in Shopov et al. (1994).

This method allows us to obtain a time series of luminescence of a flowstone from Duhlata cave, Bulgaria with resolution two months for the last 22000 yrs. This time series contains 110000 measurements. Here we show only the last 2000 years of this composite record (Fig. 15-1). The luminescence of stalactites from this cave represents mainly the solar irradiations and is very independent on the climate (Shopov et al., 1988; Shopov et al., 1991; Dermendjiev et al., 1990; Dermendjiev et al, 1991). Due to the dry climate the growth rate of this flowstone is very constant (Shopov et al., 1991).

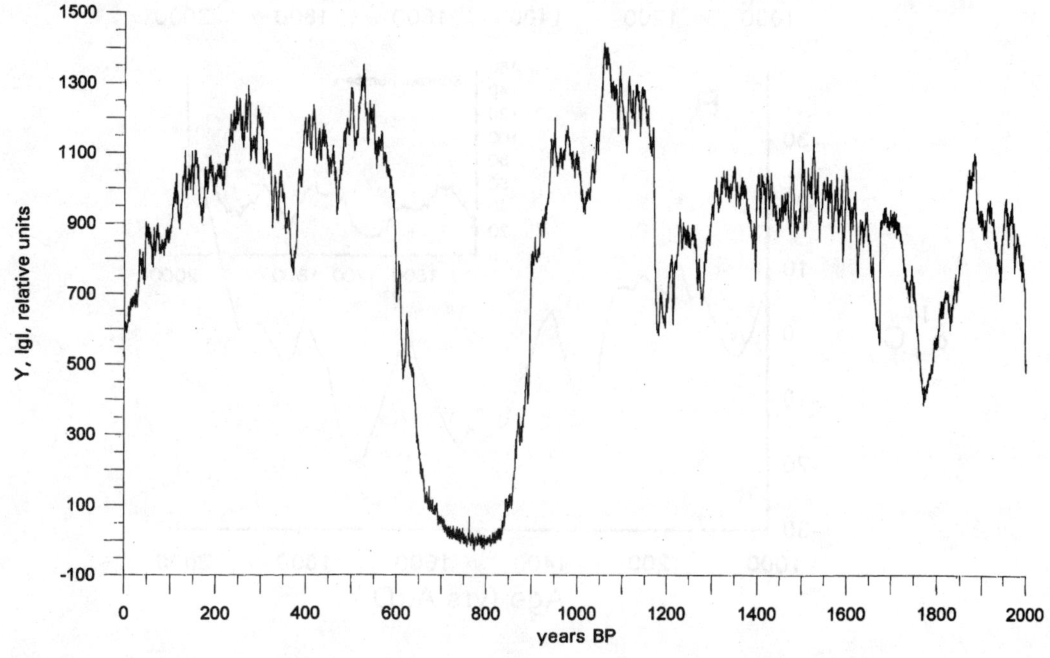

Fig. 15-1 The last 2000 yrs of a 22000 yr long LLMZA composite record of 39 scans with a resolution of 2.4 months (5 px/yr) from a flowstone in Duhlata cave, Bulgaria

The discovery of 11-year and 22-year cycles in the luminescence records of some Bulgaria speleothems (Shopov et al., 1988; Shopov et al., 1991; Shopov and Dermendjiev, 1991), leds us to inspect the North American samples for similar phenomena. These cycles are present also in the luminescence records of the samples from Cold Water Cave and McFail's Cave. The correlations of luminescent records from Duhlata Cave, Bulgaria with the inverted residual ^{14}C (Shopov et al., 1988) for the last 8000 yrs and the annual sunspot number (Alisov & Poltaraus, 1962; Dermendjiev et al., 1990; Dermendjiev et al., 1991) since 1700 AD has been demonstrated. In Fig. 15-2 the luminescence record of sample CW1 between AD 1000 and the present (resolved to 3.8 y/px), is

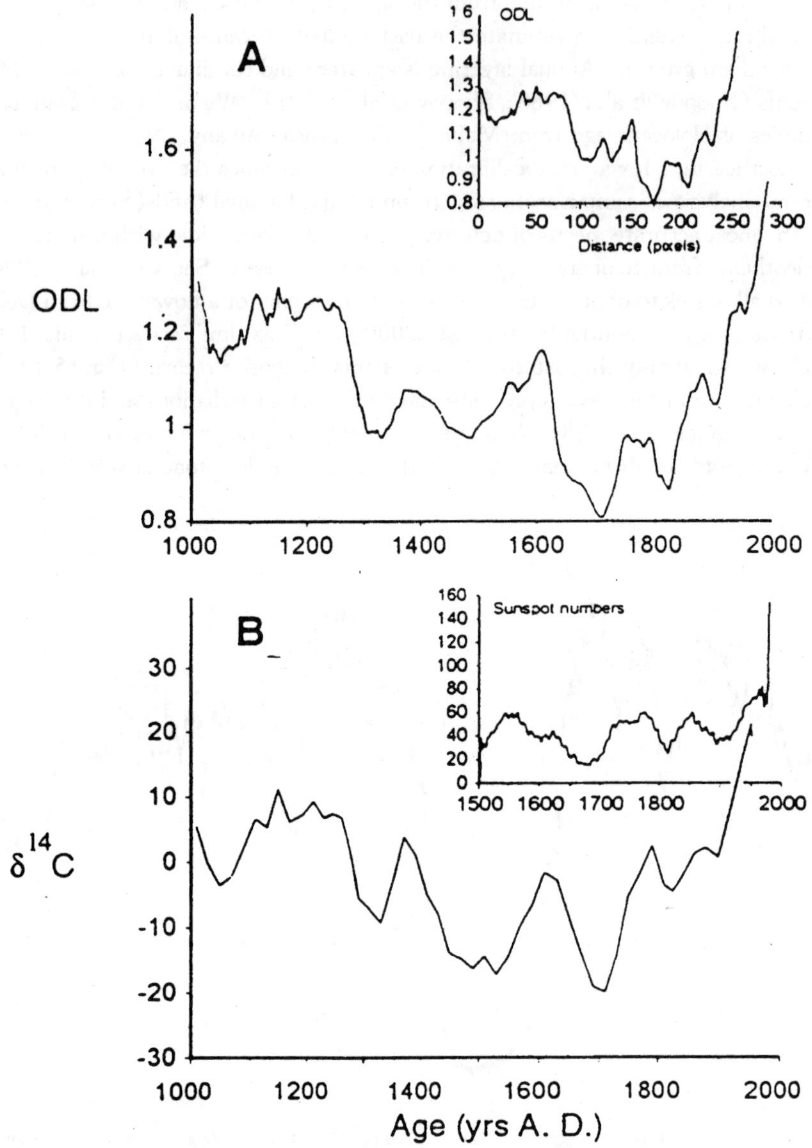

Fig. 15-2 A. Cold Water Cave; speleothem sample CW1. The luminescent record with resolution 3.78 y/px with its maxima and minima "tuned" to:-B. inverted residual ^{14}C record (with averaged resolution 20 yrs) derived from the composite 12th Radiocarbon Conference calibration record from tree rings (Stuiver, 1986). Upper inset – the original (untuned) CWl luminescent record lpx = 31.5 microns along the growth axis of the sample; Lower inset – annual sunspot numbers (Shove, 1983), (measured after 1700 A. D. and estimated from aurora frequency before 1700 A. D.) smoothed by 20 years spline average

compared to the composite calibration ^{14}C record from tree rings (Stuiver, 1986). The ^{14}C record displayed here is the inverted residual (Stuiver, 1980) with a 20-year time step. The luminescence record has been smoothed with the 5-point spline average function to find the precise positions of its maxima and minima in order to "tune" (Morner, 1973) them to the radiocarbon curve.

Such tuning reflects the fact that the true rates of calcite growth were not constant in CW1, as we have established above. The correlation coefficient between the two curves A and B is $r = 0.803$, while the original "untuned" curvefrom the upper inset of Fig. 15-2 produced $r = 0.6$. This is close to the best obtainable because C14 curve is known to contain variable experimental errors up to 10% in its amplitude (Stuiver, 1986). The best correlation obtained from two dependent solar activity indices-number and area of sunspots is 0.86 (Shove, 1983). Correlation with annual sunspot numbers known from direct observations since 1700 AD and approximated from the frequency of the auroral events between 1500 – 1700 AD (Shove, 1983) is also striking (Fig. 15-2, lower inset). A stalagmite from Rats Nest Cave, Rocky Mountains of Alberta (Yonge, 1991), demonstrates a similar though weaker, correlations between its luminescence record and residual ^{14}C record for the past millennium. Fig. 15-2 suggests that solar activity may be modulating the production of humic and fulvic acides in soils.

Sample CW1 from Cold Water Cave, Iowa is a candlestick stalagmite 16.4 cm in length, composed of clear, inclusion-free calcite. Two ^{14}C and three U series MS dates establish that growth commenced shortly before 7075 ± 295 y BP and continued to the present at an average rate of 23.2 microns/a. Autocalibration dating and independent extrapolations between MS-dated points confirm the presence of luminescence annual banding in the stalagmite.

The complete luminescent record for CW1 is given in Fig. 15-3A(1.78 y/px). A sample sequence of 23 years before 1000 AD are resolved to 2.5 day/px in Fig. 15-3B; the annual cycles are

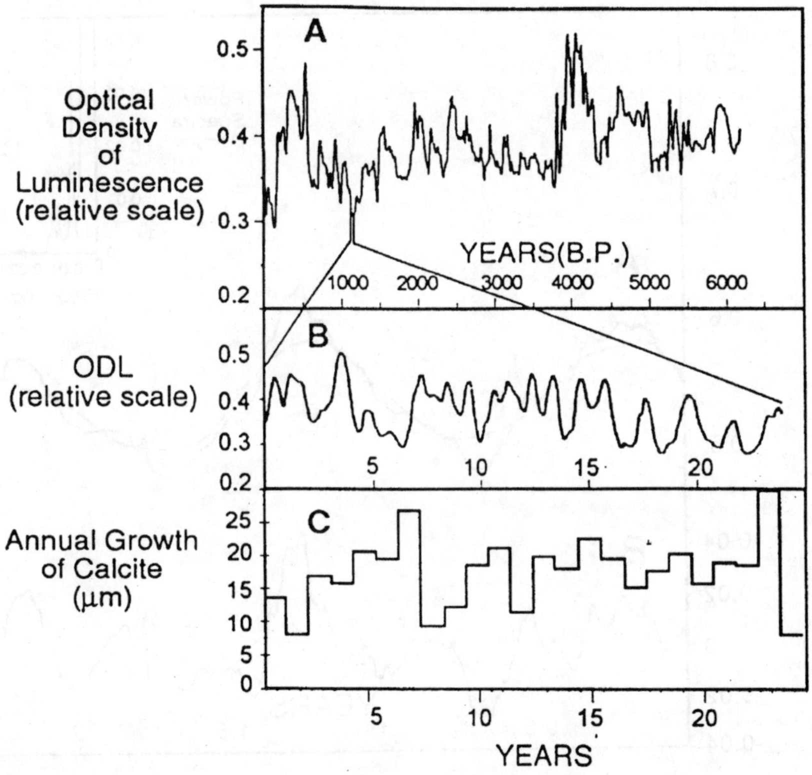

Fig. 15-3 Cold Water Cave; sample CW1. A. The luminescent record of the whole cross section; B. a 23 year part of it at a resolution of 2.5 d/px; C. Annual growth rates derived from 15-3B

clearly apparent. The measured distances between the annual maxima of Fig. 15-3B(i. e. the net growth rates of the calcite after smoothing the time series with a 5-point spline average) are presented in Fig. 15-3C. It is seen that annual accumulations of calcite at this Iowa site vary by a factor of three or more. Annual variations in the amount of groundwater recharge can be as large. Inter-annual variations in amounts of speleothems growth may be attributed chiefly to the variations in vadose zone recharge(as first suggested by (Lungershauzen, 1963) from a light microscope study), modified by the variations in the supersaturation of $CaCO_3$ in the dripping water. Fig. 15-3C is in good part a proxy measure of variations of recharge and strength of growing season in the soil above Cold Water Cave before one thousand years ago. With calibration between similar measured annual growth during the modern era and measured temperature, precipitation, etc. at nearby weather recording stations there is the potential to approximate the amounts of annual recharge/runoff during the Holocene and earlier periods.

Fig. 15-4A presents the luminescence time series of 3600 px for a span of just 2.5 yrs before 1000 y B.P. in sample CW1. Magnification is x300, yielding a mean resolution of six hours (4px/day). At this resolution each measurement (pixel) is estimated to integrate information from approximately 10^9 organic molecules. In Fig. 15-4B the time series has been smoothed by 300 px (75 days) and the smoothed curve was subtracted from the original one. The residual curve, represents only seasonal and shorter term variations in the luminescence. The power spectrum of the unmodified series (Fig. 15-4, inset) displays annual and unresolved seasonal cycles plus weaker peaks at 41, 27,23, 21 and 13.5 days. Presence of cycles as brief as 13.5 days demonstrates that significant

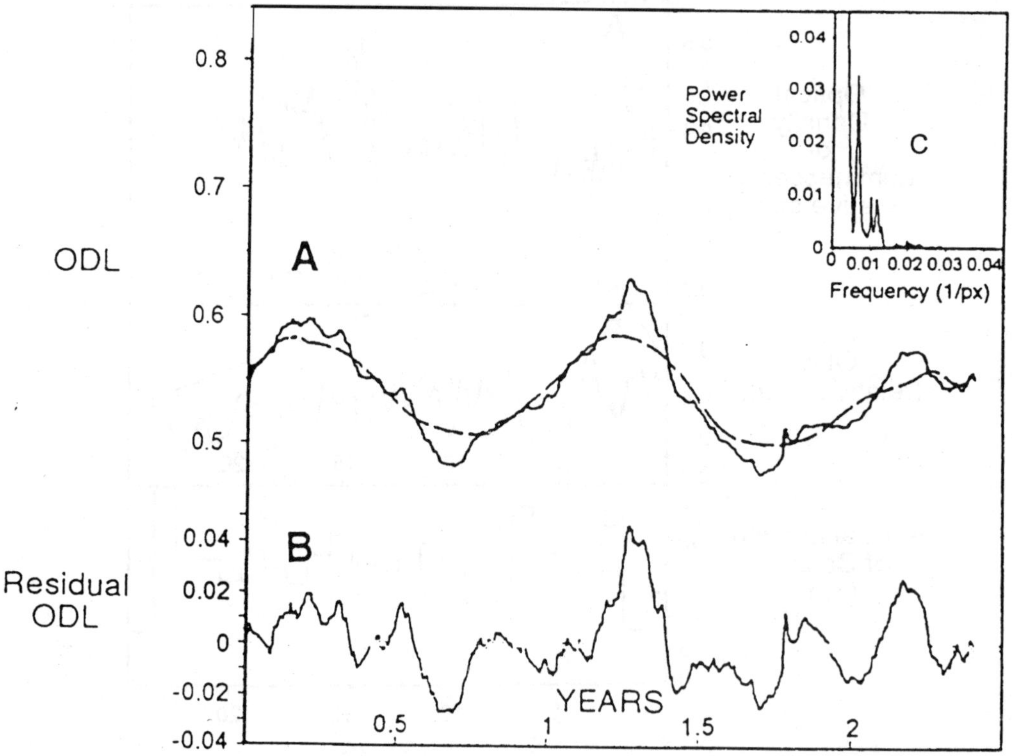

Fig. 15-4 Cold Water Cave CW1. A. a segment of 2.4 years, resolution 6 hours, magnification ×300 and its smoothed by 300 px curve, B the difference between both, presenting the seasonal variations, C. Power spectra of the original curve A

physical and chemical paleo-environmental variations in the soil water sources or along the feed water channel that occurred over periods no longer than one week can now be measured in some speleothems.

A recent communication on a "high-resolution" paleoclimatic record of Holocene speleothem from Cold Water Cave, Iowa (Doral et al., 1992) reported resolution of 100 yrs for stable isotopes and 25 yrs is claimed for such data in a South African speleothem (Talma, 1989). Our results from Cold Water Cave have 100000 times greater resolution.

We prepared a 66000-data-point (pixels) composite record covering the last 1450 ± 100 yrs with an average resolution of 8 days (45.5 px/yr) from Rats Nest Cave, Alberta, Canada(Fig. 15-5). It has been made by appending of 39 separate luminescence scans, so the general trends of the graph may be distorted by this procedure. This graph presents mostly the local climate(cloud frequency). Small parts of it has been studied by periodogram analysis (Jenkins & Watts, 1969) for presence of chaotic signal together with the periodic variability. The presence of strong chaotic behavior of the data from several weeks to several months has been demonstrated. The growth rate of this speleothem is so variable, that it is very difficult to establish a time scale of the record. The chaotic behavior may be due to the variable growth rate, local climatic peculiarities or to the presence of some trees above the cave, complicating the insolation picture by their shadows, radiation absorption etc. Further research is needed to clear the nature and significance of this chaotic signal, first detected in speleothem records.

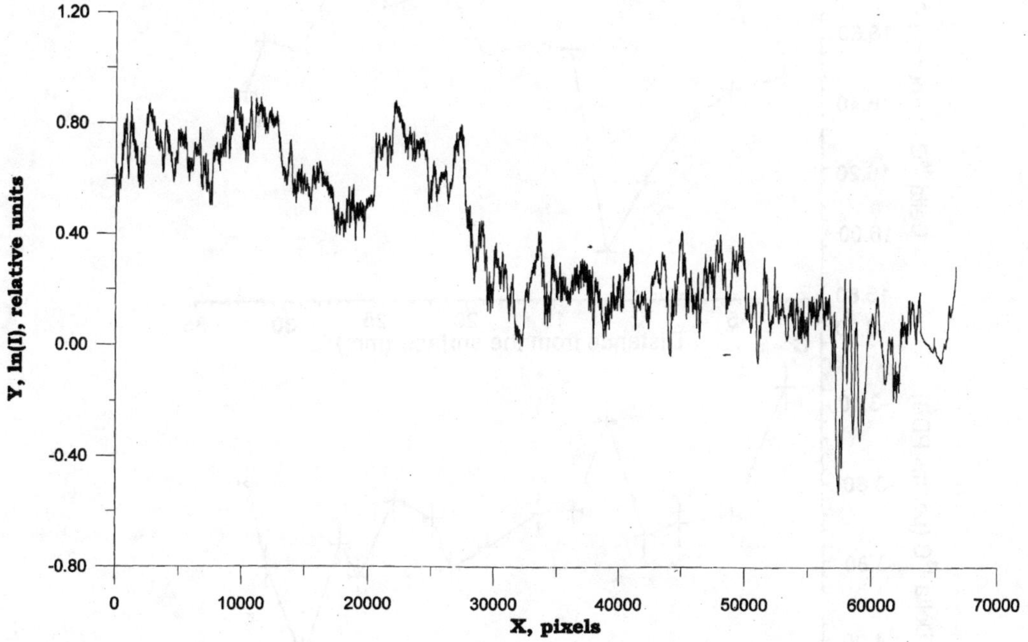

Fig. 15-5 A 66000-data-point (pixels) composite record covering the last 1450 years with an averaged resolution of 8 days (45.5 px/yr). Sample from Rats Nest cave, Alberta, Canada

A luminescent record covering the last 1400 yrs with an averaged resolution of 1.0 yr from Rats Nest Cave, Alberta, Canada is presented on (Fig. 15-6a). The stable isotope records from the same speleothem have resolution of 100 – 150 yrs, so it is hard to compare them with the luminescent one. It seems that the ^{18}O is in right correlation with the luminescence, while ^{13}C is in anticorrelation with them before 500 gears B. P. and in right correlation after. Such right correlation means, that the biological activity (respiration, etc.) prevails the CO_2 emission from soil decomposition. It may suggest, that a process of restoring of the forest appeared in the cave region at 500 years B.P.

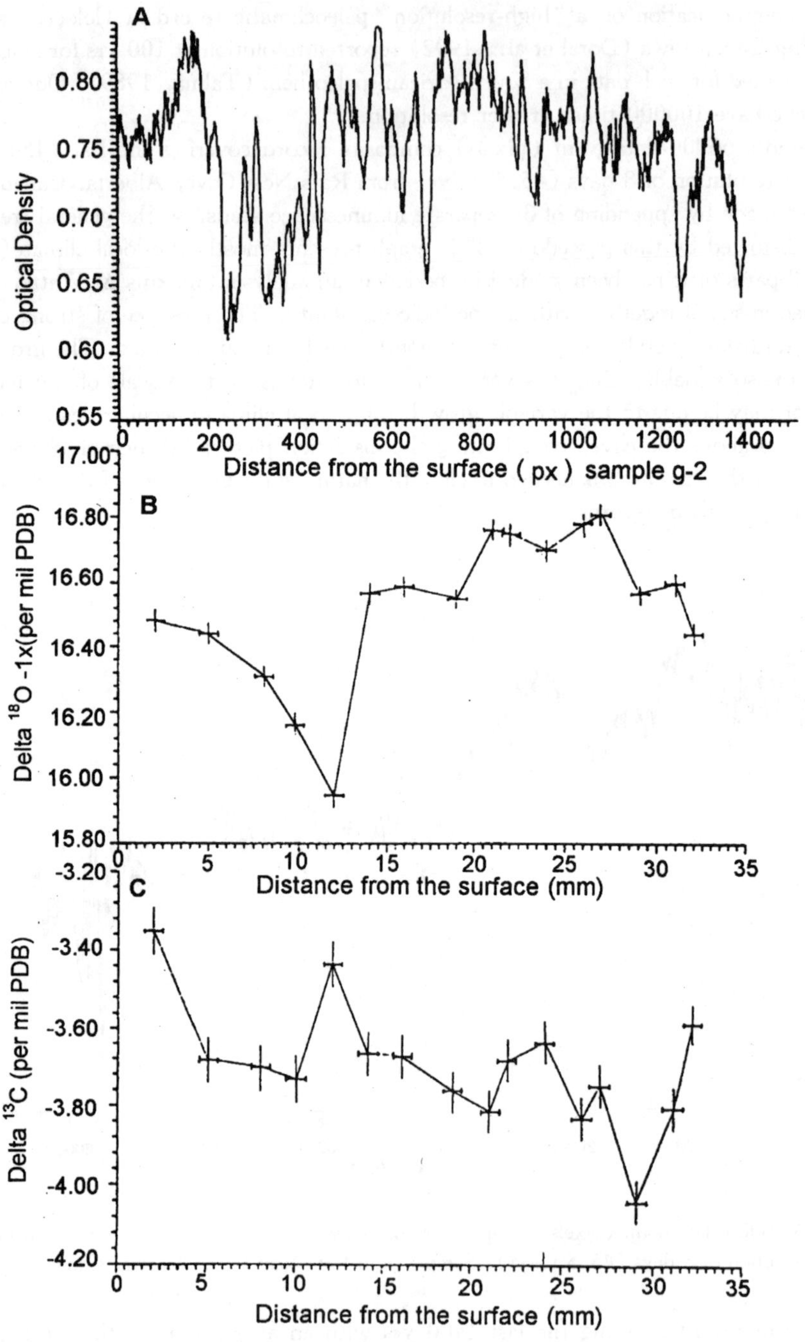

Fig. 15-6 A – A luminescent record covering the last 1400 years with an averaged resolution of 1.0 year/px (the x-axis may be read also in years B.P.) from Rats Nest cave, Alberta, Canada; B – an ^{18}O record and C – a ^{13}C record from the same sample

15.3 Solar Irradiation and Climatic Cycles from Speleothem

The strong variability of the growth rate of most speleothem obstruct their application for study of the climatic and solar cycles. The Duhlata speleothem is the only one exhibiting very stable growth rate and therefore applicable for this purpose. This site is rather unique also because speleothems here grew continuously in the last 45000 yrs (Fig. 15-7), even during the glaciation 35000 yrs ago, when the surface over the cave was completely frozen. The stable isotope study of this speleothem (^{13}C and ^{18}O) suggests, that there was no any organic carbon in the speleothem layers of this age (positive value of ^{13}C). There are no published data on other continuously growing speleothems in this time range.

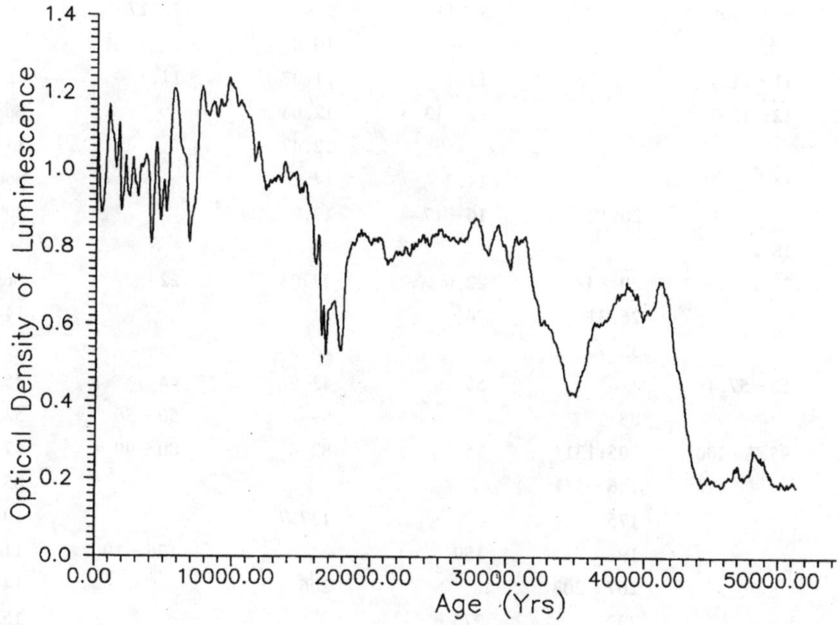

Fig. 15-7 A luminescent record covering the last 52000 years with an average resolution 15 years from a flowstone in Duhlata cave, Bulgaria

Using LLMZA time series for the last 22000 yrs with a resolution 4-5 pixels/year from Duhlata we studied some of the statistical properties of the 11-year solar cycle during 28 prolonged minima (of Maunder type) and 21 prolonged maxima (Dermendjiev et al., 1990; Dermendjiev and Shopov, 1992). It has been demonstrated, that this cycle is shorter during the prolonged minima and longer during the prolonged maxima.

A small part of this time series resolved to 125 px/yr (3 days), shown in Fig. 15-8, exhibits cycles of 2, 1 and 0, 5 yrs (Shopov et al., 1988; Shopov et al., 1989).

We used power spectra and periodogram analyses (Jenkins and Watts, 1969) to determine the cycles presented in our time series from Duhlata cave (Tables 15-1, 15-2).

The spectra in Fig. 15-9. B show that during 720 yrs (length of the used time series) the annual growth rate of the speleothem was constant.

Tab.15-1 Cycles of the solar activity (in years)

Authors	Berger	Damon Sonett	Shopov et al.	Cini et al.	Veklich	Pagava
year	(1990)	(1991)	(1989)	(1988)	(1987)	(1983)
age[BP]	3 – 303	1 – 9700	1 – 35000	70 – 1770	different	80 – 37
period	300	970 –	35000	1700yrs	< 10000yrs	43yrs
time step	12 – 1 px/yr	1 – 0.02	125 – 0.1	0.26;0.5	< 1 px/yr	1px/yr
method	Wolf index	14 – C	LLMZA	TL	1am. thick.	14-C
material	Sunspots	trees	flowst.	sea core	plant fos.	wine
cycle			1 yr	Cini 1988	1.5 yrs	
(yrs)	2.14 – 2.16		2 yrs	7.8	2;3;4;5 – 6	
	8.3 – 8.5		8.8	8.8	8.3	
	9.9 – 10		9 – 11	9.9	7 – 17	
				10.8		
	11 – 11.1		11.1	11.07	11.1	11.1
	12 – 12.2		12 – 13	12.06		Suess(1980)
				12.47		14-C. trees
	14		14.2	14.2		Sonett 1984
		20.12	16 – 17	17.7		8000 yrs BP
	18.2					
	22.2	20.83	22.0	22.03	22	Stuiver1989
		26.31	24			14-C, trees
		32.7		28.5	35	
	50 – 57.4		55	43.5	44	45
		88		59	50 – 56	52, 57
	95.7 – 100	105;131	95	82.6	80 – 90	67
		146 – 151				85
		175		137.7		104 – 110
		192	180		176 – 190	114;122 – 134
		207 – 208		206		141;142 – 155
		232	275			155;177 – 183
		299	310		~300	196 – 200;202
		353			cini1990	221;253;218
		385	390	170 – 1974	~400	279;286;290
		427;440	425			308
		504;512	550			369
		649	585		~600	399; 400
		733;805				420; 433;452
		840				487;498
		909;955	930		~900	652
			1170		1500	717;740
		2241 – 72	1180			890
		2385	2340		2200	930;955;962
		4747	3350		2700	1183 – 1486
					3000	2079
					5000 – 7000	2400

Tab. 15-2 Cycles of solar activity and insolation (in years)

Authors	Berger	Shopov
age B.P.	3 – 303	5 – 42000
period	300 yrs	420000 yrs
time step	0.083 yr	15, 0.5 yrs
method	Wolf index	LLMZA
material	Sunspots	flowstone
location	sun	Bulgaria
cycle		1 yr
(yrs)	2.14 – 2.16	2 yrs
	8.3 – 8.5	8.8
	9.9 – 10	9 – 11
	11 – 11.1	11.1
	12 – 12.2	12 – 13
	14	14.2
	22.2	22.0
		24
		47.17
		48.75
	50 – 57.4	54.27
		91;94
	95.7 – 100	95.2;97.3
		99.4;101
		106;110.1
		113.7;127
		141;152.2
		155;167.5
		207
		302;329
		399;413
		625;672
		776
		900
		1000
		1050
		1220
		1960
		2380
		5000
		16900

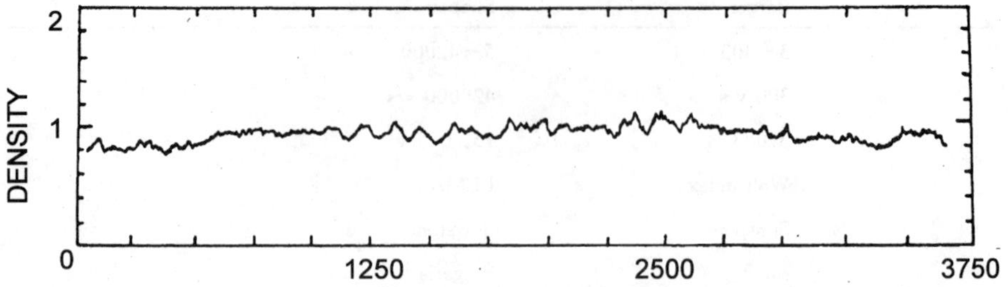

Fig. 15-8 LLMZA curve of the seasonal climatic variations with a resolution 3 days (125 px/yr) from Duhlata cave (Shopov et al, 1988)

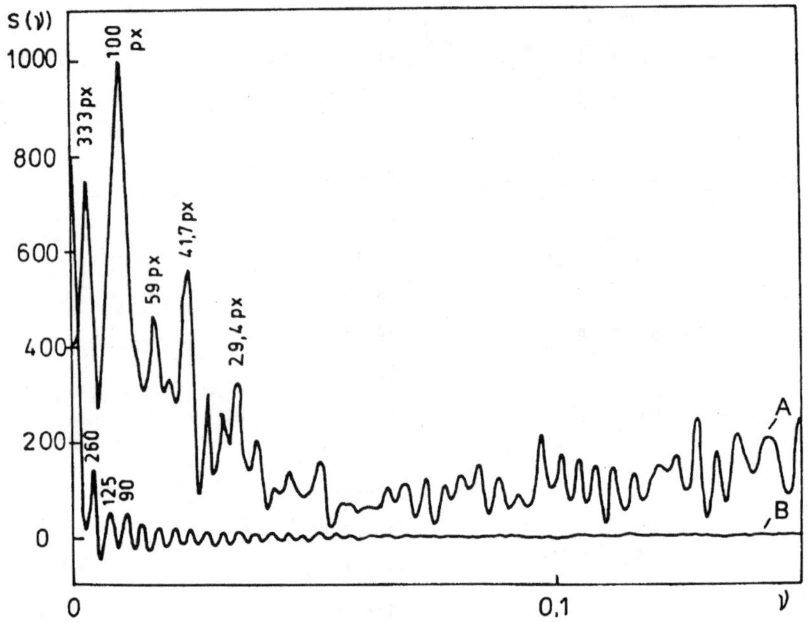

Fig. 15-9 A-Power spectra of the annual sunspot numbers from the last 300 years by (Ravin, 1989); B-High-frequency filtered spectra of LLMZA time series from Duhlata cave with a resolution 2.4 months (5 px/yr) for 720 yrs

The splitting of the 11-annual SA peak, observed in Fig. 15-9. B, is due to the availability of binary, singular, three-and four-cyclic 11-yrs cycles with different length (Veklich, 1987). It has the same form and position of the peaks as the power spectrum (Ravin, 1989) of the sunspot numbers (Fig. 15-9. A).

Power spectra from Fig. 15-9, 15-10 demonstrate possibilities of the time series of luminescent zonality for research of long and short time cyclisity of the solar insolation and activity. The spectrum from Fig. 15-10. a, b was obtained from time series with duration 35000 yrs and resolution 9.34 yrs/px from Duhlata cave. It shows convincingly the reality of cyclisity with periods of 55, 95, 180, 275, 390, 550, 930, 1170, 2340 and 3350 yrs. For existence of some of them there are data in time series of other indirect indices too, especially ^{14}C inverted production (Stuiver and Quay, 1980).

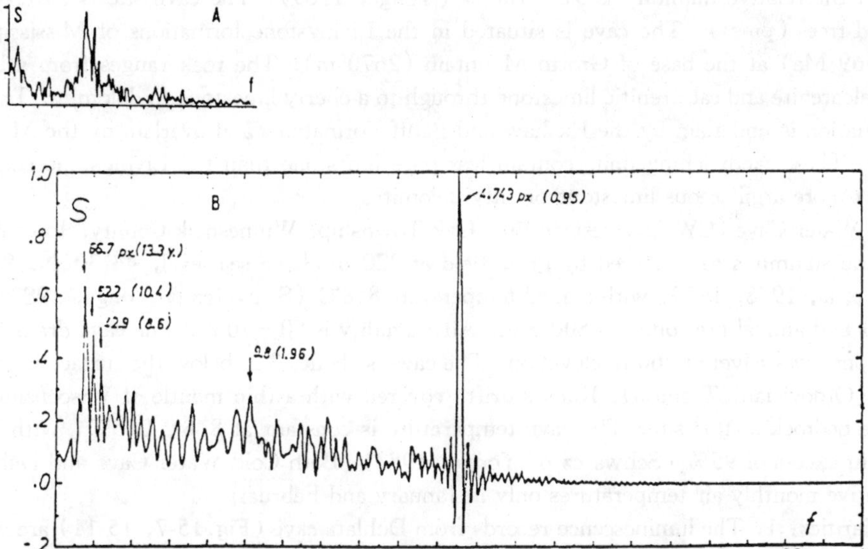

Fig. 15-10 High-frequency filtered (a) power spectrum (b) of from a 35000 years record in Duhlata with a resolution 9.34 years

15.4 Correlation of Luminescence Records from Speleothems at 40° – 50° Northern Latitude

In order to interpret obtained correlations properly we give some basic climatic and geologic data for the studied sites:

1. Duhlata Cave (18 km long) is situated in Middle-Triassic limestones at the south slope in the base of Vitosha Mts. (2200 m high) at 916 – 973 m elevation, 23° E, 42°30'N. The surface above the cave is covered by grass on thin soil layer (less than 40 cm). There are almost no any bushes or trees over the cave. The annual amplitude of the soil temperatures exceeds 70℃. The average annual temperature of the region is 8.1℃ and the annual precipitation is 685 mm. Here the air and the soil humidity is in distinct anticorrelation with the temperature, ranging from 55% in August to 85% in January. So, during the summer all plants die and speleothem growth rate remains constant in the frames of ± 5%. It is a local climatic peculiarity, missing at the other studied sites.

Mineralogy of Duhlata Cave is quite interesting. It is presented by the mineral associations of calcite-aragonite-huntite-dolomite-magnesite and aragonite-hydromagnesite plus saponite (only cave occurrence in the world) (Filipov, 1982, 1983). Magnesium in this minerals is derived from the magnesium limestone and dolomite bedrock. The solution has been enriched to Mg by the previous precipitation of aragonite or calcite. Dolomite and magnesite are products of disintegration of the metastable huntite. The luminescence of one calcite-aragonite speleothem is suggesting trace amounts of magursilite in it (Shopov, 1989). Elongated gypsum crystal up to 10 cm long has been determined by Shopov in another cave in the region.

Rats Nest Cave (RNC), 4 km long, is situated on a SW slope in Bow valley, Kananaskis county near Calgary, Alberta at 1500 m elevation, 51°N(Yonge, 1991). The averaged air annual temperature is 2.8℃ and the annual precipitation is 470 mm. There are 220 days frost, 74 days rain and 75 of snow annually. The air humidity is around 70%. In the cave air temperature is 5.0 ±

0.1℃ and the relative humidity is 97 – 100% (Yonge, 1989). The cave site is covered by rare bushes and trees (pines). The cave is situated in the Livingstone formations of Mississippian age (320 to 369 Ma) at the base of Grotto Mountain (2670 m). The rock ranges from a light grey skeletal calcarenite and calcarenitic limestone through to a cherty limestone to dolomite. The Livingstone formation is underlain by the Exshaw and Banff Formations and overlain by the Mount Head formation. These sandwiching units contain less pure limestone than the Livingstone composed as they are of more argillaceous limestone or silty dolomites.

Cold Water Cave (CWC), western Burr Oak Township, Winnesheik County, Iowa is situated in an upland summit area, covered by grass field at 320 m above sea level, 43°30'N, 91°50' W (Harmon et al, 1978, 1979) with annual temperature 8.8℃ (Schwarcz & Yonge, 1983; Metodiev, 1983) and annual precipitation 800 mm. Air humidity is 60 – 70%. The cave drains to deeply incised upper Iowa River at 260 m elevation. The cave is about 23 m below the surface in the Galena Dolomite (Ordovician, Trenton). Kansas drift, covered with a thin mantle of Wisconsinian loess, overlie the bedrock at this site. The cave temperature is constant at 8.8 ± 0.5℃, with a relative humidity in excess of 95% (Schwarcz & Yonge, 1983). Both Cold Water Cave and Duhlata sites have negative monthly air temperatures only in January and February.

Similarities: 1. The luminescence records from Duhlata cave (Fig.15-7, 15-11) are very similar to the Cold Water Cave CW1 record (Fig.15-2) and both exhibit excellent correlation with the solar luminosity records derived from sunspot numbers (Fig. 15-2, lower inset and Fig. 15-11, down) and from 14-c variations (Fig.15-2, B). This suggests, that both sites are solar irradiation sensitive and there are no significant climatic influence (perturbation) on the intensity of luminescence in this speleothems at a resolution 2 months or less. The reason for this is the lack of forest and bushes over the cave sites and the favourable exposition. 2. Stable isotope studies (Deuterium) of a Cold Water Cave speleothem growing from 25000 – 5000 yrs BP (Harmon et al, 1979) suggest that the temperature in the cave was 5℃ lower 17000 ± 2000 yrs BP. Luminescence records from Duhlata (Fig.15-7) also suggest a very cold period at this time. There are no speleothems of this age in Rats Nest Cave, because the region was completely glaciated at this time.

Differences:

1. The biggest difference between the Duhlata record and both CWC and RNC is the very constant growth rate of speleothems from Duhlata, in opposite to the variable growth rate of CWC and RNC. It is a result of the distinct anticorrelation of the air and soil humidity and the temperature at Duhlata site. The variable growth rate in CWC and RNC seems to follow the annual rainfall variations and can be used to estimate them (Shopov et al., 1994).

2. RNC records (Figs. 15-5, 15-6) do not follow strictly the solar irradiation curves as CWC and Duhlata records do. One of the reason is the presence of forest and bushes over the cave, which are complicating the local irradiation picture and decreasing the range of annual variations of the soil temperature. The second possible reason is that the cave site is 9° northern than the other sites, resulting in lower solar insolation, whose variations are overcame by the climatic variations. The last possible reason is that the site is frosted 220 days and have far shorter vegetation than the other sites.

15.5 Hydrogeology and Denudation of Bosnek Karst Region, Bulgaria

Duhlata cave is located in Bosnek karst region, Bulgaria. It is 27km^2 (Fig.15-12), consisting of : – Anisian dark grey limestones and dolomites, up to 400m thick; – Ladinian limestones and argillites up to 200m thick; – late Triassic grey dolomites and limestones up to 300 m. Duhlata cave is a labyrinth cave, with 7 levels and 2 independent rivers, one of which with 7 tributary rivers.

The cave is developed up to 12 meters under the local surface erosion basis by the "big cave river" (33.6 – 50 l/sec.). This river comes to the surface 50 – 100 m far from the end (siphon) of the cave with discharge of 97 – 300 l/sec (Shopov and Geogiev, 1987). Total length of the cave is 18000 m and denivellation-60 m. The average annual air temperature at the cave site is 8.4 – 8.1℃ and annual precipitation of 685 mm. The temperature in the cave lakes is 9.6 ± 0.1℃.

The karst denudation rate for the region has been estimated (Shopov & Geogiev, 1987) to be

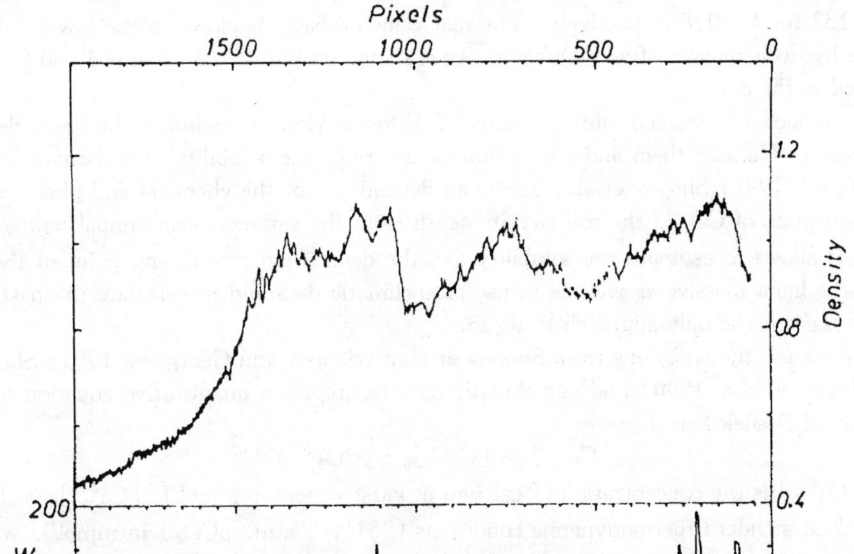

Fig. 15-11 Upper-A luminescent record covering the last 300 years with an averaged resolution 2 months from the same as Fig. 15-7 flowstone from Duhlata cave, Bulgaria; Middle-annual sunspot numbers (Shopov, 1983); Down annual sunspot numbers smoothed by 20 years spline average, presenting the solar luminosity variations

equal to 1055 t limestone/yr or 39.1 t/km^2 per year. This estimation is based on chemical analysis and the discharge of 2 main karst springs using Krubers equation. This estimation is probably quite underestimated, because : – it is based on measurements of only 2 springs, one of which just a single measurements at low waters(3.4 times less than the maximal discharge); a significant part of the waters may live in the region underground (as pointed by the water balance). The biggest spring far from the cave (point 8, Fig. 15-12) contains 212 mg/l carbonates (Mg + Ca) and the small one recharging the cave rivers (point 6, Fig. 15-12) – 241 mg/l. These concentrations are suggesting denudation rates (calculated from eq. 6, bellow) of 145 and 165 t/km^2 per year for $k = 1$, or 116 and 132 for $k = 0.8$ respectively. The real value probably is closer to the lower value.

The hydrochemical profile of Duhlata cave is shown on Fig. 15-13. Points 4 and 5 (Fig. 15-13) are located in the cave.

We conducted a detailed climatic study of Vitosha Mts. to estimate the karst denudation in Bosnek region. We used them and a quantitative theory of the solubility of carbonate rocks (Shopov and Georgiev, 1991; Shopov et al., 1989) in dependence of the chemical and phase composition, the concentration of CO_2 in the soil air, its depth from the surface, mean annual temperature or its altitude. It allows to estimate the solubility and the denudation rate in any point of the surface or depth of the karst massive as well as to use paleoclimatic data and to calculate the past denudation rates. So far it is the only approach to do so.

Here we use the equations from Shopov et al., (Shopov and Georgiev, 1991; Shopov et al., 1989; Shopov et al., 1990) and our climatic data to prepare a quantitative equation for the karst denudation of Bosnek karst:

$$[Ca^{2+}] = [Ca^{2+}]_0 \cdot pCO_2{}^{1/3} e^{-0.02t} \quad (1)$$

where, $[Ca^{2+}]$ is the concentration of calcium in karst waters in mmol/l, $[Ca^{2+}]_0$ is the solubility of the rock at standard thermodynamic conditions (25℃, 1 atm. pCO_2) in mmol/l, which had to be measured experimentally, pCO_2 is the partial pressure of CO_2 in the rock, t is the temperature in ℃.

The temperature dependence from the elevation has been determined by a climatic study of all temperature records from the meteorological stations 30 km around. This dependence is linear with scattering of less than 3% and have the form:

$$t = 13.4 - 0.0055H(℃) \quad (2)$$

where H is the elevation of the region. So for Bosnek region the equation (1) has form:

$$[Ca^{2+}] = 0.756 \times [Ca^{2+}]_0 \times [pCO_2]^{1/3} e^{0.00011H} \quad (3)$$

The partial pressure of CO_2 depends on the hydrostatic pressure Ph in the rock, because the cracks in the rock are normally filled by water

$$pCO_2 = P \times XCO_2 = (1 + Ph) \times XCO_2 = (1 + d/10) \times XCO_2 \quad (4)$$

where XCO_2-is the molar part of CO_2 in the soil (rock) air, d is the depth from the surface in m.

By combining equation (3) and (4) we obtain:

$$[Ca^{2+}] = 0.756 \times [Ca^{2+}]_0 \times (1 + d/10)^{1/3} \times XCO_2{}^{1/3} \times e^{0.00011H} \quad (5)$$

Equation (5) allows to calculate the solubility of the rock in any point of the massive for any depth. XCO_2 had to be measured experimentally. It is suggesting, that the solubility of the rock can vary up to 3.5 times in dependence of the hydrostatic pressure (due to the depth d-from the surface).

The karst denudation rates can be calculated from the equation:

$$D = k \times R \times [Ca^{2+}] \times (t/km^2 \text{ per year}) \quad (6)$$

where, k is the ratio between the amount of water passed through the karst rocks and the total precipitation, $[Ca^{2+}]$ is average concentration of calcium in the karst waters, calculated from equation (5), or measured experimentally in [g/l], R is average annual precipitation in mm. k is close to 1 for Bosnek karst region.

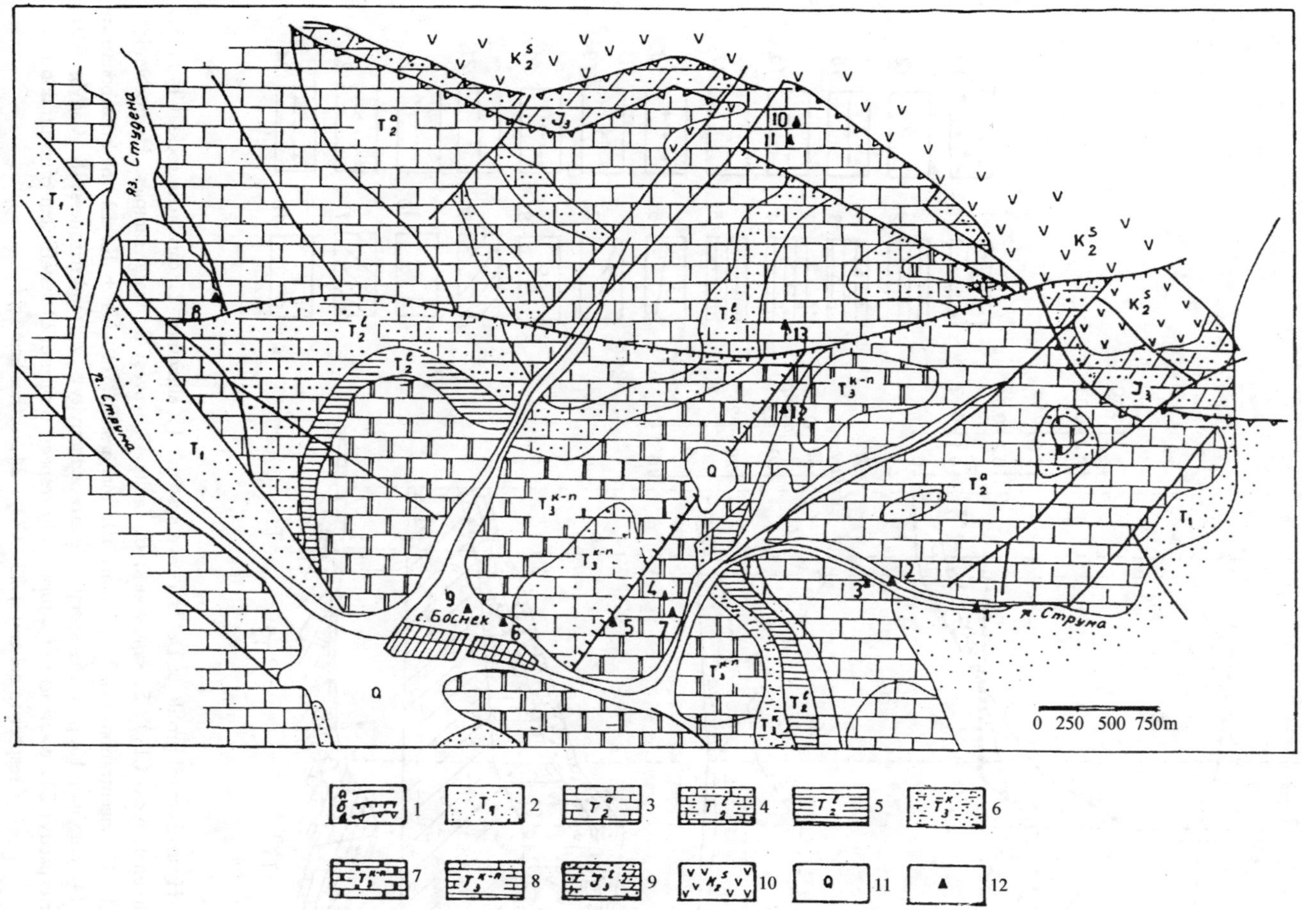

Fig. 15-12 Geological map of Bosnek karst region: -1. Fractures: a) with unclear type of movement, b) faults, c) uplift; 2-sandstones (early Triassic); 3-limestones (anisian); 4-dolomite (ladinian); 5-argillites (ladinian); 6-limestones (carnian); 7-dolomite (carnian-norian); 8-limestones (carnian-norian); 9-aleurolites and marls (tithonian); 10-vulcanite; 11-quaternary sediments; 12 sampling point: Points 4, 5 and 7 are located in Duhlata cave, point 6 is the karst spring recharging the cave rivers, point 8 is the main karst spring in Bosnek karst region

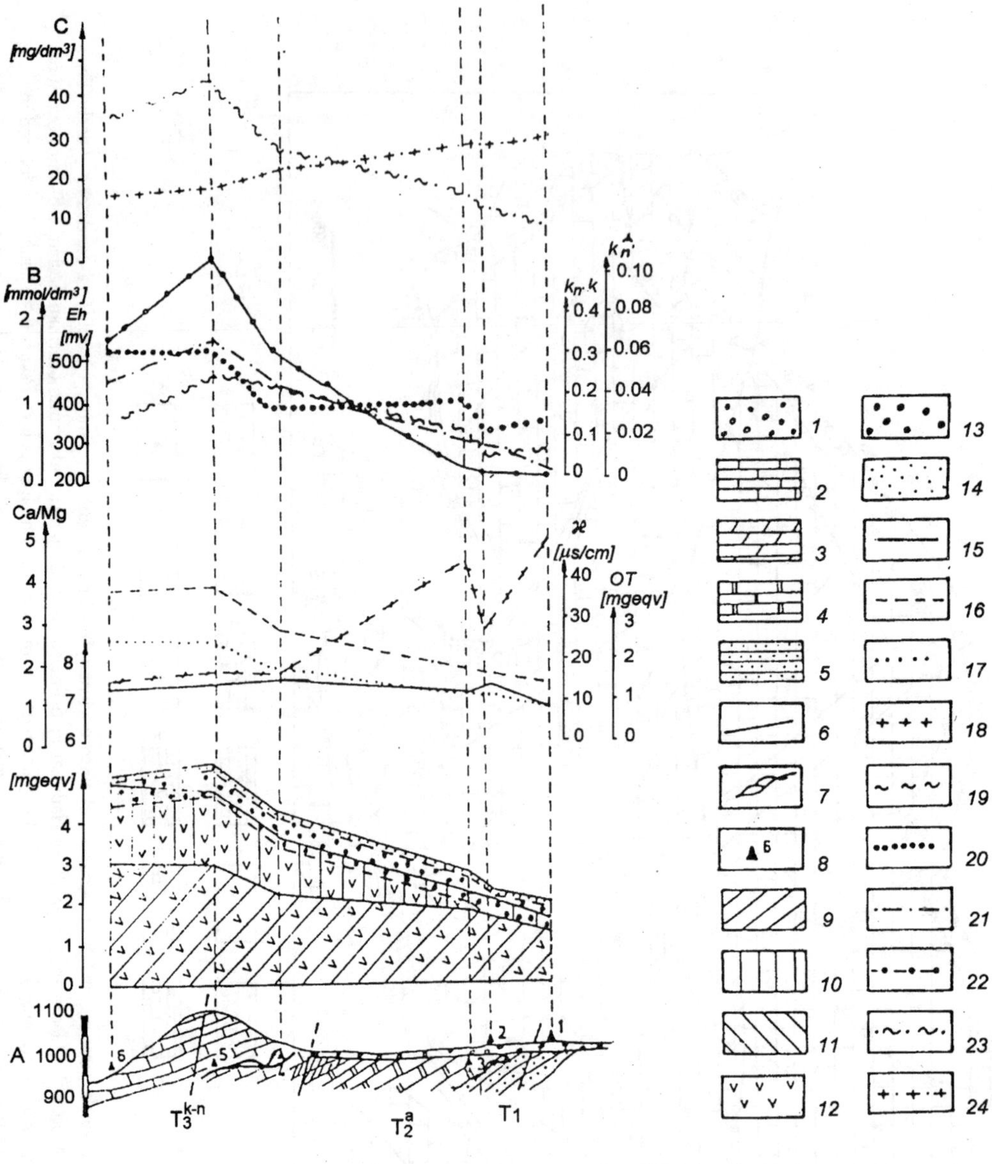

Fig. 15-13 A: Hydrochemical profile of Duhlata cave system: 1. alluvium; 2. carbonate rocks (T_3); 3. argillites; 4. carbonate rocks (T_2); 5. sandstones; 6. faults; 7. caves; 8. water samples. Hydrochemical characteristics: B: C-concentrations of: 9. calcium; 10. magnesium; 11. Na + K; 12. hydrocarbonates; 13. sulphates; 14. chlorine; 15. pH; 16. specific electroconductivity; 17. total hardness; 18. Ca/Mg; 19. EH; 20. buffer capacity; 21. coefficient of saturation in respect to calcite; 22. coefficient of saturation in respect to dolomite; 23. CO_2; 24. orthosilicic acid

The precipitation dependence on the elevation has been determined by climatic study of all precipitation records from the meteorological stations within the 30 km around. This dependence is linear with scattering of less than 10% and has the form:

$$R = 440 + 0.33H \quad (7)$$

By combining the equations [5, 6 and 7] we obtained the denudation rates in dependence of H, d, XCO_2 and $[Ca^{2+}]_0$:

$$D = 0.756k(440 + 0.33H)(1 + d/10)^{1/3} \times XCO_2{}^{1/3} \times e^{0.0011H} \times [Ca^{2+}]_0 \text{ (t/km}^2\text{ per year)} \quad (8)$$

Form equation (8) can be made full reconstruction of the denudation in the massive in any point of the space and time. This equation is written for equilibrium dissolving (the most common case inside the solid rock). If there are any disequilibrium processes (in fast flowing waters through the rock) an additional disequilibrium coefficient (taking into account, that the water is only partially saturated) should be introduced. This coefficient is equal to the ratio between the concentration of the karst water and saturated water at the same conditions.

Additional data for Duhlata cave can be found in (Shopov and Geogiev, 1987, 1991; Shopov et al., 1989, 1990; Shopov et al., 1991; Shopov et al., 1993; Shopov et al., 1994).

15.6 Conclusions

In conclusion, it has been suggested that the luminescent records of vadose zone speleothems may preserve a wealth of information depending on the cave site (the way of the underground waters, local climate, etc.), the resolution of the record and the experimental technique (autocalibration dating, measurement of the annual growth, intensity of luminescence).

Temporal resolution is 1000 – 10000 times greater than that obtained so far with other paleoenvironmental methods applied to terrestrial (continental) materials. It is possible to measure the annual growth rates of ancient speleothems, which are related mainly to ground water recharge and its variations.

The long minima of Maunder and Spoerer, the Medieval maximum and other well known long lasting minima and maxima can be seen in the obtained time series.

Cycles of the Solar Activity and insolation with periods of 1, 2, 11 – 12, 22, 55, 95, 180, 300, 400, 600, 900, 1200, 2300, 3350, 5000 and 16900 years are determined by LLMZA of speleothems.

The Cold Water cave, Iowa and Duhlata Cave, Bulgaria have not been glaciated, while Rats Nest cave, Calgary, Canada site was glaciated during the last glacial maximum 17000 yrs B.P.,

Acknowledgements

This research was supported by a Strategic Research Grant to Ford and Schwarcz from the Natural Sciences and Engineering Research Council of Canada. We are indebted to Professor T. Timusk (Physical, McMaster) for his help in preparation of the equipment for luminescent analysis and Dr. J. Morrison (Geology, McMaster) for the technical help. We thank Professor M. Stuiver for supplying his 12th Radiocarbon Conference ^{14}C record. ^{14}C dating was carried out by Iso trace Ltd, University of Toronto. MS dating was undertaken by W.-X. Li and K. Goodger at McMaster University. Ing. M. Zlatkova (Higher Mining Institute, Sofia) provided useful help in the selection and preparation of the samples. The spectral measurements was done in Bulgarian National Solid State Spectroscopy lab. at Sofia University under grant 439 of Bulgarian science foundation to Y. Shopov.

References

Alisov, B. and B. Poltaraus, 1962. Climatology. Moskow University, Moskow, 227p. (in Russian)

Baker, A. et.al., 1992. Nature, v.364, p.518 – 520.

Berger, A.L., 1990. Evolutive spectral analysis of sunspot data over the past 300 years. -Phil. Trans. R.Soc. Lond., 330, p.9 – 541.

Broecker, W.S. and P.C.Orr, 1960. Nature 185 (4706), 93.

Chromov, S.P., 1964. Meteorology and climatology for geographers. Hydrometeorologicheskoe zdatelstvo, Leningrad, 499 (in Russ.)

Cini, C. G., 1988. Proc. of the Int. School of Physics "E. Fermi", Cource XCV, Elsevier, Amsterdam, p. 317 – 328.

Cini, C. G., G. Bonino and A. Provenzale, 1988. The termoluminescent profile of a Recent sea sediment core and the Solar Variability. -Solar Physics, 117, 187 – 197.

Cini, C. G., G, Bonino, A. Provenzale and M. Serio, 1990. -Solar physics, 117, 357 – 377.

Damon, P. and C. Sonett, 1991. in The Sun in Time (eds. C. Sonett, M. Giamapa, M. Matwthews) 360 – 388.

Dermendjiev, V., Y.Y. Shopov and G. Buyukliev, 1990. Solar activity in the past and the problem of Solar Dynamo. -Solar physics 128, pp.217 – 225 (199).

Dermendjiev, V., G.T. Buyukliev and Y.Y. Shopov, 1990. The prolonged minima of Solar activity and the problem of Solar Dynamo. -in book "The sun and cold stars: -Activity, Magnetism and Dynamos" (ed. by l. Tuominen, D. Moos, G. RUdiger), Springer-Verlag, pp.268 – 270.

Dermendiev, V., Y.Y.Shopov, G.Buyukliev and I. Panayotova, 1991. One New indirect Solar Activity index-Geomagn. andAeronomy, V.31, 5, p.739 – 740.

Dermendjiev, V. and Y.Y. Shopov Y.Y., 1992. in: Solar-Terrestrial Variability and Global Changes, W.Schoder, J.-P. Legrand (eds.), Bremen-Roennebeck, p.145.

Doral, J.A. et.al., 1992. Science, 258, 1626.

Filipov, A: F., 1982. Hydromagnesite from the "Duhlata" cave, Bosnek village, District of Pernik. -Annual of Solia University, Geolo-Geogr., V.72, 1, Geol., pp.205 – 218.

Filipov, A.F., 1983. Hydromagnesite, aragonite, niddle-calcite, sapomite and brusite forming "moon milk" in "Duhlata " Cave, Bulgaria-proc. European Regional Conference of Speleology, v.2, p.86 – 103.

Gilson, R.J., E.Macarthney and J.Ashford, Speleo.Soc., p. 1(1954) ; R.J.Gilson and E. Macarthney, International J. Speleogy

Harmon, R. et al., 1978. Late Pleistocene Paleoclimates of North America as inferred Stable isotope studies of speleothems. -Quaternary Res., 9, 54 – 70.

Harmon, R. et al., 1979. An isotopic paleotemperature record for late Wisconsinian time in northeast lowa. -Geology, v.7, p.430 – 433.

Jenkins J.M. and D.G. Watts, 1969. Spectral analysis and it's applications. Holden day, San Francisco.

Kononova, M.M., 1966. In Soil Organic Matter (Pergamon Press), p.543

Lauritzen S.-E., D. C. Ford and H. P. Schwarcz, 1986. Proc. 9th International Speleogy Congress, Vol.2, 77 – 79, (Barcelona). Li et al., 1989. Nature, 339, 534.

Lungershauzen, G., 1963. In problemy planetarnoy Geologey, (Gosgeolizdat), pp.7 – 49.

Malinin, A. and K. Burenin, 1987. Physical Geography (school textbook), 3rd edition, Sommer and Co., Wien, 144p. (in Russian)

Metodiev, R., 1983. Proc. European Regional Conference of Speleology, v, 1, p. Morner, N.A., 1973. Boreas 3(2:1) 33.

Rivin, U.R., 1989. Cycles of the Earth and Sun, Moskow, Mauka, p. 165, (in Russian)

Schwarcz, H. and C. Yonge, 1983. Isotopic composition of paleowaters as inferred from speleothem and its fluid inclusions. -in: paleoclimates and paleowaters: A collection of environmental isotope studies, IAEA, Wien, pp.115 – 33.

Schwarcz, H., 1986. In Handbook of Environmental Isotope Geochemistry (Elsevier, New York, 1986), part B, pp. 397-421.

Shopov, Y.Y., 1987. Laser Luminescent Microzonal Analysis-A New Method for investigation of the Alterations of the Climate and Solar Activity during Quaternary-in "problems of karst Study of Mountainous Countries" (Proceedings of the international Symposium of Speleogy 5 – 12 Oct.1987), MEISNIEREBA, Tbilisi, pp.228 – 232.

Shopov, Y.Y. and L.N. Geogiev, 1987. Quantitative Theory of the Solubility of Carbonate Rocks in Dependence of the physico-Chemical and Climatic Conditionns. -in abstracts of the International Symposium on "Problems of karst Cmplex Study of Mountain. Countries" (ed. by T. Kiknadze), MEISNIEREBA, Tbilisi, p.32.

Shopov, Y.Y., V.N. Dermenjiev, G.I. Buyukliev, L.N. Georgiev, T.S. Stoychev, 1988. Investigations on the Variations of the Solar Activity during the Holocene by means of LLMZA of Cave Flowstone. Communications of the Int. Symp. on Phys., Chem and Hydrogeological Research of Karst, May 10 – 15, 1988, pp.97 – 100

Shopov, Y.Y., S.L. Georgiev and L.N. Georgiev, 1989. Climatic bases for karstification of pirin Mts. -Expedition Annual of Sofia University, V.3/4, pp.42 – 53.

Shopov, Y.Y., 1989. Bases and Structure of the international Programme "Luminescence of Cave Minerals" of the Commission of Physical Chemistry and Hydrogeology of karst of UIS. -Proc. 10th internat. Congress of Speleology, 13 – 20 August 1989, Budapest, V. 1, pp. 98 – 100.

Shopov, Y. Y., V. Dermendjive and G. Buyukliev, 1989. Investigations on the Old Variations of the Climate and Solar Activity by A New Method-LLMZA of Cave Flowstone from Bulgaris. -Proceedings of 10th International Congress of Speleology, 13 – 20 August 1989, Budapest, v. 1, pp. 95 – 97.

Shopov, Y. Y., V. N. Dermendjiev and G. Buyukliev, 1990. Methods for Research of the Solar Activity in the past and Flowstone Luminescent Records of the Solar Activity. -Studia Carsologica, v. 2. pp. 139 – 149.

Shopov, Y. Y., V. N. Dermendjiev and G. Buyukliev, 1990. Solar Activity in the last 35000years, from data of luminescence of Cave Flowstones from Bulgaria. -Annuals Geophysicae, Special issue, p. 300.

Shopov, Y. Y. and L. N. Georgiev, 1991. Quantitative Theory of the Solubility of Carbonate Rocks in Dependence of the physico-Chemical and Climatic Conditions. -Exped. Annual of Univ. of Sofia, A-Speleology, v 5, pp 9 – 16.

Shopov, Y. Y., L. Gerogiev, L. Tsamkov, V. Dermendjiev and G. Buyukliev, 1991. Methods for Research of Luminence of Cave MInerals and Speleothem Records of the Paleoclimate and Solar Activity in the past. -IGCP 299 Newsletter, v. 2. 52 – 58.

Shopov, Y. Y., V. Dermenddjiev and G. Buyukliev, 1991. Astrophysical Effects and Solar-Terrestrial Relationships Recorded by the Conventional Indirect Indexes and the new LLMZA index of the Solar Activity in the Past, -in book: - "ICSU Round Table on Space and Solar influences on the Environment", 25 – 30 Sept 1990, Rozhen, Bulgaria (ed. by S. Radicella and K, Seratimov), pp. 56 – 72.

Shopov, Y. Y. and V. Dermendjiev, 1991. Microzonality of Luminescence of Cave Flowstones as a New Indirect Index of Solar Activity. -Comptes rendus de I'Academie bulgare des Sci., v. 43, No 7, pp. 9 – 12.

Shopov, Y. Y, V. Dermendjiev and G. Buyukliev, 1991. A New Method for Dating of Nature Materials with periodical Macrostructure by Autocalibration and its Application for Study of the Solar Activity in the past. -Quaderni del Dipartimento di Geografia, n. 13, Universita di Padova, pp. 17 – 22.

Shopov, Y. Y., D. C. Ford, J. Morrison, H. P. Schwarcz, L. N. Georgiev, M. E. Sanambria, V. Dermendjiev and G. Buyukiev, 1992. High resolution records of Quaternary Solar Activity, Climate and Variations-GSA Abstracts, 24, (7), P. a268.

Shopov, Y. Y., D. C. Ford, L. N. Georgiev, T. Timusk, J. Morrison and H. P. Schwarcz, 1993. Very high resolution paleo-environmental data from the luminescence of speleothems. -Abstracts of the 1993 jiont Annual Meeting of the Geological and Mineralogical Associtions of Canada, Edmonton, 17 – 19 May 1993, p. 96.

Shopov Y. Y., D. C. Ford, C. J. Yonge, W. Macdonald, L. N. Georgiev, M. E. Sanambria, V. Dermendjiev and G. Buyukliev, 1994. High resolution records of Climatic Variations and Solar Forcing in the last 2000years from the luminecence of speleothems. -Abstr. of NATO Advanced Research workshop: Climatic Variations and Forcing Mechanisms of the last 2000 years, 11 Ciocco, Italy, 3 – 7 Oct. 1994; in press in NATO series, Springer Verlag.

Shopov, Y. Y., D. C. Ford and H. P. Schwarcz, 1994. Luminescence Microbanding in speleothems: High resolution chronology and paleoclimate. -Geology, v. 22, p. 407 – 410, May 1994.

Shove, D. J., 1983. In Sunspot Cycles, D. Shove, Ed., (Hutchinson Ross Publishing, 1983) pp. 1 – 28.

Sonett, C. P., 1984. Reviews of Geophysics and space physics 22(3), 239 – 254.

Stuiver, M. and P. Quay, 1980. Nature 207 (4426), 11

Stuiver, M. and R. Kra (Eds), 1986. Radiocarbon, Callibration issue, 28.

Stuiver, M. and T. Braziunas, 1989. Atmospheric 14C and century-scale solar oscillations. Nature, V. 388, 30 March 1989, p. 405 – 408.

Suess, H. E, 1980. The radiocarbon record in tree rings of the last 8000years. -Radiocarbon, V. 22, No. 2, p. 200 – 209.

Talma, A. S., 1989. Bull. of the South African Speleological Asssocition 30, 75

Veklich, M., 1987. Problems of Paleoclimatology. Kiev, Naukova Dumka, 188p. (in Russian)

White, W. and E. Brennan, 1989. Proc. X Int. Congr. Speleogy, (Budapest), v. 1, 212. Yonge, C. J. et al., 1985. Stable isotope studies of cave seepage water. -Chemical Geoleogy, 58, pp. 97 – 105.

Yonge, C. J., 1989. The Rats Nest Cave Project-proceedings of 10th international Congress of speleology, 13 – 20 August 1989, Budapest, v. 1 pp. 170 – 171. Yonge, C. J., 1991. Cave Science, 18 (3), 119

Global Karst Correlation
Edited by Yuan Daoxian and Liu Zaihua
Science Press and VSP BV, 1998

Chapter 16 Perspectives of Karst Science

Yuan Daoxian
Institute of Karst Geology, CAGS, Guilin, China

The progress of IGCP 299 in five years' time has brought about some new enlightenments to karstology.

16.1 The Application of Earth System Science (ESS) in Karst Study

It has deepened the understandings on the mechanism of karst formation remarkably. The ESS has been developing since a couple of decades ago. While investigating geological processes, especially epigenic processes, ESS requires doing it on the bases of understanding the rules of matter and energy transfer on the interfaces between lithosphere, hydrosphere, atmosphere and biosphere. The involvement of CO_2 in karst processes made this approach even more important in karst research. In the course of IGCP299, we did every efforts to catch the moving track of carbon cycle, water cycle and calcium(magnesium) cycle in karst by using a set of portable field instruments to measure parameters as indicated in Fig. 1-3. Moreover, we had taken the advantages of the broad trans-continental correlation over varied natural environments provided by the Project, to discover the relationship between karst formation and the different forms of carbon, water and calcium (magnesium) cycle under varied environments. Following the researches on the issues, such as the geochemistry in karst processes, the role of allogenic water in karst formation, the origin of calcareous tufa and the biokarst processes, the application of ESS in karst study has extended and penetrated into depth our knowledges on the mechanism of karst formation, and brought about some new ideas.

The importance of cycling intensity. We have long been aware of the relationship between intensity of water cycle and karst processes, but the intensity of carbon cycle and calcium cycle is important as well. For instance, a water with low pH and low carbonate hardness was considered to be undersaturated and aggressive to carbonates, and thus favourable for karstification. The assertion is although not wrong, but incomplete. Because from a viewpoint of ESS, or from the point of cycling intensity and to look at the environmental background as a whole, a water like that is exactly the result of slow moving karst process. The swamp water in the Taiga of Siberia, Russia could be an example. It is the reflection of a slow process under the environment of very low annual mean temperature. In contrast, in the subtropical karst of south China, the karst waters usually show higher pH, higher carbonate hardness, and higher saturation with respect to calcite and dolomite. It seems to be not favourable to karst process, but is exactly the expression of intensive karstification. The debates in world karstological circle 40 years ago (Corbel, 1959) on whether karst process is more intensive in cold region or in warm region will become straightforward from a viewpoint of ESS.

The synthetic effect of matter and energy transfer on Earth. Some examples are enlightening. Global correlation shows, under the environments of middle and high latitude with low temperature, the carbon cycling is slower. Speleothem are usually very few in such region, even it is humid. Abundant speleothem in caves under such conditions are generally considered to be the relics of previous warm humid period. However, a great deal of modern speleothems are growing in caves under dense forest of Victoria, SE Australia (Buchan caves, photo47), but it is in a humid temperate climate of 38° southern latitude. It is believed that the biosphere environment of dense forest has intensified the carbon cycle and also karst process, as being evidenced by the high P_{CO_2} in some East Australian caves. A lot of carbonate speleothems are formed in Spipola cave, Bologna, Italy, which is developed totally in pure gypsum of giant swallow-tail twin. It tells that under definite biogeochemical background, sulphates can also be replaced by carbonates.

Karst types according to source of CO_2. From the effects of karst processes on the source and sink of atmospheric CO_2, karst can be classified into: Atmosphere-biogenic Karst; Geothermal Karst and Anthropogenic Karst. Most of the Karst Dynamic Systems studied and monitored in IGCP 299 fall in the atmosphere-biogenic type. The results show that, from a global view, this type of karst is more a sink than a source to the atmospheric CO_2. From the investigation in karst regions of modern volcanism or active tectonism, such as Huanglong Ravine, China, Pamukale, Turkey and Central Italy, it is discovered that the deep source or mantle-originated CO_2 plays an important role in karst process. This direction should be more studied in the future because of its unique action on karst formation and the importance of its parts in the source-sink of atmospheric CO_2. The burning of fossil fuels is regarded as the major anthropogenic source of atmospheric CO_2. However, the making of lime, the hydration or consolidation of cement and the hydrotechnical structures on hydrological system can all change the intensity or direction of water, carbon and calcium cycles, and thus become a particular source or sink of atmospheric CO_2, and bring about unique karst features, named as anthropogenic karst.

16.2 Karst Feature Complex (KFC) and Its Environment of Formation

IGCP 299 used KFC rather than individual karst feature as a tool for world karst morphological correlation. It is defined as a set of karst features, including macro and micro forms, surface and subsurface forms, as well as dissolutional and depositional forms that require similar environmental background for their formation. The advantages of using KFC as basis of karst correlation are, to overcome the uncertainties in macroscopic karst geomorphologic comparison, and meanwhile, to avoid the confusions brought about by isomorphism or the mixture of historical karst features developed in other environments (Paleokarst) with the modern ones. In the 8 major excursions of the Project, it was exactly by this approach, we have got better understanding on the morphological differences of different types of karst. Moreover, by comparing such differences with their geological, climatic, hydrological and vegetational background and relevant characteristics of water, carbon, and calcium (magnesium) cycle, the essential distinctions in mechanism of formation for different karst types were revealed.

16.3 Karst Proxies for Global Change Study

To reconstruct the course of paleoenvironmental change from karst records for testing the output of general circulation model is another important objective of IGCP 299. This is particularly important in those regions without other paleoenvironmental proxies (ice core, lake sediments, etc.). The sensitivity of karst dynamics system to environmental change also makes it sensitive in recording change, as demostrated by the studies of Winograd (1992), Dorale (1993), Railsback (1994), Shopov (1994) and Richards (1994) amongst others. The sites where karst records are taken for global change study cover almost all the continents (Fig. 16-1). A 1.22 m high stalagmite taken from Panglong Cave, 37 km south of Guilin, China was used for reconstructing the environmental change course of the past 36,000 years and got a resolution of 100 years (Fig. 9-7, Photo 48). In southeast Australia, the study on the content and paleotemperature information from dark bands in stalagmites had made it possible to trace back the history of bush fires to middle Pleistocene. G.A. Brook (USA) reported his works on high resolution paleoenvironmental data from speleothem and clastic sediments in Drotsky's Cave, NW Botswana. A 40 cm stalagmite consists of alternating layers of calcite and aragonite. Layer counts and radiocarbon ages indicate that the calcite-aragonite pairs are annual layers representing about 1500 years of deposition. Ar-laser induced luminescence shows that there are more organic substances in the calcite than the aragonite. Therefore the calcite layer is supposed to represent warm wet season. In a study of the most recent 600 layers in the deposit, covering the period A.D. 1374 – 1973, periodicities at 10, 20, 40, 75 and 150 years were isolated. The 10, 20 year periodicities were also apparent in rainfall data from 4 stations near the cave.

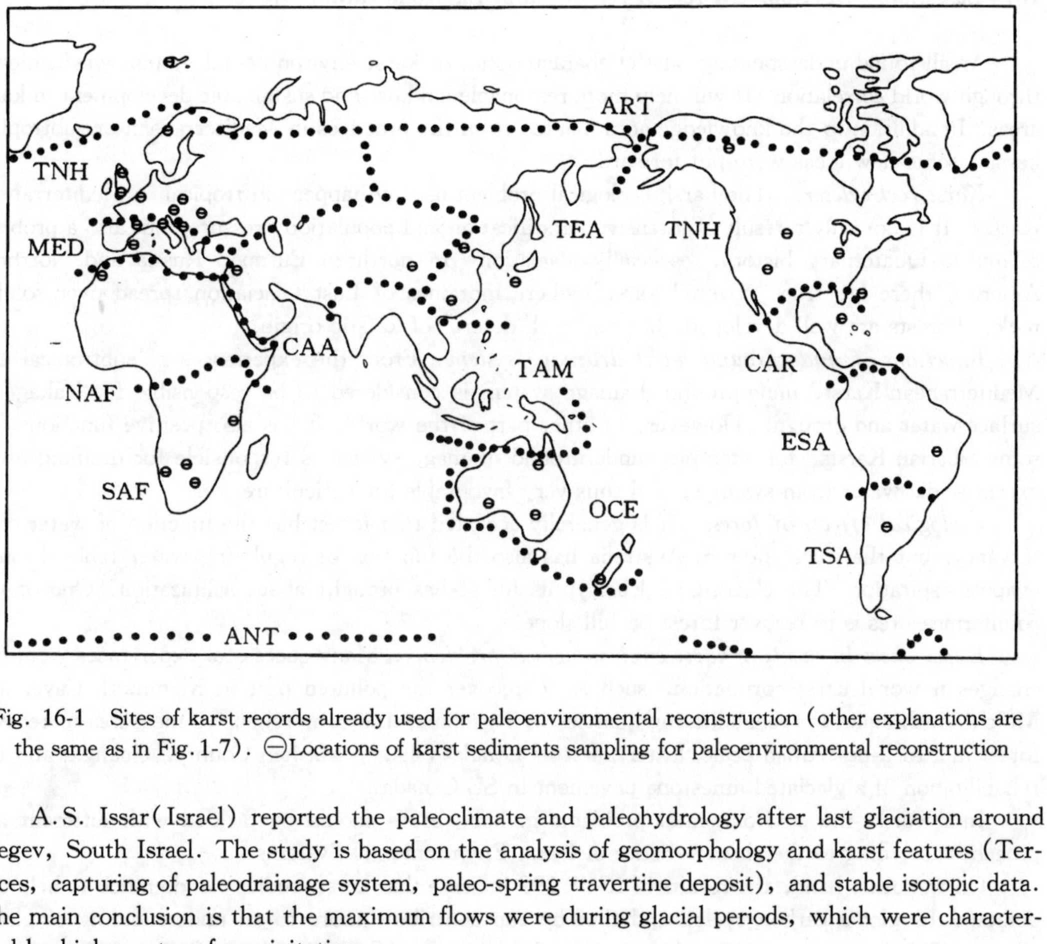

Fig. 16-1 Sites of karst records already used for paleoenvironmental reconstruction (other explanations are the same as in Fig. 1-7). ⊖Locations of karst sediments sampling for paleoenvironmental reconstruction

A.S. Issar (Israel) reported the paleoclimate and paleohydrology after last glaciation around Negev, South Israel. The study is based on the analysis of geomorphology and karst features (Terraces, capturing of paleodrainage system, paleo-spring travertine deposit), and stable isotopic data. The main conclusion is that the maximum flows were during glacial periods, which were characterized by higher rates of precipitation.

In Tumen karst, Yiyuan County, Shandong Province of North China, paleohydrology of middle Pleistocene was reconstructed through dating and investigating the sedimentation relation between allogenic pebble layers and flowstone in caves. The dating of calcite, gypsum, and halite speleothems from Nullarbor caves threw light into the changing course from a humid climate to an arid one in late Pleistocene and Holocene. It is considered to be the result of strengthening in cold dry circulation following the northward moving of Australian Continent and expansion of Southern

Ocean. Italian colleagues found seismic records in speleothems as the direction change in the growth axis of stalagmite, and the collapse events in caves. By analyzing karst feature complex of different elevations on some Pacific coral reef islands, Japanese group reconstructed the course of sea level change. In a joint research between Britain (Heather Viles and others, 1994) and Germany (Karl Heinz Pfeffer), nine sites of tufa deposit in the two countries were examined as an attempt to find out the origin of tufa deposition declining in North Europe during Holocene. The result suggests that increased erosion within catchment, following land use change and climate fluctuation, have been recorded in tufa deposits, and were responsible for their decline. All these examples show that karst records are very potential in global change study, especially in some broad continuous karst regions without other paleoenvironmental proxies.

16.4 Sustainable Development for Different Karst Environmental Systems

An all-round understanding on the characteristics of karst environmental system was achieved through world correlation. It will help more reasonable land use and sustainable development in karst areas. In addition to the knowledge accumulated from the practices in Mediterranean or subtropical karsts, some new ideas were put forward.

Karst rocky desert. The harsh ecological problem usually happens in tropical or Mediterranean Karsts. It is not only a result of intensive karstification and population pressure, but also a problem related to Quaternary history, especially glaciation. In northern Europe, Russia and Northern America, there are true "covered karst" where moraines of Last Glaciation spread over soluble rocks. Forests are well developed, but no "rock desert" of karstic origin.

Functions of underground karst drainage system. From the experiences of subtropical and Mediterranean Karst, underground drainage system is considered to be responsible for leakage of surface water and drought. However, in other part of the world, it has also positive functions. In some Siberian Karsts, for example, underground drainage system is responsible for draining away excess acidic water from swamps, and thus very favourable for agriculture.

Ecological effects of forest. It is generally accepted that forest has the function of water conservancy, but the Eucalyptus in Australia has also the function of regulating water table through evapotranspiration. The clearing of Eucalyptus forest has brought about salinization. One of the countermeasures is to recover forest on hill slope.

Experiences in tackling karst environmental problems. Many successful experiences were exchanges in world karst correlation, such as to recover the polluted part in Mammoth Cave, the Mulches techniques for rehabilitating quarries in Tasmania, the comprehensive measures to recover forest in a rock-desertified peak cluster karst of Longla Village, Mashan County, Guangxi and the rehabilitation of a glaciated limestone pavement in SE Canada.

In a word, the environmental problems in karst areas should be tackled with different approaches according to the characteristics of Karst Environmental Systems.

On the other hand, the results of IGCP 299 indicate that karst studies can do much to help understand the global carbon cycle, and thereby can contribute more to an understanding of global change. This is not only in regard to the greenhouse gas problem, but also in finding more paleoenvironmental proxies to test the output of general circulation models. Accordingly the objectives of the successor project IGCP 379 "Karst processes and the carbon cycle" (1995 – 1999) are:

(1) To assess the contribution of carbonate rocks to the content of CO_2 in atmosphere;

(2) To compare the annual balance of CO_2 between the atmosphere and karst system under different geological, climatic and ecological environments;

(3) To determine the origin and amount of annual emission of CO_2 into the atmosphere from

karst areas with geothermal, volcanic activities or active faults, especially those near plate margins; and

(4) To provide information about the processes of environmental change after the late Pleistocene in major karst regions of the world, especially those without other paleoenvironmental proxies.

Now the new project is going smoothly. Its information are available at:

http://www.gxnu.edu.cn/igcp379/index.htm.

We wish the new round of international cooperation would be as fruitful as the previous one.

References

Baker, A., 1993. Annual growth banding in a cave stalagmite. Nature 364: 519-520.

Corbel, J., 1959. Erosion en terrain calcaire. Ann. Geog. 68: 97-120

Dorale, J.A., 1992. A high resolution record of climate change in speleothem calcite from Cold Water Cave, northern Iowa. Science 256: 1626-1630.

Railsback, B.L., 1994. Environmental controls on the petrology of a late Holocene speleothem from Botswana with annual layers of aragonite and calcite. J. Sediment. Res. A64: 147-155.

Richards, D.A., P.L. Smart and R.L. Edwards, 1994. Maximum sea levels for the last glacial period from U-series ages of submerged speleothems. Nature 367: 357-360.

Shopov, Y.Y., D.C. Ford and H.P. Schwarcz, 1994. Luminescent micro-banding in speleothems: high resolution chronology and paleoenvironment. Geology 22: 407-410.

Viles, H., A. Goudie and A. Pentecost, 1994. The sensitivity of tufas to Human interference. Cave and Karst Science 21: 21

Winograd, I.J., 1992. Continuous 500,000 year climate record from vein calcite in Devil's Hole, Nevada. Science 258: 255.

APPENDIX 1

Karst Feature Complex Developed Under Different Climatic Environment

Karst Features \ Climatic Environment		Arid, Semi-arid	Humid		
			Arctic and Alpine	Temperate	Tropical Subtropical
Surface Featrues	Macro form	Normal shape Mts.	Normal shape Mts.	Hill-doline, Stone knob-doline	Tower karst
	Big form	Dry valley	Dry valley, shallow doline	Dish shape doline, Solutional basin	Polygonal doline, Solutional basin, Stone forest
	Micro form	Individual karren	Sharp karren	Sharp karren, Sub-soil round karren, kamenitza	Sharp karren, Sub-soil round karren, kamenitza
	Depositional form	Limestone scree; Calc-case; Calc-concretion	Limestone scree, Stream tufa	Stream tufa, little outside stalactite, sometimes limestone scree are available	Terra rosa, Abundant outside Stalactite
Subsurface Featrues	Big form	Wind erosion rock shelter and through cave. Scarcely any cave except those under snow Mts.	Large caves under snow Mts. or modern glacier	Large cave system, its feature depends on hydraulic conditions	Large cave system, with features depending on hydraulic conditions
	Micro form	Scallop, pothole in caves under snow Mts.	Little scallops, potholes and notches	Potholes, scallops, notches, rock pendants are ofter seen	A lot of minor solutional forms
	Depositional form	Small secondary carbonate deposit in caves under snow Mts.	Glacial varve, collapse deposit, little secondary chemical and cold biotic deposit.	Collapse and alluvial deposit are often seen, more secondary chemical deposit, and temperate biotic deposit.	Abundant secondary chemical deposit, collapse, alluvial, tropical and subtropical biotic deposit.

APPENDIX 2

IGCP 299 "Geology, Climate, Hydrology and Karst Formation" Registration Form for A Typical Karst Area

(*Fill in the form after reading the instructions carefully*)

Name of the karst area ______

Location: province(state) ______, country ______

latitude ______, longitude ______

Karst type ______, area coverage ______ km^2,

Altitude: highest ______ m, lowest ______ m,

Soluble rock: chronological period ______, thickness ______ m,

stratigraphic feature ______,

lithology ______, CaO content ______ %,

MgO content ______ %, acid nonsoluble material ______ %, porosity ______ %,

compressive strength ______ kg/cm^2, permeability ______ m/d.

tensile strength ______ kg/cm^2, Shearing strength ______ kg/cm^2

maximum continuous thickness of soluble rock ______ m.

Geological structure:

folding ______,

faulting ______,

fracture pattern ______.

major orogeny ______,

intrusion ______,

Neotectonism: Cenozoic uplift ______ m.

Present climate: annual mean precipitation ______ mm,

annual maximum potential evaporation ______ mm,

annual mean temperature ______(℃).

thickness of max. snow accumulation ______ mm,

thickness of ice accumulation ______ mm,

thickness of permafrost zone ______ m.

Hydrology : pattern ______, area of catchment ______ km^2,

depth of water table: general ______ m, perched ______ m,

amplitude of fluctuation:

discharge: max. ______ l/s, min. ______ l/s,

water table: high ______ m, low ______ m,

availability of allogenic water ______,

percentage of nonsoluble rock area involved ______ %.

Vegetation ______.

Soil: description ________________, thickness ______ m,
organic content ____________ %, permeability __________,
Concentration of CO_2 in soil air: max. ________________ ppm,
min. ________________ ppm,
pH of soil water: min. ____________, max. __________.

Hydrochemical features:

pattern of system	T(℃)	pH	TDS mg/l	Na^+ mg/l	K^+ mg/l	Ca^{2+} mg/l	Mg^{2+} mg/l	HCO_3^- mg/l	SO_4^{2-} mg/l	Cl^- mg/l
open										
semi-open										
closed										

Limestone denudation rate:
based on Hydrochemical data ________________ mm/ka,
based on surface measurement ________________ mm/ka,
based on limestone tablets approach:
subaerial __________ mm/ka, on surface __________ mm/ka,
subsoil __________ mm/ka, subaqueous __________ mm/ka.

Karst feature complex matching present climate:
surface features (with morphometric description):
macro forms ____________________,
big forms ____________________,
micro forms ____________________,
sedimentation ____________________.
subsurface features (with morphometric description):
caves: total number ____________, total length
__________ m,
major types ____________________,
longest cave: name ____________, total length ______ m,
deepest cave: name ____________, depth ______ m,
biggest hall: name ____________, area ______ m^2
micro solutional feature ____________________,
cave deposit:
major types of speleothem: ____________________,
allogenic deposit ____________________,
translocation deposit ____________________,
numbers to the attached slides, photos ____________________

Karst Feature Complex Basically Formed in previous Paleoenvironment:

karst feature complex	altitude (m)	chronology(B. P.)	Dating approach
surface forms: macro form ______			
big form ______			
micro form ______			
sediments ______			
subsurface forms: cave ______			
micro solutional forms ______			
cave deposits ______			

Numbers to the attached slides, photos ______

Description of paleoenvironment as indicated by the above karst feature complex ______

______

Evidences of paleoenvironment change by other techniques (SEM, isotope, and etc.)

______

______

Other Karst Features:

Mineral deposits in karst ______

______

oil gas reservoir in karst ______

______

Thermal water karst ______

______

Environmental Problems:

Natural:

soil shortage ______

soil nutrient deficiency ______

shortage of water from leakage ______

flooding in karst depression ______

______

natural collapse ______

diseases associated with karst ______

Human induced problems:

deforestation:

from over－timbering ______

from air pollution ______

water table declining ______

water intrusion in mines ________________________
water pollution ________________________
surface collapse ________________________
Trends of environmental change in the past thousands years from written history or karst record ________________________
____

Trends of environmental change in the past decades ________________________
____

Registrar: Name ________________________
Address ________________________
Date ________________________

INSTRUCTIONS

1. This form is sent to geoscientists who are willing to take part in the IGCP 299 "Geology, Climate, Hydrology and Karst Formation" to be filled in as a basic measure for international correlation. The immense field of karst study makes it almost impossible to carry out an intimate comparison merely by exchange of papers through a meeting or a proceedings even dedicated to definite problems. The advantage of this form is to attract attention from participants to the priorities of correlation on geological, climatic, and hydrological backgrounds of karst formation; the relationship between the karst feature complex and its environment of formation; the resources and environmental problems of karst; and the reconstruction of paleoenvironments by means of karst informations. However, it is not in any sense meant to use this form to replace the role of research reports, scientific papers and proceedings, which have the advantages to discuss the problems and give data in detail and more systematically, and create new fields and ways of karst correlation.

2. This registration form includes about 150 items that are the most essential for international correlation on karst. However, accuracy and common understanding on each item is critical for the feasibility of such a correlation. Accordingly, registrars are required to read the instructions carefully before filling in the form.

3. As karst type and not administration division is the basic unit of comparison, therefore, the data coverage for each registration form should be limited to a region characterized by a special karst type. Consequently, each country should have several forms if it enjoys different karst types. Several participants can share one form if they are dealing with the same region of the same karst type. On the other hand, every participant is encouraged to fill in more than one form if he/she is very familiar with different karst types of different regions in the world.

4. It can be seen that the data required in the form may not be fully available until the end of the project. However, to make this project work smoothly, and to facilitate exchange timely, registrars can only fill in a part of the form according to available data when it is first sent to the IGCP 299 Secretariat. The remaining items can be replenished in the next year, or year after year during the implementation of the project. Registrars can also fill in new forms for the same work region in the following years if there are major changes. Meanwhile, the contents of the form may be changed according to the comments and suggestions from the participants year after year.

5. The first form for the participating karst region should reach the Secretariat by the end of 1990.

6. Karst type refers to arctic karst, glaciokarst, temperate karst, subtropical karst, tropical karst, arid zone karst, high mountain karst, coastal karst, evaporate karst, deep karst, buried

karst, thermal water karst and etc.

7. Soluble rock: Stratigraphic feature refers to continuous (hundreds meters of soluble rock without any non-soluble rock intercalation); individual (tens of meters of soluble rock intercalated in a major non-soluble rock sequence); alternative (soluble rock and non-soluble rock in similar thickness appear alternatively); intercalative (major soluble rock formation with many minor non-soluble bed intercalated); and etc.

Lithology refers to limestone (further refers to grainstone, packstone, wackestone), crystalline limestone, marble, dolomite, dolomitic limestone, impure carbonate rock, evaporite-carbonate mixture formation, evaporate rock, and etc.

8. Geological structure:

Folding refers to gentle folding, close folding, major anticline, syncline or monocline.

Faulting refers to the occurrence of a major fault and its geomechanic features.

Orogeny refers to major unconformities or disconformities of the regions, and their chronology.

9. Hydrology:

Pattern is a general description for a karst hydrological system, which is in accordance with the space distribution of soluble rock, and configured by the combination of relief, stratigraphic and geological structural features, e.g. it may be a vadose pattern (in bare karst), phreatic pattern (in covered karst), or deep slow flow pattern (in buried karst), or association of the three. For a vadose pattern, it should be further distinguished as narrow belt pattern (close folding with intercalative soluble beds), broad pattern (gently folded area), gorge pattern (with steep hydraulic gradient), etc.

Allogenic water refers to surface water being accumulated in the neighboring non-soluble rock area, and flowing into the studied karst region.

10. Vegetation refers to virgin forest, jungle, bush-wood, grassland, stony bare rock, swamp, and etc.

11. Soil description refers to its colour, particle size, sorting, and type, such as brown forest soil, calcareous soil, black steppe soil, loam, terra rossa, laterite, and etc.

12. Hydrochemical features:

Open, semi-open, or closed karst hydrochemical system refers to system with different degree of CO_2 exchange between lithosphere/hydrosphere and atmosphere/biosphere. Thus the vadose part of bare karst is usually an open system, covered karst and phreatic part of bare karst is usually a semi-open system, whereas buried karst is usually a closed system.

Referring to an open system, type of karst water, such as perched spring, dripping water or sheet flow in caves, or subterranean stream should be further remarked.

For pH value in an open system, measuring in-situ is a prerequisite. For pH value of semi-open, or closed system , not only in-situ, but also quick measuring is necessary to avoid the effect of degassing on the turning of a closed system into an open system.

13. A karst feature complex is a combination of karst features, including macroforms and microforms, surface forms and subsurface forms, solutional forms and depositional forms. The advantages of using karst feature complex as the basis for international karst correlation is to avoid the confusion of isomorphism which usually happens when dealing with individual karst forms.

Macro surface forms refer to such landforms as tower karst, doline field, normal shape limestone mountains, glaciated limestone mountains.

Big surface forms refer to such karst forms as doline, polje, dry valley, isolated peak, frost limestone pinnacles.

Micro surface forms refer to karren, grike, kamenitza, and etc.

Surface karst sedimentation refers to limestone scree, terra rossa, surface tufa dam, outside-cave stalactite, and etc.

Micro subsurface solutional feature refers to scallop, notch, pothole, halftube, bone-yard, anastomosis, and etc.

Allogenic cave deposit refers to deposit brought into the cave by allogenic water, such as gravels composed of non-soluble rock.

Translocation cave deposit refers to a deposit brought into the cave by fissure water, such as a clay layer in cave.

14. Environmental problems:

Soil shortage refers to thickness of cultivable soil, and percentage of cultivable land against the whole studied karst area.

Natural collapse refers to whether collapse happened in soluble rock brought about by the natural enlargement of underground cavity, or collapse happened in overburden following natural fluctuation of water table or heavy rainfall.

Human induced collapse refers to surface collapse, mostly in overburden, caused by human activities, such as pumping karst water for water supply, or dewatering in mines.

APPENDIX 3

Rbbstaler Alfen Eastern Alps, An IGCP 299 Correlation Site of Ausrtia

Rudolf Pavuza
Museum of Natural History, Vienna

1. General

Topography. The area described lies at the Northern Boundary of the Eastern Alps in Central Europe at about 47°55' N, 14°45' E. It mainly consists of moderate relief mountains and has an altitude range from 360 to 1170 m a.s.l. Only a few small plateaus can be observed.

Vegetation and soil. Mostly mixed woodlands (80%) with minor grasslands at low altitudes and a few alpine meadows at about 1000 m. Brown loamy soil dominates the soil profile with thicknesses up to 1 m.

Climate. A mean annual precipitation of 1400 mm and temperature of 6.7℃ yields an actual runoff of nearly 1000mm per year being typical for the northern margin of the Eastern Alps.

Geology. The area lies in the (Cretaceous) overthrust belt of the "Northern Calcareous Alps" with at least two tectonic nappes and some internal overthrusts. One can find a stratigraphy from the lower Triassic up to the older Cretaceous with upper Triassic dolomites, limestones and evaporites as main karst rocks. Intense folding and several generations of faults finally yield a rather complex karst system.

Hydrology. Estimated water balances for the different catchment areas lead to the conclusion that the greater part of the infiltrating water (50% - 90%) does not reappear in springs and creeks but flows directly into the ground water systems of the adjacent valleys. Runoff for springs and creeks is in the range from 400 to 900 1/s—depending on the actual meteorological circumstances—for the 70 km^2 area.

2. Hydrochemistry

Based on the geological situation there are three types of karst waters: dolomite, limestone and sulfate water with higher mineralisations in the areas with evaporites. TDS varies from 350 mg/1 in open system to 1100 mg/1 in closed systems of ascending waters (due to high sulfates contents). Basing on this data only, an overall denudation rate of 15 mm/ka can be calculated but most of this dissolution may occur in the near surface zone.

3. Karst features

Due to the fact that dolomite are dominating in most areas not so many of the well known karst features can be observed. For the dolomite areas dry valleys—only active for short periods during flood events—are quite typical. In the limestone/evaporite areas there are caves up to 500m long (mostly canyons near the actual base of the local karst complex), some dolines but no karren. Cave deposits are from local origin mostly. Rather typical are numberous tufa-deposits, maybe related to somewhat higher sulfate contents. Tufa ages may range up to several hundred of years. Some of the dolines and the small plateaus are related to an ancient (upper Cretaceous) landscape with nearly no relief.

Over all there seems to be a discrepancy between the potential subsurface dissolution and the extent of the caves mapped so far even in the limestone areas.

4. Paleoenvironmental records

There are only a few hints to this matter so far. Variations in the chemistry of the tufas may indicate climatic changes in the last centuries or even some changes within the catchment areas. As the dry valleys in the dolomite areas are clearly older than the Pleistocene valley fillings it is obvious that the karst water table has reached deeper parts of the aquifer already before the Pleistocene even in the dolomite areas where a higher "porosity" occurs due to more intensive jointing.

5. Environmental and resource problems

Problems occur mainly due to intensive forestry with numberous roads, doubtful forestry measures combined with an increased input of atmospheric chemicals(SO_2, NOx). Local hygienic problems arise because of illegal dumping.

There is still plenty of high quality karst water available in this area. As dolomites diminish, there are good filtration capacities combined with good aquifercharacteristics. There are good possibilities for groundwater exploitation in the adjacent valleys.

6. Geothermal karst

At several points there are ascending springs with water temperatures up to 5℃ above the annual air temperature at the spring location. These springs show nearly no annual variation of chemistry and discharge.

APPENDIX 4

Major Publications of IGCP 299 (1990 – 1994)

Books

Yuan Daoxian, Zhu Dehao, Weng Jintao, Zhu Xuewen, Han Xingrui, Wang Xunyi, Cai Guihong, Zhu Yuanfeng, Cui Guangzhong, Deng Ziqang, 1991. Karst of China. Geological Publishing House, Beijing, 224 pages, 48 colour photos.

William Back, Janet S, Herman, Henri Paloc (Editors), 1992. Hydrogeology of Selected Karst Regions. IAH International Contributions to Hydrogeology. Vol. 13. Verlag Heinz Heise, Hannover, 494 pages, 32 papers.

Yuan Daoxian (Editor), 1992. World Karst Correlation. Proceedings of the International Symposium on Karst of Inner Plate Region with Monsoon Climate, July 1991, Guilin, China, Suppl. Issue of Carsologica Sinica. No. 16, 230 pages, 28 papers.

Wang Fuxing, Cao Jianhua, Huang Junfa, Jiang Lideng, Huang Jifu, Wang Jing, 1993. Biokarst. Geological Publishing House, Beijing, 130 pages (In Chinese with extended English Summary)

Zoran Stevanovic, Budimir Filipovic (Eds), 1994. Ground Waters in Carbonate Rocks of the Carpathian-Balkan Mountain Range. Allston Holding Co. Ltd, Jersey, UK., 237 pages. 6 papers.

M. M. Sweeting, 1995. Karst in China. Spring-Verlag, Berlin Heidelberg, 265pages. with 82 figures and 36 photographs.

Liu Zaihua, 1997. The Rate-determining Mechanisms for the Dissolution and Precipitation of Calcite in $CO_2 - H_2O$ Solutions with Turbulent Motion. Guangxi Teachers University Press. Guilin, China. 135 pages (English version, with detailed Chinese abstract)

Yuan Daoxian (Ed.), 1998. Globol Karst Correlation. Science Press, Beijing. Final report of IGCP 299, with 16 chapters. (this volume).

Abstracts of Papers

David J Lowe and John Gunn, 1994-1995. Papers Presented at the International Symposium on Changing Karst Envirnonments, Oxford and Huddersfield, UK, September 1994, In Cave and Karst Science, the Transactions of the British Cave Research Association. Vol. 21, Nos. 1, 2, 3. 64 Abstracts

Guidebooks for Excursions

Liu Zaihua (Ed.), 1991. Guidebooks for International Symposium and Field Seminar on Karst of Inner Plate Region with Monsoon Climate. July 8-Aug. 1, 1991. The Institute of Karst Geology, Guilin, 72 pages, 42 figures.

David Gillieson (Ed.), 1992. Guidebook for Field Symposium in Australia, Humid Temperate Impounded Karst, Sub-humid Temperate Syngenetic Karst, Arid Temperate Karst. Department of

Geography and Oceanography, The University of New South Wales, Special Publication No., 4. Canberra, 115pages, 60 figures.

Part of Papers in International Journals

Yuan Daoxian & William Back, 1991. IGCP Project 299: Geology, Climate, Hydrology, and Karst Formation. Episodes, International Geoscience News Magazine, Vol.14, No.1, pp. 80–81, Herndon, USA.

G. Malcolm Brown, 1994. Limestone, Climate and Groundwater, in Examples of Recent IGCP Research, Nature and Resources, Vol.30, Nos.3 & 4, pp. 25–27, UNESCO, The Parthenon Publishing Group, UK & USA.

Liu Zaihua and He Dianbin, 1994. Two Mechanisms of Tufa Formation in the Cement Grouting Tunnels at Wujiangdu Hydropower Station of Guizhou. Chinese Science Bulletin 39, 1468–1472 (in English)

Liu Zaihua, U. Svensson, W. Dreybrodt, Yuan Daoxian and D. Buhmann, 1995. Hydrodynamic Control of Inorganic Calcite Precipitation in Huanglong Ravine, China: Field Measurements and Theoretical Prediction of Deposition Rates. Geochimica et Cosmochimica Acta, Vol. 59, No. 15, pp.3087–3097, printed in USA.

Daoxian Yuan, Bin Li and Zaihua Liu, 1995. Karst in China. Episodes. International Geoscience News Magazine, Vol.18, Nos.1 & 2, pp. 62–65. Keyworth UK.

Yuan Daoxian, 1995. Modern Karst Study Related to Global Change. In China Global Change Report No.2, pp. 126–132, Science Press, Beijing.

Yuan Daoxian, 1997. Sensitivity of Karst Process to Environmental Change along the PEP Ⅱ Transect, Quaternary International, Vol.37, pp. 105–113, Printed in Great Britain.

Yuan Daoxian, 1997. The Carbon Cycle in Karst, Z. Geomorph. N. F, Supple.-Bd 108:91–102, Berlin, Stuttgart.

Yuan Daoxian, 1997. Rock Desertification in the Subtropical Karst of South China, Z. Geomorph. N.F, Supple.-Bd 108:81–90, Berlin, Stuttgart.

Liu Zaihua, Yuan Daoxian, and He Shiyi, 1997. Stable Carbon Isotope Geochemical and Hydrochemical Features in the System of Carbonate-H_2O-CO_2 and Their Implications-Evidence from several typical karst areas of China. Acta Geologica Sinica 71, 446–454 (in English)

Liu Zaihua and Dreybrodt, W., 1997. Dissolution Kinetics of Calcium Carbonate Minerals in H_2O-CO_2 Solutions in Turbulent Flow: The Role of the Diffusion Boundary Layer and the Slow Reaction $H_2O + CO_2 \rightarrow H^+ + HCO^{3-}$. Geochimica et Cosmochimica Acta 61, 2879–2889

Newsletters

Wang Fuxing, Lin Xinghong, Liu Zaihua(Eds.), 1990. IGCP 299 Newsletter, recent research by IGCP 299 Participants. The Institute of Karst Geology, Guilin. 111 pages with 6 figures and photos.

Lin Xinghong(Ed.), 1991. IGCP 299 Newsletter, The Institute of Karst Geology, Guilin. 138 pages with 41 figures and photos.

Lin Xinghong (Ed.), 1992. IGCP 299 Newsletter, The Institute of Karst Geology, Guilin. 66 pages with 20 figures and photos.

Xu Shengyou (Ed.), 1993. IGCP 299 Newsletter, The Institute of Karst Geology, Guilin. 79 pages with 34 figures and photos.

Xu Shengyou (Ed.), 1994. IGCP 299 Newsletter, The Institute of Karst Geology, Guilin. 125 pages with 47 figures and photos.

1. Calcareous tufa cascades at Pamukale geothermal karst spring, Turkey, result of deep source CO_2 outgassing.

2. A quarry on Quaternary calcareous tufa at Cisterna, south of Rome, Italy. This kind of tufa is the main source of building stone for Rome and Vatican.

4. Low, rounded subtropical cockpit karst, developed on soft porous Tertiary carbonate rocks. Puerto Rico (courtesy of W.H.Monroe).

5. Low flat karstland at Yucatan Peninsula, Mexico, result of gentle Cenozoic uplift, and porous carbonate rock.

6. Deep, sharp karren developed on Permian limestone under humid subtropical climate. Stone Forest, Lunan, Yunnan.

3. Tall, steep subtropical tower karst, developed on hard compact Devonian limestone, Guilin, South China.

7. Tiny karren developed on Proterozoic carbonate rock and semi-arid temperate climate, Jixian, Tianjin, North China.

8. Ulupinar karst spring, near Kalkan, southwest Turkey, with low temperature and very few travertine deposit as a result of water recharged from high mountain.

9. Outlet of Dudenbasi Underground Stream, with many outside stalactites, Antalya,Turkey.

10. Limestone scree in Alvani Polje, Southwest Turkey.

11. Vegetation line on Taurus Mt., lower than 2000m a.s.l., photo taken from Aspendos, east of Antalya, Turkey.

12. Hierapolis aqueduct (200BC), with calcareous tufa encrustation, Pamukale, Turkey.

13. Thick calcareous tufa deposited on modern stream, Xiaoqikong resort, Maolan virgin forest, Libo County, Guizhou, China.

14. Frost denudation limestone pinnacles, an alpine karst feature at Huanglong Ravine, 4000m a.s.l., Songpan county, Sichuan, China.

15. Limestone scree at Huanglong Ravine, 4000m a.s.l., Songpan County, Sichuan, China.

16. Tower karst at Zashui County, Shaanxi Province, the northmost of macroscopic subtropical karst landform in China (33°40'N, at the southern slope of Qinling Mt.)

17. Tufa dam at Huanglong Ravine, Songpan County, Sichuan, China, result of deep source CO_2 outgassing,

18. Frost denudation limestone pinnacles in Beijing suburb, a relic of Pleistocene pereglacial feature resembling those of modern ones at Huanglong (photo 14), and Bassano, Italy (photo 42)

19. Taiga forest along Kama Reservoir, Perm, Russia, with collapse bank on gypsum beds.

20. Shallow dish shaped dolinen on Sinkhole Plain, Kentucky, USA.

21. Shallow, dish shaped dolinen on Kungur Plateau, Perm, Russia.

22. Bog in Taiga forest, with acidic water, Berezniki, Central Ural, Russia.

23. Solutional feature in Skyline Cave, Virginia, USA.

24. Abundant speleothem which looks to be old in Luray Cave, Virginia, USA.

25. Salt stalactites in Berezniki Potassium Mine, Central Ural, Russia.

26. Ice flowstone, ice flower in Kungur Cave, Russia.

27. Exsudation phenomena in Gorringe Cave, Nullarbor, Australia, the earlier carbonate speleothems were fallen as a result of exsudation caused by the later grown evaporite speleothems.

28. An enclosed depression containing water, considered to be a dissolutional feature on silicate minerals, being seen on Granite Batholith in Wudina, South Australia.

29. Potato field near Kungur, southeast of Perm, Russia, showing the advantage of underground karst drainage system for agriculture.

30. Salt karren, a technogenic karst feature developed on waste pile of Potassium Salt Mine, Berezniki, Russia.

31. Big collapse occurred January, 1986 in the Taiga above Berezniki Potassium Mine, Russia (Fig.4-8)

32. A natural tunnel in Ordovician dolomitic limestone, Southwest Virginia, USA.

33. Sinkholes in doline, Droop Mountain region, West Virginia, USA.

35. Coastal towers on Tertiary limestone, Campbell, Victoria, Australia.

36. Niagara Fall, Ontario, Canada, the Silurian dolomite escarpment is formed by both the hard litholoical feature of the gently dipped dolomite strata, and the scouring of ice sheet during the last Glaciation.

34. An installation to conduct cave air for greenhouse, Sloan Valley, Kentucky, USA.

37. Glaciation striation on dolomite pavement, near Cyprus Lake, Bruce Peninsula, Canada.

38. Tufa deposit on the bottom of Cyprus Lake, fed by a karst spring, Bruce Peninsula, Canada.

39. Glacial pavement and grikes on Silurian dolomite, near Lion Head, Bruce Peninsula, Canada, with forest rehabilitated on bare rocks during the past 60 years.

42. Frost denudation limestone pinnacles on Triassic dolomitic limestone slope, north of Bassano, northern Italy. They resemble those of Huanglong Ravine (Photo 14), or Beijing suburb (Photo 18) from points of both morphology and origin.

40. A CO_2 geyser well at the Ferrarelle Mineral Water field, Central Italy.

41. Giant swallow-tail twin gypsum on the entrance of Spipola Cave, Bologna, Italy. The cave is totally under the Miocene gypsum bed, but there are many calcite speleothems in it as a result of incongruent dissolution.

43. Glacial pavement on Triassic dolomitic limestone at Southern Alps, Rifugio Sennes, Northern Italy, similar with those of Canada (Photo 39) or UK (Photo 45), but originated from mountain glaciation rather than continental ice sheet.

44. Chalk quarry at Playhatch, near Reading, UK, with chert beds being seen on the quarry wall, but very few karst feature on this deep fresh exposure.

45. Glacial pavement on Carboniferous limestone, Great Asby Scar Nature Preserve, Cumbria, UK.

47. Abundant unique speleothem in Fairy Cave, Buchan Karst, Victoria, Australia.

48. Sedimentary structure of a 1.22m high stalagmite taken from Panlong Cave, Guilin, China. Environmental change course of the past 36000 years was reconstructed with the section. Big trapezium holes: sampling points for C-14 dating; small rectangular holes: AMS C-14 dating sampling points; small round holes: stable isotopic sampling points.

46. deep sharp karren on the glacial pavement, Great Asby Scar Nature Preserve, Cumbria, UK.

49. Hydrothermal cavities, filled with calcite spar, as exposed in the walls of a cave in Blomstrandsøya.

50. Suffosion doline developed in cryoclastic regolith and glacial drift above the blow-hole of a sea-cave, Blomstrandsøya.

51. Geothermal talik dolines on raised abration platform at Hilmarfjellet.

52. Irgenstjernet, a large doline situated on the (NW) summit of Blomstrandsøya (see Fig. 3-6). The relict form is inundated due to present-day permafrost.

53. Rundkarren on bare karst surface, Blomstrandsøya.

54. Exceptionally deep, decantatio rinnenkarren formed beneath a major snowpatch,Blomstr-andsøya.

55. Scalloped wall of Hilmargrotta, situated about 100 m above the Vitkovski glacier in the Hilmarfjellet karst. The paleodischarge of the passage was approximately 4 m^3/s .

56. Trollosen, the largest spring on Spitsbergen (B, Fig.3-7), here at a discharge of about 12 m^3/s. Note the turbid water of glacial origin.

57. "Stone Board", height 2.7 m, in the Kostivere karst field, Estonia.(Photo:A.Miidel)

58. Niakaev ("Witch Well", depth 2.0 m) in the Kata karst field during the spring flood. (Photo: R. Tiirmaa)

59. Drop Dents in a Calcite Crust (photo: R.A. Jameson).

60. Features of Condensation Corrosion in the North Canyon of Snedegar's Cave (photo: R.A. Jameson).

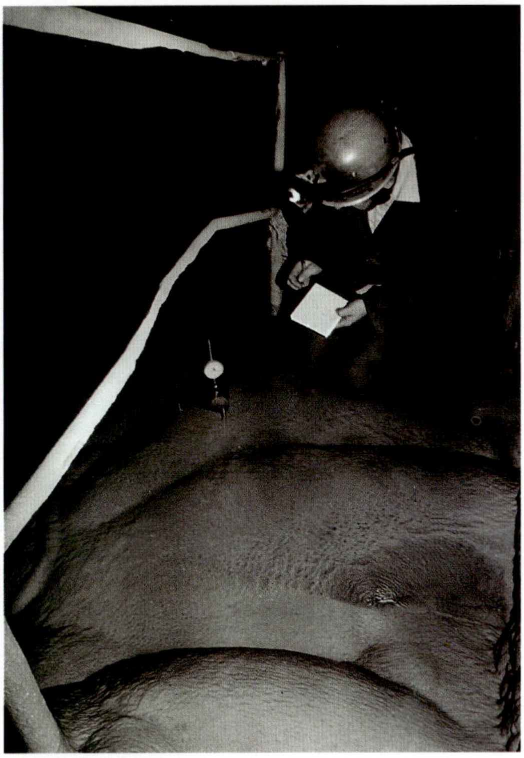

62. The measurement of the flowstone deposition on old tourist path in Hankejev canal. The fence, and the steps are about 100 years old (photo: A. Mihevc).

61. Calcite Drip Hole Rings (photo: R. A. Jameson).

63. Tower karst of the Morown cliffs in the Napier Range, Kimberleys, Australia .

64. Trickett's Cave, Yarrangobilly Caves, New South Wales. A typical former spring in impounded karst which is now hanging due to valley incision .

65. Collapse doline with infill of aeolian sand, Nullarbor Plain, South Australia .

66. The Hindenburg Wall, PNG. Section shown is 750m high with a major landslide and springs emerging at the contact of the Darai Limestone and the underlying Ieru Formation .

67. A large doline near Atea Kananda on the Muller Range, PNG.